D0240475

Proceedings

Volume 2

1981 Rapid Excavation and Tunneling Conference
San Francisco, California, May 3-7, 1981

Editors

Richard L. Bullock, AIME
Henry J. Jacoby, ASCE

Sponsored by

American Institute of Mining, Metallurgical, & Petroleum Engineers
American Society of Civil Engineers

Cooperating Societies

Canadian Institute of Mining and Metallurgy
Engineering Institute of Canada

Society of Mining Engineers
of
The American Institute of Mining, Metallurgical, and Petroleum Engineers, Inc.
New York, New York • 1981

Printed in the United States of America by
Port City Press, Inc., Baltimore, Maryland

Library of Congress Catalog Card Number 81-65517
Volume 2 ISBN 0-89520-284-0
Set ISBN 0-89520-285-9

FOREWORD

Few professions hold a greater breadth of challenge than engineering. Furthermore, few disciplines tax the engineer's overall abilities more than the excavation of holes in the earth and the creation from them of usable facilities and avenues of productin for the raw materials of industry. Yet from the engineering of this relatively small group of professionals who succesfully challenge the subterranean forces comes much of the basis for that quality of life which is simply taken for granted by our modern society. As Herbert Hoover observed, "The engineer himself looks back on the unending stream of goodness which flows from his successes with satisfaction that few professions may know. And the verdict of his fellow professionals is all the accolade he wants." So it is that the common interest of underground tunneling, excavation, and mining within ASCE and AIME should come together periodically to review and pass judgment on their technical progress and productivity in the forum of the Rapid Excavation and Tunneling Conference (RETC).

The Theme of RETC 1981 is "Tunneling Excavation and Mining Productivity" —in short, TEAM.

TEAM is an appropriate acronym for two reasons: First, because the efficient development of the underground will depend to a great extent on the teamwork of those who plan, design, and construct underground facilities, of those who supply the equipment and materials to do the work, and of users of the underground space; second, because of the intercommunication and sharing of ideas and methods RETC promotes between mining engineers and civil engineers to increase productivity in underground techniques.

This has been the thrust of our conference since its inception in Chicago in 1972. The steady rate of inflation, the increasing restrictions required for a clean environment, and the diminished availability of surface spaces, particularly in urban areas, have only heightened the problems.

The scope and importance of our problems are highlighted by a 1979 report of the US Bureau of Labor Statistics indicating a steady decrease in labor productivity in all segments of US economy, with the two poorest segments being construction and mining. This trend obviously must be reversed. In fact, productivity must be increased to control inflation and to provide the increasing facilities in both civil construction and mining which our economy requires to sustain and improve the production of necessary services and materials.

We are proud to provide this forum for the interchange of ideas for all who attend and participate in our sessions. The steady increase in interest and attendance at the RETC conferences demonstrates the need of our efforts and their success. Undoubtedly, these forums will stimulate innovation and reduce overlap of effort. Our *Proceedings* has become an important information source in our field.

The 22 sessions of the 5th RETC held in San Francisco May 3-6, 1981 were prepared by your program cochairmen, 35 session chairmen, and 199 authors and coauthors. Sixty-eight of these authors, representing 14 countries outside the US, prepared 42 of the 121 technical papers of the Conference. Highlights of problems common to both civil and mining engineers were identified and practical solutions were presented from which, hopefully, underground tunneling, excavation, and mining can take place with greater safety and productivity.

Richard L. Bullock
Henry J. Jacoby
Cochairmen

February 1981

1981 RETC EXECUTIVE COMMITTEE

Conference Chairman

Alfred C. Maevis
McLean, VA

AIME

Richard L. Bullock
Golder Associates
Golden, CO

William A. Hustrulid
Colorado School of Mines
Golden, CO

Bruce A. Kennedy
Golder Associates
Golden, Colorado

John W. Wilson
Smith International Inc.
Houston, TX

ASCE

Henry J. Jacoby
Grow Tunneling Corp.
New York, NY

Martin Kelley
Peter Kiewit Sons Co.
Omaha, NB

John W. Leonard
Morrison-Knudsen Co.
Boise, ID

Harry Sutcliffe
Bechtel Corp.
West Somerville, MA

Staff

Claude L. Crowley
SME-AIME
Conference Manager

Ruth M. Orologio
SME-AIME
Assistant Conference Manager

A.J. Favata
ASCE
Exhibit Manager

Marianne Snedeker
SME-AIME
Proceedings Coordinator

1981 RETC PROGRAM COMMITTEE

Conference Program Chairmen

Richard L. Bullock
Exxon Minerals Co.
Houston, TX

Henry J. Jacoby
Grow Tunneling Corp.
New York, NY

Session Chairmen

J.S. Bhore
Perini Corp.
Framingham, MA

A.R. Biggart
Edmund Nuttall Ltd.
London, England

T.L. Brekke
University of California
Berkeley, CA

R.L. Brittain
Dames & Moore
Golden, CO

G.S. Brierley
H&A of New York
Rochester, NY

E.F. Casey
Mason & Hamger-Silas Mason Co.
New York, NY

G.W. Clough
Stanford University
Stanford, CA

H.H. Einstein
Massachusetts Institute of Technology
Cambridge, MA

J. Franklin
University of Wisconsin
Madison, WI

C. Gerity
Occidental Minerals Corp.
Lakewood, CO

B.C. Hamilton
University of Wisconsin
Madison, WI

D.G. Hammond
Daniel, Mann, Johnson & Mendenhall
Baltimore, MD

C. Heever
Cyril Heever & Partners, Inc.
Carletonville, South Africa

J. Henneke
Mannesmann Demag AG
Duisberg, Germany

R.J. Jenny
Jenny Engineering Corp.
South Orange, NJ

D.A. Johnson
Al Johnson Construction Co.
Minneapolis, MN

W.H. Lane
American Mine Service
Denver, CO

J.W. Leonard
Morrison-Knudson, Inc.
Boise, ID

R.L. Loofbourow
Multi-Purpose Excavation Group
Minneapolis, MN

C.D. Mann
Exxon Minerals Co.
Houston, TX

S.C. Matthews
Battelle Memorial Institute
Columbus, OH

S.L. Milne
Pincock Allen and Holt Inc.
Tucson, AZ

D. Pentz
Golder Associates, Inc.
Kirkland, WA

C.M.F. Peters
Consultant
San Francisco, CA

C.R. Peterson
Massachusetts Institute of Technology
Cambridge, MA

A.G. Provost
Harrison Western Corp.
Denver, CO

R.J. Redmond
MacLean Grove & Co., Inc.
Greenwich, CT

J.S. Redpath
J.S. Redpath Ltd.
North Bay, Ontario
Canada

S. Serata
Serata Geomechanics, Inc.
Berkeley, CA

G.L. Tiley
G.L. Tiley & Associates Ltd.
Hamilton, Ontario
Canada

J.G. Warnock
Acres American Inc.
Columbia, MD

G.L. Wilhelm
Exxon Minerals Co. USA
Houston, TX

M. Young
Ozark Lead Co.
Sweetwater, MO

TABLE OF CONTENTS

SECTION 20 Ground Control in Mining

SECTION 21 Instrumentation in Ground Control

SECTION 22 Increasing Productivity Through Better Contractual Arrangements & Management

Volume 1

SECTION 1 Site Investigation I: Shafts and Underground Caverns

SECTION 2 Site Investigation II: Tunnels and Subways

SECTION 3 Mine Development Planning

SECTION 4 Current Techniques in Soft Ground Tunneling

SECTION 5 Current Techniques—Small Diameter Tunnels

SECTION 6 Mixed Face Tunneling Special Problems

SECTION 7 Current Tunnel and Shaft Lining Techniques

SECTION 8 Recent Development and Performance of TBMs In Large Urban Projects

12

Shaft Sinking for Civil Projects

Chairman: A.G. Provost

Harrison Western Corp., Denver, CO

Chapter 55

THE HELMS UNDERGROUND PUMPED STORAGE PROJECT SHAFT DEVELOPMENT

by Scott F. Andersen

Underground Systems Manager
Transco Northwest, Inc.
Portland, Oregon

ABSTRACT

Discussion to include location and description of the project from upper lake through powerhouse to lower lake, noting locations and size of shafts. Discuss evolution of shaft development concepts in conjunction with owner, contractor and CAL OSHA. Discuss elevator shaft equipment, T1 gate shaft, T2 surge shaft equipment, T3 surge shaft and the incline shaft equipment. Question and answer period.

INTRODUCTION

Pacific Gas & Electric Company's Helms Underground Pumped Storage Project is being constructed high up in California's Sierra Nevada Mountains by the joint-venture: Granite-Ball-Groves. Some seventy miles east of Fresno and at elevations above 1830 meters (6000 ft), this elaborate water storage complex will complement P. G. & E.'s power deliveries from the recently completed Diablo Canyon nuclear generating facility.

Three pump-turbine units, each rated at 160 megawatt will be located in the underground powerhouse, which measures 26 meters (85 ft) wide, by 111 meters (365 ft) long by 52 meters (170 ft) high. The powerhouse is located between two lakes, each at different elevations and the three connected through some 8 kilometers (5 miles) of roughly 9 meters (30 ft) diameter water carring tunnels. Peak power demands will be met during the day as water from the upper Courtright Lake flows down the incline shaft, through the turbine-pumps and into the lower Wishon Lake. At night excess power from Diablo Canyon will be used to drive the pump-turbines, drawing water from the lower lake and pumping it through a 457 meter (1500 ft) elevation difference to the upper lake.

The upper lake can be isolated from the down stream power tunnel system by closing the gate housed in the Gate Shaft. With 49 meters (160 ft) between shaft collar and the tunnel below, the Gate Shaft measured 4 meters (12 ft) by 8 meters (26 ft).

A 15 meter (50 ft) diameter vertical Surge Shaft Number 2 is located approximately 90 meters (300 ft) upstream of the intersection of the power tunnel and the Incline Shaft. This Surge Shaft's collar, at 20 meters (65 ft) diameter, is approximately 180 meters (600 ft) above the power tunnel below and can only be reached on foot or by helicopter.

The 10 meter (32 ft) diameter Incline Shaft carries the water from the upper power tunnel down at an angle of fifty-five degrees from horizontal to the lower penstocks and into the powerhouse, a drop of 457 meters (1500 ft).

A 300 meter (1000 ft) deep, 6 meter (20 ft) diameter Elevator Shaft serves both as powerhouse access and as a power cable conduit to the switch yard above.

The tailrace tunnel, or Tunnel Number 3, connects the powerhouse and the lower lake. Surge protection is provided by Surge Shaft Number 3. This shaft is 275 meters (900 ft) deep and developed to 14 meters (47 ft) diameter for 90 meters (300 ft), with 150 meters (500 ft) of 3 meter (10 ft) diameter shaft leading up to the collar and 40 meters (130 ft) of oriface shaft droping to the tunnel below.

All shaft development concepts evolved through close cooperation between P. G. & E., Granite-Ball-Groves, CAL OSHA and the equipment designer-fabricator, Morgan Manufacturing, Inc.. The safety of the workmen was established as the primary criteria for both shaft development concept and equipment design. Sound granite, spiling bolts, the requirement of helicopter access to T2 Surge Shaft, and the economic desire for the least number of pieces of equipment consistent with maintaining the construction schedule, were also set as design criteria.

VERTICAL SHAFTS

All shafts were initially developed by raise boring, either to 2.5 meters (8 ft) diameter as with the Elevator and Gate Shafts or 3 meters (10 ft) diameter in the T2 and T3 Surge Shafts. The tunnel and shaft development schedules were coordinated to keep both crews working effectively, with the tunnels driven under the shaft prior to shaft pilot bore penetration, allowing the raise bore head to be subsequently attached and work continued without interuption.

The initial development concepts called for one jumbo to ring drill the two surge shafts from within the raise bore, and a second jumbo conventionally slashing the Elevator and Gate Shafts into the raise bore. As the schedule required two shafts being opened at the same time, two headframes, jumbo hoists, mancars and mancar hoists were envisioned and built.

Each jumbo was suspended on a pair of 5 centimeters (2 in) wire ropes and hoisted by two sycronized, continous pull or payout Lucker pull machines. Each puller was mounted vertically atop the headframe, adjacent to its automatic wire rope spooling reel. The puller is comprised of two selflocking, hydraulically opened cable grips, in guides: each cycled back and forth by hydraulic cylinders to effectively pull or payout out of the rope in a hand over hand fashion. The force of pull and speed are controlled at the operator's console. The console and hydraulic power unit were housed in the operator's shack, located on the groud adjacent to the shaft collar. The systems used for the vertical shafts were rated at 68180 kilograms (150,000 lbs) combined line pull with variable speeds of up to 9 meters per minute (30 ft per min). Connected horsepower was approximately two hundred and forty.

This vertical puller mounting provided several advantages, both in weight and cost, when compared to conventional heavy hoist systems: There is no need for massive head sheaves with a resultant headframe designed for greater vertical and horizontal loads. Large and syncronized mine type hoists, with fleetangle requirements in site and headframe size, are elimated. Another feature, that of the puller grips selflocking on the wire rope under load, was considered important. Each puller weighed under 3180 kilograms (7000 lbs), a requirement for installation by helicopter.

The jumbo hoist ropes were centered at 2 meters (7 ft) as wire rope guides for the mancar, providing access to the jumbo. The mancar was provided with a broken hoist rope safety. Lighting and communication were provided in an eight conductor, internal messenger cable as spooled onto a hydraulically powered, headframe mounted cable reel. An 3 centimeter (1-¼ in) rope led from the mancar safety over a head sheave in the headframe and to an hydrostatically driven mancar hoist.

Prior to fabrication, the use of a hydrostaticly driven hoist for hoisting personnel was discussed at length with officials of CAL-OSHA to assure safety compliance. Rated at 13600 kilograms (30,000 lbs) and 30 meters per min (100 ft per min), with infinately variable speed in either direction, these hoists met and exceded all Federal and State safety requirements. The hoist operator controlled service brakes, speed and direction with a single joy stick. Load and car position were digitally displayed at the console. The requirement for automatic car deceleration and stop some 6 meters (20 ft) above the jumbo was met and the action triggered with a pendant suspended system riding the mancar. An override button on the operator's console allowed a "talked in" stop above the final limits at the jumbo. Upper limits were mounted in the headframe.

With the scheduled need to work two shafts simultaneously, two identical headframes were conceived and built. The use of the Lucker pullers allowed a design where ten welded pannels, each capable of being flown by helicopter, could be pinned or bolted together on the ground, and through the use of snatch blocks, self errected, with subsequent installation of the pullers and mancar head sheave. The headframe base pannels were designed for installation over any of the four shafts, with a welded truss system provided for spanning to 20 meters (65 ft) diameter collar at T2 Surge Shaft. An hydraulically powered electric cable reel was mounted on the base mat to provide power to the jumbos. The design enabled the contractor to dismantle, move and reerrect the headframe at another shaft in less than a weeks time.

Shaft lining for the Elevator, T2 and T3 Surge Shafts was to be slipformed, with concrete delivery via special 3 cubic meter (4 c yd) Garbro buckets, as suspended below the mancar. The buckets were designed with pneumatic, metering discharge gates, where the concrete could be delivered to a collecting, swivel chute attached below the bucket, either directly to the form, as in the Elevator Shaft or to revolving belt conveyors, as required in the larger T2 and T3 Surge Shafts. For safety reasons all concrete for these shafts would be loaded in the tunnel below and hoisted through the slip form structure, where the pour forman would hook up his gate control valve to operate the bucket gate. Finply form sheeting was to be carried on structural steel form carriers, one for the Elevator Shaft and a second adjustable, modular structure for use in T2 and T3 Shafts. The Gate Shaft forms were field fabricated and concrete delivered by drop pipe.

INCLINE SHAFT

The initial concepts and schedule called for reuse of the vertical shaft hoisting equipment and the pneumatic drills as removed from the slashing jumbo. As with the vertical shafts, inital development was done with a raise bore, here at 3 meters (10 ft) diameter. With P. G. & E.'s approval in allowing the Incline Shaft allignment to follow the raise bore, the raise bore invert was to be located. 6 meters (2 ft) below incline shaft "A" line, serving two purposes: As undisturbed control for the development and concrete operations, and as a roadway for the Slashing Jumbo's lower trucks. A modularized rail system, in 3 meter (10 ft) lengths, would carry the upper trucks and have a safety rail , water and air pipes preattached. This rail system would key and rock-bolt into the raise bore "sub invert", and be carried far enough behind the face to prevent blast damage, a feature allowed by running the jumbo's lower truck on this sub-invert. In concept and practice, the jumbo could be lowered to the face immediately after a shot, where a jumbo mounted, traveling backhoe would muck the face down the raise bore, and at the same time another rail module was passed into the jumbo structure for installation.

Stability for the moving jumbo was provided by a traveling outrigger, which would be extended to the invert and the jumbo lowered or raised through the stationary outrigger structure.

Rail modules and other materials were lowered on a material car, which trailed below the incline shaft mancar. The mancar would be provided with a safety rail gripping, broken hoist rope safety and electrically operated cable take up reel for lighting and communication. The hydrostatic mancar hoist, as well as the jumbo cable pullers, would be located under a access trestle to be erected in the elbow area at the intersection of the incline shaft and upper power tunnel. After fabrication, factory assembly and breakdown for shipment, the jumbo would be reassembled on rail mounted atop the trestle, then moved onto a tilt table hinged at the trestle's end, and as restrained temporarily with the mancar hoist, allowed to tilt over to a position where the jumbo could be lowered, by the Lucker cable pullers, onto the first sections of inclined rail.

A bridge crane would be installed above the trestle, extending out over the end of the trestle for use in erecting the jumbo and subsequently to handle and place rebar on a Rebar Carrier.

The incline shaft jumbo design was to allow for its structure to double as a form carrier on completion of shaft development. The six pneumatic drills were to be located, and articulated man decks provided for use in both the installation of spiling bolts and normal drill and loading operations. A knuckle boom crane was envisioned for use in handling materials and maintainance.

While the afore mentioned concepts were generally adhered to, numerous circumstances arose, requiring some modification. Where earlier site investigations implied sound granite at the shaft sites, as work progressed raise bore operation logs gave indications of less than ideal rock conditions at T2 Surge, and the Incline Shaft. The ring drill concept was abandoned for use in T2 and consequently T3 shafts because of this system's lack of provision for reaching the shaft walls to control rock fall outs, should it occur. The fear of a continued drought necessitated the unscheduled impounding of water in the upper lake and forced a change in sequence in shaft development, with resultant need for additional equipment. Three shafts were eventually under development at the same time.

ELEVATOR SHAFT

The first to be developed was the 6 meter (20 ft) diameter Elevator Shaft. A 2.5 meter (8 ft) diameter raise bore was pulled 300 meters (1000 ft) from a construction adit off the powerhouse access tunnel. Development to "A" line was accomplished with a three drill slashing jumbo as depicted on figure 1. The jumbo was raised prior to a shot. Three meter (10 ft) rounds were normally pulled.

The slashing jumbo was built with a center core section, to which were bolted three drill module assembles; a fourth would be added for slashing the Gate Shaft. The center core housed an hydraulic power-unit, motor control center, air receiver and a hoist system, which held the raise bore plug. The core was bolted below an equalizing crosshead to which the two 5 centimeter (2 in) diameter hoist ropes were attached. Gardner Denver JTTI telescoping rollover booms, mounting 3.7 meters (12 ft) feed shells, with PR55 drifters were factory assembled and plumbed to the drill modules.

Drill and boom as well as stinger controls were factory plumbed into the drill modles. Each module housed a hydraulically driven stinger which was run out into the shaft wall for jumbo stability during the drill cycle. Access to the bench was provided by a retractable ladder, which too acted as rails for a powered powder and materials transport.

As in all shafts jumbo access was by means of an enclosed mancar, using the jumbo hoist ropes as guides. The mancar was hoisted and lowered with the hydrostatically driven mancar hoist. The requirement for a second means of egress was provided by the Lucker cable pullers hoisting the jumbo to the collar if necessary.

Wire meshing was attached to the shaft walls from the jumbo's top deck. Mucking was primarily accomplished with blow pipes. On several occasions, three rounds per day were attained, not withstanding the requirements for installation of spiling bolts prior to a shot.

A 5.5 meter (18 ft) diameter slipform was assembled complete outside, less the hanging finish deck, and trucked into place at the bottom of the shaft. The Heede jacks were mounted on the headframe mat and jack rods assembled from the jumbo as it was lowered after checking tights.

As previously mentioned, concrete was delivered to the form in a special concrete bucket with integral swivel chute, as suspended from the mancar (see figure 2). The bucket was filled at the shaft bottom and hoisted through the form, where it was discharged into a revolving pour chute. Slip rates in excess of .6 meters (2 ft) per hour were achieved.

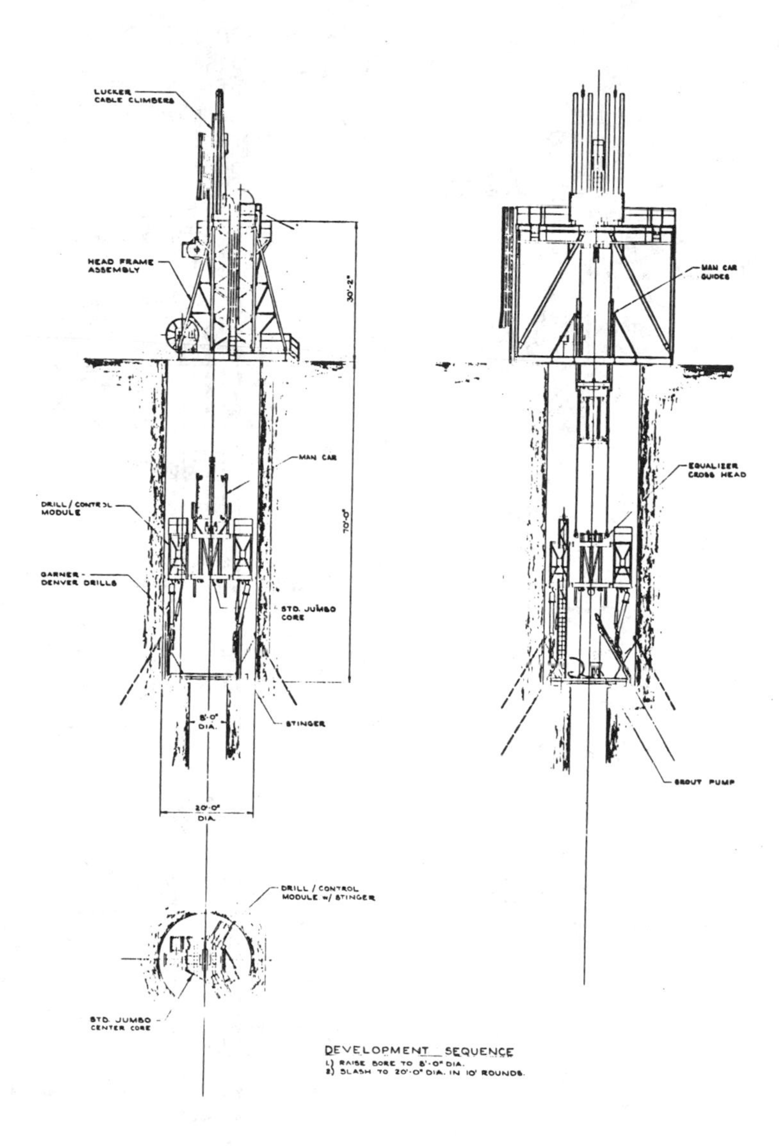

Fig. 1 Elevator Shaft Development

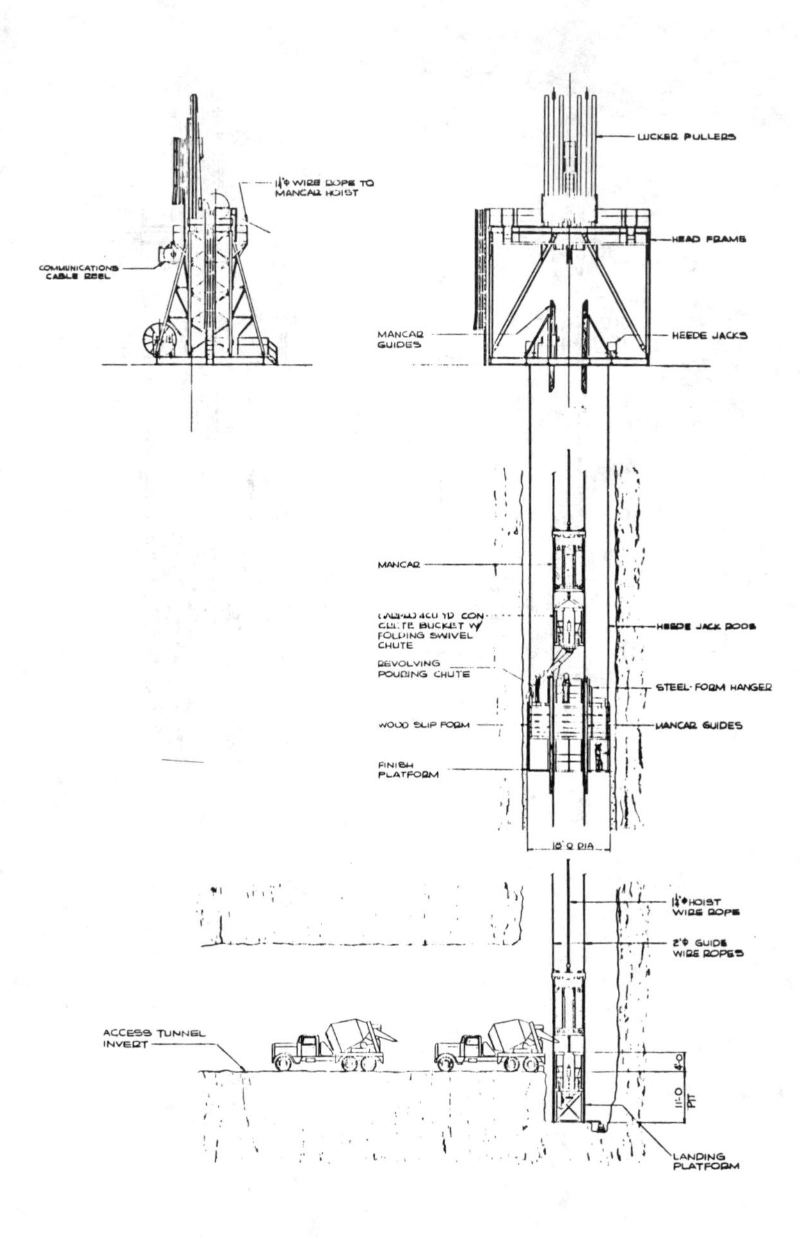

Fig. 2 Elevator Shaft Concrete

GATE SHAFT

On completion of the Elevator Shaft, the equipment was disassembled and brought to the Gate Shaft. The headframe and hoists were reinstalled and the slashing jumbo modified to develop this rectangular shaft.

To the jumbo core were bolted two adapter sections and in turn two drill modules were assembled to each adapter. An operational modification made in the Elevator Shaft was incorporated at the outset here: Drill and boom controls were relocated on the raise bore plug for better sight in collaring.

Shaft development proceeded along lines as in the Elevator Shaft. Production was slower principally due to muck hang up on the longer benches. With the drills removed from the jumbo after holing through, the jumbo was decked over and used as a form carrier. Concrete was delivered by drop pipe, through a bull hose and into the forms.

T2 SURGE SHAFT

For enviromental considerations, T2 Surge Shaft was developed without any road access to the collar. All materials and equipment were either walked in or ferried by helicopter. The I.R. raise bore machine was disassembled, for helicopter lift, then set up and a 3 meter (10 ft) diameter bore hole reamed. A thirty-five ton stiff leg derrick was found, modified and installed. A new and modified mancar hoist was supplied to handle the derricks load line, rated at 22725 kilograms (50,000 lbs) and 18 meters per min (60 ft per min).

Collar development was performed with air tracks using a teathered Cat 951 for mucking. When the 20 meter (65 ft) diameter collar was developed to 18 meters (60 ft) depth, concrete lining was placed. Inserts were set in this pour to later accept the slipform jack supports.

At this stage a new eight boom jumbo was hoisted up through the 3 meter (10 ft) raise bore hole, in modules, using the stiffleg derrick. Because of previously mentioned schedule changes and the anticipation of blocky ground, the ring drill method of shaft development had to be abandoned. Several main line tunnel jumbos were now in surplus with their eight Atlas Copco COP 1038 hydraulic drills and BUT15 booms available. It was readily determined that these drills could provide adequate coverage for the remaining 140 meters (460 ft) of 15 meter (50 ft) diameter shaft, and could long hole drill the last 9 meters (30 ft) of 9.5 meters (31 ft) diameter oriface shaft. The jumbo was designed to operate in both T2 and T3 Surge Shafts.

Bench mucking using the CAT 951 track loader with sidedump bucket basically controlled the dimensions of the jumbo, as well as the slip form carrier, which was to be used as a work platform for meshing above the bench. The loader, as lowered with the stiff-leg derrick after a shot, would have to pass both inside the form carrier structure and by the jumbo to reach the muck pile. The mucker would then be unshackled from the hoist rope for effecient operation. For the safety of the operation, the lower portion of the jumbo was designed as a grizzly, allowing muck to pass but preventing the loader from falling into the raise bore (see figure 3).

While drilling, the grizzly structure would also act to stabilize the jumbo, when fully lowered into the raise bore. Hydraulically acturated wedges were fitted into the bottom of the eight grizzly bars to aid this effort. The grizzly bolted to the underside of the jumbo core.

The jumbo core stood some 9 meters (30 ft) from drill deck to top deck and housed the four double hydraulic power units, air receiver, transformer and switch gear. One drill, boom and hydraulic power unit were factory assembled into the jumbo and all air, water and hydraulic runs for the remaining seven prefabricated.

Before hoisting the drills through the raise bore they were assembled to their drill modules and plumbed. The drill modules with larger boom swing cylinders mounted as required for vertical drill operation, bolted onto the top deck core structure, and final plumbing to the power units was completed. A 10 centimeter (4 in) thick equalizer bar assembly was connected to the core structure and the two 5 centimeter (2 in) jumbo hoist ropes pinned.

After the jumbo was assembled, the two collar spanning trusses were set and the headframe erected. The headframe, mancar hoist, Lucker pullers and mancar were identical to those used at the Elevator Shaft.

Steel sets, as well as spiling bolts, were required the entire lenght of the shaft. Often only one 1.5 meter (5 ft) round per day was attained. The use of the steel sets precluded the necessity of suspending the form carrier above the jumbo. On holing through, the sixteen module form carrier was assembled and the Finply form attached. Sixteen Heede wire rope jacks were placed on knee braces at the collar and the mild plow steel ropes lowered and attached to the form. As in the Elevator Shaft, concrete was hoisted from below in the special buckets, but here two revolving transfer conveyors were used to place the concrete in the forms. Rebar was also hoisted from below with the stiffleg derrick and placed from the rebar deck atop the form. The average slip rate for this 140 meter (460 ft) pour was in the order of .3 meters (1 ft) per hour.

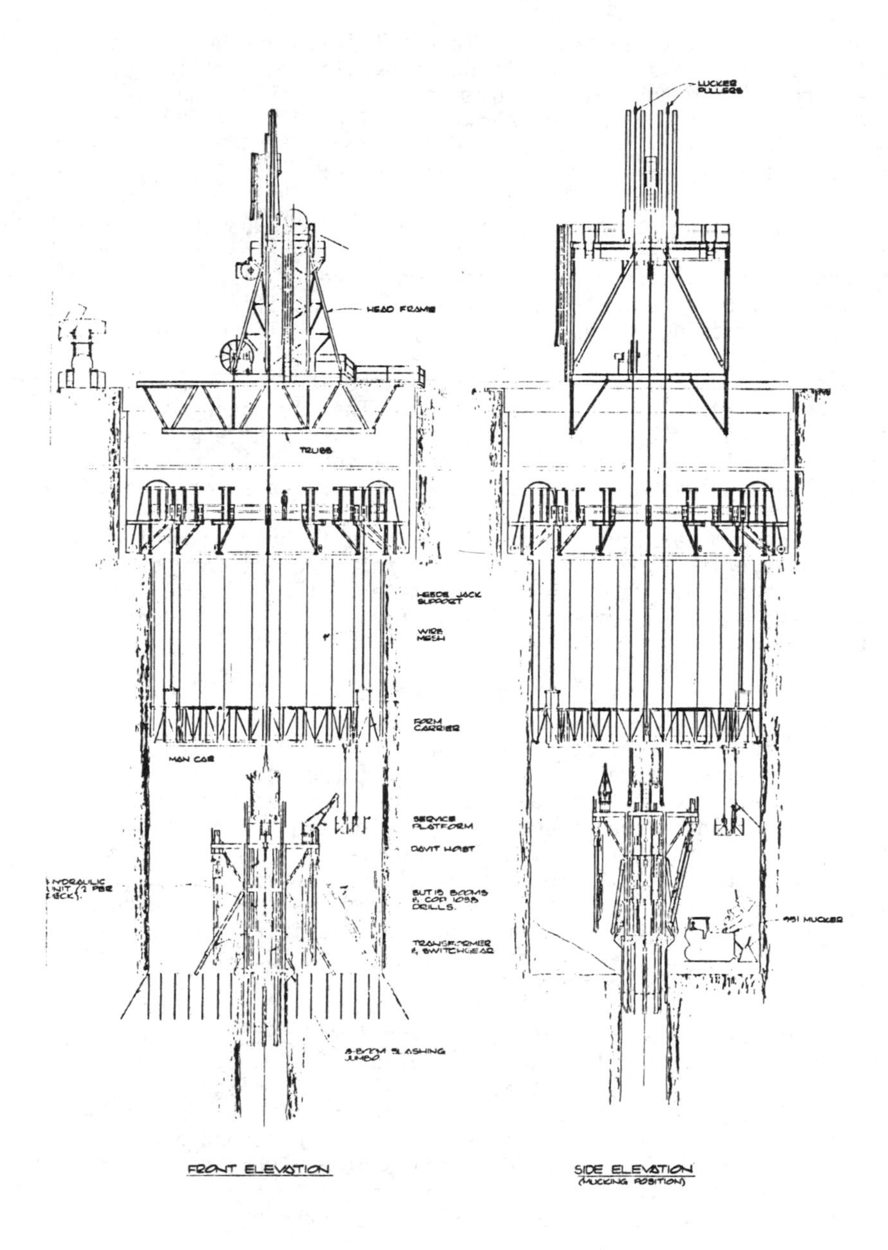

Fig. 3 T2 Surge Shaft Development

T3 SURGE SHAFT

The Schedule dictated that the T2 Shaft jumbo not be reused in T3 Surge Shaft. This shaft bells out from its 3 meter (10 ft) raise bore to 14 meters (47 ft) diameter, at an elevation some 150 meters (500 ft) below the headframe. There is only 90 meters (300 ft) of this 14 meter (47 ft) shaft before it necks down to 9.5 meters (31 ft) diameter for another 40 meters (130 ft).

Modified Gardner Denver AT-50 air tracks with PR55 drills were slung below the mancar and lowered to a grizzly-raise bore plug structure which was suspended by the two Lucker pullers. (see figure 4). The grizzly structure mounted two modified J. D. 510 backhoes for mucking. A round every day and a half were averaged.

A work deck with four air tuggers mounted aboard was used to wire mesh the shaft as it was developed. The work deck was to be tied off to the conical shaft umbrella later to act as a Heede jack support platform during the slip form show; this in lieu of the planned placing of the curb and knee braces as depected.

The slip form carrier used at T2 Shaft is to be reassembled in the T3 Shaft, with spool pieces removed to bring the form surface to the required 13.4 meter (44 ft) diameter. (T2 Shaft was placed at 14.3 meters (47 ft) diameter). As of this writing no concrete has been placed.

INCLINE SHAFT

The incline shaft concepts discussed previously generally were adhered to in the design and fabrication of the equipment, (see figure 5). Atlas Copco hydraulic drills and booms were used on the jumbo instead of the pneumatic drills, as they were again available from surplus tunnel jumbos. Where a lifting platform was designed and installed to work and load the face, it was subsequently removed, when it was found that the face could be laid back and walked on, without significantly increasing the amount of muck left after a shot. A single man basket was added to serve the drilling equipment.

When bad ground was encountered, several modifications were required. The sub invert raise bore surface fell away in several locations with one result in that the rail system alignment could not be maintained to the degree necessary for the mancar as designed. A new broken rope mancar safety was designed and installed along with an additional rail system. When steel sets were required, they were placed by hand at the face. The lower jumbo truck was raised and made to ride set spanning rail.

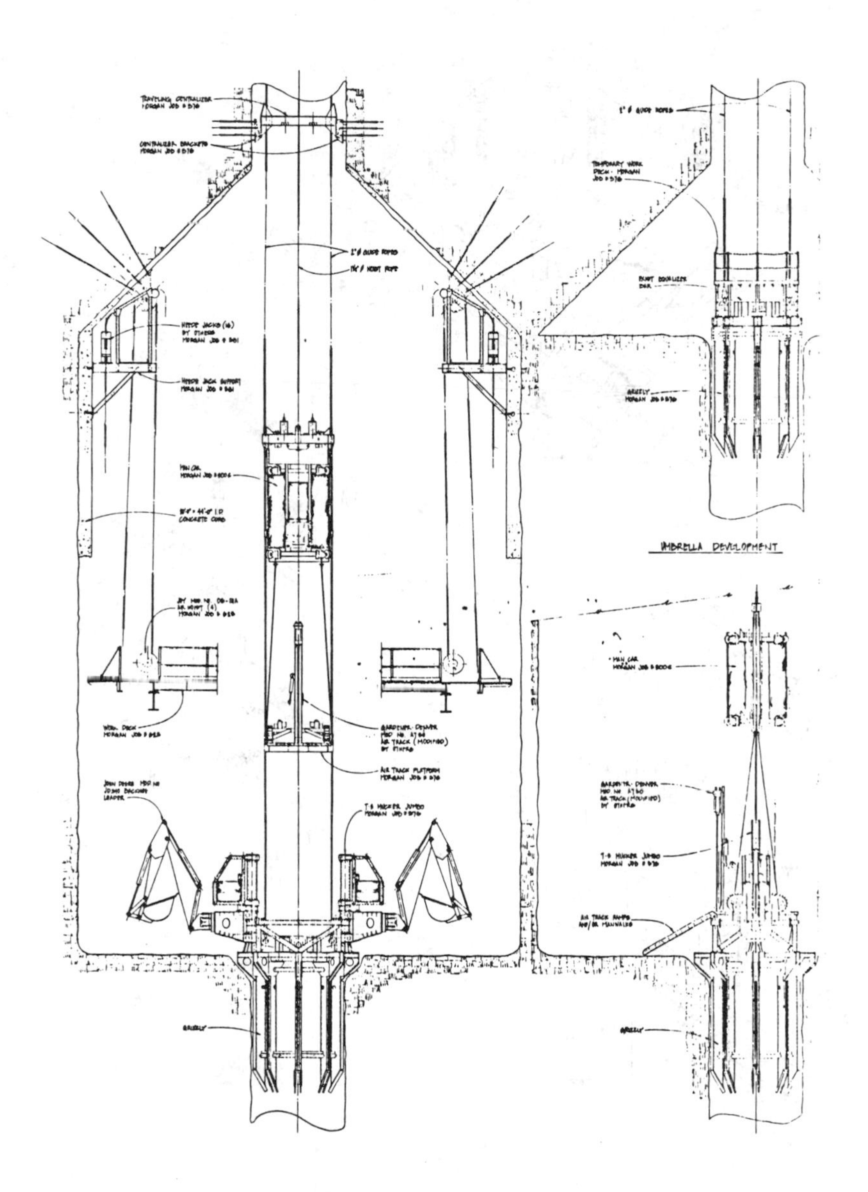

Fig. 4 T3 Surge Shaft Development

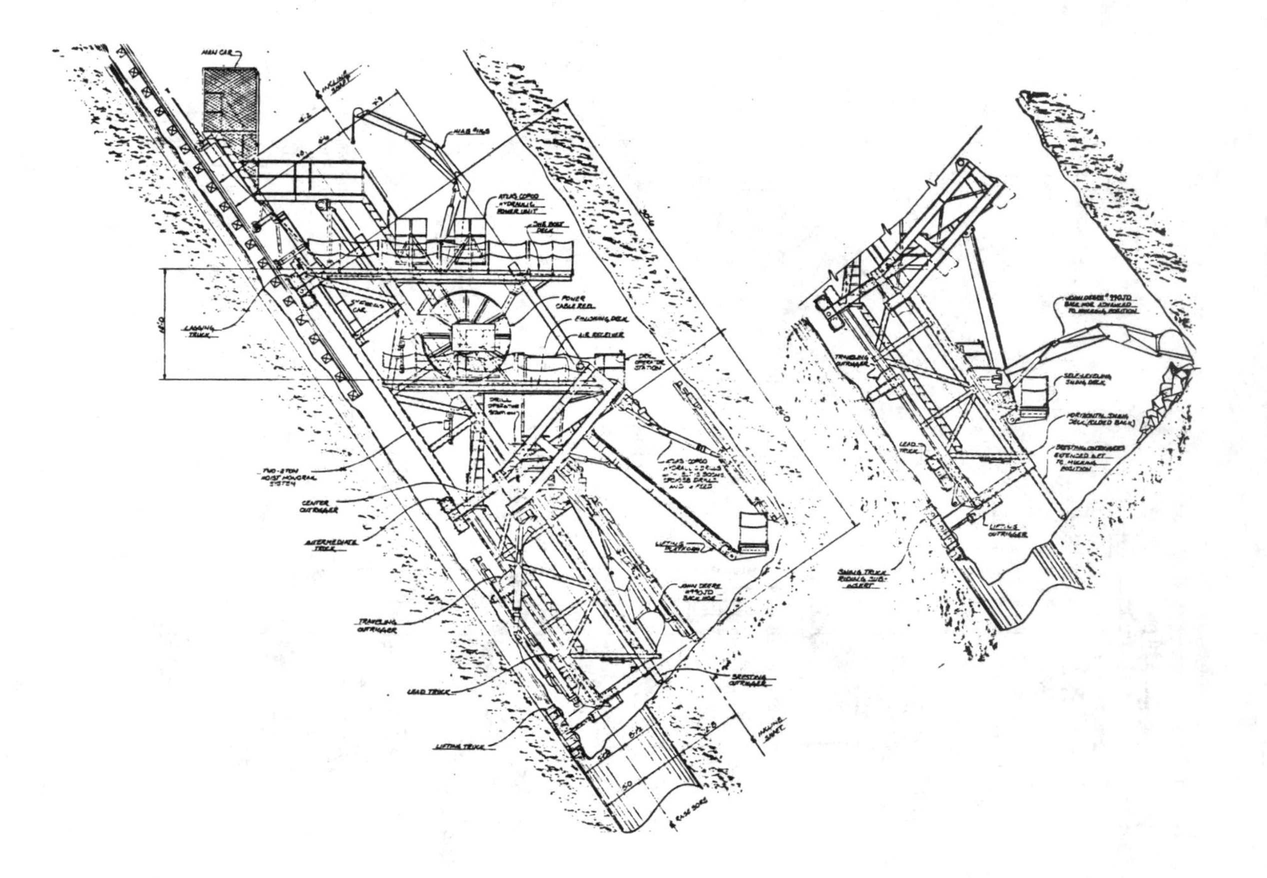

Fig. 5 Incline Shaft Jumbo

To inspect and remedy potential problems in the shaft walls above the jumbo, a gantry type inspection car was installed. It was designed to allow the mancar to pass through it and would later be used to set rebar above the concrete lining operation. This inspection rebar car is hoisted and lowered on two ropes, without the need for a broken rope safety. The dual drum hoist system again was hydrostatically driven, through here the drums were not mechanically locked, but load syncronized, allowing the drums to rotate a differential speeds should the hoist ropes be on different wraps while operating. The operator's control, as with the other mancar hoists, was with a single joy stick.

To date, in good ground, better than a round a day are maintained. The concrete lining will be placed in 9 meter (30 ft) lifts.

CONCLUSION

There were many equipment firsts employed in the development of the shafts at the Helms Project. The use of the Lucker cable pullers to support the jumbos proved cost effective both in initial cost and in the resultant savings in the headframes and site preparation costs. The hydrostatically driven hoists too provided substantial cost advantages over conventional hoists and continue to perform safely and effectively. Here was the first American use of hydraulic drills in shaft sinking, with bit penetration ratesof up to 2 meters per min (6 ft per min). The traveling outrigger system on the incline shaft jumbo, tied with riding on the raise bore subinvert proved a effective method of combining several drill cycle tasks, shortening the cycle time.

The development of the equipment used at the Helms Project required close cooperation between the owner, the contractor, CAL OSHA, the craftmen and the fabricator. The author would thank all those involved, for without their counsel and desire to "make it work", the methods and equipment described herein would not have been successful.

Chapter 56

DESIGN AND INSTALLATION OF LARGE DIAMETER SUB-SEA CONNECTING SHAFTS FOR THE SEABROOK STATION COOLING WATER SYSTEM

by Allen J. Hulshizer and Jean-Pierre Nossereau

Supervising Structural Engineer
United Engineers & Constructors Inc.
Philadelphia, Pennsylvania

Project Manager-Marine Construction
Morrison-Knudson Company, Inc.
Boise, Idaho

The main thrust of this paper covers the design, installation techniques and experience associated with the installation of eleven 1.5 m (4'-11") and three 2.87 m (9'-5") diameter shafts in 15 to 23 meters (50 to 75 ft) of water over 1.6 Km (a mile) out in the Atlantic Ocean. The approach implemented, permits the use of pre-fabricated shaft linings and incorporates a safe dry-tap method for connecting the offshore shafts to tunnels driven blind from deep land shafts over 4.8 Km (3 miles) away. This tunnel-shaft system is a unique venture employed at the Seabrook Nuclear Power Station to meet plant cooling water requirements.

INTRODUCTION

The Seabrook Power Station, presently under construction, is a two unit, nuclear powered electric generating station located at Seabrook, New Hampshire. Each unit has a rated capactiy of 1150 megawatts (electric) and combined require approximately 53.63 m^3/s (850,000 gpm) of water essentially for condensor cooling. One of the main siting features of the plant was its proximity to the limitless water supply of the Atlantic Ocean, whose shore line is about 3.22 Km (2 miles) from the plant. A deep tunnel system was chosen as the most suitable environmental scheme to convey the water to and from points over 1.6 Km (a mile) at sea to the plant, resulting in 10.25 Km (6.4 miles) of hard rock tunnels.

The once through cooling system utilizes two independent tunnels to obtain the cooling water and to discharge the heated water. Both tunnels start at the plant site 79.25 m (260 ft) below the surface and extend out under the ocean, terminating about 48.8 m (160 ft) below the ocean's surface (MSL).

The intake tunnel is connected to the ocean by means of three, 2.87 m (9'-5") finished diameter shafts, spaced 33.53 m (110 ft) apart and located approximately 2.13 Km (7000 ft) off the Hampton Beach shoreline in 18.3 m (60 ft) of water. A 9.3 m (30'-6") diameter concrete velocity cap is mounted on top of each shaft to reduce the intake velocity.

The discharge tunnel connects to the ocean by means of eleven 1.5 m (4'-11") finished diameter shafts, spaced about 30.5 m (100 ft) apart and located about 1.52 Km (5000 feet) off the Seabrook Beach shoreline. A diagramatic sketch of the cooling water tunnel system is shown in Figure 1.

The tunnels are machine bored to a 6.71 m (22'-0") diameter and concrete line to a finished diameter of 5.79 m (19'-0").

Since the cooling water system is indispensable and maintenance and repairs to the tunnel-shaft system are impossible during plant operation, it is imperative that they perform virtually maintenance free for the minimum 40 year design life of the $3.2 billion plant. Current replacement cost of power for plant shut down is about $3 million/day.

Driving of these tunnels, accurately for over 4.83 Km (3 miles), to the precise shaft locations represents a formidable task. However, the ultimate success of the tunnel concept lies in a safe, efficient and effective means of linking the underlying hardrock tunnels to the ocean above.

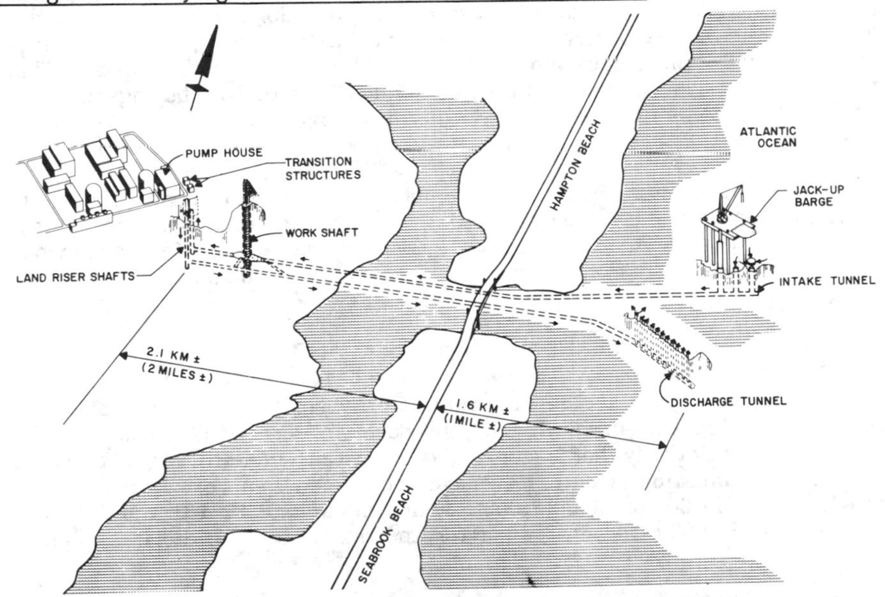

PERSPECTIVE OF TUNNEL ARRANGEMENT

FIGURE 1

The basic drilled-in, dry-tap scheme developed for Seabrook was presented at the 1976 RETC by Hulshizer, Desai and Dave [1]. Since that time the shafts have been drilled, the pre-fabricated lining grouted in place and, as of mid January, 1981, the tunnels excavated to within 274m (900 ft) and 530m (1700 ft) of the first intake and discharge shafts respectively. Description of the land shaft and tunneling work is given in References 2 and 3.

It is the purpose of this paper to further describe the design details and to relate the general construction experience associated with the drilling and installation of the ocean shafts.

The referenced presentation[1] should be consulted for general background information regarding the alternate consideration of an open caisson with a conventionally sunk shaft and other historical information involving the use of drilled-in, dry-tap shaft connections.

SHAFT LOCATIONS

The optimum location for the water intake and discharge would be as close to the shore line as possible, but because of the great concern to preserve the marine ecology, offshore locations in 15 to 23 m (50 to 75 ft) of water, remote from the shore line were selected.

Concurrent with environmental investigations, a major underground geologic study was carried on to determine the best available tunnel routes and most feasible and economical location to sink the linking offshore shafts. This program, utilizing over 9,144 lineal meters (30,000 feet) of core borings at costs over two million dollars has been extensively described in the paper listed under Reference 4.

Final shaft locations represent a compromise between tunnel and shaft construction requirements as best fitted within the environmental parameter confinements and are not therefore always located where subsurface conditions are the most desirable cost or construction wise for shaft sinking operations.

SUB-SURFACE CONDITIONS

Overburden throughout the general shaft area varies from clays to sands to dense boulder filled tills in varying depths down to elevation (-)36 m (120 ft) MSL. Rock is relatively hard, generally consisting of either quarzites or diorites or a combination of both. Average unconfined compressive strength of 83 and 124 MPa (12,000 psi and 18,000 psi) and maximums of 131 and 234 MPa (19,000 psi and 34,000 psi) were found for the quartzites and diorites respectively.

The quartzites, which are predominate in the intake area, exhibited petrofabrics dipping deeply subvertically, with closely spaced joints, some weathering and randomly oriented strikes so that the rock tends to be blocky.

Occasional difficulties in maintaining open holes during rock coring were encountered apparently due to the close fracturing.

The intake shaft area is generally level at elevation (-)18 meters (60 feet) MSL and is characterized by 9 to 12 meters (30 to 40 feet) of clay and gravel till overlaying the bed rock.

In contrast to the intake shaft area the ocean bottom at the discharge shaft area is irregular, varying in elevation from (-)15 to (-)23 meters (50 to 75 feet) MSL with abruptly changing bedrock contours outcropping over significantly large zones. Overburden is generally clay in varying thicknesses up to 9 meters (30 feet).

DRILLED-IN SHAFT CONCEPT

The overall objective of the offshore shaft installation work is to provide a safe, economic and sound means of connecting the ocean to the underlying tunnels. Failure in this linking-up process could have catastrophic consequences both in terms of life and property and could cause an extensive delay in putting the power plant on line.

Essentially the Seabrook drilled-in shaft concept is comprised of the following phases. A schematic shaft detail identifying the pertinent features is shown in Figure 2.

Jack-Up Barge Mobilization: The jack-up barge is towed to location and is positioned by means of its six anchor mooring system in conjunction with onshore survey station monitoring. (See Plan Figure 3 and Photograph Figure 4). The legs of the jack-up barge are then dropped, fixing the relative position. When sufficient accuracy in location has been achieved toallow for final adjustments within the tolerances of the guidance fixtures on the outrigger, the barge is jacked up to provide about 4.5 to 5.5 meters (15 to 18 feet) of clearance between the water and the underside of the barge. (See Photograph Figure 5). This distance can be increased to allow for the barge to ride out most storm conditions; eliminating the need to de-mobilize and put in to safe harbor in all but extreme storm cases. Once the barge is jacked to its operating elevation, remaining equipment transferred to the jack-up deck, and the outrigger guide assembled, work on the shaft sinking can proceed much like a land based operation.

Although the use of a jack-up barge is costly, its use for long duration open sea work is more than compensated for by the efficient use of equipment and personnel on the fixed platform operation. In comparison, a floating operation would have incurred numerous shutdowns and greatly reduced efficiencies during the less than ideal weather and sea state conditions.

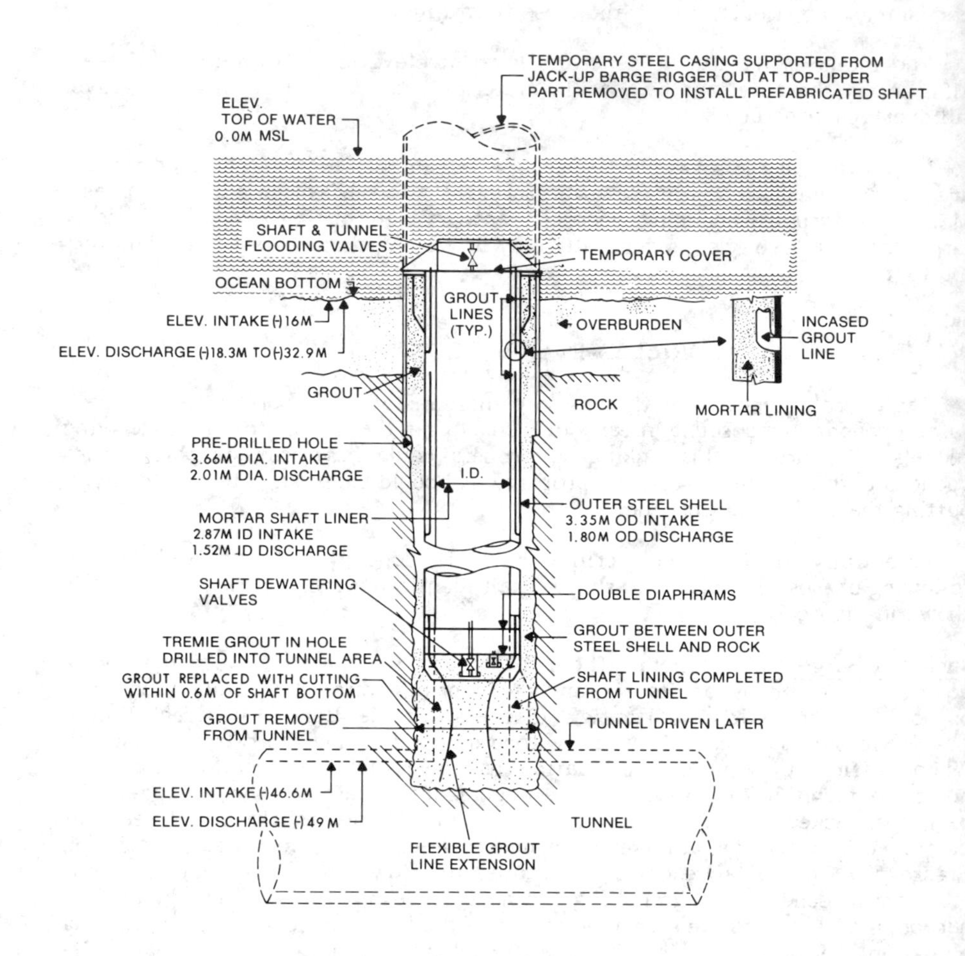

SCHEMATIC SHAFT DETAIL

FIGURE 2

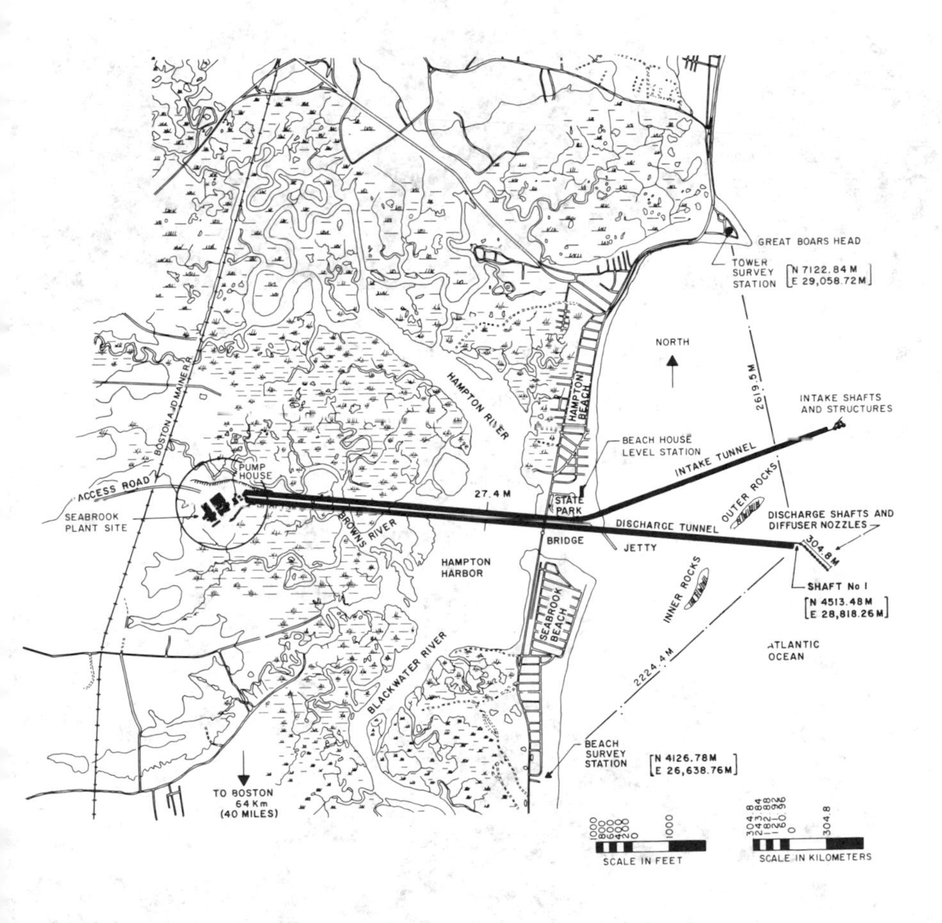

TUNNEL PLAN

FIGURE 3

JACK-UP BARGE UNDER TOW

FIGURE 4

JACK-UP BARGE IN POSITION

FIGURE 5

Driving The Casing: The initial step is to drive a temporary casing (or drill sleeve), slightly larger than the hole to be drilled, through the overburden and somewhat into the rock (See Figure 2). A core boring may be taken prior to driving the casing to verify or determine rock condition. At that point the overburden is removed down to the rock by claming or drilling. The presence of overburden is desirable to stabilize the temporary casing and to seal the casing to the rock. Once the casing has been seated and cleaned, the drilling work can commence.

Drilling: The rotary drill drive table is set up on the temporary casing and the drill bit, stabilizer and drilling weights inserted into the casing and drilling started (See Figure 6 and 7). Apart from special problems, drilling continues until it is necessary to extend the drill string length in 3m (9.8 ft) increments, adjust the stabilizer diameter or to perform maintenance. The hole is drilled "blind" utilizing the reverse circulation, method which removes the cuttings by air lift while the drilling is in progress. All cuttings and drill water is collected and filtered, with the cuttings being stored for transfer to a land disposal area and the clean water returned to the drill sleeve. See photographs of drill table arrangement, drill bits and filtering system, Figures 8 to 11.

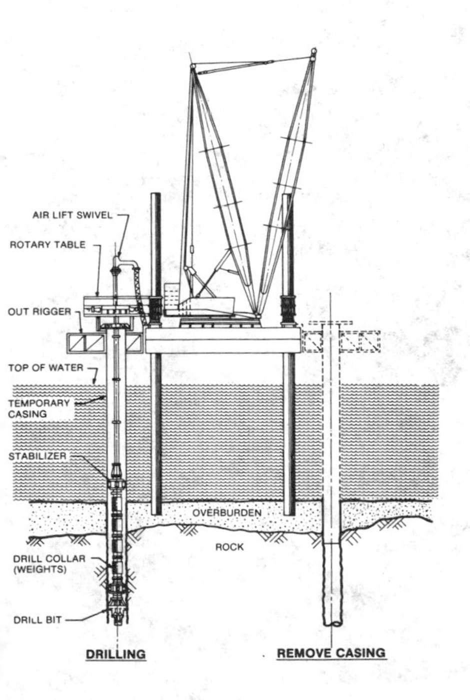

DRILLING SET-UP

FIGURE 6

INTAKE - 3.66 METER DIA
DRILL AND STABILIZER

FIGURE 7

DISCHARGE DRILL CASING AND DRILL TABLE

FIGURE 8

DISCHARGE - 2 METER DIA. DRILL BIT

FIGURE 9

INTAKE - 3.66 METER DIA. DRILL BIT

FIGURE 10

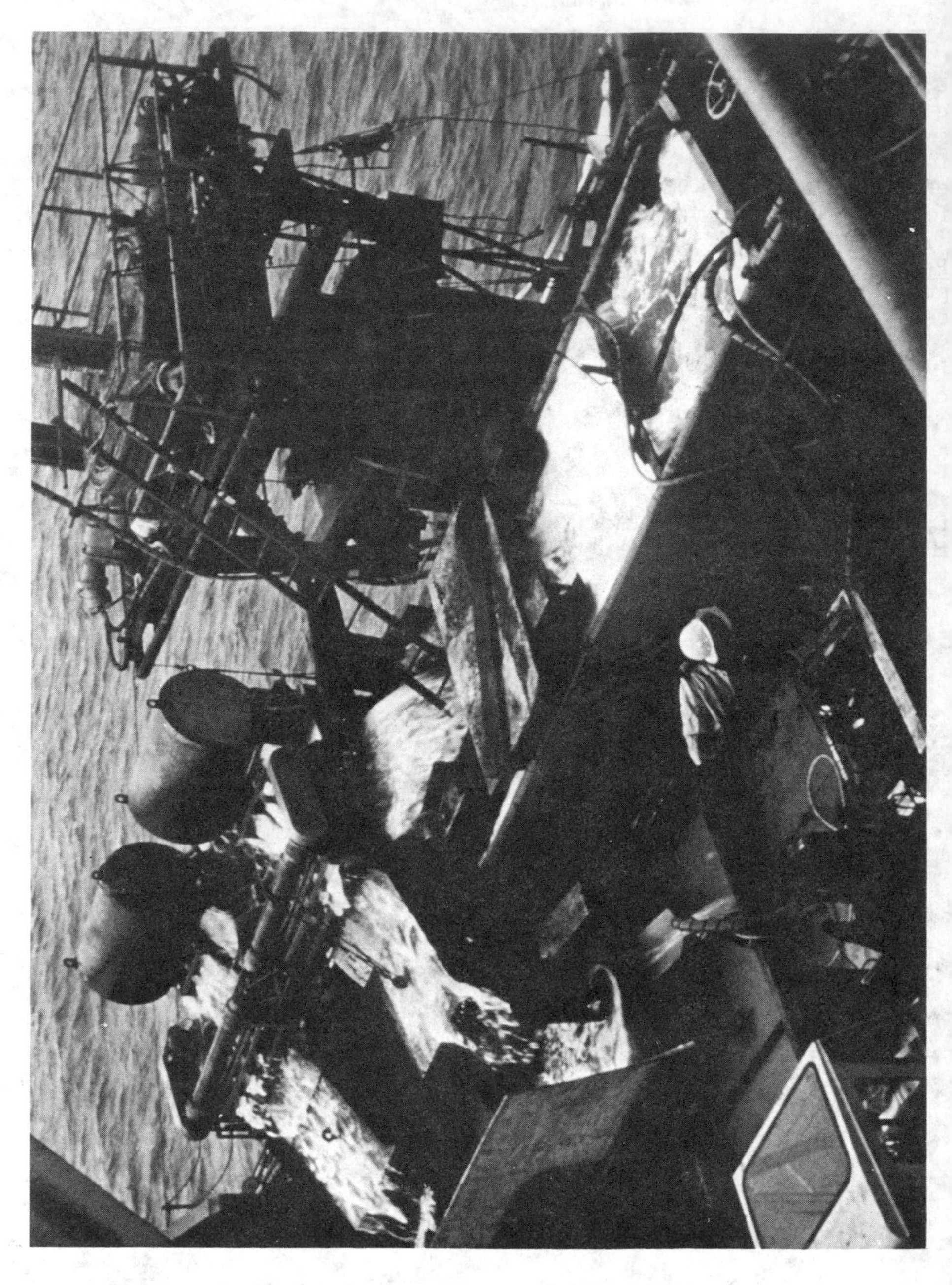

DRILL TABLE AND FILTERING SYSTEM

FIGURE 11

Casing Removal: After completion of the drilling and de-mobilization of the drilling equipment, the upper portion of the temporary casing is cut off at the desired elevation by divers. (See Figures 2 and 6). The main cut is made from a special template platform within the casing and the final "freeing" cuts made from the exterior. The upper casing is then removed and utilized with a new extension length and outfitted with a "driving shoe" in order to provide guidance for the next shaft drilling sequence.

Prefabricated Shaft Installation: After removal of the outrigger guide, the prefabricated shaft is lifted into position over the open drilled hole by the onboard crane, grout lines attached to the top of the suspended prefabricated shaft and the shaft assembly lowered into hole (See Figure 12 and 13) until the flange of the prefabricated shaft is resting on the remaining portions of the casing.

One of the limiting factors associated with the drilled-in shaft concept is that of being able to handle the length and/or weight of the pre-fabricated shaft during off loading and installation. The 81.6 ton (90 short tons) air weight for the empty discharge shafts is within the safe range of the crane (even if filled with water) so that handling of these shafts is more or less routine for this type of work. (See Photograph Figure 13).

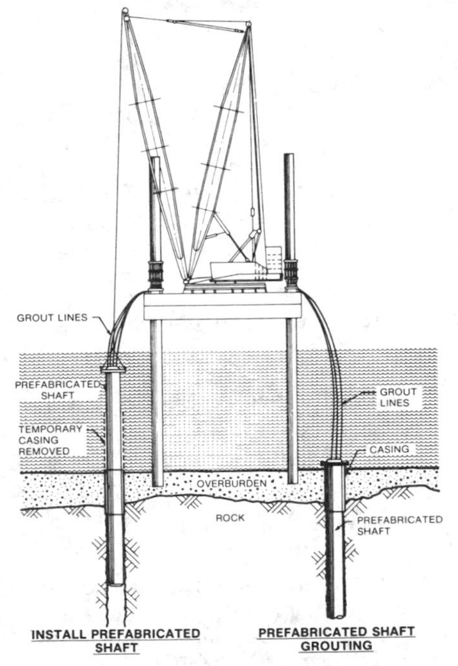

SHAFT SETTING AND GROUTING SET-UP

FIGURE 12

PRE-FABRICATED DISCHARGE SHAFT

FIGURE 13

The intake shafts however, weigh approximately 213.2 tons (235 short tons) air weight and exceeded the crane capacity without further allowance for impact or internal water. Special handling techniques were used for the intake shafts which employ the jacking systems on the barge along with reduction in weight through buoyancy. This technique will be described later under Intake Shaft Construction Experience.

The intake velocity cap is mounted during the offshore shaft work utilizing a two stage location of the temporary cover (See Figure 14). Like the pre-fabricated intake shaft, the weight of the intake velocity cap exceeds the crane's capacity and advantage of special rigging off of the jack-up barge platform was required to set the caps and is described under Intake Shaft Construction Experience.

Prefabricated Shaft Grouting: The annulus between the rock and the prefabricated shaft is grouted to seal and secure the shaft in place (See Figures 2 and 12). The grout is pumped in stages through the lines incorporated in the prefabricated shaft lining. Grout injection is controlled to insure that the shaft is not floated out of the hole by the greater grout density and injection pressure. Apart from the velocity cap and nozzle attachments to the ocean side of the shafts the offshore shaft installation work is essentially complete with grouting in of the shaft, and awaits the final "dry-tap" operation when the tunnels reach that location.

Dry Tap: As the tunnels reach each shaft locations the material filling the drilled space between the bottom of the prefabricated shaft and the tunnel (about 2.4 meters or about 8 feet deep) is removed exposing the bottom diaphragm of the shaft (See Figure 2). The shaft is drained and checked for water tight integrity through valves built into the lower diaphragms. The shaft diaphragms remain until the tunnel and shaft linings are ready to be connected with a smooth transition section. The "dry-tap" of the shafts to the tunnels is now complete.

Once the diaphragms are cut the entire security of the tunnels is dependent on the integrity of the shaft and the temporary cover at the top of the shaft.

When the tunnel lining work has been completed, the tunnels are flooded by diver operated valves located in the temporary shaft cover. The temporary shaft covers are removed and discharge nozzles mounted, completing the linking of the ocean to the land based pumphouse.

SHAFT WORK DESIGN ASPECTS

The drilled-in shaft concept includes many pre-engineered construction features. Close coordination between engineering and construction is necessary to finalize the construction related features. Because the many engineered features of the drilled-in concept are an integral part of the handling and installation techniques it is difficult to separate the basic design from the installation techniques. Many small steps and detailed features, too numerous to discuss, make up a vital compliment necessary to a successful drilled-in, dry-tap, shaft intallation.

The following represent the major design parameters, construction details and system developments associated with the basic design.

Design Loadings: In addition to forces associated with handling and installation techniques, the shafts and bulkhead diaphragms are designed for full hydrostatic pressure, lateral overburden pressures and rock loadings determined from an evaluation of the surrounding rock jointing and postulated failure planes. Forces acting on the structures protruding above the ocean bottom are transferred to the shafts and incorporated in the total design loading. Hydrodynamic wave forces have been computed on the basis of a design wave of 17.68 meters (58 feet) high as determined from a refraction analysis of the deepwater significant wave corresonding to a wind velocity of 40.23 m/s (90 mph) and a 12 hour duration. Stillwater depth was considered 22.1 meters (72.5 feet) including 3.81 meters (12.5 feet) of tide surge. A load factor of 1.5 was used as an added safety factor for calculated hydrodynamic forces.

Materials

Steel Plate: 5.08 cm (2 inches) thick and under ASTM A285 gr C; over 5.08 cm (2 inches) thick ASTM A515 gr 55.

Shaft Mortar Lining: 50% Sand, 50% ASTM C Type V Cement by volume.

Concrete: 34.47 MPa (5000 psi) Compressive Strength, Type V Cement or Modified Type II with C_3A Less than 5%.

Grout: Type V Neat Cement with anti-bleeding agent.

Concrete Reinforcing: ASTM A615 gr 60, with 25 to 50 MicroM (1-2 mil) wrought nickel coating.

Cladding: 90-10 Copper Nickel Sheeting.

Codes and Standards

Steel: American Water Works Association (AWWA) - Standard D100 for all but temporary handling loads where American Institute of Steel Construction, Design Specification was used.

Concrete: American Concrete Institute Standard 318 (ACI 318).

Mortar Lining: AWWA - Standard C100 and ACI 318.

Welding: American Society of Mechanical Engineers, Section IX Specifications.

Miscellaneous Features

Mortar Lining: The spray mortar pipe lining technique was adopted to line the shafts through a series of full scale mock-up tests. Various destructive tests were made to ascertain the effectiveness and soundness of the application.

Grout: Load tests were performed on neat cement with and without an anti-bleed agent and a non-shrink, premixed grout. Specimens were designed to obtain bond values while simulating in place conditions. Although the non-shrink grout produced bond values 3 to 4 times greater than the neat cement, the less costly neat cement provided sufficient bond values to satisfy the design requirements with a 4 to 1 safety factor.

Copper Nickel Cladding: The entire exterior surface of the intake velocity caps are clad with copper nickel sheeting to eliminate marine growths that may serve to attract fish and increase the chance of fish being drawn into the system.

Nickel Coated Reinforcing: Although good design and construction practices were employed to obtain durable concrete intake velocity caps in the marine environment, the presence of the copper nickel cladding and cover seats provided an added potential corrosion problem. Tests on nickel coated concrete reinforcing bars in marine envirionments have indicated very good resistance to corrosion[5]. Additionally the nickel coating process produces an "inert" diffusion zone of steel and nickel which serves to negate the potential corrosion problem of the dissimilar steel reinforcing and the copper nickel metals.

EQUIPMENT

Essential to operating a construction effort of this type, is the obtaining of equipment suitable to meet the necessary performance requirements yet with sufficient re-use demands to enable recovery of investment cost making the overall concept justifiably economical. In the case of the Seabrook shaft project, fabricating and collecting the required equipment was a formidable task. It was further complicated by the fact that very little work of this nature has been done in this section of the world.

In addition to the compliment of tugs, barges, crew boats, compressors, generators, etc. necessary to support the effort, the following represents the major pieces of special equipment that were vital to the successfull Seabrook shaft installation work.

Jack-Up Barge: Commissioned the JAY ROBERTSON, the jack-up barge was designed and fabricated on the east coast. The platform is 25.6 meters wide by 48.8 meters long (84 x 160 feet) with a deck design pay-load of 27.4 Kg/m^2(650 psf). The barge has facilities and provisions to support short term live-on requirements. Six, 1.8 meter (71 inch) diameter legs are used to lift and hold the platform, utilizing a 1088 ton (1200 short ton) holding capacity, DeLong Air Operated jack on each leg. Jacks are capable of lifting 454 tons (500 short tons). Provision for the addition of two more legs has been built into the platform.

The jack-up was outfitted with a Manitowac Model 4100 crane with a ringer, which was load tested at 193 tons (212.5 short tons). The outfitted barge meets the approval of the American Bureau of Ships (ABS) and the U.S. Coast Guard.

Hammer: MENCK, Model MRBS 1500/2 (used)
Rated Striking Energy per blow - 183,876 Nm (135,620 foot pounds)
Falling weight - 18,000 Kg (33,000 pounds)
Maximum stroke 1.25 meters (49.25 inches)
Anvil Outside Diameter - 1.75 meters (68.77 inches)
Total Net Weight - 53,790 Kg (118,580 pounds)

Drilling Equipment: WIRTH, Reverse criculation Rotary Table Size 2110S (used)
Maximum Torque - 352,513 Nm (260,000 foot-pounds)
Table Opening - 2.11 meters (83 inches)
Air Lift Inside Diameter - 31.75 cm (12.5 inches)
Maximum Rock Drill Diameter 4.06 meters (13'-4")
Hydraulic Power Pack - 2 - 1148 Kw (154 HP) motors

Drill Bits: REED Tool Company, Big Hole Products Division, Special Fabrication
Discharge Shaft 2.0 meters (79 inch) diameter
Intake Shaft - 3.66 meters (144 inch) diameter
Cutters - Discharge & QC 1, 2, 3 & 4;
Intake - QKC 1, 2, 3 & 4; with replaceable inner roller bearings, average life of roller assembly, 200 drilling hours.

Surveying Equipment:
Positioning - Wild, Mode T2, Theodolite
Distance Checking - K&E, Ranger IV
Level - Ziess, Double Columniation, Valley Crossing

Underwater Cutting: Ciucas Diving and Marine Engineering Ltd.
KERIE Cutting Cable

Caisson Clam: Casagrande & Company, Italy
Single line Hammer Grab Bel, 1.78 meters (70 inch) diameter

DISCHARGE SHAFT CONSTRUCTION EXPERIENCE

After considerable, unplanned, legal, licensing and labor related delays, release was finally given to proceed with the Seabrook offshore work and on October 7 1977 the jack-up barge was towed to sea from its storage in Portsmouth, New Hampshire and positioned on location between Discharge Shafts No. 1 and No. 2 (nearest shafts to shore). As time would show, the delayed start shifted the entire operation into less than desirable weather conditions, forcing further delays in work and initially, reduced efficiencies. Several attempts were necessary to position the jack-up because of rough seas, which continued to hamper the mobilization and transfer of supplies and equipment for several weeks. Positioning of the jack-up was directed from two shore line stations about 3840 meters (12,600 feet) apart, having lines of sight to the jack-up of about 2621 and 2225 meters (8600 and 7300 feet) (See Plan-Figure 3). During this mobilization period the rock was cored for shafts to be installed from that location. (Note: The jack-up is outfitted to enable two shafts to be installed from one location in between the two, with differing work being done at the same time, i.e., drilling on one side, grouting on the other.)

In general, two - 10 hour shifts are utilized per day and no work performed on weekends or holidays except for maintenance and watch.

Further problems were encountered with getting equipment to function properly due to long storage, but finally on October 31, 1977 the temporary steel casing (or drill sleeve) for Discharge Shaft No. 2 was driven to rock through 8.5 meters (28 feet) of silt and clay overburden to elevation (-)26.8 meters (88 feet). When mucking of the overburden commenced using the drill bit, the settling basin provided to clean up the drill water proved to be inadequate to "filter" the water to meet the stringent environmental discharge requirements. One major contributor to the problem was over 0.126 m^3/s discharge of frothy, silty water from the air lift which kept the fine particles in suspension. Modifications to the filtering systems were made to obtain a satisfactorily clean discharge water. Limited deck space was further crowded by the necessity to extend the water cleaning system.

On November 15, 1977 rock drilling commenced for the 79 inch diameter hole and bottomed out at elevation (-) 49 meter (161.0 feet) on November 29. Some further problems were encountered in initiating this new phase of the work with the recently un-tried equipment but most all problems were corrected during this start-up period so that no future significant delays occurred. Drill string weight was about 99.8 tons (110 short tons) (air weight) producing an average drilling rate of about one foot per hour for the 2 meter (79 inch) diameter hole in the diorite. During the initial drilling stage in the surface weathered rock the drill sleeve followed the drill for about 1.8 meters (six feet) before locking up apparently due to "raveling" of the poorer quality rock.

On November 30, 1977 work was started on Discharge Shaft No. 1 with the driving of the drill sleeve through the overburden to elevation (-) 26.5 meters (87 feet) and extended by a welded additional section the following day. In marked contrast to Shaft No. 2, the 7.9 meters (26 feet) of overburden in Shaft No. 1 was mucked out with little incident in only 8 hours utilizing the Caisson Clam.

After re-mobilizing the filtering system, drilling was started on No. 1 on December 28 and bottomed out on January 13, 1978 at elevation (-)49.2 meter (161.5 feet) with interruptions due to holidays and bad weather. The drill sleeve on this hole followed the drill for about 3.7 meters (11.2 feet) into the rock before locking up and sealing off.

During the drilling of No. 1 discharge Shaft, work continued December 22 on Shaft No. 2 with the cutting of the drill sleeve by divers just above the mud line on December 28 in preparation for the installation of the prefabricated shaft. On December 30 the prefabricated shaft was barged out, set in the water (Photograph Figure 12), re-slung, righted and inserted into the open hole while flooding without any difficulties.

The first stage (about 9.1 meters or 30 feet up the shaft from the bottom) of Shaft No. 2 was grouted in 13 hours on January 4, 1978 and allowed to set-up to insure against floatation prior to completing the grouting of the remainder of the shaft. Grouting was completed in 4-1/2 hours, two days later. An air lift was inserted down into the annulus through designed holes in the top of the prefabricated shaft to determine the proper elevation to cut off the first stage grouting and also to know when to initiate the third stage tremie grouting to prevent the grout from being discharged into "free" water. Of special note was the fact that the actual grout "take" was only 13% greater than the neat hole volume calculated with a one inch allowance for over break. This indicates that very little loss of the side walls occurred during drilling.

On January 17, 1978, Shaft No. 1 drill sleeve was prepared for removal by cutting the sleeve just above the mud line which left only 3 places about 15 cm (6 inches) long to be cut when the upper part of the sleeve was to be removed. Further work was deferred due to an impending storm.

A change in sea conditions permitted the final cutting and removal of the sleeve on January 19. Total cutting time was about 4 hours for the preparatory cut and one hour for the final cut. Due to very low temperatures and problems with oxygen manifold freezing it was necessary to make the sleeve cuts with a carbon arc in place of the KERIE cutting cable.

On January 23, Discharge Shaft No. 1 was set in place, the first stage grouted in 5 hours, allowed to set for 12 hours and the next day the remaining annulus grouted in 8 hours. Again good correlation between the calculated and actual grout take was found indicating a neatly drilled hole.

Unlike the first shaft installed, the space below the inserted pre-fabricated shaft was filled with drill cuttings to within 60 cm (2 feet) of the bottom of the inserted shaft. This not only reduces the amount of grout to be placed and any of its associated problems but also facilitates the removal of the material from the tunnel to access the bottom of the pre-fabricated shaft.

In all 91 tons (100 short tons) of cement was used to grout in the two pre-fabricated shafts.

On January 30th the jack-up barge was moved to its next position between Discharge Shafts No. 3 and No. 4, uneventfully, in good weather, in only 9 hours. Positioning was within one foot of an "exact" location, and although closer tolerances could be obtained, available outrigger adjustments did not warrant further re-positioning.

The details associated with the drilling and installation of Shafts 1 and 2 have been elaborated on to provide a description of the general characteristics and envolvements of the work. Accomplishment dates for key events are provided for comparative purposes for Shafts 3 through 11. Dates are given instead of durations in order that seasonal weather conditions associated with the New England Atlantic Ocean may be appropriated.

Discharge Shaft No.	Casing Set	Drilling Start	Drilling Finished	Shaft Set	Shaft Grouted
	On Location 1-3-78; Ready to Relocate 3-29-78				
3	2-10-78	2-15-78	3-3-78	3-24-78	3-29-78
4	3-1-78	3-8-78	3-22-78	3-24-78	3-29-78
	On Location 3-30-78; Ready to Relocate 5-5-78				
5	3-31-78	4-5-78	4-14-78	5-2-78	5-5-78
6	4-17-78	4-17-78	5-1-78	5-2-78	5-5-78

Discharge Shaft No.	Casing Set	Drilling Start	Drilling Finished	Shaft Set	Shaft Grouted
	On Location 5-19-78; Ready to Relocate 6-30-78				
7	6-7-78	6-8-78	6-26-78	6-77-78	6-29-78
8	5-22-78	5-23-78	6-6-78	6-27-78	6-29-78
	On Location 6-30-78; Ready to Relocate 7-20-78				
9	7-3-78	7-6-78	7-17-78	7-19-78	7-19-78
10	7-3-78	-	-	-	-
	On Location 7-20-78; Ready to Relocate 9-15-78				
10	8-14-78	8-17-78	8-29-78	8-30-78	9-1-78
11	8-29-78	9-1-78	9-12-78	9-13-78	9-15-78

The following are some of the more significant events and details relating to the installation of Shafts 3 through 11.

- About five days were lost while on Shafts 3 and 4 due to the blizzard of 1978. Storm lasted about 2½ days, tearing off Shaft No. 3 casing and outrigger. About 2½ days were required to bring up, repair and reinstall the casing and outrigger.

- Almost two weeks were lost while waiting for calm seas to move from Shafts 3 and 4 to 5 and 6.

- After drilling and setting Shaft No. 9 the Jack-up was located between Shafts 10 and 11 and secured during a temporary shut-down by the NRC lasting from 7-20-78 to 8-14-78.

- Overburden at shaft locations 5 through 11 was shallow or non-existant. Shafts 6 and 11 required minor blasting of rock-out crops to level surface sufficient to seat casing and start drilling. Out-croping very irregular, varing as much as 6 m (20 ft) in 30.5 m (100 ft).

- Drilling rates were generally about 305 mm per hour (1.0 ft/hr) with rates as low as 140 mm per hour (0.46 ft/hr) in some of the harder diorite.

- For the most part very little driving of the casings was required. Raveling of upper weathered rock surface and the weight and vibration of the drilling operation were sufficient to socket the casing in the rock. The drilling weight on the casing was always more then the weight of a flooded shaft. Grout was calculated to take the full weight of a flooded shaft without the need to count on casing support.

- The tops of each shaft were sealed against the casing for grouting by the use of a 101 mm (4inch) diameter rubber hose, which became crushed into the annular space between the two when the pre-fabricated shaft was inserted.

- Typical down-time during the operation involved regular removal of drill-string to tighten bolts and replace cutter bearings, equipment repairs, hydraulic repairs and transfering of equipment and supplies to and from the jack-up barge.

INTAKE SHAFT CONSTRUCTION EXPERIENCE

The scheme for drilling of the Intake Shafts is essentially the same as that described for the Discharge Shafts. (See Photograph - Figure 14) Installation of the pre-fabricated shafts and velocity caps required special handling techniques because of weights in excessive of onboard crane capacity. Work on the intake shafts started shortly after the completion of the discharge shafts with the following key dates and details of drilling:

Intake Shaft No.	Casing Set	Drilling Start	Drilling Finished	Shaft Set	Shaft Grouted
	On Location 9-19-78; Ready to Relocate 1-13-79				
1	10-10-78	10-26-78	11-24-78	1-10-79	1-13-79
2	10-18-78	12-4-78	12-20-78	1-5-79	1-11-79
	On Location 1-13-79				
3	1-24-79	2-1-79	2-14-79	2-22-79	2-28-79

Setting of velocity caps and grouting were completed on the following dates:

Intake Shaft No.	Cap Set	Cap Grouted
3	3-16-79	3-23-79
2	3-28-79	3-30-79
1	4-18-79	4-25-79

The rock conditions in the intake shaft is very block quarzites having low RQD's (See Ref. 1) which brought original concern over the ability to maintain a stable hole during drilling for such a large hole. Hole stability never did become a problem. The hole walls raveled very little as conformed by the actual grout take. Average rate for drilling of the 3.66 m (12 ft) diameter holes was about 152 mm (0.5 ft) per hour.

Clamming time, utilizing the caisson claim averaged about two days per shaft.

Drilling Intake Shaft No. 1

Casing was driven by hammer 10.5 m (34.5 ft) into the over burden from the seabed elevation of (-) 16 m (52.4 ft). Casing was then clammed out to the top of rock at elevation (-) 29.5 m (96.8 ft) allowing the casing to follow down an additional 3 m (10 ft). Rock drilling was introduced and casing followed drill an additional 5 m (16 ft) into the rock until it finally seized up. Drilling continued to elevation (-) 47 m (154.3 ft) giving a total depth of hole from seabed of 31 meters (102 feet).

Drilling Intake Shaft No. 2

Casing was set on location at seabed elevation (-) 16 m (52.4 ft) and clammed out allowing the casing to follow down to the rock at elevation (-) 27 m (89 ft). Rock drilling commenced with casing following an additional 4.6 m (15 ft) into the rock. Rock was drilled out to a final elevation of (-) 46.6 m (153 ft) giving a total depth of hole of 30.7 meters (100.6 feet).

Drilling Intake Shaft No. 3

Casing was set on location at seabed elevation (-) 16.8 m (55 ft) and clammed to within 1.1 m (3.5 ft) of rock which was at elevation (-) 30 m (85 ft). Casing continued to follow the clamming. The remaining over burden was removed by drilling. Casing followed the drill only 0.9 m (3 ft) into the rock. Hole was drilled to elevation (-) 46.1 m (151.3 ft) for a total depth of 29.3 meters (96.3 feet).

Setting of Pre-fabricated Intake Shafts

Due to the reach-load limit of the on-board crane it was necessary to derive and alternative scheme to handle the 213 ton (235 short ton) pre-fabricated shafts utilizing already available equipment and facilities. The basic scheme vas to utilize the excess capacity of the jack-up barge jacking system and 'educe the effective weight on the crane by taking advantage of the shaft ›ouyancy.

Since the shafts were bouyant, they could be barged to the area, rolled off he barge and floated into the desired position under the jack-up barge just ıbove the drilled hole. (See Photograph Figure 15) The shafts were previously ›ut-fitted with temporary trunions to which cable slings were attached with the ack-up in a lowered position. The barge was then elevated, raising the shaft Photograph - Figure 16) sufficient to clear the casing when the shaft was ighted by the on-board crane (Figures 17 and 18). Once the shaft was righted, ufficient bouyancy was available to allow the shaft to be handled by the crane. \fter re-slinging the crane to the top of the shaft and the load taken up, the emporary trunnions were cut free allowing the shafts to be lowered into the ıole and seated on the casing. Grouting was carried out similar to that lescribed for the discharge shafts with the actual grout take coming out very :lose to the calculated annulus volumes with only about 50 mm (2 inches) ıllowed for over reaming.

;etting of the Velocity Caps

Unlike the discharge shafts, which would be out-fitted with nozzles after looding of the tunnels, the three intake shafts were to be completed by the ıddition of a 9.3 m (30.5 ft) diameter, 227 tons (250 short ton) Velocity Cap cap). This cap, as shown in Figure 19, was designed to utilize the temporary :over from the shaft to re-seal the shaft once the cap was in place.

Again the on-board crane load-reach capacity was exceeded, requiring a lifferent concept of handling. All three caps were constructed on a large barge ıt a dock facility on the Piscataqua River, up stream from Portsmouth, New ɬampshire. From there, they were towed approximately (17 miles) to the shaft ;ite. A special out-rigger was fabricated and out-fitted with two pairs of ten ;heave blocks. The twin line pull was provided by a 13.6 (15 short ton) line pull Manitowac deck winch. Since the rate of assent (pick) was critical to have the :ap clear the barge to prevent being smashed by the rising swell, jacking of the ›arge was utilized to make the final lift.

Due to the deep peneteration of the jack-up barge legs into the thick over-›urden and subsequent reduction in leg height, the distance available to have :he cap clear the floating barge become critical and could only be acheived at :he time the tide was at its lowest. Photographs of the cap and operaton are ;hown in Figures 20 and 21.

All three caps were set, grouted and temporary cover replaced by May 1, 1979 to complete this phase of the shaft installation.

DRILLING SET-UP FOR INTAKE SHAFTS

FIGURE 14

INTAKE SHAFT FLOATED INTO POSITION FOR LIFTING

FIGURE 15

INTAKE SHAFT LIFTED BY TEMPORARY TRUNNIONS

FIGURE 16

INTAKE SHAFT RIGHTED ON TEMPORARY TRUNNION

FIGURE 17

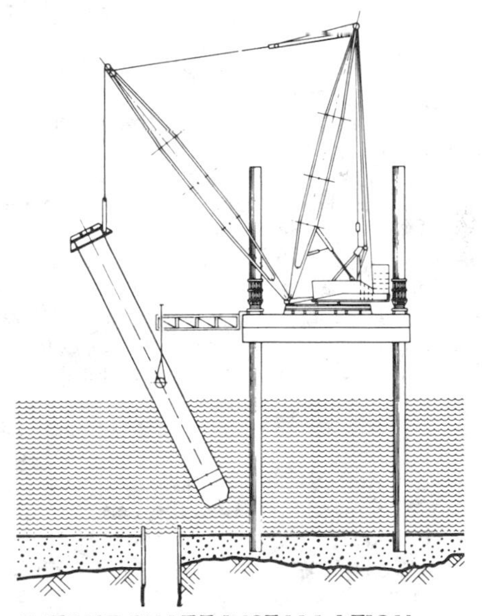

INTAKE SHAFT INSTALLATION SET-UP

FIGURE 18

SUMMARY

Numerous storms occurred during the offshore shaft work, producing seas with 6 m (20 ft) waves, winds 80 to 97 km (50 to 60 miles) per hour, gusts up to 145 km (90 miles) per hour, and sub freezing temperatures and icy conditions, which required a virtual halt to all work and the transfer of personnel, and the necessity to secure the crane boom on a number of occasions. Of particular difficulity was the inability to predict with any accuracy the short range sea state closer than 3 or 4 hours which created near hazardous situations with nearby moored vessels being utilized to transfer materials and equipment.

The Seabrook marine shafts do not represent a special acheivement because of their depth or diameter of the holes drilled but rather because of the uniqueness of the combination of construction conditions, prefabricated shaft and cap sizes and rigid controls necessary to acheive a successful and dependable installation.

The concept of underwater drilling and lining of shafts in not entirely new and has been successfully utilized on several projects to connect large bodies of water to subsurface tunnels. (References given in Ref. 1) The Seabrook shafts, while utilizing the same general concept, represents significant differences in geological conditions, shaft diameter and length so than when coupled with the necessity to install the shafts in 15 to 21 meters (50 to 70 feet) of water 1.6 km (a mile) or more out in the Atlantic Ocean presents a challenge that has, to the writers' knowledge, no known precedent.

The drilled-in concept discussed, presents a method of installing reasonably large diameter shafts for safe connection to under water chambers that is more desirable and economical than that of the conventional caisson or cofferdam approach.

The drilled-in shaft concept is particularly attractive where geological conditions permit the drilling of large diameter holes in the rock without the need for a full depth casing. Under these conditions, the only basic limitations to shaft size and depth will be that of available drilling equipment and the ability to handle the size and weight of the prefabricated shafts and associated structures. Prefabricated shafts can be installed and joined in sections, so that depth is not limited to a single length of shaft lining.

CONCLUSIONS

A complete shaft connection for marine environments cannot be seperated from the installation of the required lining and finishing structure. The efforts carried out for the Seabrook shafts have proven that a safe, ecconomical method is available for dry-tapping into underwater chambers, even at considerable distances out into the ocean.

The Seabrook offshore shaft installation represents a major undertaking and the experience gained through this installation has provided valuable information and confidence that will further the development and use of underwater connecting shafts.

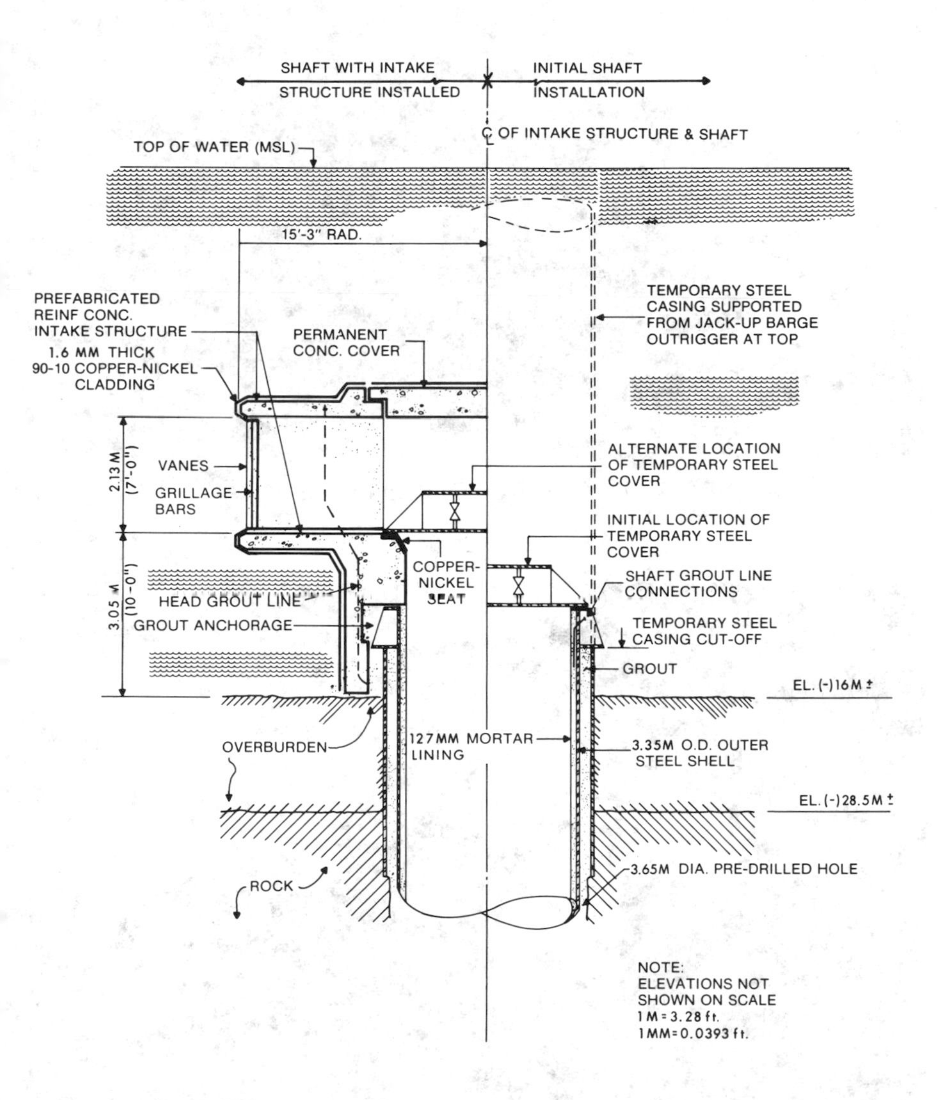
SHAFT WITH INTAKE STRUCTURE INSTALLED
INITIAL SHAFT INSTALLATION
℄ OF INTAKE STRUCTURE & SHAFT
TOP OF WATER (MSL)
15'-3" RAD.
PREFABRICATED REINF CONC. INTAKE STRUCTURE
1.6 MM THICK 90-10 COPPER-NICKEL CLADDING
PERMANENT CONC. COVER
TEMPORARY STEEL CASING SUPPORTED FROM JACK-UP BARGE OUTRIGGER AT TOP
2.13 M (7'-0")
VANES
GRILLAGE BARS
ALTERNATE LOCATION OF TEMPORARY STEEL COVER
INITIAL LOCATION OF TEMPORARY STEEL COVER
COPPER-NICKEL SEAT
SHAFT GROUT LINE CONNECTIONS
3.05 M (10'-0")
HEAD GROUT LINE
GROUT ANCHORAGE
TEMPORARY STEEL CASING CUT-OFF
GROUT
EL. (-)16M ±
OVERBURDEN
127MM MORTAR LINING
3.35M O.D. OUTER STEEL SHELL
EL. (-)28.5M ±
ROCK
3.65M DIA. PRE-DRILLED HOLE
NOTE:
ELEVATIONS NOT SHOWN ON SCALE
1M = 3.28 ft.
1MM = 0.0393 ft.

TYPICAL SECTION THROUGH TOP OF INTAKE SHAFT AND VELOCITY CAP

FIGURE 19

9.3 METER (30'-6") DIA. INTAKE VELOCITY CAP

FIGURE 20

INSTALLATION OF 227 TON (250 SHORT TON) VELOCITY CAP

FIGURE 21

ACKNOWLEDGEMENTS

The Seabrook Station Power Plant is jointly owned by a number of utilities. Public Service Company of New Hampshire is the major shareholder and agent for the Owners. Yankee Atomic Electric Company is the Engineering supervisor for the Owners.

United Engineers & Constructors Inc. are the Architect-Engineers and Construction Manager for the plant including the circulating water tunnels and shaft system. Morrison-Knudsen Co. Inc. is the contractor for the tunnel and shaft work.

REFERENCES

(1) Hulshizer, A.J., Desai, A.J. and Dave, B.J., "Drilling and Lining of the Ocean Shafts - Seabrook Power Project," Proceedings - Rapid Excavation and Tunneling Conference, Las Vegas, Nevada, June, 1976, pp 148-168.

(2) Hulshizer, A.J., et al, "Land Shaft Construction and Initial Station Development for Seabrook Station Cooling Water Tunnels," Proceedings - Rapid Excavation and Tunneling Conference, Atlanta, Georgia, June 1979, pp 1300-1316.

(3) Hulshizer, A.J., et al, "Production Experience and Computerized Evaluation of the Seabrook Tunnel Excavation," Proceedings - Rapid Excavation and Tunneling Conference, San Francisco, California, May 1981.

(4) Desai, A.J., et al, "Geologic Investigation, Prediction and Construction Evaluation For Cooling Water Tunnels - Seabrook, N.H., Nuclear Power Station," Proceedings - Rapid Excavation and Tunneling Conference, Las Vegas, Nevada, June, 1976, pp 39-63.

(5) Baker, E.A., et al, "Marine Corrosion Behavior of Bare and Metallic - Coated Steel Reinforcing Rods in Concrete," ASTM Special Technical Publication 629, Chloride Corrosion of Steel In Concrete - (June, 1976), pp 30-50.

Chapter 57

DESIGN AND CONSTRUCTION OF SHAFTS BY THE WET METHOD

by Safdar A. Gill

Principal Engineer, Soil Testing Services, Inc.
Northbrook, Illinois

ABSTRACT

The technique of installing small diameter caissons (drilled piers) through soft clays and water bearing ganular soil is well established for constructing building foundations. Over the past few years, the method has been utilized for constructing a large number of shafts extending into rock for the Chicago's Deep Tunnel Project. This paper will discuss design considerations for obtaining the most economic ground support system, the impact of construction procedures on the support and lateral pressures for design. Construction procedures will be described along with performance of the shafts.

INTRODUCTION

Excavations in urban areas have alway presented great difficulties and the construction problems are compounded when the digging is required through water bearing granular soils, soft squeezing clays, sands, gravels, and boulders, and it ends in bedrock with artesian water pressure. The technique of installing rock bearing caissons (drilled piers) through such strata for high rise buildings in the Chicago area has been well established for several decades. Rock caisson foundations for buildings require a relatively small diameter shaft; for example, the John Hancock Center caissons were mostly less than 214 cm to 305 cm (7 ft to 10 ft) in diameter and the Sears Tower, the world's highest building, had 114 caissons, 183 cm to 214 cm (6 ft to 7 ft) diameter and only two with maximum diameter of 305 cm (10 ft). Over the past few years, the Metropolitan Sanitary District of Greater Chicago has been constructing Tunnel and Reservoir Project

(TARP) for controlling overflows from combined sewers into the various rivers and canals in the area. This project includes a large number of connecting structures intercepting the sewage overflows, drop shafts, access shafts, vent shafts and manholes extending through the overburden soils into the deep tunnel which is being drilled through Silurian dolomite rock at depths of 61 to 91 m (200 to 300 ft) below the street level. The writer has designed excavation support for many of these shafts for construction by an extension of the method conventionally used for installation of rock bearing caisson foundations. This paper presents design considerations and construction procedures for these shafts and will discuss the impact of the construction procedures on ground support and lateral pressures for design.

TYPICAL SOIL PROFILE

The typical soil profile in the downtown Chicago area, where several of the drop shafts and access shafts are located, is shown in Figure 1. The near surface fill consists of sand, cinders, brick, wood, and miscellaneous materials. Below the fill is natural sand which is typically in a medium dense to very dense condition. Both these layers are water bearing with the water table a few feet above the level of Lake Michigan or that in the several branches of the Chicago River. Along the river where the drop shafts are located, the upper water table would be about 1.5 m to 2.4 m (5 ft to 8 ft) below the existing ground surface.

The strength and natural moisture content of the soft "blue" clays vary from place to place. They are normally consolidated to slightly overconsolidated deposits of glacial Lake Chicago of Wisconsinan Glacial age. Unconfined compressive strengths range from 19.2 kPa to 57.5 kPa (0.2 to 0.6 tons/sq.ft) with slight increases in strength with depth. Once the natural water content exceeds about 30% and its strength is below 38.3 to 47.9 kPa (0.4 to 0.5 tons/sq.ft), experience has shown that squeezing of the uncased auger hole would occur even at a rapid excavation rate. The unconfined strength of the stiff to hard silty clay layers ranges from 144 kPa to over 431 kPa (1.5 to over 4.5 tons/sq.ft). The "hardpan" consists of overconsolidated glacial till and it is made up of silty clay, clayey silt, silt, sand, gravel, pebbles, etc. Seams, pockets or layers of granular soils are randomly encountered in the "hardpan" as well as in the silty clay. These soils are water bearing and the water head may be the same as in the underlying rock. However, if these are confined pockets, water pressure quickly releases and excessive water inflow does not occur.

RESTRAINTS ON CAISSON INSTALLATION PROCEDURES

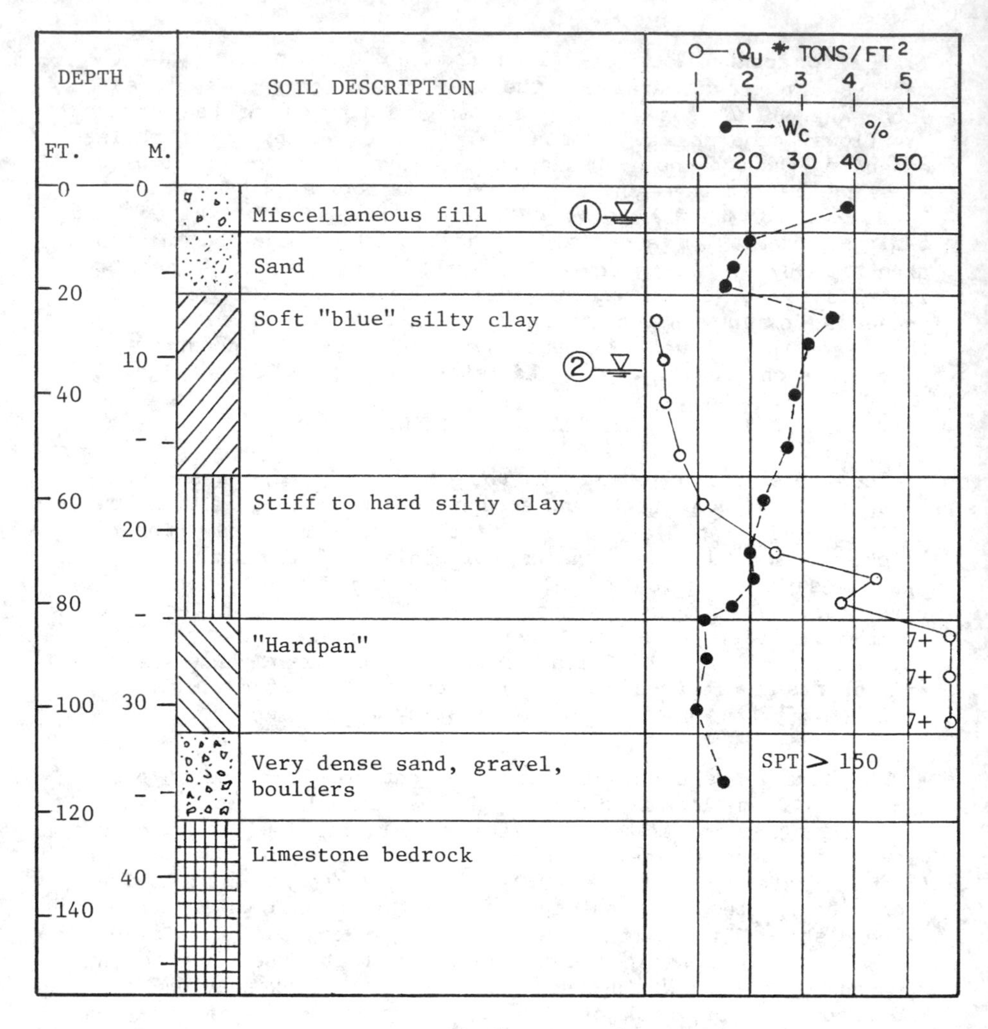

① Upper Water Table
② Water Table in Rock
o Q_u = Unconfined Compressive Strength
● W_c = Water Content
1 Ton/sq.ft = 95.8 kPa

FIGURE 1. Typical Soil Profile in Downtown Chicago

The Chicago method of caisson installation has been developed to suit local soil conditions and the environmental restraints. The shafts are typically located close to existing buildings, bridges, dock walls and outfall structures which must be maintained and continue to function during the construction of the new work. The excavation system must be safe for the workmen, prevent excessive deformations of surrounding property, should be able to be executed without excessive contraints on the contractor and finally, the method should be economical and expeditious.

The amount of deformation and settlement which is acceptable for the surrounding property varies with the location and the ownership of the property. Sometimes less restraints are enforced by public ownership than by private ownership. Even for the former, the constraints might be smaller when the damage can be easily repaired, for example, by repaving of the street surface or reconstructing curbs and gutters and sidewalks of the street as compared to the case where there is danger to gas lines and water mains.

Rock bearing caisson foundations for buildings typically require cleaning of the rock surface and inspection of the base to verify bearing capacity and absence of seams, etc. That requires that the shaft be dry and protected when the workmen are working inside. A full length steel casing is essential in such situations. Considering the typical soils in the Chicago area, there are three main considerations, namely:

1. Preventing water inflow and sloughing in of the fill soils and the granular soils near the surface.

2. Squeezing in of the soft clays.

3. Control of artesian water in the granular soils overlying the bedrock as well as in the fractured zones of the upper surface of the bedrock.

Many of the high rise buildings in the Chicago area as well as bridge structures are supported on caisson foundations bearing on the "hardpan" layer which overlies the granular layer containing artesian water pressure. There are many instances of blow-up occuring at the base of excavations for "hardpan" bearing caissons where there is insufficient thickness of the cohesive "hardpan" layer below the base of the excavation to resist the uplift pressures or when the diameter of the enlarged base becomes excessive. Sometimes this blow-up has been triggered by a probe hole or an improperly plugged soil boring hole. In any event, it is practically impossible to drill an uncased hole in the dry through the "hardpan" and extending into rock. The construction procedures normally utilized for rock bearing caissons provide for balancing the water head in the lower aquifer by keeping the shaft flooded when the excavation has reached some depth into the "hardpan". It is for this reason that the method of installation is called the wet method.

TYPICAL CONSTRUCTION PROCEDURES

Foundation Caissons

Caisson shafts for foundations are typically excavated by rotary auger attachments on large crawler mounted cranes. The attachments include telescoping kelly bars and have been developed for the drilling to the required depth upto and into rock.

On a typical site, the area of the shaft is excavated to remove old foundations and surface obstructions including old timber piles, if such exist in place. An oversized hole is then drilled in the fill and granular soils with the aid of drilling mud and an oversize temporary casing is set. It is keyed a few feet into the underlying clay to obtain a seal and the mud is pumped out from inside. Further excavation is done by auger flights. If squeezing of clays is encountered, which is easily detected during removal and insertion of the augers, then the hole is stabilized by drilling mud or a telescoping temporary steel casing is inserted through the upper casing and driven as the excavation proceeds. When squeezing of soft clays is predicted with certainty, then the first stage drilling with mud extends to the bottom of the soft clay stratum and the oversize temporary casing is sealed into the lower very stiff clays. A criteria suggested by Lukas and Baker (1978) is that squeezing is very likely when the ratio of effective overburden pressure to the undrained shear strength is on the order of 8 to 9 or more.

The drilling of shafts in the very stiff to hard clays and through the "hardpan" is made in the dry by means of auger flights if the squeezing clays are contained by a steel casing. On the other hand, if the shaft is stabilized by drilling mud, then the rest of the excavation will continue in the wet still utilizing the auger flights for the excavation in the zone of clay and "hardpan". For the former case, the hole is flooded with drilling mud once refusal to the auger flight is reached or if granular zones are indicated or when it is estimated that the remaining cohesive hardpan is insufficient to balance the water head in the lower aquifer. Thereafter, the remaining excavation would be done under a slurry head. If the excavation is through granular soils, the auger is turned and also moved up and down to form a slurry of the granular soils with the drilling mud. The material may remain in suspension if the slurry is not excessively heavy or it may be removed by a bailing bucket. Once refusal to excavation by this method is reached, or in some cases even before excavating fully through the hardpan, a heavy wall steel casing called core barrel which has hardened carbide cutting teeth at the bottom, is set within the surface temporary steel casing. The core barrel is turned by the drilling rig and screwed through the dense silt, sand and gravel, into the underlying bedrock. This casing would remain permanently in place and form an outer shell for the caisson.

The carbide teeth at the bottom of the core barrel permit socketing it into rock. The bottom of the casing is inserted at least 1 ft into rock and deeper where the upper zone of the rock is fractured and excessive water inflow is expected. The intention is to obtain a seal between the core barrel and the rock to minimize, and possibly prevent, inflow of water from the rock into the shaft. After a seal has been obtained in the rock, the mud inside the casing is pumped out. If water enters the shaft from the bottom, it would be evident from a rise in the level of mud as the pumping continues. In that case, the core barrel is screwed deeper into the rock in an attempt to obtain a good seal.

Pumping from within the caisson invariably removes silt and fine soil particles from the strata above the rock unless the casing has effected a seal. Migration of soil particles also occurs into the zone of boulders and fractures in the upper zone of the rock. This causes settlement of the adjoining ground. Observations have shown surface settlements as much as 15 to 20 cm. in area as far as 18 to 24 m. from a caisson, from the effect of excessive and prolonged pumping. In the Chicago area, the City Building Department has usually required that maximum pumping from a caisson be limited to about 57 liters per minute. To meet this requirement, pregrouting of the rock with a chemical grout (a mixture of sodium silicate, water and organic reactants) was done for the Northern Trust Company building and for the New Harris Trust Company building in downtown Chicago (Cunningham and Robins, 1974). Cement grouting the rock during construction of the caissons has been done at many projects where problems develop during installation of some caissons.

The technique ususally utilized consists of removing the fractured rock before installing the steel casing, putting tremie concrete or rich cement grout to the level of the top of the rock and then advancing and turning the permanent steel casing through this green concrete block and socketing it into the unexcavated rock. This allows a seal between the casing and the fractured rock and also fills some fractures, outside the excavation created by removal of the broken rock fragments. This method has been successfully applied for obtaining a tight seal and controlling water inflow in a number of shafts.

The excavated shaft is usually 15 to 30 cm (6 inches to a foot) larger than the diameter of the steel casing which is inserted and sealed into rock. After a seal has been obtained, the annular space outside the casing will normally be grouted as far as is practical and the casing left permanently in place. Only the upper temporary casing is removed when the concrete has been placed in the shaft but it is still green and not bonded to the casing. Careful operations are required during the removal of the temporary casing in that the head of concrete inside the casing is always kept a few feet higher than the bottom of the casing to prevent contamination of the concrete by inflow of the drilling mud or water from outside the casing. Problems also occur if the concrete sets before the casing is pulled. Several case histories on failure of caissons by improper techniques of construction as well as improper pulling of temporary casing have been described by Osterberg (1968) and by Baker & Khan (1971).

Application of the Wet Method For Shaft Construction

The method described above is equally applicable for the construction of relativley small diameter shafts such as those for manholes and vent shafts. It can also be extended for relatively large diameter shafts in which case the capacity of the drilling machines imposes the limiting diameter. Two of the largest caisson contractors in Chicago namely: Caisson Corporation and Case International Company, have successfully constructed several drop shafts with a finished diameter of 3.8 m (12.5 ft) and to depths as much as 41.1 m (135 ft) below grade. Comparing these shafts with those required for caisson foundations, there are three different conditions, namely:

1. The diameter is relatively large and the shafts are deeper, extending several tens of meters into rock.

2. The shafts have to be kept open for a long period of several months and possibly years before the permanent inside lining can be installed. The supporting casing must be designed for permanent conditions.

3. The upper portions of the shaft to a depth of 7.6 m to 13.7 m (25 to 45 ft) require an enlarged diameter and an opening on one or two sides for future connections to the overflow structure.

Another feature is that the shafts are located very close to a river or a canal or an existing dock wall where obstructions from existing piles, anchor walls, sheet piles and anchor piles as well as dock walls exist to considerable depths. In addition, at certain locations, there are problems of head room because the drop shafts are constructed under or adjacent to overhead bridges. This gives low head room for working and tight space for operation of the drililng equipment. It is to be further recognized that the potential for squeezing in of the soft clays increases significantly with the time of excavation which, of course, increases by the square of the diameter of the shaft. In addition, the problem of basal heave is also compounded by the shaft diameter and the potential for heaving increases with the time that the base is left exposed. Another very important influencing factor is the weight of the casing to be handled by the installation equipment. Transportation of this large diameter casing from the fabricating yards to the site and the installation of the casing in the shaft, especially the socketing into rock, are difficult problems which also limit the size of the shaft which can be installed by the wet method.

Because of the above described reasons, the shafts for TARP did not have temporary (removable) casings. The oversize shaft at the top was supported by conventional systems such as sheetpiles, ribs and lagging, or by fabricated corrugated steel plates. The circular corrugated pipe was installed in an oversize shaft about 45 cm (18 inches) larger than pipe diameter, dug by the caisson drilling methods and the annular space grouted before preceeding with the drilling by wet method for the lower shaft. This grouting assures stability and minimizes ground loss. One shaft 5 m (16.5 ft) diameter, excavated within 30 cm (1 ft) of a bridge abutment and wing wall footings did not cause any noticeable settlement or distress to the existing structure.

Another large diameter shaft, 3.66 m (12 ft) finished diameter, 34 m (112 ft) deep was installed under an overpass with a head room of only 11 m (37 ft) and within 91 cm (3 ft) from the edge of an existing valve junction structure which was located 8.5 m (28 ft) below grade. Drilling was performed by using telescoping kelly, in stages, using 3.66 m (12 ft) diameter auger with reamers to core a 4.11 m (13.5 ft) diameter shaft. All excavation was done under a slurry head. Permanent steel casing, 31.7 mm (1.25 inch) thick was fabricated in 9.1 m (30 ft) along sections. The lowest section had carbide teeth on 1.83 m (6 ft) centers and twister ears for socketing into rock. The next section had a special collar that would telescope over the lower section after that was cored and sealed into rock. The entire operation was done under a slurry head. After pressure grouting the annular space, the slurry was pumped out and a nearly bone dry shaft obtained. The entire work of shaft installation was completed in three weeks. (Reference 7)

Photographs No. 1, 2, and 3, furnished by Caisson Corporation, show steel casing and some of the equipment used for installing the shafts.

LATERAL PRESSURES FOR CASING DESIGN

For conventional excavations, there are two basic approaches for arriving at design lateral pressures. These are semi-empirical approaches based on observations and measurements for various types of soils and theoretical approaches based on an assumed failure mechanism or plastic equilibrium. The former approach is nearly always used for braced excavations, both rigid and flexible, as well as for conditions of no drainage (e.g., excavation supported by interlocking sheet pile walls or slurry walls) and for situations where drainage of ground water is permitted such as where wood lagging or contact sheeting is utilized. The technical literature is abound with papers comparing the design pressures and actual measurements for a variety of soil conditions and discussing the validity of the various empirical pressure diagrams suggested by the various authors. The latest state-of-the-art papers suggest that the methods and empirical diagrams proposed by Terzaghi and Peck (Peck, 1969) are most valid and most frequently utilized for braced excavations.

The theoretical approach is utilized for design of permanent structures and has gained additional application for analytical analysis utilizing digital computer and for soil structure interaction studies.

For the case of shaft linings, several theories of earth pressures are discussed in the paper by Prater (1976). There is a considerable variation in the earth pressure on vertical shafts computed by the various methods discussed in that paper. It is concluded that below a certain depth no earth pressure exists or it stops at a certain value. Similarly, the design pressures recommended in NAVFAC DM-7 (1971) for vertical shafts indicate that for shafts in granular soils, the horizontal soil pressures do not increase below a depth of about 3 to 4 times the shaft diameter and for cohesive soils, also, soil arching and mobilized shear resitance causes reduction in lateral pressures for deep shafts. However, because of the differences in the various available theories, considerable engineering judgement is necessary in arriving at design pressures for cylindrical shafts especially in mixed soil conditions. Considering the wet method of installation where ground movements are minimal and probably insufficient to mobilize active pressures, the writer recommends designing the circular shaft for at-rest earth pressures in addition to the hydrostatic pressures. It has been found that the design of casing or linings is not controlled by the earth pressures at-rest but rather by the conditions of buckling under hydrostatic pressures before the casing is grouted in place. This is for the reason that buckling pressures are much higher when the casing is in contact with the soil and passive pressures are mobilized and react to prevent buckling.

For the design of casing or temporary lining for excavation support of circular shafts installed by the wet method, two different pressure conditions must be considered; namely:

1. The differential hydrostatic pressures outside and inside the casing before the annular space between the casing and the excavation is grouted, and,

2. Hydrostatic pressures and earth pressure at-rest on the casing after it is grouted.

For the former case, the soil pressures are stabilized or balanced by the drilling mud inside the shaft and need not be considered for the design of casing for the buckling mode of failure. For the latter case, the earth pressure at various depths can be determined by using the at-rest coefficient given by Jaky (see Dramola, 1980) which is:

$$K_o = 1 - \sin \phi$$

or the expression given by Brooker and Ireland (1965) i.e.:

$$K_\theta = 0.95 - \sin \phi$$

These are for normally consolidated soils. For unconsolidated clays K_{or} is related to K_o by

$$K_{OR} = K_0 (OCR)^{\lambda}$$

where:

OCR = Overconsolidation ratio

λ = Empirical coefficient which can be obtained from:

$$PI = -281 \ \text{Log}(1.85 \lambda)$$

PI = Plasticity Index

For overconsolidated sands, λ ranges between 0.4 and 0.5 and decreases for larger values of OCR. It is not difficult to estimate the effective angle of internal friction ϕ for different strata. As mentioned above, even pressures determined from a conservative assumption of ϕ usually do not control the design of steel casing.

DESIGN OF CASINGS

As mentioned above, two conditions of casing design must be considered. These are:

1. The conditions prior to and during the grouting of the annular space between the casing and inside of the excavation, and,

2. The final conditions after the casing is grouted and the inside is dewatered.

For the former conditions, the lining is subjected to an all around radial hydrostatic pressure. Differential pressures develop on the casing and result from the difference in the level of mud outside and inside the casing or the higher pressures outside from the wet grout outside the casing. It is, of course, necessary that the grout be placed uniformly all around so that unequal radial loading is avoided.

The most critical condition is when outside pressures are higher than those inside as this creates combined compression and bending in the casing and the failure mode is that of buckling. When inside pressures are higher, the casing is in tension and buckling is not critical.

The analysis for buckling of a circular tube under combined axial compression and bending from uniform external pressure is given by Timoshenko (1936). For a tube of uniform thickness h and radius r, the critical pressure at buckling q_{cr} is given by:

$$q_{cr} = \frac{E}{4(1-\nu^2)} \cdot \left(\frac{h}{r}\right)^3$$

where:

E = Modulus of elasticity (29 X 10^6 psi for steel)*
and ν = Poisson's ratio (0.3 for steel)

* 1 psi = 6.89 kPa

If the tube has an initial ellipticity, or out-of-roundness, the pressure at buckling "q_{yp}" can be determined by solution of the following quadratic equation:

$$q_{yp}^2 - [\frac{\sigma yp}{m} + (1 + 6mm)q_{cr}] + \frac{\sigma yp}{m} \cdot q_{cr} = 0$$

In which:

σyp = yield stress of the tube material
m = r/h
n = w/r
w = initial radial deviation of the tube from a true circle

It should be noted that the external pressure determined from the second equation is smaller than that at which collapsing of the tube would occur for the perfectly round tube. The difference between the two increases exponentially with increase in eccentricity or out of roundness and also as the diameter increases. This can readily be seen by solution of the equations by a simple computer program. To illustrate this point, buckling pressures for representative diameters and different eccentricities are given in Table 1 below:

TABLE 1
Buckling Pressures (pounds per square foot)*

Casing Dia.	6' - 0"		7' - 0"		8' - 0"		9' - 0"		10' - 0"	
Wall Thick.	1/2"	5/8"	1/2"	5/8"	1/2"	3/4"	5/8"	3/4"	3/4"	1.0'
Eccentricity (% of Dia.)										
0	2490	4500	1770	3040	1390	3510	1780	2670	2160	4280
1	2140	3670	1570	2580	1280	2950	1600	2330	1930	3550
2	1890	3130	1430	2260	1190	2570	1480	2070	1760	3090
3	1700	2740	1320	2000	1120	2300	1380	1890	1630	2750
4	1560	2450	1230	1850	1060	2090	1300	1740	1530	2500

* 1 psf = 47.9 Pa
1 ft = 30.5 cm
1 in. = 25.4 mm

It is evident from the above table as well as from a solution of the above equations that for a certain external pressure, the thickness of casing required increases considerably as the diameter increases. In actual practice, it has been difficult to obtain casings with eccentricity less than 2% of the diameter. At that eccentricity and a shaft diameter of 3.0 m (10 ft), wall thickness of 19 mm (3/4 inches) is required for a hydrostatic pressure corresponding to a differential head of 6.1 m (20 ft) and allowing for a safety factor of 1.33.

It is essential that the differential head be controlled to minimize the required thickness of casing. Of course, one has also to consider a practical limit of grouting speed and the time of setting of grout at arriving at the design differential head. Experience shows that it is possible to install a casing and maintain a differential head of about 3 to 6 m (10 ft to 20 ft) of water without hampering construction operations. The differential head of the same amount is usually sufficient to detect if the casing has been adequately socketed into rock to exclude water inflow into the shaft.

No cases of casing buckling have been observed after grouting has been done in the annular space. The first case of buckling of a casing was experienced for the foundations of the John Hancock building in 1965. In that case, a 3.0 m (10 ft) diameter casing with a uniform wall thickness of 22 mm (7/8 inches) buckled while the inside was being dewatered to see if a seal had been obtained. The annular space had not been grouted before the dewatering. Another case of buckling of a casing occured in 1967 during construction of rock caissons for Illinois Bell Telephone building in Chicago. Analyses of these collapses indicated failure by buckling under external pressure from differential fluid head. Prior to these collapses, little attention was paid to the design of casing and the casing size was selected arbitrarily by the contractors based on their experience or possibly for compressive stresses only similar to a flexible conduit buried in soil. All the casings designed for the drop shaft and access shaft for the TARP by the writer recognized possible buckling failure of the casing and allowed for a possible out-of-roundness of 5 cm (2 inches) or 2% of the diameter of the casing, whichever was greater.

It will be readily seen from the buckling equations given above that the buckling resistance is dependent upon the moment of inertia of the casing. In order to get a larger moment of inertia and yet using a smaller thickness of the casing, a design improvement was made by installing stiffening ribs in the casing. The ribs consisted of bands 23 cm to 30 cm (9 inch to 12 inches) wide and 19 mm to 30 mm (3/4 inch to 1.25 inches) thick welded to a casing pipe 13 mm to 16 mm (½ inch to 5/8 inch) thick at a spacing of 1 to 1.5 times the casing diameter. They were welded outside or inside the casing at the option of the contractor or fabricator. For diameters larger than about 3 m (10 ft), the stiffeners consisted of bent rings of channel sections c 9 X 20 or c 10 X 20, welded continuously inside the pipe. These rings projected about 7 cm (2.75 inches) inside the pipe wall and did not create any undue hardship during the drilling of the shaft in the rock. The analysis of the casing with stiffener rings indicated considerable improvement in allowable differential head as illustrated in the following Table 2.

TABLE 2
External Differential Pressure at Buckling (psf)

Casing Diameter (ft)		8		10		12	
Wall Thickness (in.)		3/8	1/2	1/2	5/8	1/2	5/8
Stiffeners							
Size	Spacing (ft)						
9"X3/4"	8	1660	2270	1300	1780	820	1120
	10	1400	1960	1120	1570	700	990
	12	1230	1750	1000	1420	630	900
12"X1/2"	8	1160	1770	990	1490	620	920
	10	1000	1570	890	1350	550	840
	12	890	1430	810	1250	500	780
12"X3/4"	8	2060	2770	1590	2120	990	1340
	10	1740	2370	1360	1850	850	1170
	12	1520	2100	1200	1660	760	1050
12"X 1"	8	3330	4160	2420	3020	1540	1920
	10	2800	3510	2040	2580	1300	1640
	12	2410	3060	1780	2270	1130	1450

In addition to an increase in allowable differential head, the weight of the casing pipe is reduced considerably by using the stiffener bands or rings.

It was not considered necessary to design the casing pipe as spanning between the rows of stiffeners. This is analogous to conventional tunnel liner plates, 46 cm or 61 cm (18 inches or 24 inches) wide and supported by steel ribs at 91 cm to 122 cm (3 to 4 ft) apart. The liners and the casing function in compression and not in bending between the ribs. With the arched section of the casing pipe and the stiffening provided by the stiffener bands, the buckling of the casing between the stiffener rings spaced at 1.5 times the diameter of the casing did not appear possible. This is brought out by the experience and actual performance of several dozens of casings designed with stiffeners and installed successfully over the past few years.

The design for permanent conditions, after the casing is grouted in place, can be made for compressive stresses resulting from radial loading only. The casing pipe, even with stiffeners, can be considered as flexible and would deform so that the lateral pressures act radially. For such a loading, the stresses are compressive and no bending stresses exist. The analysis must, however, consider and provide for sufficient rigidity to limit radial deformation to about 5% of the diameter, similar to the criteria adopted for a flexible culvert. The empirical design procedures for design of flexible culverts can be utilized for the permanent conditions following the grouting in place of the casing. (see Handbook of Steel Drainage & Highway Construction Products, 1971). The minimum required stiffness is given by:

$$\text{Minimum Stiffness} = \frac{EI}{D^2}$$

Where:

D = diameter
E = modulus of elasticity
I = moment of inertia

Buckling pressure, f_c can be determined from the following formulas:

For diameter less than $\frac{r}{k} \cdot \sqrt{\frac{24E}{f_u}}$

$$f_c = f_u - \frac{f_u^2}{48E} \left(\frac{KD}{r} \right)^2$$

and, for diameters greater than $\frac{r}{k} \cdot \sqrt{\frac{24E}{f_u}}$

$$f_c = \frac{12E}{\left(\frac{kD}{2}\right)^2}$$

In which:

f_u = minimum specified tensile strength
k = soil stiffness factor which varies from 0.22 for soils with $\emptyset > 15^o$ to 0.44 for $\emptyset < 15^o$
r = radius of gyration

A factor of safety of 2 is recommended against buckling computed from the above equations. It has been found that for shaft diameters of about 3.8 m (12.5 ft) and depths of about 41 m (135 ft), the design is controlled by stability against buckling prior to grouting and not by resisting the final at-rest soil and water pressures.

In practically all the shafts installed for the Tunnel and Reservoir Project, an oversize shaft has been installed in the upper 7.6 m to 13.7 m (25 to 45 ft). For relatively large drop shaft structures, the upper shaft has been conventionally excavated and supported by steel sheet piles, or circular steel ribs and liner plates or wood lagging. In many instances, the upper shaft has also been machine excavated using caisson drilling methods and supported by a corrugated casing or steel liner plates. Because of limitations of caisson drilling equipment, the excavation for the upper shaft has been limited to 5.0 m (16.5 ft) diameter and the furnished shaft has been maximum of 4.59 m (15.5 ft) diameter. These shafts were supported by 152 mm X 51 mm (6 inch X 2 inch) X 7 guage corrugated metal liner plates fabricated at the job site. These casings were installed in the dry and not excavated under water by the wet method. The casings were grouted and placed before drilling for the lower casing by the wet method.

The upper shaft has also been supported by specially fabricated corrugated liner plates, as made by Young Metal Products Co. of East Chicago, Indiana. These plates give moment of intertia greater than a standard 152 mm X 51 mm (6 in X 2 in.) corrugated metal plate and therefore has greater resistance to buckling. Furthermore, these are easier to fabricate at site.

The upper casing is also designed to resist unequal lateral pressures developing from heavy crane loading which from necessity must be seated on one side of the shaft. Buckling analysis was performed for non-uniform loading on the site with the reactive forces from passive pressure on the two opposite sides as shown in Figure 2.

CONCLUDING REMARKS

At present, locally available auger drilling equipment are capable of drilling 5 m (16.5 ft) diameter shafts in overburden. The wet method of shaft construction can be applied to shafts of larger diameters which would be possible with advance and development of caisson drilling equipment. Recently a shaft of 20 ft 3 in. diameter has been bored mechanically for Monterey Coal Company's No. 1 mine near Carlinville, Illinois. In that case, excavation of shaft in the overburden was made by

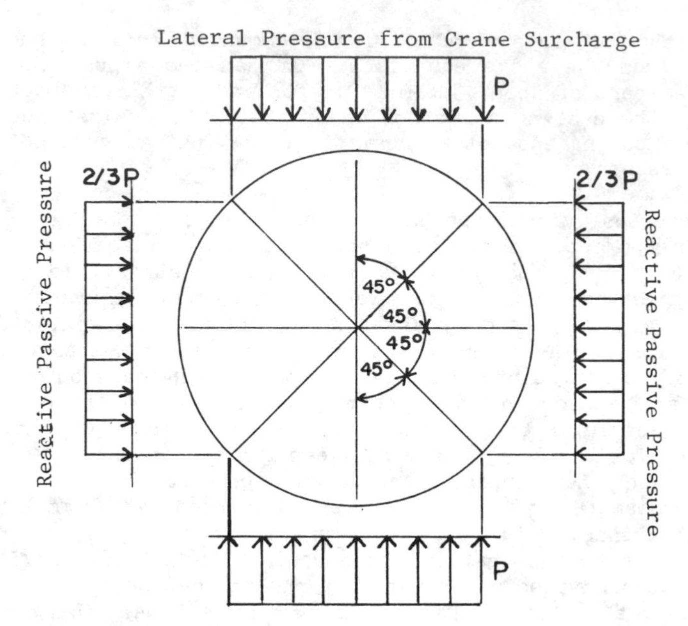

FIGURE 2: Pressure Diagram for Surcharge Loading

conventional methods. One can foresee similar developments for caisson drilling equipment in overburden soils. Steel casing with stiffener ribs could be installed for these shafts for the support in overburden, especially where the soils consist of water bearing sands or soft squeezing clays.

For shafts larger than about 3.8 m (12.5 ft), transportation of shop fabricated of the casing to the site would be impractical. Hence, site welded segmentally fabricated casing or casing made from liner plates and fabricated at site would be required. Installation procedures for such casing in a slurry filled trench also need to be devised.

This wet method of construction allows utilization of relatively economical excavation support casing besides speedier installation. Detrimental effects of dewatering during construction are avoided and ground loss in adjoining areas is minimum. This construction technique is also possible for intake shafts in water and for the mining industry.

REFERENCES

1. Baker, C.N., and Khan, F., (1971), "Caisson Construction Problems and Correction in Chicago", Journal of the Soil Mechanics and Foundation Division, ASCE, Vol. 97, No. SM 2, February, pp. 417-440.

2. Brooker, E.W., and Ireland, H.O., (1965), "Earth Pressures at Rest Related to Stress History", Canadian Geotechnical Journal, Vol. 2, pp. 1-15.

3. Cunningham, J.A., and Robbins, J.R., (1974), "Rock Caissons for the Northern Trust Building in Chicago's Loop", ASCE-IABSE Regional Conference on Tall Buildings, Bangkok, January.

4. Dramola, O., "On Estimating K_o for Overconsolidated Granular Soils", (1980), Geotechnique, Vol. XXX, No. 3, pp. 310-313.

5. Handbook of Steel Drainage & Highway Construction Products, (1971), American Iron and Steel Institute, New York, NY, pp.264-265.

6. Lukas, R.G., and Baker C.N., (1978), "Ground Movement Associated with Drilled Pier Installations", ASCE Spring Convention and Exhibit, Philadelphia, April 24-28, Preprint No. 3266.

7. Martin, R.L., (1980), Case International Company, Personal Communication.

8. NAVFAC DM-7, (1971), Naval Facilities Engineering Command, U.S. Govt. Printing Office, Washington, D.C. pp.7-14-3 to 7-14-4.

9. Osterberg, J.O. (1968), "Drilled Caissons - Design, Installation, Application", Chicago Soil Mechanics Lecture Series, Dept. of Civil Engineering, Northwestern University, Evanston, Illinois. pp. 151-208.

10. Peck, R.B. (1969), "Deep Excavation and Tunneling in Soft Ground", Proceedings, Seventh International Conference on Soil Mechanics and Foundation Engineering, Mexico City, State of the Art Volume, pp. 225-290.

11. Prater, E.G., (1971), "An examination of Some Theories of Earth Pressure on Shaft Linings", Canadian Geotechnical Journal, Vol. 14, pp. 91-106.

12. Timoshenko, S., (1936), Theory of Elastic Stability, 1st Edition, McGraw-Hill Book Co., New York; pp. 204-225.

FIGURE 1. Auger mounted on crane and large casing transportation by truck.

FIGURE 2. Upper shaft casing raised for installation.

FIGURE 3. Lower shaft core barrel.

13

Shaft Sinking Practices for Mining

Chairmen: J.S. Redpath
C. Heever

J.S. Redpath Ltd., North Bay, Ont., Canada
Cyril Heever & Partners, Inc., Carletonville, South Africa

Chapter 58

SHAFT SINKING AT NOSE ROCK
by

Mr. James O. Greenslade
Phillips Uranium Corporation
Vice President of Mining & Milling
Crownpoint, New Mexico

Mr. Cherie Tilley
Phillips Uranium Corporation
Development Manager
Crownpoint, New Mexico

Mr. Gerald G. Griswold
Harrison Western Corporation
Vice President of Engineering Services
Denver, Colorado

Mr. Richard Reseigh
Harrison Western Corporation
Manager of Engineering & Administration
Crownpoint, New Mexico

INTRODUCTION

The Harrison Western Corporation, a leading Denver based mine contracting and engineering concern, is presently engaged in sinking two 1,006 m (3,300 ft) shafts for the Phillips Uranium Corporation at their Nose Rock Project, approximately 13 miles northeast of the small community of Crownpoint in McKinley County, New Mexico. The Nose Rock Project is the first attempt by the Phillips Uranium Corporation to tap the deep uranium reserves in what has become known as the Grants Mineral Belt. (See Figure 1)

Project Description

Phillips Uranium Corporation's plan for the large 2700 metric ton per day (2950 tons/day) mining facility calls for a series of deep access and ventilation shafts ranging from 4.27 m (14 ft) to 5.49 m (18 ft) in diameter to approximate depths of 1,006 m (3,300 ft). The initial pair of shafts consists of one production shaft and one ventilation shaft separated by a distance of 91 m (300 ft). The interbedded layers of sedimentary sandstones and shales to be penetrated by the shafts contain several major water producing aquifers, the deepest being the mineralized zone called the Westwater Canyon Member of the Morrison Formation.

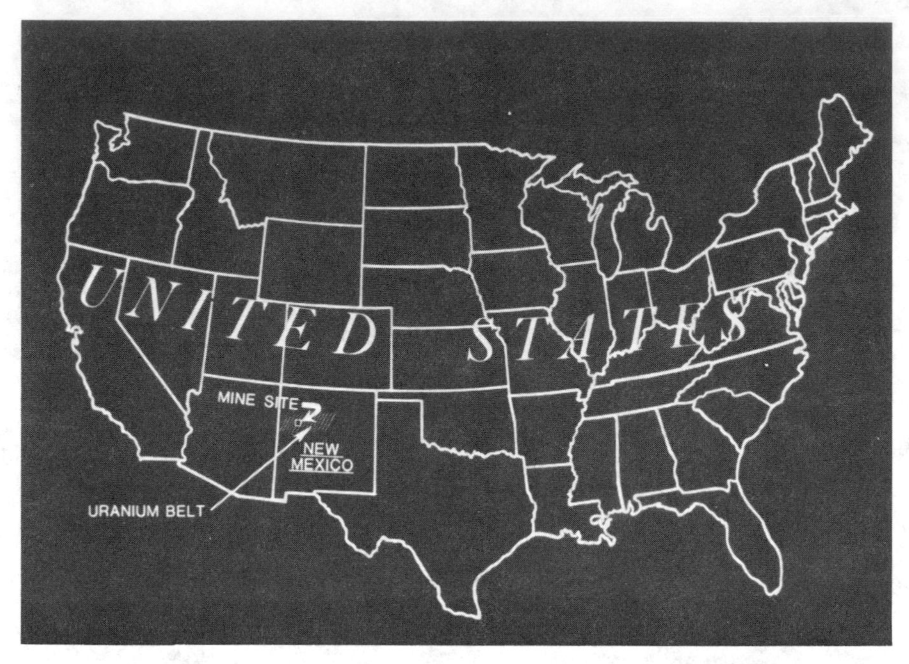

FIGURE 1. PROJECT SITE

A series of temporary and permanent water pumping stations is planned. Generally, the temporary stations are located above major aquifers to facilitate water removal while sinking through the aquifer and the permanent stations constitute what, in the final mode, will be the mine dewatering system. In addition, Phillips Uranium Corporation has installed and is maintaining a system of depressurization wells that temporarily pump the major aquifers and considerably reduce the water inflows during shaft construction. The major aquifers are also chemically grouted prior to sinking.

Site work for the project was initiated in the fall of 1976. Full scale shaft sinking commenced in November of 1977 on the 4.88 m (16 ft) diameter ventilation shaft and on the 5.49 m (18 ft) production shaft by another contractor. Harrison Western Corporation began work on the project on November 4, 1979 with the production shaft at a depth of 633 m (2,076 ft) and the ventilation shaft at a depth of 474 m (1,554 ft). This paper will address only the portion of shaft sinking completed by Harrison Western.

Geology and Hydrology

The Nose Rock Project is located on the Chaco Slope in the southern extreme of the San Juan Basin in northwest New Mexico. The southern San Juan Basin is generally bound by the Defiance Uplift to the west, the Zuni Uplift to the south and the Nacimiento Uplift to the east. The Grants Mineral Belt occupies most of the southern portion of the San Juan Basin and this project is located on the northern extreme of the Grants Mineral Belt. The San Juan Basin is comprised of sedimentary rock of continental, marginal-marine and marine origin, that dip northward from the Zuni Uplift and Chaco Slope into the interior of the San Juan Basin. (See Figure 2)

Major Formations The major geologic formations to be penetrated range from mudstone and shales to siltstones and sandstones. The sandstones are highly productive aquifers which, under static conditions, would flow artesian. Water temperatures in the aquifers are high and therefore are a force to be dealt with. Temperatures range from 18°C (65°F) in the upper aquifers to 48°C (118°F) in the lower. The mudstones are generally bentonitic. (See Figure 2)

GALLUP SANDSTONE: The Gallup Sandstone is the first major regressive wedge in the San Juan Basin of the Cretaceous era and at this project is about 35 m (115 ft) thick. It is medium grained and prior to depressurization carried a hydrostatic water pressure of over 72.5 kg per cm^2 (1,031 psi) which is artesian. Compressive strength ranges from 334.7 kg per cm^2 (4,760 psi) to 421.8 kg per cm^2 (6,000 psi). Water temperature is approximately 30°C (86°F).

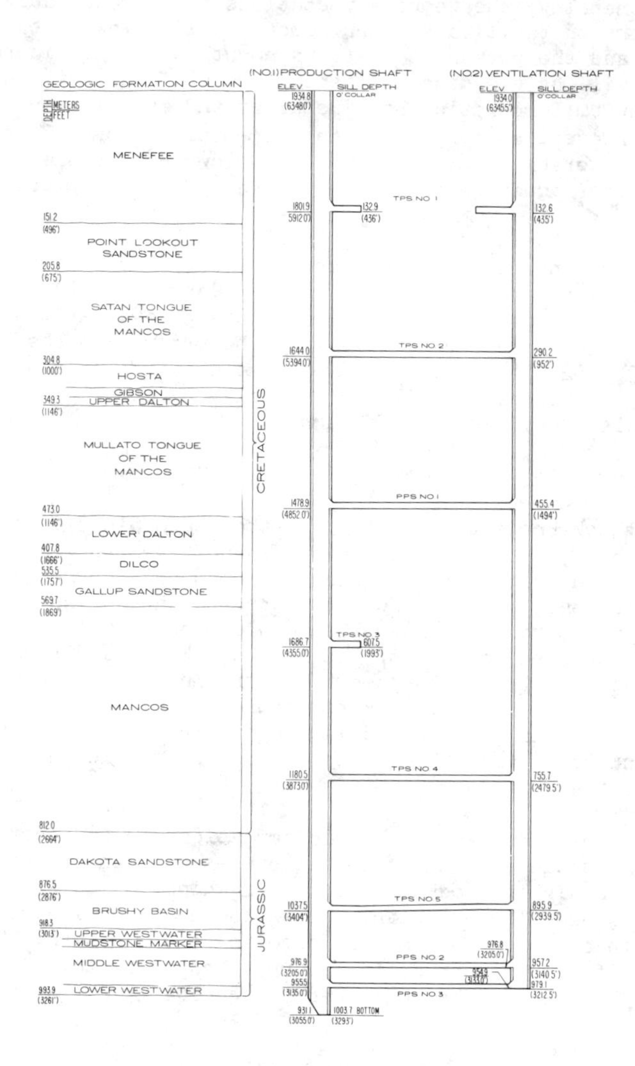

FIGURE 2. SHAFTS VERTICAL CROSS SECTION

MANCOS SHALE: The Mancos Shale comprises the bulk of marine deposits in the San Juan Basin and represents deposition in deeper, quieter water in offshore areas where energy levels were lower and finer clastics could settle out. At Nose Rock, the Mancos Shale is roughly 207 m (680 ft) thick. Compressive strengths range from 188.4 kg per cm^2 (2,680 psi) to 400.7 kg per cm^2 (5,700 psi). It is not water bearing.

DAKOTA SANDSTONE: The Dakota Sandstone and its corresponding Twowells member is approximately 98 m (322 ft) thick at Nose Rock. The main body of the Dakota Sandstone is a fine grained sandstone with the so called Twowells sandstone tongue actually being a siltstone. Prior to depressurization, water in the Dakota was under a hydrostatic pressure of 108.1 kg per cm^2 (1,537 psi), also artesian. Compressive strengths range from 386.0 kg per cm^2 (5,490 psi) to 562.4 kg per cm^2 (8,000 psi). Water temperature is approximately 43°C (109°F).

BRUSHY BASIN SHALE: The Brushy Basin Member is the upper-most member of the Morrison Formation which marks the approximate boundry between the Cretaceous and Jurassic eras. Locally, it is composed of a sequence of fine grained sandstones, siltstones and mudstones which grade into one another, although disconformities are sometimes distinguishable. The mudstones and siltstones constitute the greater part of the section. Overall, it is 44 m (143 ft) thick and some of the sandstones are water bearing. Compressive strengths range from 456.3 kg per cm^2 (6,490 psi) to 954.8 kg per cm^2 (13,580 psi).

WESTWATER CANYON MEMBER: The Westwater Canyon Member of the Morrison Formation was deposited in a continental environment during the Jurassic era and is the ore bearing sandstone for the Nose Rock Project. It is actually comprised of three submembers called Upper, Middle and Lower. The Westwater Canyon Member is a classic example of an artesian aquifer with water being recharged from topographically higher outcrops on both the Zuni and Defiance Uplifts. Prior to depressurization, the hydrostatic pressure was 120.2 kg per cm^2 (1,710 psi). Grain sizes range from medium to coarse, and compressive strengths range from 94.9 kg per cm^2 (1,350 psi) to 348.7 kg per cm^2 (4,960 psi). Note that the lower range for compressive strength is lower than the original hydrostatic pressure, indicating a possible running sand condition if sinking should be attempted in the absence of depressurization or grouting. Water temperature is approximately 48°C (118°F).

Depressurization Wells The Phillips Uranium Corporation has put into operation and maintained a series of depressurization wells in the area of the shafts to reduce the hydrostatic pressure in the major aquifers in order to facilitate shaft sinking. Six wells were drilled through the Gallup Sandstone, four wells in the

Dakota Sandstone and six wells in the Westwater Canyon Member. The casing was slotted throughout the total length of each aquifer and the pump settings were generally just above each aquifer.

Formation	Number Wells	Months Pumped	Yield	Initial Pressure	Residual Pressure	Effect
Gallup	6	17	1080 gpm	1038 psi	135 psi	82%
Dakota	4	14	1120 gpm	1537 psi	350 psi	77%
Westwater	4-6	6	1760 gpm	1711 psi	238 psi	86%

Table 1. Summary of Results of Depressurization Wells

As can be seen from the results summarized in Table 1, the program has been highly effective. More perspective concerning residual formation pressures can be gained by the following estimates, prepared by Phillips Uranium Corporation geologists, of potential inflows to both shafts with and without the depressurization wells.

Formation	With Wells	Without Wells
Gallup	1,080 gpm	2,307 gpm
Dakota	1,120 gpm	2,562 gpm
Westwater	2,212 gpm	5,020 gpm

Table 2. Potential Inflow Estimates

Although these potential yields with the benefit of the wells would by no means prohibit shaft sinking, the water inflow from the upper aquifers was further reduced by chemical grouting of the formations prior to sinking.

Grouting

Carrying large volumes of water on the shaft bottom during sinking probably possesses the greatest single detriment to high shaft sinking productivity. For the most part, the system of depressurization wells had the effect of reducing potential inflows from the upper aquifers during sinking to around 4,160 liters per minute (1,100 gpm). As mentioned above, these inflows would not necessarily prohibit sinking, although carrying these volumes of water would have the dual effect of increasing capital expenditures caused by slower shaft sinking rates and increasing future operating expenses caused by pumping larger quantities of water over a significant portion of the mine life.

From the above, it was apparent that further reduction of potential inflows from the major aquifers would be beneficial if the reductions could be obtained at a reasonable cost. Owing largely to the success of Harrison Western's chemical grouting program at the Gulf Mineral Resources Company's Mt. Taylor Project, it was decided to instigate a similar program at the Nose Rock Project for the upper aquifers. No grouting is planned for the mineralized Westwater Canyon Member since any potential inflows will be fully realized during mine development.

It should be recognized that the grouting process itself is expensive as it is not uncommon to spend one to two months treating 30 m (100 ft) of shaft. In addition, initial applications are highly beneficial but time spent attempting to obtain a "perfect curtain" is subject to the law of diminishing returns. Theoretically, the right amount could be determined by adding the cost of grouting to the incremental savings of shaft sinking costs due to grouting, and comparing the totals to the after tax discounted cash flow savings of incremental mine life pumping expense. Supposedly, if this comparison yielded a positive net present value, further grouting would be warranted. The extreme difficulty of estimating accurate values for the above parameters is obvious and therefore, the outcome of any attempt must be viewed with suspicion.

Grout Materials The grouting agents used at Nose Rock were selected primarily on the basis of successful use on other similar projects in the Grants Mineral Belt.

CEMENT: All of the sandstone aquifers requiring grout treatment were of fine enough porosity to preclude the use of suspension type grouting agents. Cement grout was used primarily to stabilize the rock mass around the concrete grouting pad and to seal leaks where the pad joined the shaft lining.

Pumped cement grout was mixed with water in water to cement ratios that varied from 12:1 to 1:1 by weight.

CHEMICAL RESIN GROUT: A water soluble resin prepolymer was the primary grouting agent used at Nose Rock. The resin is supplied as a fine powder which readily dissolves in water, and in the presence of catalysts and accelerators, forms an irreversible, impermeable gel. The mixture normally has a viscosity close to that of water and can therefore be injected into formations of low porosity.

The set time or "gel time" is the time elapsed to form a stiff gel after the chemicals are mixed. For the most part, gel times can be predicted and controlled by varying the concentration of the solution and/or the addition of a sodium silicate accelerator. Gel times are also a function of temperature with the relationship being inverse.

Two variations of chemical grouting agents were used at the Nose Rock Project. The first type was characterized by the resin and caustic soda catalyst being packaged separately. The second type is packaged together with other modifications. Care in transportation and storage of the second type must be exercised to prevent the reaction from taking place in the bags prematurely.

Grouting Equipment The equipment selected was based on successful experience on similar projects elsewhere.

PUMPS AND MIXING TANKS: A double-acting recirculation type pump capable of pumping at 345 kg per cm^2 (4,900 psi) at 8 kg per cm^2 (100 psi) air pressure was used. The pump is modeled after the South African type grout pump. Two mixing tanks were equipped with air powered mixing and agitation paddles with one tank elevated above the other. The tanks were sized to mix the contents of one 23 kg (50 lb) bag in the most diluted mix of 129 l (34 gal). One bag was mixed in the upper tank while a solution was being pumped from the lower tank.

JUMBO AND DRILLS: The grout jumbos consisted of two drill buggies which circled the shaft on a single track from a pivot in the center of the shaft. High speed, air powered, chain fed rotary drills with 1.5 m (5 ft) feed were used with EX diameter drill rod.

MISCELLANEOUS EQUIPMENT: Schedule 80 pipe of 5 cm (2 in) diameter was used for stand pipes. These were coupled with drill through ball valves of similar diameter. Blow-out preventers capable of closing an EX drill rod were also used for added safety.

Grouting Procedure Normally, one or more probe holes were drilled into each aquifer from a safe distance above. The probe hole served the dual purpose of determining the exact location of the aquifer and finding suitable strata to pour the grouting pad. Normally the pad was located from 6 m (20 ft) to 9 m (30 ft) above the aquifer.

GROUT PAD: When the predetermined depth was reached, the excavation was done for the grout pad. The "curb" or lower ring of the shaft form was removed and the pad poured, forming a solid concrete plug poured tight against and keyed under the shaft lining. The plug was designed to withstand the anticipated grouting pressure. While the pad was curing, the jumbo was set up and the standpipes installed. Before grouting commenced, every standpipe was tested to full grouting pressure.

Upon completion of the above, the holes were drilled 3 m (10 ft) to 6 m (20 ft) and the rock mass between the pad and the aquifer was injected with cement to consolidate the mass and seal leaks between the pad and the shaft lining.

GROUTING: Due to widely varying porosities and local fracturing conditions, experience has shown that precalculated grout quantities for a given aquifer are unreliable. As a result, holes were pumped to refusal at a predetermined pressure instead of a predetermined quantity. The grouting pressure was determined by the amount of residual formation pressure to be overcome and the acceptability of the formation due to grain size, porosity, fractures and other characteristics. Normally, this pressure was approximately twice the hydrostatic pressure calculated from the surface, and many times the residual hydrostatic pressure due to the effect of the depressurization wells. A curtain length of 30 m (100 ft) was the approximate maximum depth that could be grouted from one pad.

The hole pattern was designed to intercept as many fractures as possible with the distance between holes at the base of the curtain not exceeding 1.4 m (4.5 ft). The aquifer was grouted from the top down in stages of 3 m (10 ft) and all holes in the pattern were grouted to refusal before deepening the holes to advance the cover. (See Figure 3)

Generally, 75% - 90% of the potential inflows were sealed off by the grout curtains.

SHAFT SINKING

For the most part, the shaft sinking methods used at the Nose Rock Project can be classified as conventional. Methods and techniques employed on any project depend, to a large extent, on safety and health regulations promulgated by appropriate regulatory agencies at both state and federal levels. At the federal level, the project falls under the Federal Mine Safety and Health Act of 1977 (Public Law 95-164) and is administered by the newly created Mine Safety and Health Administration of the Department of Labor. Subsequent to enactment of the 1977 Act, the New Mexico Mine Safety Code has adopted the federal standards as their own. In addition, the state of New Mexico periodically develops stricter standards, mostly as a result of previous serious accidents. The most important of these to the shaft sinker is a requirement limiting unsupported ground in vertical shafts to 3 m (10 ft).

The two shafts are generally scheduled to be sunk together. The resulting plan represents the earliest possible completion

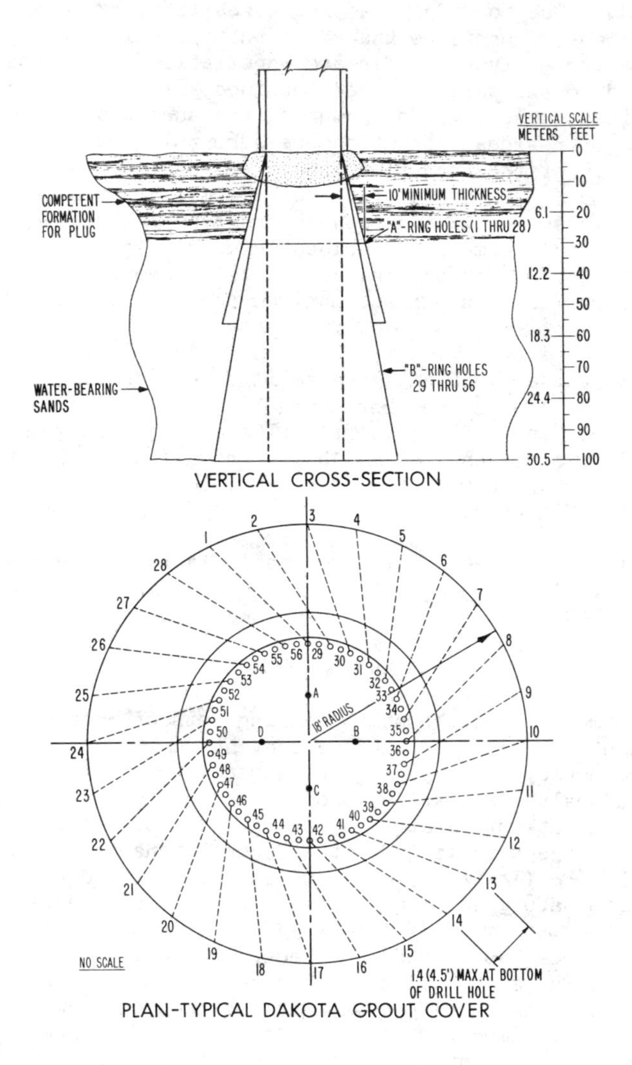

FIGURE 3. PLAN-TYPICAL DAKOTA GROUT COVER

date and allows the fresh air base to be lowered when connecting stations are reached in order to counteract the high temperatures caused by hot water emanating from various aquifers.

Sinking Equipment

The permanent production hoist and headframe are used for sinking the 5.5 m (18 ft) diameter production shaft. The hoist is a 1,119 kw (1,500 hp) double drum, double clutch unit, capable of 610 meters per minute (2,000 fpm) line speed. A temporary hoist and headframe are used for sinking the 4.9 m (16 ft) ventilation shaft. The hoist is a 1,007 kw (1,350 hp) double drum, single clutch unit capable of 579 meters per minute (1,900 fpm) line speed. Hoist ropes are 38.1 mm (1.5 in) diameter and are of 18 x 7 non-rotating right lang lay construction.

Compressed air is supplied to both shafts by seven electrically powered rotary compressors located on the surface. A portable concrete batching plant is used to supply concrete into transit trucks that mix and deliver it to the respective shafts. Concrete is transported underground in 2.7 m^3 (95 ft^3) buckets.

Galloway stages are suspended by four 25.4 mm (1 in) locked coil ropes and are used in each shaft as work platforms. Each Galloway consists of four decks and weighs approximately 31,070 kg (65,000 lb). The locked coil ropes serve as crosshead guides for the counterbalanced buckets. The Galloway stages are raised and lowered by four winches that are electrically wired to operate together, although any winch can be clutched out by hand in order to periodically balance tension between the ropes. The rope speed of the Galloway winches is about 2.4 meters per minute (8 fpm).

The Cryderman shaft mucker anchored to the lining with brackets is used for mucking (excavation of blasted material). Invented and developed in Canada, the mucker is essentially an air powered clamshell mounted on a telescoping boom. Positioning cylinders and the telescoping features of the boom itself allow positive crowd at any location on the muck pile. The machine is controlled by levers actuating two four-way valves, with the left hand controlling boom position and the right hand controlling the clamshell and the telescoping feature of the boom. Two units are used in the larger production shaft and a single unit in the ventilation shaft. In all cases, the units are suspended on cable winches located on the surface with the rail and bracket anchoring systems allowing vertical movement only. Muck bucket sizes range from 2.7 m^3 (95 ft^3) in the ventilation shaft to 3.5 m^3 (123 ft^3) in the production shaft.

Drilling is done with 28 kg (62 lb) hand-held sinkers with a piston diameter of 67 mm (2-5/8 in). Drills are lowered in a specially designed basket containing all materials required for the operation.

The concrete forms are of all steel construction of the appropriate diameter with a length of 3 m (10 ft). The forms are constructed of four vertical sections of .75 m (2.5 ft) length to enable any multiple of .75 m (2.5 ft) pour to be made if ground conditions are poor. The curb ring is of blast proof construction and contains the ring blockout necessary to enable pouring the subsequent pour below. The top "matcher" ring laps the previous pour and contains the guillotine doors that are closed after the form is filled with concrete. The form itself is suspended from the previous pour by six hanging rods.

Typical Sinking Cycle

Due in most part to the wet conditions, the benching method of excavation is used. This technique provides a lower area for an electric submersible pump to be placed after each blast. Moreover, the "blowover" process of cleaning the bench in preparation for drilling allows a thorough examination for misfires and the rock mass thrown by the blast is directed at the shaft walls instead of the Galloway, thus minimizing damage.

The cycle described below may vary in duration from as little as 14 hours to as much as 34 hours, depending on conditions. Sinking rates for both shafts are comparable. The larger production shaft has an advantage with the additional Cryderman mucker, but this seems to be offset by the lesser volume of muck and a somewhat faster concrete cycle in the ventilation shaft.

Drill and Blast This segment of the cycle begins with a thorough blow over of loose muck into the sump created by the preceding bench. Forty to fifty 2.4 m (8 ft) holes are drilled and charged with a semigelatin dynamite. The dynamite selected is a reasonable compromise between the desired characteristics of adequate strength, low fumes, good water resistance and cost. A non-electric delay blasting cap system has been used for detonating explosives with reasonable success. The crews remain on the surface for a few minutes while the smoke clears. (See Figure 4)

Mucking The Cryderman mucker(s) are lowered and mucking begins. Normally, the bucket chains remain attached to the hoist hook and swivel during loading. Since the boom lift (not in or out) operation is the most time consuming, Cryderman operators soon learn to excavate a hole for the next bucket which tends to save time. While the loaded bucket is hoisted and dumped, the Cryderman operator(s) can move muck from hard to reach to convenient places which also conserves time. Buckets are dumped with a lazy chain controlled by a toplander from the "crow's nest" in the headframe. (See Figure 5)

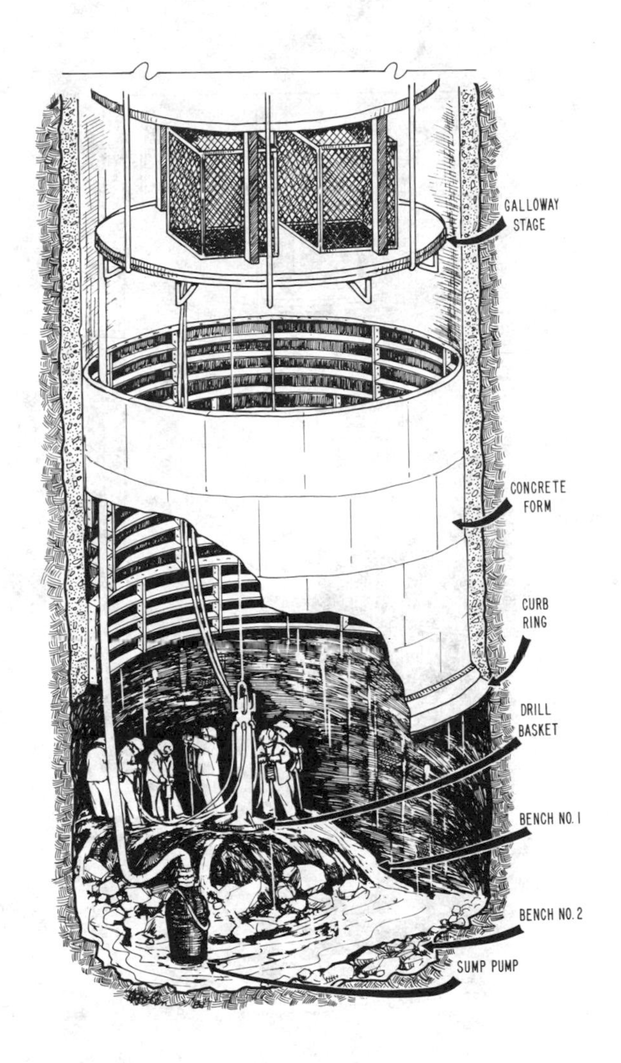

FIGURE 4. DRILLING THE BENCH

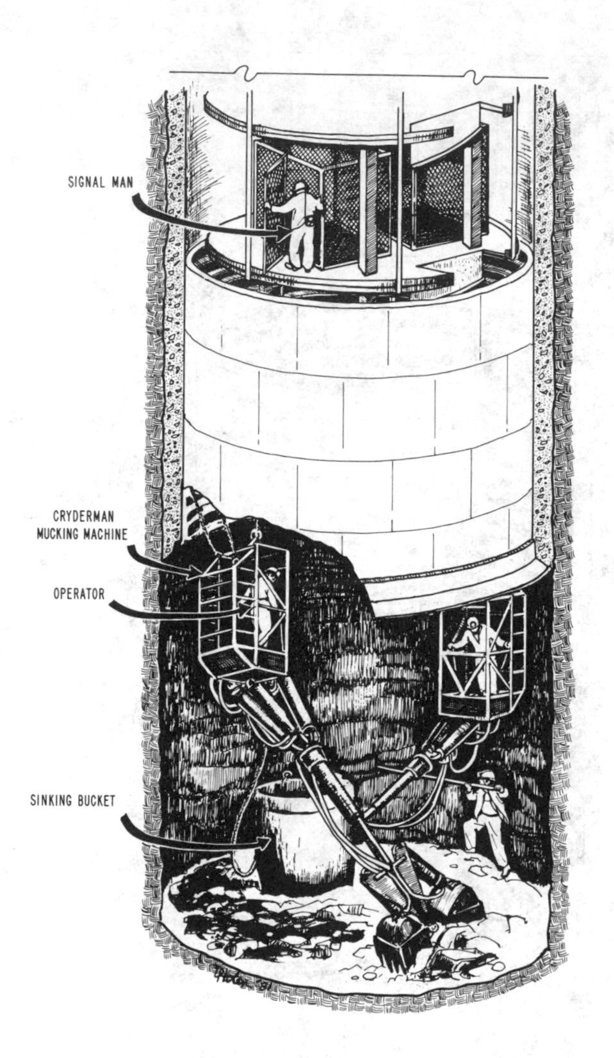

FIGURE 5. MUCKING

Level Off On the average, 2-1/2 benches is about 3 m (10 ft) of excavation, which normally results in cycles consisting of either 2 or 3 benches. At any rate, when enough excavation is made for the 3 m (10 ft) pour, mucking ceases and the remaining pile is "leveled off" or flattened, usually slightly lower than the 3 m (10 ft) below the preceding pour.

Concrete Lining This segment of the cycle begins with the removal of the "cone nuts" from the hanging rods of the previous pour. Six 28.6 mm (1-1-8") high strength hanging rods are installed with the cone nuts reinstalled at the lower end of the new hanging rods. At this time, the curb ring segment of the concrete form is lowered by slings attached to the Galloway, aligned and leveled. Required inserts are installed and gravel is placed to provide a smooth base for the concrete. It is then poured. An 8 sack concrete mix has been used almost exclusively, which, after some initial modifications, has provided excellent strength and workability. In addition, an accelerator is placed in the curb ring pour to assure initial set before mucking resumes. Concrete is placed directly from the concrete buckets with "elephant trunks" hung from the gates of the buckets. (See Figure 6)

Upon completion of the curb ring pour, the remaining 2.3 m (7-1/2 ft) of form is lowered into place from the poured curb ring to the bottom of the previous pour. Concrete is placed through the guillotine doors of the uppermost matcher ring which slightly laps the previous pour.

Utilities These are installed every other cycle and consist of a 61.0 cm (24 inch) ventilation tube and a 30.5 cm (12 inch) pipe for pump discharge, a 20.3 cm (8 inch) compressed air line, a 10.2 cm (4 inch) drill water pipe, a 10.2 cm (4 inch) seal water line, and a 10.2 cm (4 inch) drain line.

Water Control Techniques

Instrumental to the attainment of high sinking rates is a program which controls water that leaks through pour joints in the lining and falls on the crew below. Left uncontrolled, this water would eventually build to levels that adversely affect every facet of a shaft sinking operation from equipment maintenance to overall crew morale.

Backsheeting Also known as panning, this operation basically consists of placing thin sheets of metal against the exposed rock when sinking through productive aquifers and bringing the water through the lining in pipes. After 3 m (10 ft) is excavated through the aquifer and before the curb ring is lowered, backsheeting and weep pipes are placed against the upper 2.4 m (8 ft) of the shaft to be poured. The weep pipes consist of a perforated leg placed between the metal and the aquifer, a 90° ell, a nipple that extends from the perforated leg to the form and a coupling

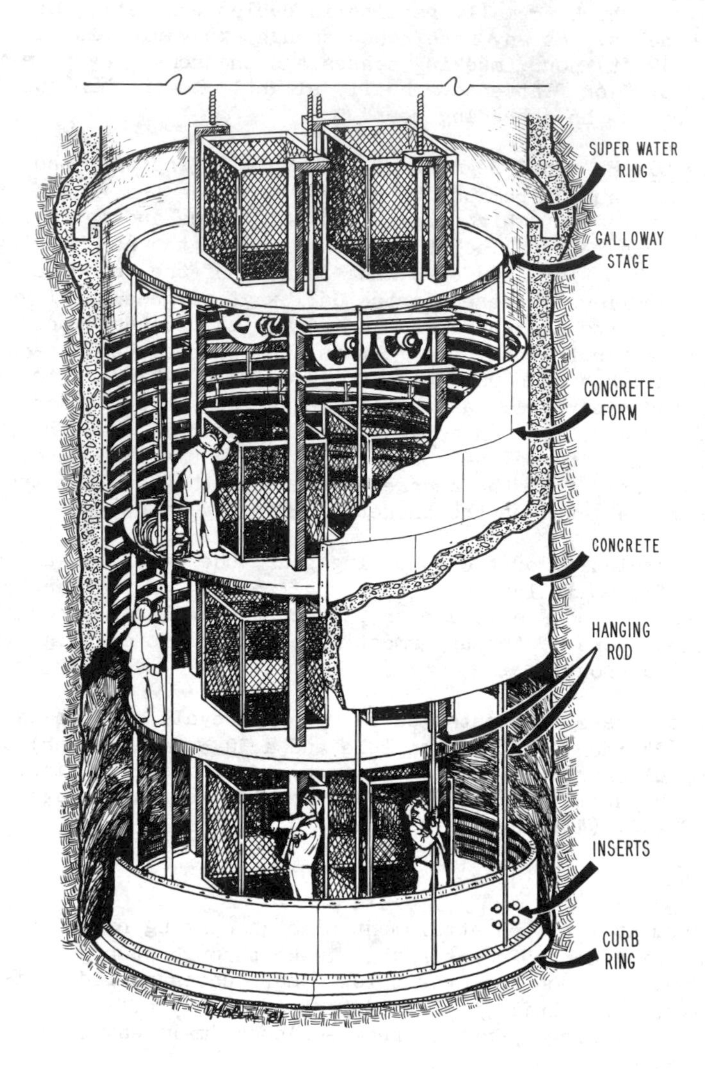

FIGURE 6. SETTING CONCRETE FORMS

that attaches the weep pipe to the form. After the curb ring is lowered, the pipes are attached to the form with a fastening device that threads into the coupling and allows the water to come through the form. The curb ring is then filled with concrete forming a tight seal for the bottom of the pour. After the remaining form is lowered and poured, the water flows freely through the weep pipes. These are later connected to a 10.2 mm (4") drain line which carries the water into a pump station or a "super water ring" discussed further below.

Super Water Rings The in-shaft pumping system consisted of 43 kw (58 hp) submersible pumps on the bottom and staged up the shaft wall in distances not exceeding 61 m (200 ft). The electric submersible pumps of this type require frequent maintenance and normally this must be done on the surface. To facilitate pump changeout and provide a sump for staged pumps, Harrison Western engineers developed the "super water ring." Essentially, the super water ring is the enlargement of a 3 m (10 ft) vertical section of the shaft by .6 m (2 ft) in radius with a .6 m (2 ft) steel dam installed flush with the shaft lining. Submersible pumps in these rings eventually transfer water to temporary or permanent pumping stations.

Fiberglass Water Rings The purpose of the fiberglass water ring is to collect water running on the inside of the shaft lining. The rings are installed above pump stations, super water rings or periodically when needed, and are connected with hose or piping to the drain line, super water ring or station. They are fabricated to attach to the concrete form and are easily installed.

Bonus and Incentives

In recent years, industrial managers have gravitated towards the theories of motivation espoused by such management theorists as Fredrick Herzburg et al. These theories stress "job enrichment" or other such enlargement of an individual's task or area of responsibility as a motivating force in order to otherwise offset the boredom and dissatisfaction that often accompanies the modern industrial work setting.

For the most part, these theorists would deny that additional remuneration is a motivating factor per se, although admitting that substandard pay scales can be a source of considerable dissatisfaction amoung a work force. Underground construction and mining in the Rocky Mountains and in a large portion of Canada are some of the last bastions of the piece work system still existing in North America, albeit in modified form.

Seemingly in defiance of modern management theory, the Nose Rock Project has successfully applied two forms of bonus incentives affecting all contractor personnel on the project. The first is a direct bonus which is paid only to those working below the shaft collar. This bonus is basically a piece rate system applied to the crew as a whole with a guaranteed minimum base rate for each man. The second form of bonus is paid to all others not receiving the first and is based on a review of the overall project status compared with the original project schedule. This bonus is paid (if earned) every calendar quarter as a percentage of the base wage rate.

Sinking Rates Attained

Shaft sinking rates of 3 meters per day (10 ft per day) were regularly attained, even through most major aquifers, and rates of 30 meters per week (100 ft per week) were regularly attained through much of the Mancos shale. The production shaft crew achieved an area record of 36.3 meters (119 ft) of completed shaft in one week of seven days. The ventilation shaft crew achieved a one month production of 132.6 meters (435 ft) of completed shaft, also believed to be an area record.

PUMPING SYSTEM - TEMPORARY AND PERMANENT

Dependable pumping systems are an absolute necessity to the construction and operation of a mine such as this one with the shafts penetrating five major aquifers and the ore itself having been deposited in the matrix of the fifth, the Westwater Canyon Member. Extensive planning was required by both the Phillips Uranium Corporation and Harrison Western Corporation to insure that the system was reliable for sinking, mine development and later for ore extraction. The two permanent pump stations represent the system requirement for mine development and ore extraction. Unfortunately, this system is not entirely adequate for sinking the shafts and as a result, the permanent system was augmented by a series of temporary pumping stations for sinking.

Of prime consideration when locating pumping stations is the capability of the equipment itself and the selection of suitable strata in which to locate the station. The sandstones to be mined can be expected to yield a certain amount of sand particulate to the discharge water and even with the benefit of a desanding facility, the pumps must be able to pump water containing sand particulates. For this reason and the fact that desanding equipment is not available for sinking, less efficient slurry type centrifugal pumps were selected. These pumps enjoy wide popularity at other mines in the Grants Mineral Belt, mainly for their ability to pump water containing abrasive solids over long periods of time with low maintenance costs.

Permanent Pump Stations

The two permanent pump stations at the Nose Rock Project were designed for a sustained pumping capability of 22,700 liters per minute, (6000 gpm) with an additional 11,350 liters per minute (3,000 gpm) backup. These stations consist of three banks of five pumps per bank with each bank being capable of pumping 11,350 liters per minute (3,000 gpm). Provisions were made in each station to install a fourth bank of equal capacity sometime in the future, should conditions dictate.

The primary pumps of each bank are 313 kw (500 hp) electrically powered, direct driven centrifugal slurry pumps, each capable of 11,350 liters per minute (3,000 gpm) at a total discharge head of 137 meters (450 ft). These pumps are connected in series to attain the desired system head and in all cases are force fed with high volume, low head feed pumps, to minimize the effects of cavitation. The last pump of each bank is equipped with a fluid coupling which, in conjunction with electric metering and feed back of sump water levels, can automatically regulate output to allow continuous operation at levels as low as 6,050 liters per minute (1,600 gpm).

The upper permanent pump station is located 457 meters (1,500 ft) below the surface. Each bank of pumps on this station consists of three main pumps connected in series and force fed by two feed pumps, also connected in series. The lower permanent pump station is located at 957 meters (3,140 ft) below the surface and when completed will discharge into sumps on the upper station. The typical bank on the lower station consists of four main pumps in series force fed by a vertical centrifugal pump which will be located in a sump on the haulage level 23 meters (75 ft) below.

Temporary Pump Stations

Temporary pump stations are normally located above major aquifers in order to minimize the less reliable in-shaft super water ring system described earlier. These stations are equipped with either the primary pumps described earlier or a smaller version capable of 7,570 liters per minute (2,000 gpm) at a total discharge head of 98 meters (320 ft). The maximum lift for a temporary station was 305 meters (1000 ft).

Five temporary pump stations were used for shaft sinking at the Nose Rock Project. These stations either discharged into higher temporary stations or permanent stations. As permanent stations were completed and became available, they were incorporated into the system.

CONCLUSION

The Nose Rock Project is currently running approximately three months ahead of schedule. Although no methods or techniques have been used that could be classified as unconventional, through a combination of experienced management, proven water control techniques, well structured bonus incentive plans, and a positive overall relationship between owner and contractor, record sinking rates have been attained.

When completed, the Nose Rock Project will unlock for public use a considerable amount of uranium ore from deep underground. Combined managment and technical achievements of both Phillips Uranium Corporation and Harrison Western Corporation are responsible for this success.

REFERENCES

Chenowith, W.L., 1977, "Uranium in the San Juan Basin - An Overview," New Mexico Geological Society Guidebook, 28th Field Conference, San Juan Basin III, pp. 257-262.

Greenslade, W.M., Sprouls, E.P., 1977, "Geotechnical and Hydrologic Investigation, Production Shaft, Mining Unit 1, Nose Rock Project," Dames and Moore, Phoenix, Arizona.

Griswold, G.G., White, L.G., 1980, "Water Control During Shaft Sinking Utilizing Depressuring Wells and Resin Grouting Techniques," Harrison Western Corporation, Denver, Colorado.

Kelly, T.E., 1977, "Geohydrology of the Westwater Canyon Member, Morrison Formation, of the Southern San Juan Basin, New Mexico," New Mexico Geological Society Guidebook, 28th Field Conference, San Juan Basin III, pp. 285-290.

Molenaar, C.M., "Stratigraphy and Depositional History of Upper Cretaceous Rocks of the San Juan Basin Area New Mexico and Colorado, with a Note on Economic Resources," New Mexico Geological Society Guidebook, 28th Field Conference, San Juan Basin III, pp 159-166.

Vanderwoude, M.D., 1980, Mine Geologist, Phillips Uranium Corporation, Private Communication.

Chapter 59

SHAFT SINKING CONCEPTS AND TWO INDEPENDENT SYSTEMS
OF CONCURRENT DEVELOPMENT THROUGH THE SHAFTS BEING SUNK

BY

P.J.L. NEL

TECHNICAL ASSISTANT TO CONSULTING ENGINEER

GOLD AND URANIUM DIVISION
ANGLO AMERICAN CORPORATION OF SOUTH AFRICA LIMITED

ABSTRACT

The paper describes several successful concepts used in the sinking of shafts on the Elandsrand Gold Mine. The concepts enabled the shaft sinking time to be reduced as well as the period in which development would normally take place to establish initial ore reserves.

INTRODUCTION

Elandsrand, the first new independent gold mine venture by the Anglo American Corporation for seventeen years, has come "on stream" faster than any other major deep level mine since mining began on the Witwatersrand.

The first chapter of the Elandsrand story opened in mid 1974 when Anglo American Corporation of S.A. Limited approved a feasibility study for developing a new gold mine approximately 80 kilometres south west of Johannesburg, close to another Anglo American gold mine, Western Deep Levels Limited. Due to economic pressures of constantly escalating costs set against a fluctuating gold price, it was necessary to ensure a reduction in all time schedules to bring the mine into production. This was to be achieved as rapidly as possible with due regard to safety.

In the achievement of this time trimming objective, several stimulants came into play. The Elandsrand project team introduced many innovations which were made possible by Elandsrand's consulting engineer, Mr W.R. Lawrie, who once he had set and obtained committment to broad yet comprehensive objectives, held the reins of control with a light hand. Mr Harry Oppenheimer, Chairman of the Anglo American Corporation and Elandsrand at the first shaft sinking blast in 1976 epigrammed Elandsrand by stating "this mine by any standards is a big project and one which we like to think is in the character of our group, to do big things and to do them fast".

Rocks outcropping in the Elandsrand's lease area consist of quartzite, shale and lava of the Pretoria group and are underlain first by 1 300 metres of dolomite and then by the Black Reef series. This in turn rests unconformably on Ventersdorp and Witwatersrand rocks and truncates the Basal member of the Ventersdorp super group, the Ventersdorp contact reef (VCR), near the northern boundary of the lease. The Ventersdorp group is composed of lava and varies in thickness from nil in the north of the lease area to 1 000 metres in the south. The VCR, less than 100cm thick, dips 27° to the south and lies between 1 786 and 3 386 metres below datum.

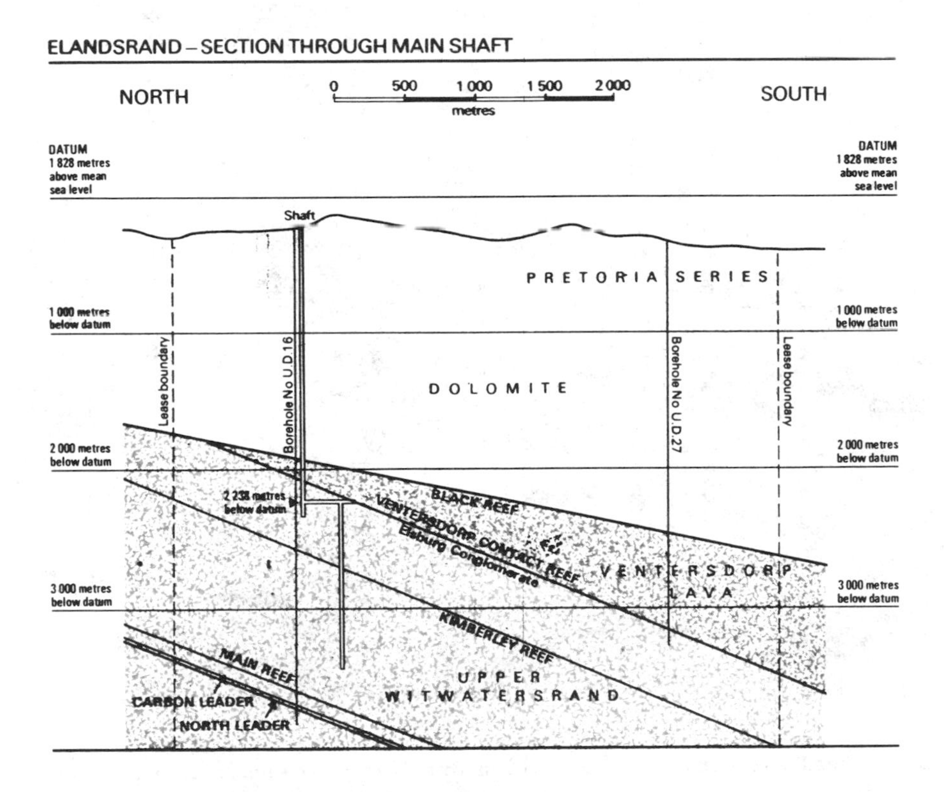

SHAFT SINKING CONCEPTS

Pre-sinking Cementation

Full economic value of specialised mechanical equipment such as is used during shaft sinking can only be obtained by an uninterrupted sequence of operations and it was therefore planned to reduce the chances of water being intersected thereby delaying the progress of the shaft as the shaft had to transverse the water-bearing dolomite formations.

Man-material shaft headgear (on left) and rock-ventilation shaft headgear with pre-cementation drill-rigs adjacent to the headgears.

The two proposed shafts at Elandsrand namely the man/material (M/M) 8,35m diameter, and rock/ventilation (R/V) 9,78 m diameter, shafts were sited well within and above a gravimetrically determined 200 metre 'safe-limit' contour of the northern slope of the Gatsrand. Two pre-cementation holes were drilled and the cementation holes were kept within a 9 metre annulus round each shaft to seal any water bearing pockets in the proximity of the excavation during sinking through the overlying dolomites.

Casing of holes

114mm casings were set throughout the upper shales in both holes. 76mm casings were set at 205 metre depths and 60mm casings at 830 metre depths. The reason for setting the casing as deep as possible was to increase the theoretical pre-split pressure at the base of the casing, to reduce the amount of re-drilling of cement, and to gain better control of the direction of the boreholes by drilling 76mm size holes. All casings were grouted in by lowering them to within 10cm of the bottom of the holes, attaching the grouting range, pumping water to establish a circulation down the inside of the casing and up between the casings and the holes, then pumping the final grout in which the casings were set, when the thick grout was seen to return to surface the injection was terminated, the casings lowered to the bottom and a setting period of three days allowed. Casing grout used has a cement, water ratio of 2 : 1 (as thick as the cementation pumps could handle.)

Deflections

Hole No. 1 (Fig. 1) serving the M/M shaft was collared 22m from the shaft centre, in order to accommodate sub-bank constructing. There were two phases in controlling the direction of this hole, the first being to guide the borehole into position (9m annulus) and the second to maintain it in that position. For the former, in particular, it is advisable to have a definite plan of action which should include a specific aiming point marking the end of each phase. In the case of hole No. 1 the aim was to have it back into the 9m annulus when reaching the dolomites at 340m below collar.

In planning holes No's 1 and 2, the natural drift was estimated from the behaviour of holes drilled in the surrounding area. The selection of aiming points was influenced by the fact that control in phase two would be easier within the line where the natural drift in the dolomites were tangential to the stipulated limits, a circular zone extending from five to fifteen metres from the shaft centres. These limits ensured that the holes, and in particular any casing, wedges or rods left in the holes, remained clear of the shaft sinking operations that followed and yet placed injections close enough to be completely effective across the shaft area.

Re-drilling

Re-drilling was done using non-coring tungsten carbide crowns and limiting the life of each crown to 200 metres. Drilling further than this resulted in the necessity for reaming or even having the crown stuck in the hole.

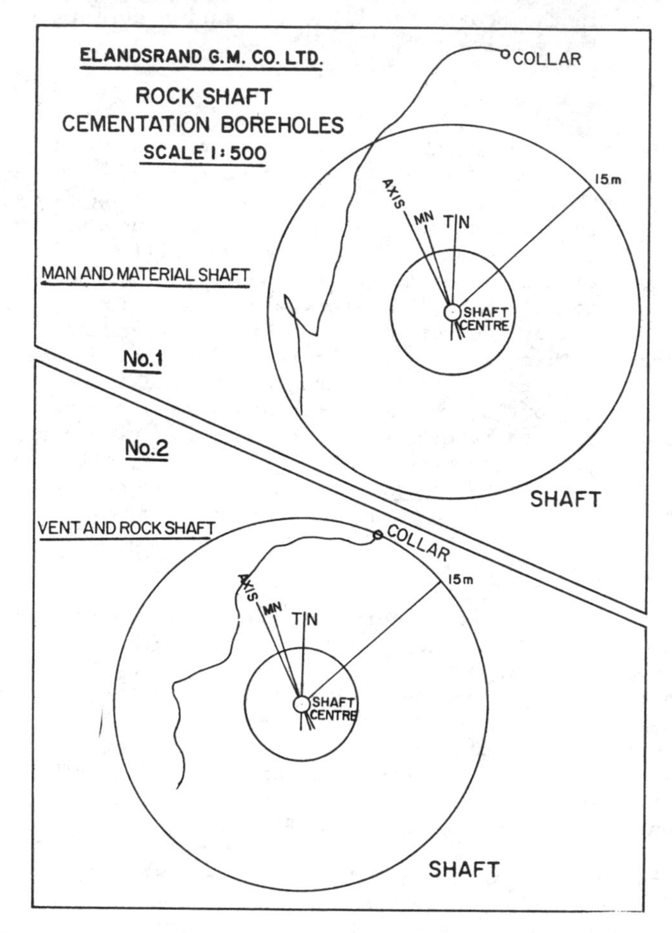

Fig. 1. Plan view on pre-cementation drill holes.

Decisions when to inject

The decision was taken to inject when water losses occurred. In cases of partial water losses it may become critical to decide when to inject. With a water loss of 50 percent or more the hole was injected at the completion of a run. When smaller losses occurred, the hole was drilled on to determine if the loss increased (this was normally the case) the ruling was that not one of the holes would be continued for more than fifty metres with a partial water loss without taking a pressure test to establish the flow which the hole would accept under pressure.

Grouting procedure

When the decision to inject had been made it became standard practice to measure the water level in the hole and where applicable, to do a water pressure test. It was standard practice that by the time an injection was started in one hole, the rods should at least be in the process of being pulled from the other. On only one occasion an injection inter-connected between the two holes. At the start of each injection clear water was pumped for one hour in order to flush the fissure, to clear drilling cuttings from the hole and to create a flow within the fissure which added momentum to the injection.

A starting mix with a water, cement ratio of 6 : 1 (density 1,10) was used. Depending on the course of the injection, the density of the mix should be increased at four hourly intervals by 0,05. Sealing pressure used was 40 bar. This was based on the fact that pressures tended not to increase above that level due to the fast pumping rates and the increase in pressure at the point of injection imposed by the column of cement mix in the hole. Although this pressure was well below, the theoretical pre-split level at the base of the casing it is always considered necessary to be aware of that maximum.

Injections were terminated by pumping 800 litres of cement with a density of at least 1,50 followed by a calculated volume of water sufficient to clear the casing.

General

The stated intention of the pre-grouted holes was to pump cement ahead of the shaft sinking operations, in order to seal off any water bearing zones, to improve ground conditions and to provide geological information which could assist with shaft and station planning. Logging of the shafts indicated clearly that cement had permeated the ground thoroughly and cement grout was consistently detected in both shafts.

Notwithstanding the pre-cementation programme, one water pocket of 35 bar pressure was intersected in the M/M shaft when a shaft cover hole was drilled to a depth of 36 metres and a pre-cementation rock drilling machine was catapulted to the stage, 12 metres above the shaft bottom and the shaft was flooded.

TYPE 30 SHAFT LASHING GEAR

The first of these units was supplied to Anglo American Corporation of South Africa and were used during sinking both shafts at Elandsrand Gold Mine. The type 30 lashing gear was designed and manufactured by a South African company.

Although a young company, it has at its disposal the accumulation of many years of experience in the designing and construction of shaft sinking lashing gears and this experience enabled the company to produce a lashing gear in which the basic design parameters and the design of every component has been considered on the basis of past operational performance.

As anticipated this completely new design overcame many of the problems experienced in the past under the very arduous operating conditions which these machines must endure.

The type 30 lashing gear (Fig. 2) was designed with the specific objectives of providing :

(i) a rugged construction giving reduced down-time as a result of damage, wear or mechanical failure;

(ii) improved rope life;

(iii) reduced maintenance by virtue of a centralised lubrication system;

(iv) improved operator control;

(v) four point mounting onto the bottom deck only of the sinking stage.

The standardised turntable assembly made the type 30 suitable for use in shafts up to ten metres in diameter and capable of handling a 'Cactus' grab of 0,85 m^3 capacity. The lashing gear is of robust construction, but designed so that all components will pass easily through the kibble openings on the sinking stage. The base support is designed to be mounted at four points onto the lower platform and carries the main support bearing and slew ring-gear.

The turntable is mounted on the main support bearing and carries on its upper surface the hoist winch, the slew motor and gearbox as well as the rope reel.

The boom which is attached to the underside of the turntable by support pins, is heavily reinforced at the attachment points and has the main side members cut from plate in one piece to avoid welded joints.

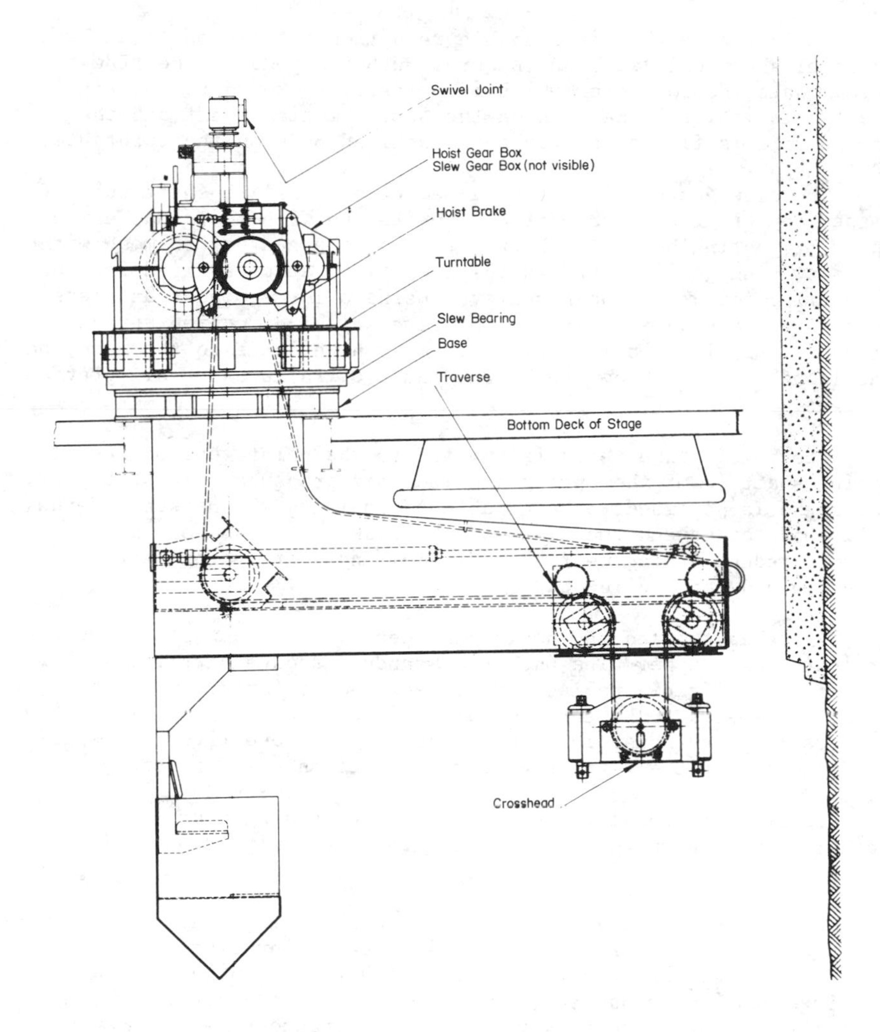

Fig. 2. Type 30 shaft lashing gear used during shaft sinking at Elandsrand Gold Mine.

The main support bearing is a massive ball race of approximately 1,7 m diameter and carries both the axial thrust due to the mass of the lashing gear and its load, as well as the turning moment produced by the boom load. The bearing is designed to be capable of withstanding loads far in excess of the maximum loads which would be imposed in service. The ring gear for the slew drive is cut in the inner race of the bearing.

The hoist gearbox is a double reduction totally enclosed parallel shaft unit with an integral outboard pedestal bearing to accommodate the rope drum which is pressed and keyed to the final shaft. The hoist brake acts on the second motion shaft and the entire unit is flange-mounted onto machined pads on the turntable.

The slew gearbox is a triple reduction parallel shaft unit of dished construction with vertical shafts and with the final drive shaft projecting below the bottom face of the gearbox to mesh with the slew ring-gear. Although the reduction ratio required for the slew drive could have been achieved using a more compact and less costly worm and wheel hearbox, the reversal of direction during slewing operations would apply extremely high loads to the worm and wheel and has been known to be the cause of failures on all previous designs.

The hoist brake which is applied to the hoist gearbox second motion shaft is of the spring-applied, air pressure release type. The brake is designed to be capable of applying 200 percent of the full load torque and the width of the brake path has been made very wide to reduce lining wear to a minimum and so reducing bearing pressure and heat build-up.

All sheaves used in the lashing gear are of cast steel and are of 'cartridge' type. The use of a standard sheave cartridge makes for simple and rapid replacement of any sheave, and reduces the number of spares to be carried. The diameter of the sheave has been made as large as possible in order to improve rope life. A magazine reel-mounted on the turntable carries three changes of rope.

In order to reduce shock loads on the lashing gear, the grab anchor points on the grab crosshead are fitted with compression springs.

All gears with the exception of the slew ring gear are fully enclosed and oil lubricated. The ring gear is protected and grease lubricated. All other moving parts, with the exception of the carriage and grab crosshead, are supplied from a centralised grease lubrication system, thereby reducing maintenance to a minimum.

The normal use of air hoses, which are, of course, susceptible to damage, has been avoided on the type 30 lashing gear and all air lines have been piped in steel. Small diameter air lines are further protected by being grouped together inside a steel channel. The use of a pilot valve to actuate the main grab valves resulted in improved operator control.

CONCRETE MIXING AND DELIVERY

With the introduction of lining and sinking concurrently the expeditious delivery of concrete from the batching plants on surface to the shuttering rings has always been a matter of great importance in shaft sinking.

The normal practice is to place two concrete batching plants (one as a standby) close to the shaft being sunk. During lining operations the concrete is fed into a receiving hopper situated on the bank (surface) by means of a conveyor belt, from where it is passed down the shaft in a special pipe 150mm in diameter. At the bottom, attached to the concrete column, is an overflow pot or kettle.

Fig. 3. The two shafts being sunk with the central batching plant. (Left bottom corner).

Fig. 4. Batching plant feeding into two hydraulically operated concrete pumps.

During the initial planning stage of the Elandsrand shafts it was realised that if the standard method was to be adopted, four batching plants (two per shaft) were required, two plants adjacent to each shaft. This would have resulted in delaying other construction work, close to the shafts, which was scheduled to run concurrently with shaft sinking, as the batching sites were required until the completion of sinking. In order to allow operations to be implemented and carried out concurrently rather than consecutively it was decided to embark upon a concept new to shaft sinking practice.

A central batching plant serving both shafts was positioned 180 metres west of the sinking shafts. (Fig. 3). The central plant consisted of two batching plants feeding directly into two hydraulically operated concrete pumps of 35m^3 per hour capacity. (Fig. 4). Suitable piping arrangements from the pumps to the two shafts, ensured concrete deliveries with constant feeds even in cases of one pump and one plant being out of operation due to breakdowns. This lay-out enabled construction work adjacent to the shafts to continue and also resulted in a 50% saving in capital expenses and a 30% reduction in batch plant personnel.

In between shaft lining shifts, the plant with the pipe lines extended to wherever required were used for concrete lining the bank area.

The kettle or overflow pot attached to the bottom of the concrete column is designed to break the fall of the material as well as re-mixing the aggregate before passing it by means of two rubber armoured hoses to behind the shuttering.

It is a known fact in South African shaft sinking that once depths of approximately 800 metres are exceeded the buffer plate in the kettle, 225mm thick bright steel or manganese, lasts for approximately two lifts or eight hours of concreting. The kettle and hoses (approximately 1½ tons) are brought to surface after each concreting shift for cleaning, inspection and any necessary repairs. It is of extreme importance that this is done as a "break-through" the kettle during concrete lining could result in long delays and serious accidents.

A special kettle (Fig. 5) was designed and proven during the sinking of the Elandsrand shafts. The kettle is supplied with a buffer plate and tube liners made from "Brantwil metal" which has a composition of 5 percent cobalt and 95 percent tungsten carbide. Kettles of this design proved to be very successful during the sinking of both Elandsrand's shafts and has become standard practice on all new deep shafts. A kettle of the above design which remained underground for three months during which, approximately 432 metres were sunk and passing approximately 3 000m^3 of concrete through was brought to surface and inspected for wear. The wear on the buffer plate was less than 15mm. Recently two kettles of similar design completed the 2 300m, 10,6m diameter, Vaal Reef's No. 9 shaft. The use of this new type of kettle resulted in a tremendous saving in sinking time and effort.

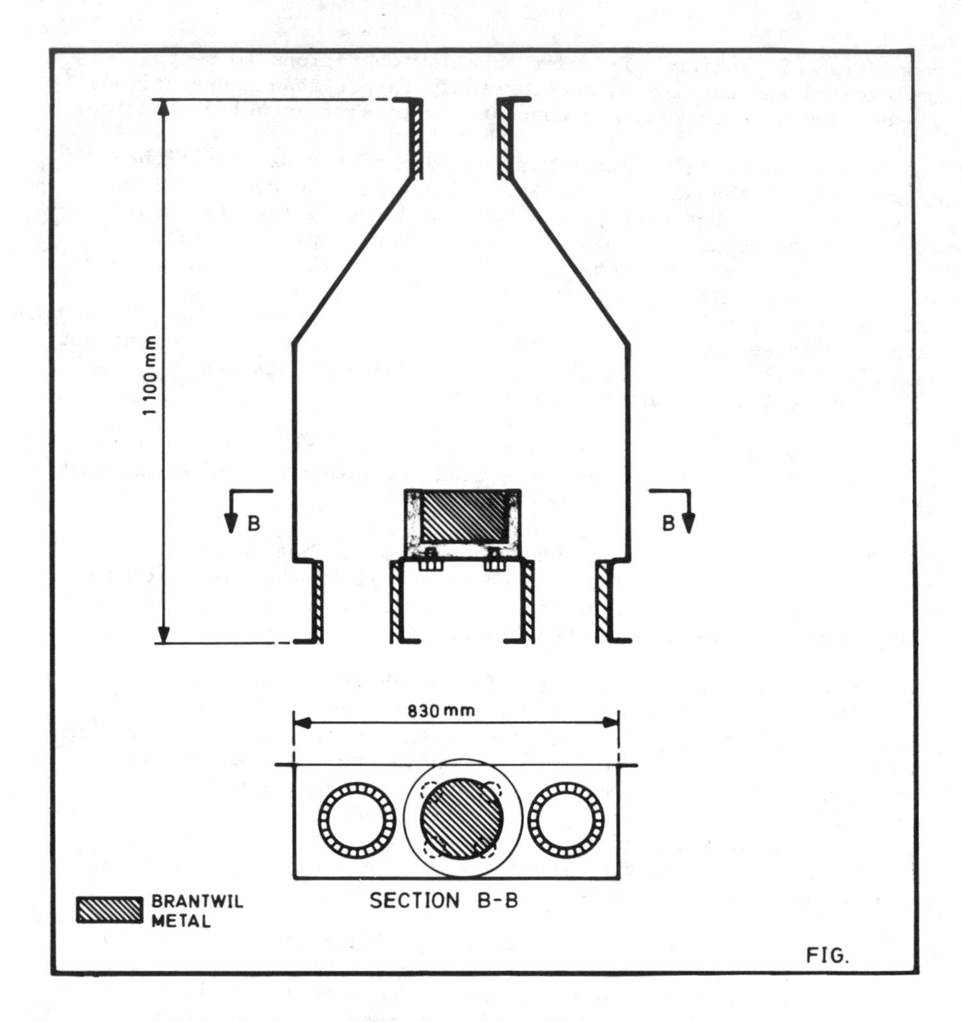

Fig. 5. Concrete kettle with "Brantwil Metal" liners.

TWO INDEPENDENT SYSTEMS OF CONCURRENT DEVELOPMENT THROUGH SHAFTS BEING SUNK

Due to the success achieved with the pre-sinking and headgear construction, alternative plans had to be implemented to bring the whole Elandsrand programme in line with the changing production date which after twenty-one months was already a year ahead of schedule. The overall gain in time threw sharp attention on the bar chart schedules for the development in the R/V shaft of the main pumping levels, the two main working levels on the M/M shaft (Fig. 6), both vital steps in the programme to commission these shafts as quickly as possible. If this object could be achieved we would eliminate delays usually associated with shaft commissioning that could run into months.

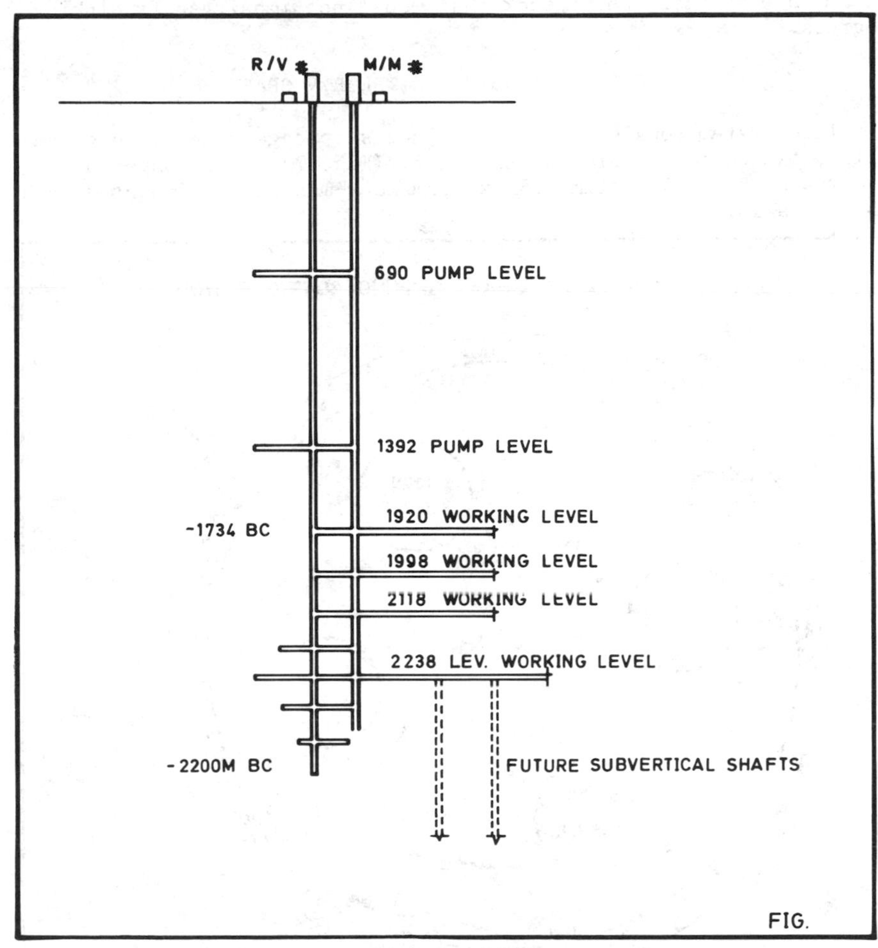

Fig. 6. Section through shafts indicating different levels.

Only one mine, Vaal Reefs South has managed to sink and develop a shaft simultaneously but then development - by some of the shaft sinkers - could be carried out daily only for limited periods when sinking kibbles were available for men, material and rock conveyance while drilling was in progress. Rock loading was achieved by swinging out a cylindrical drawbridge from the level under development. However, this scheme was too restrictive for Elandsrand's purposes because if the new goals were to be achieved much more than the twenty percent of the twenty-four hour cycle shaft operating time allocated to development at Vaal Reefs South would be needed. In order to meet our goal we required an independent conveyance system in each shaft being sunk that would not impair shaft sinking progress.

MID SHAFT LOADING ON THE R/V SHAFT

This system consisted of a combined skip cage running on guide rails attached to the side of the shaft (Fig. 7). The conveyance used was an unusually slim 1,5m x 1,2m four-man cage surmounted by a 4,5 tons skip.

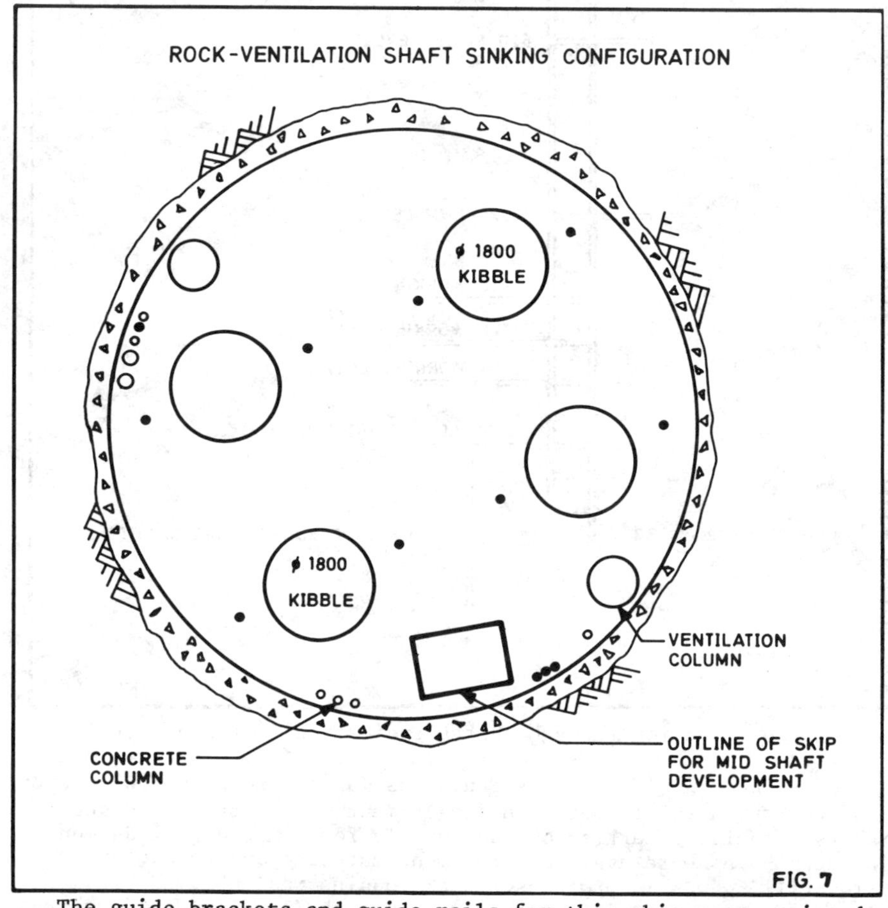

FIG. 7

The guide brackets and guide rails for this skip were equipped concurrently with the sinking up to the first pumping level, i.e. 690 level. The level was profiled only and sinking continued for an additional 90 metres. The mid shaft loading arrangement consisting of a basket arrangement, a rock bin and measuring flask (Fig. 8) were installed after which the sinking crew continued sinking the shaft whilst the mine's development teams were able to develop, support and fully equip each of the two pump levels, i.e. 690 metre level and 1392 metre level. The 1392 metre level was done after completion of 690 metre level when the mid shaft loading system was dismantled and re-installed at the 1392 metre level.

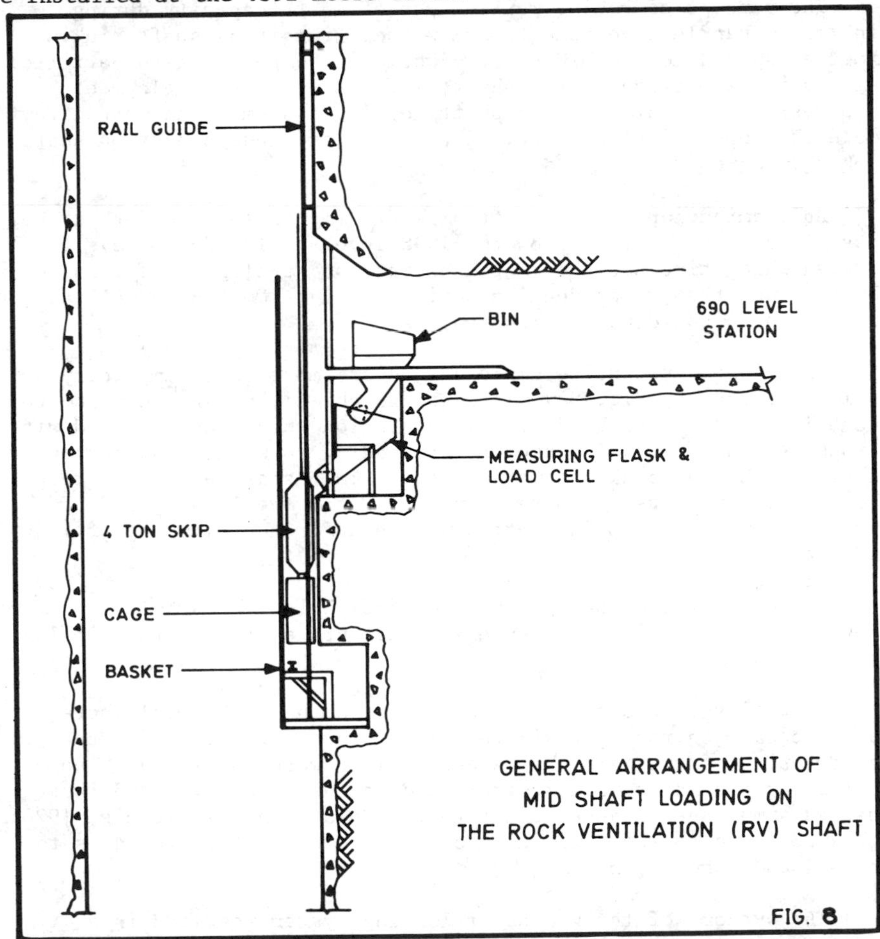

GENERAL ARRANGEMENT OF MID SHAFT LOADING ON THE ROCK VENTILATION (RV) SHAFT

FIG. 8

This basket arrangement was essential to protect the shaft sinking crew from any falling material or rocks from the levels being developed. A similar type of basket, with a double deck collar door was also installed from 4 metres below the shaft collar and extended up into the headgear to above the tipping position to ensure that no material or rocks could fall down the shaft whilst loading material or tipping broken rock.

This system was used on the two levels stated and approximately 1 500 metres of development or 19 000 m^3 of rock was excavated, resulting in a significant time saving in the shaft commissioning of approximately six months.

MID SHAFT LOADING ON THE M/M SHAFT

The concept of making maximum use of shaft capacity during sinking to handle development work without impairing shaft sinking progress spread to the M/M shaft - would it be possible to partition temporarily a portion of the shaft, exclusively for development purposes; to establish a mid shaft loading system; and what effect would the appropriation of one of the sinking winders have on shaft sinking progress?

An examination of the shaft sinking time-table showed that the loss of one winder from below the 1998 level would add 16 days to commissioning time but the increased rate of development envisaged would reduce the pre-production period by eight months as well as the time taken to build up ore reserves.

The system eventually employed had an impressive simplicity and is illustrated in (Fig. 9). It consists chiefly of an ore pass, to a sub-level 27 metres below the main station which was equipped with a rock bin and a swivel conveyor for loading rock into the respective kibbles. The sub-bank excavation on the main station carried the cross-head arrestors and were mainly used for the loading and off-loading of men. The main station was used for the slinging of long material.

The whole system was partitioned from below the sub-level to above the main station to ensure adequate protection to the sinking crews below.

Initially this system was installed on the 1920 level where it was in operation for approximately four months at which time the raise-boring of the main ore passes to 1998 were completed. The system was dismantled and re-installed on the 1998 level and thus enabled simultaneous development to take place on both levels, 1920 and 1998. Due to the simplicity of the system it took ten days to install and commission.

The outcome of the mid shaft loading system resulted in a reduction in the pre-production period of fifteen months (Fig. 10), and an improvement of the discounted cash flow of 6,3 percent. The last blast heralding the end of shaft sinking was on 5th January 1978 at which time Elandsrand had already developed 24 000 metres of waste rock and 1 500 metres of reef tunnels.

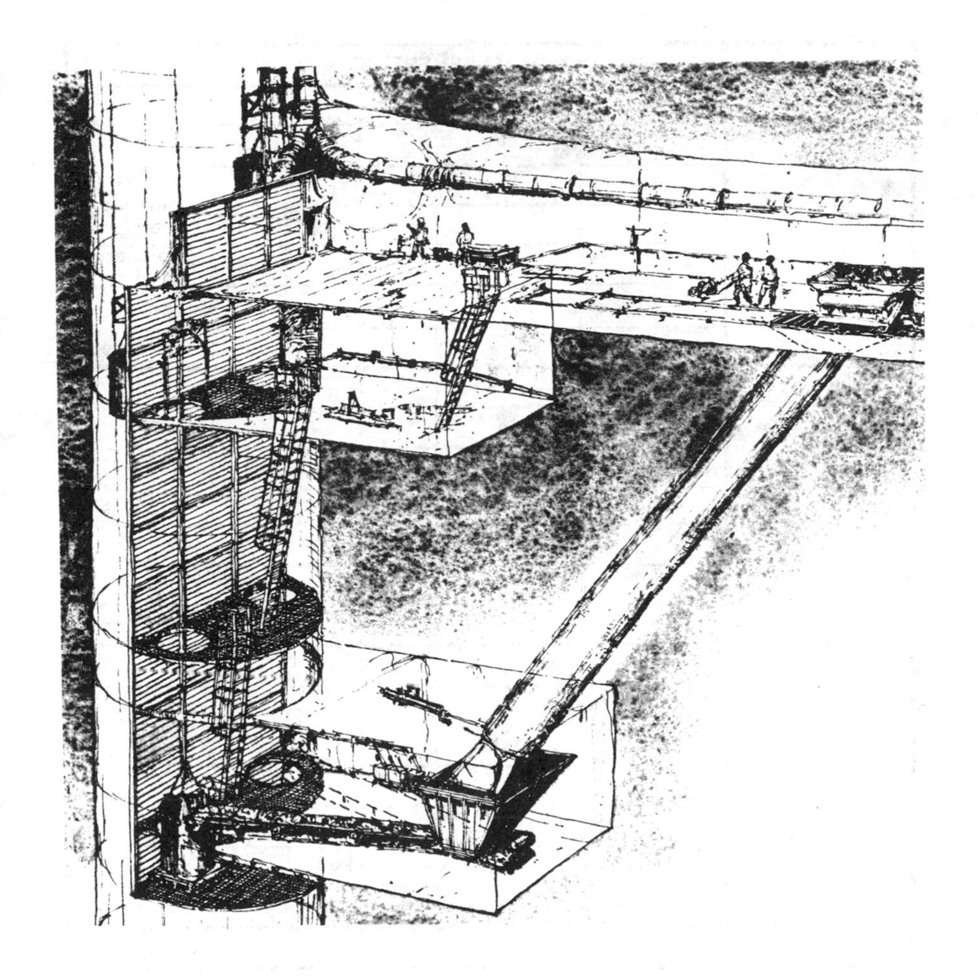

Fig. 9. Simultaneous sinking and mid-shaft development on MM shaft was heavily shielded to prevent rock and materials dropping upon shaft sinkers working far below.

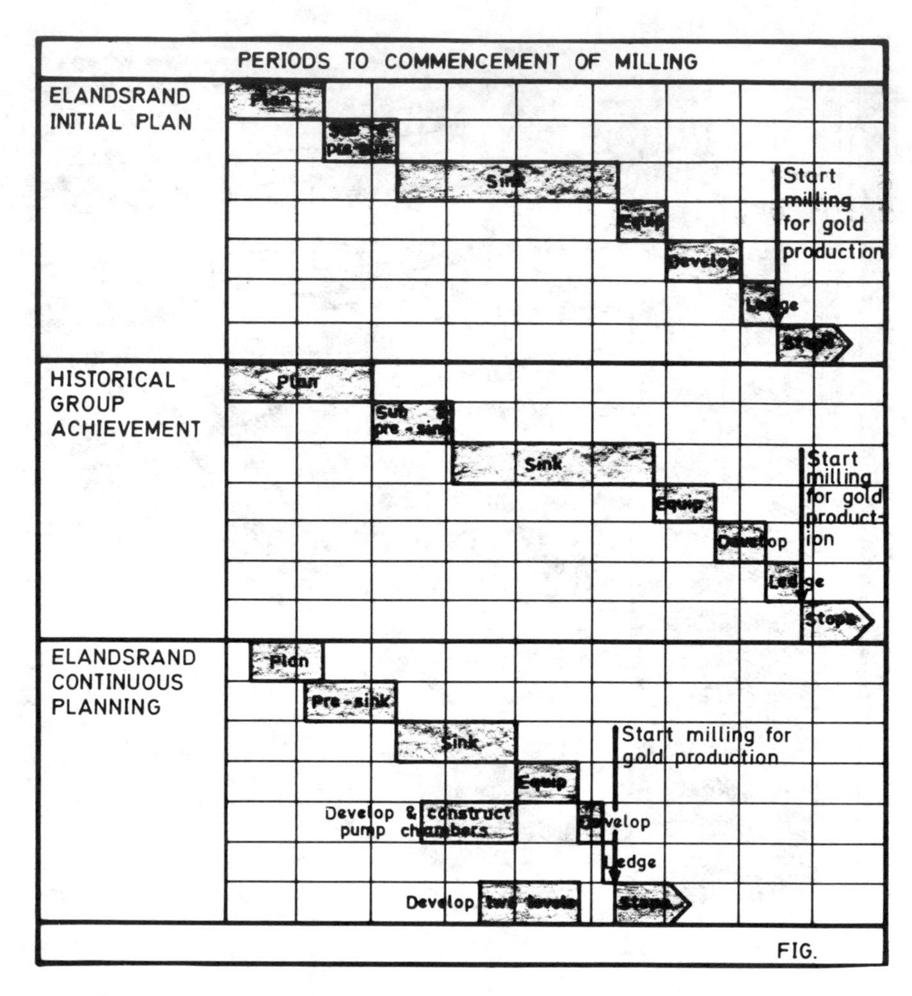

Fig. 10. Periods to commencement of milling.

CONCLUSION

The enormous capital expenditure required to open-up and develop new deep level gold mines has placed tremendous effort on the development of rapid shaft sinking methods in order to reduce the pre-production period. With new deep level mines costing about $600 million it is easy to see the motivation for reducing the pre-production period to the absolute minimum. With regard to further advances in sinking speeds, those engaged in sinking operations are confident that many improvements in practice can still be obtained.

ACKNOWLEDGEMENTS

The author is indebted to the photographic section of the Anglo American Corporation of South Africa Limited and Optima Magazine for the use of photos and diagrams. Mr W.R. Lawrie, Deputy Managing Director Gold and Uranium Division, Anglo American Corporation of South Africa Limited for permission to publish this paper.

Any views expressed in this paper are those of the author.

Chapter 60

NEW TECHNIQUES IN DEEP PRE-SINKING OF MINE SHAFTS

CYRIL HEEVER

CONSULTING ENGINEER

ROCKS outcropping in Elandsrand's lease area consist of quartzite, shale and lava of the Pretoria group and are underlain first by 1 300 metres of dolomite and then by the Black Reef series. This in turn rests unconformably on Ventersdorp and Witwatersrand rocks and truncates the basal member of the Ventersdorp Super group, the Ventersdorp Contact Reef (VCR), near the northern boundary of the lease. The Ventersdorp Super group is composed of lava and varies in thickness from nil in the north of the lease area to 1 000 metres in the south.

The VCR, less than 100 cm thick, dips 21° to the south east and lies between 1 786 and 3 386 metres below datum. The Oberholzer dyke straddles the north-western corner of the property and separates the dewatered Oberholzer compartment, over which most of Elandsrand lies, from the as yet un-dewatered Turffontein compartment. As so much of the lease area is covered by thick impermeable rocks, the water-bearing capacity of the underlying dolomite was expected to be low.

The man-material (MM) and rock hoisting ventilation (RV) shafts were sited well within and above a gravimetrically determined 200-metre 'safe-limit' contour of the northern slope of the Gatsrand. Two pre-cementation holes were drilled and the cementation rigs were placed within a 15 metre annulus round each shaft to seal any likely water-bearing pockets in the proximity of the excavation during sinking through the first 300 metres of shales and the surface water-table.

To counter the cavernous nature of the dolomite and the likelihood, remote in our view, of inter-connecting cavities being intersected by either shaft, different coloured dyes were injected into the holes: although cement grout was consistently detected in both shafts down to 400 metres no dye was ever seen. In fact, the excellent pre-cementation programme notwithstanding, one water pocket of 35-bar pressure was intersection in the MM shaft - when a shaft bottom cover hole was drilled to a depth of 36 metres and a pre-cementation rock-drilling machine was catapulted to the stage, 22 metres above - and the shaft was flooded.

As the site establishment, civil construction and the shaft pre-sinking programmes began to take shape, and we began to apply our concept, described in the preceding article, of running as many activities in parallel as possible to advance Elandsrand's production date, so our planning was concentrated upon the design and use of mobile headgears on a 'floating raft' to provide the necessary hoisting and shaft cleaning capacity, an idea which had never before been implemented in shaft sinking.

The raft, constructed of bolted standard uni-girders, carried two headgears; a conveyor mounted between the headgears was designed to load directly into 10 m^3-capacity end-tipping trucks. Also on stage were two 18-kilowatt single-drum stage winders with a rope speed of 30 metres/second to support the two-deck sinking stage; another 110 kW single-drum winder; and a mini-substation.

Initially, MM shaft sinking operations were slow because of the absence of permanent power - the winders and compressors had to be powered by a generator and portable diesel units - but by the third phase a neighbouring mine was able to provide 600 KVA to site.

THE MM SHAFT

It should not be construed that there was an overall plan for concurrent civil engineering and shaft sinking operations: each stage of progress was thought out, evaluated, costed, measured against the original plan and the alternatives before being implemented. Everyone concerned was involved in this 'think tank' process. In all there were five phases.

Phase 1

While the 'raft' was being constructed nearby, the square excavation with vertical sides was being cut to a depth of 12 metres for the headgear foundation by a ripper-equipped bulldozer; loading of the spoil was by Caterpiller Traxcavator on to 4 m^3-trucks.

Access was by way of a ramp which later was brought into use as a conveyor incline. To prevent collapse, the sidewalls were supported by concreting or by 400-kilonewton ground anchors.

Phase 2

Using compressed air rippers and occasional blasting, and a construction crane for hoisting and cleaning, the excavation was taken to the founding or 'toe-in' level of 12,5 metres and then to 30 metres, the maximum depth to which sinking can legally be taken using unguided kibbles, while simultaneously the civil engineering contractor proceeded with concreting and reinforcing of the headgear foundations.

Phase 3

Using bulldozers, the 'raft' was slid on rails over the excavation in three hours: sinking was able to continue as soon as the stage ropes and stage were placed in position. The crane, slightly re-positioned, was used solely as a rock kibble winder, the kibbles being guided by ballast frames. Men and materials were hoisted by the 110 kW winder. Sinking to 100 metres took only a few days.

Phase 4

Depth was now a limitation. Shaft bottom cleaning, using first Eimco track-type loaders and then diesel track-type loaders usually used on surface, was no longer economic. Faced with three months' shaft 'dead time' during headgear erection and equipping, sinking hoist installation and other services and before the shaft headgear could be 'slid', the 'think tank' decided to replace the crane with a more powerful winder (to be used also in the RV shaft) so that sinking could continue. Within 24 days of financial evaluation, the contractors had purchased, transported, modified and installed a 300 kW Emil Wolf winder and for six weeks sinking proceeded to a depth of 200 metres concurrently with civil work.

Phase 5

To allow pre-sinking to continue while the shaft headgear was being slid the raft was removed. In only 14 days, a remarkable achievement, one of its headgears, served by the 300 kW winder for conveyance of men, material and rock, and with loading conveyor, was installed on a temporary sub-bank established at the permanent headgear's founding level; blasted rock was transported from conveyor to surface by trucks using the exit ramp.

Pre-sinking had reached 246 metres by the time permanent headgear construction and equipping were completed. Concurrent operations ceased only when the temporary headgear protruding above the shaft collar began to obstruct the final stages of shaft equipping.

THE RV SHAFT

Using MM shaft experience, we were better able to plan each stage of the RV shaft pre-sinking programme and the simultaneous development of the ventilation drift, which nevertheless called for extraordinary co-operation and assistance from the civil engineering contractor in executing the headgear sub- and superstructure.

The first two phases were almost identical to the MM programme.

Phase 3

The raft with a single headgear and conveyor was transported by two 40-ton cranes and slid over the excavation when it had reached a depth of 30 metres. For 12 weeks, the construction crane again served as a kibble winder, to hoist rock from the ventilation by-pass excavation and the shaft as pre-sinking took it to 35 m while concreting proceeded of the headgear foundations and its sub-structure.

Phase 4

The raft was removed, to be used later over the ventilation drift excavation, and one of its headgears with conveyor was placed solidly on a temporary bank over the shaft collar for rock kibble hoisting. The only concession made in headgear erection was provision of temporary openings in the superstructure (for winder ropes) and in the foundations for the kibble winder ropes.

Phase 5

The raft headhears were used to sink the ventilation drift to 91 metres. The permenent headgear was erected to 67 m (in 16 days) and equipped, the ventilation by-pass was concreted and other incidental work was completed while pre-sinking took the shaft depth to 250 m.

The additional cost of pre-sinking equipment was R382 000.

Overall, this programme together with the subsequent mid-shaft programmes in both shafts where development was carried out concurrently with shaft sinking helped to reduce the pre production timetable by 15 months and to improve the forecast discounted cash flow by 6,53 percent.

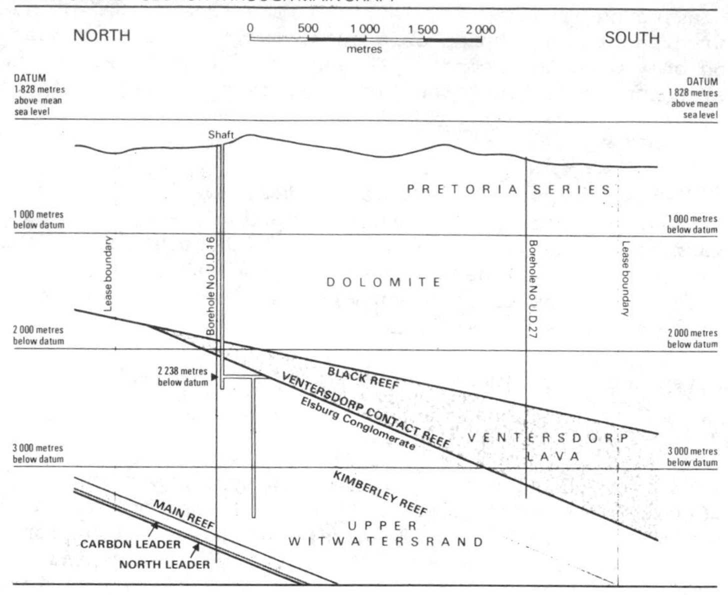
ELANDSRAND – SECTION THROUGH MAIN SHAFT
NORTH
SOUTH
0 500 1 000 1 500 2 000
metres
DATUM
1 828 metres above mean sea level
DATUM
1 828 metres above mean sea level
Shaft
PRETORIA SERIES
1 000 metres below datum
1 000 metres below datum
Lease boundary
Borehole No U.D.16
DOLOMITE
Borehole No U.D.27
Lease boundary
2 000 metres below datum
2 000 metres below datum
2 238 metres below datum
BLACK REEF
VENTERSDORP CONTACT REEF
Elsburg Conglomerate
VENTERSDORP LAVA
3 000 metres below datum
3 000 metres below datum
KIMBERLEY REEF
MAIN REEF
CARBON LEADER
NORTH LEADER
UPPER WITWATERSRAND

Phase 1

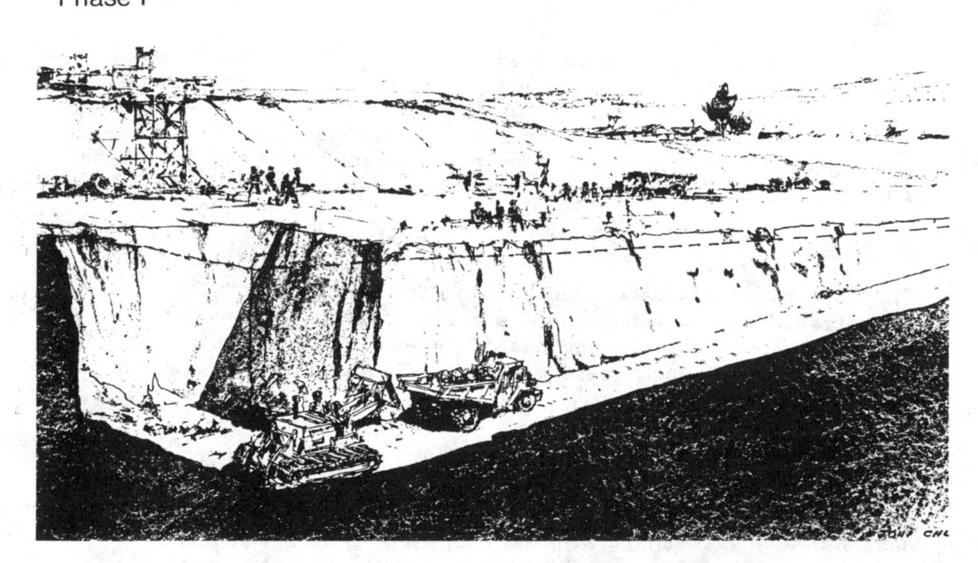

Phase 2

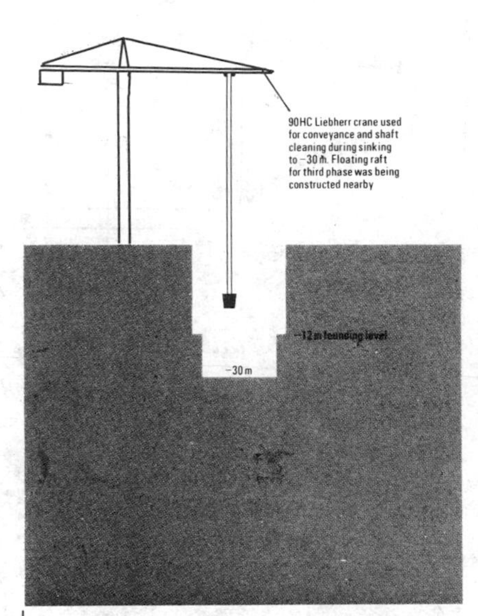
90HC Liebherr crane used for conveyance and shaft cleaning during sinking to −30 m. Floating raft for third phase was being constructed nearby
−12 m founding level
−30 m

Phase 3

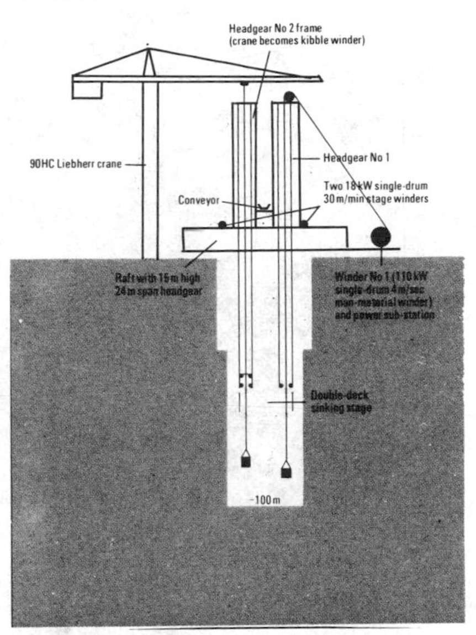
Headgear No 2 frame (crane becomes kibble winder)
90HC Liebherr crane
Headgear No 1
Two 18 kW single-drum 30 m/min stage winders
Conveyor
Raft with 15 m high 24 m span headgear
Winder No 1 (110 kW single-drum 4 m/sec man-material winder) and power sub-station
Double-deck sinking stage
−100 m

Phase 4

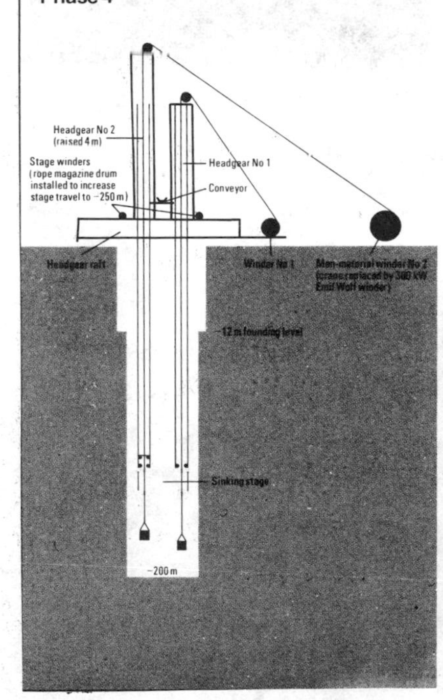
Headgear No 2 (raised 4 m)
Stage winders (rope magazine drum installed to increase stage travel to −250 m)
Headgear No 1
Conveyor
Headgear raft
Winder No 1
Man-material winder No 2 (crane replaced by 300 kW Emil Wolf winder)
−12 m founding level
Sinking stage
−200 m

Phase 5

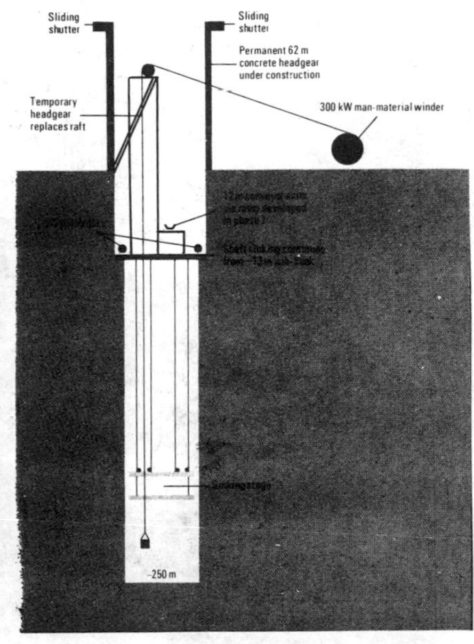
Sliding shutter
Sliding shutter
Permanent 62 m concrete headgear under construction
Temporary headgear replaces raft
300 kW man-material winder
−250 m

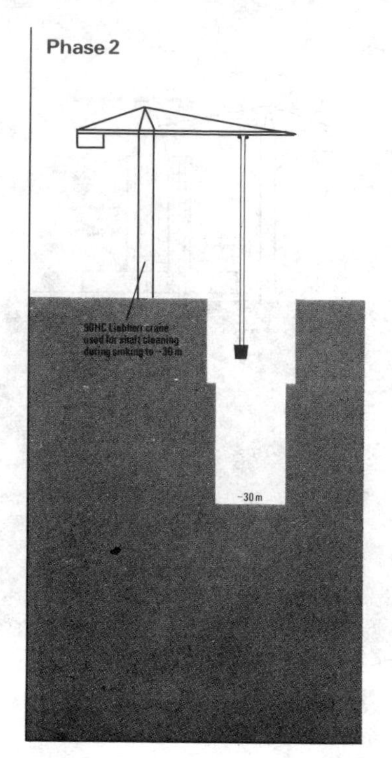
Phase 2
90HC Liebherr crane
used for shaft cleaning
during sinking to −30 m
−30 m

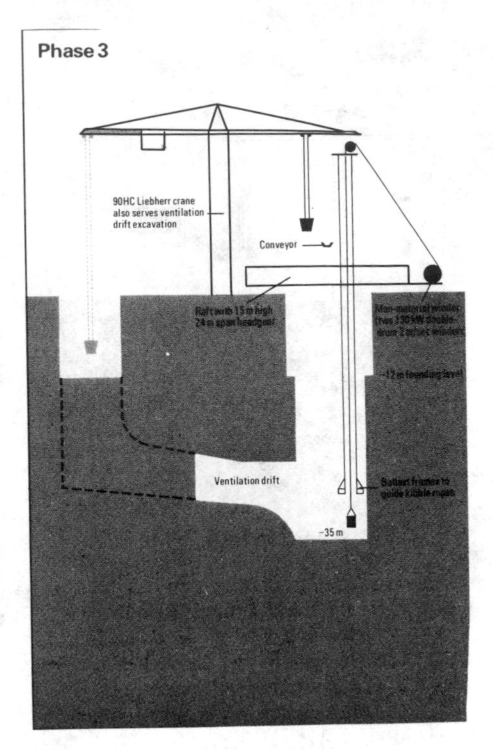
Phase 3
90HC Liebherr crane
also serves ventilation
drift excavation
Conveyor
Raft with 15 m high
24 m span headgear
Ventilation drift
−35 m

Phase 4

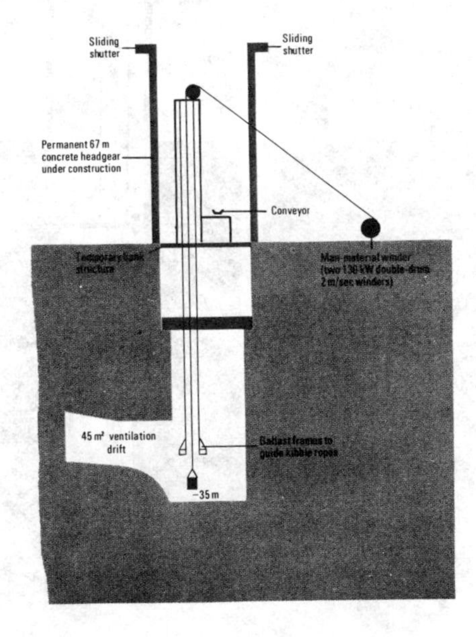
Sliding
shutter
Sliding
shutter
Permanent 67 m
concrete headgear
under construction
Conveyor
Man-material winder
(two 130 kW double-drum
2 m/sec winders)
45 m² ventilation
drift
Ballast frames to
guide kibble ropes
−35 m

Phase 5

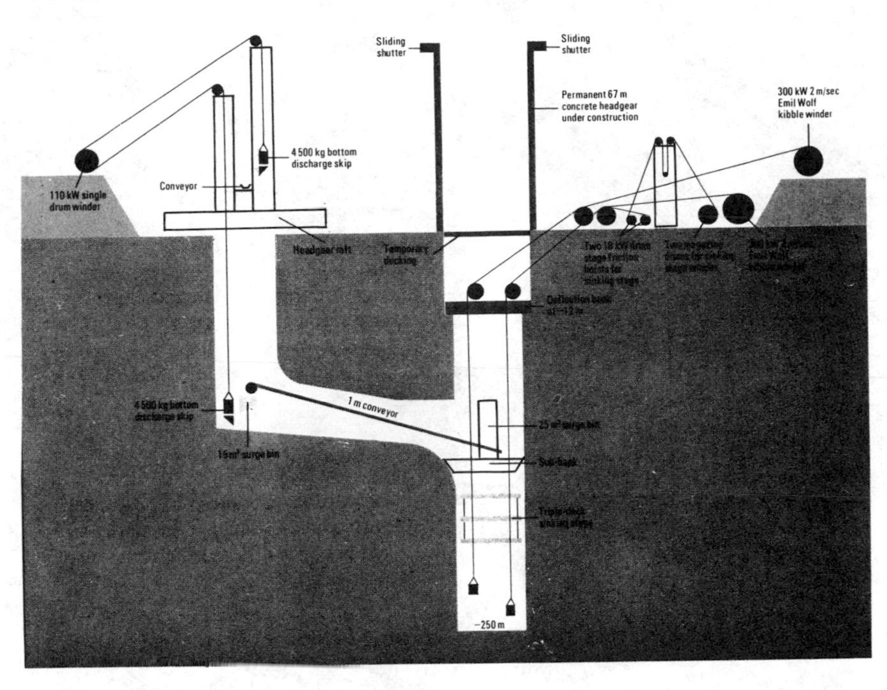
Sliding shutter
Sliding shutter
Permanent 67 m concrete headgear under construction
300 kW 2 m/sec Emil Wolf kibble winder
4 500 kg bottom discharge skip
Conveyor
110 kW single drum winder
Headgear mft
Temporary decking
1 m conveyor
4 500 kg bottom discharge skip
15 m³ surge bin
25 m³ surge bin
Sub-bank
Triple-deck sinking stage
–250 m

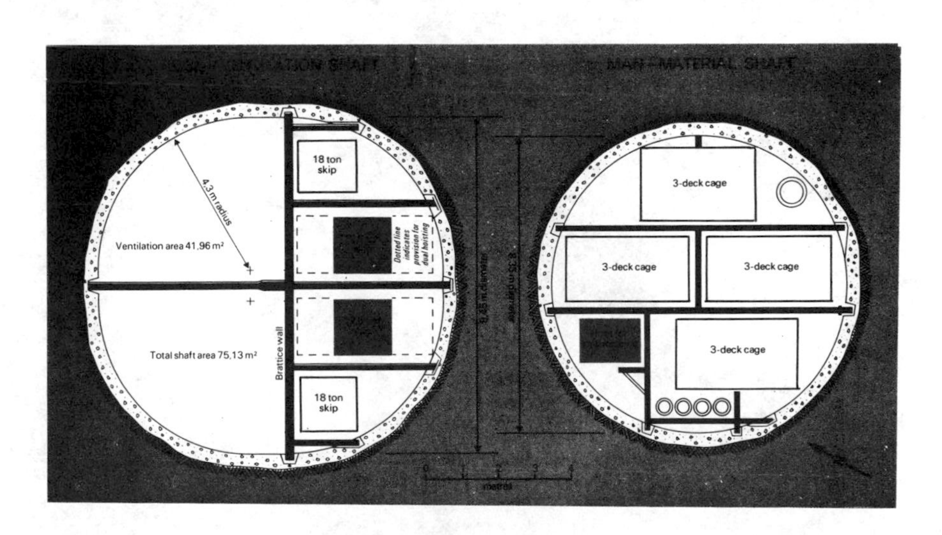
18 ton skip
4,3 m radius
Ventilation area 41,96 m²
Dotted line indicates provision for dual hoisting
Total shaft area 75,13 m²
Brattice wall
18 ton skip
3-deck cage
3-deck cage
3-deck cage
3-deck cage
metres

14

Development Execution Underground

Chairmen: G.L. Wilhelm
S.L. Milne

Exxon Minerals Co. USA, Houston, TX
Pincock Allen and Holt Inc., Tucson, AZ

Chapter 61

PREGROUTING IN A FULL-FACE BORED TUNNEL

by Thor Skjeggedal, BSc, MNIF

Site manager, A/S Høyer-Ellefsen,
OSLO, Norway.

ABSTRACT.

The Norwegian contracting firm A/S Høyer-Ellefsen has for the last 2.5 years carried out substantial pre-grouting in a 7600m long tunnel just outside the city of Oslo. This has been done to avoid groundwater lowering and consequent damage to surface structures. A WIRTH TBM is used in combination with a 2 boom Atlas Copco hydraulic jumbo for the drilling of groutholes in front of the machine.

The detailed procedure for the drilling and grouting will be discussed, and the results obtained will be presented.

PROJECT.

Presently the City of Oslo together with the two neighbouring municipalities Baerum and Asker are building a new sewage treatment plant on the west side of the inner Oslofjord.

For transport of sewage and storm water from the Citysentre and the two neighbouring areas, a 36 km tunnelsystem has to be excavated.

The tunnelsystem is devided into 4 seperat contracts, from which A/S Høyer-Ellefsen has one. This contract consists of a main tunnel of 7600m (3.35m dia.), access tunnel of 250m and a branch tunnel of 1000m.

Construction started in the spring of 1977 and is scheduled for completion late 1981. By the end of 1980, a total of 6400m of the main tunnel and 700m of the branch tunnel have been completed.

GEOLOGY.

Within the region of the contract, the rock originate from two geological periods, the Cambro Silurian sedimentary and Permian ignious rocks. The sedimentary rocks consists of limestone, shale and sandstone, which are folded in the direction NE-SW. This is also the strike of the bedding and the direction of the tunnel, i.e. the strike and the tunnelline are parallel. Due to this some extra stability and pregrouting problems have occured, and it has also reduced the rate of penetration of the tunnelboring.

The limestone is present in more or less even layers, nodular layers and isolated nodulis. In some parts of the tunnel massive limestone or massive nodular limestone also occure.

The Permian ignious rocks appear as dykes in the Cambro-Silurian sediments and constitutes approx. 10% of the tunnel length.

The dykes are mainly diabase, but sometimes maenaite and syenite also appear. Thickness of these dykes varies from less than 0.5m and up to 25m. Some of them are heavily fractured, especially against the neighbouring rocks, and some others especially the syenite can be quite massive.

In the north-south direction a number of faultzones occur. Here, materials as clay, chlorite and talc have been found.

The following typical figures shows the compressive strenght of the rock to be:

For sedimentary rock	8 - 900 kg/cm2.
For ignious rock	17 - 1800 kg/cm2.

PREGROUTING.

In the Oslo area there are many clay deposits on which buildings and other structures are founded.

The ground water table is in most places just under the surface of these deposits.

If the ground water is lowered, it will lead to an increase in effective pressure and will again lead to a certain amount of settlement, dependent upon how much the pore water pressure has been reduced and the thickness of the deposit.

Some of these ground water reservoars are quite small and may be in direct contact with the tunnel, which is only 30-60m beneath the surface.

A leakage into the tunnel can lower the ground water table with several meters in a very short time, and then settlements are following quite rapidly. Post-grouting or in-situ concrete behand the TBM would therefore be of no use.

Fig. 1 shows an example from the centre of Oslo where no pregrouting was done. Experience from this and other tunnels in the area has showed great damage to some buildings, and millions of dollars have been necessary for restoring.

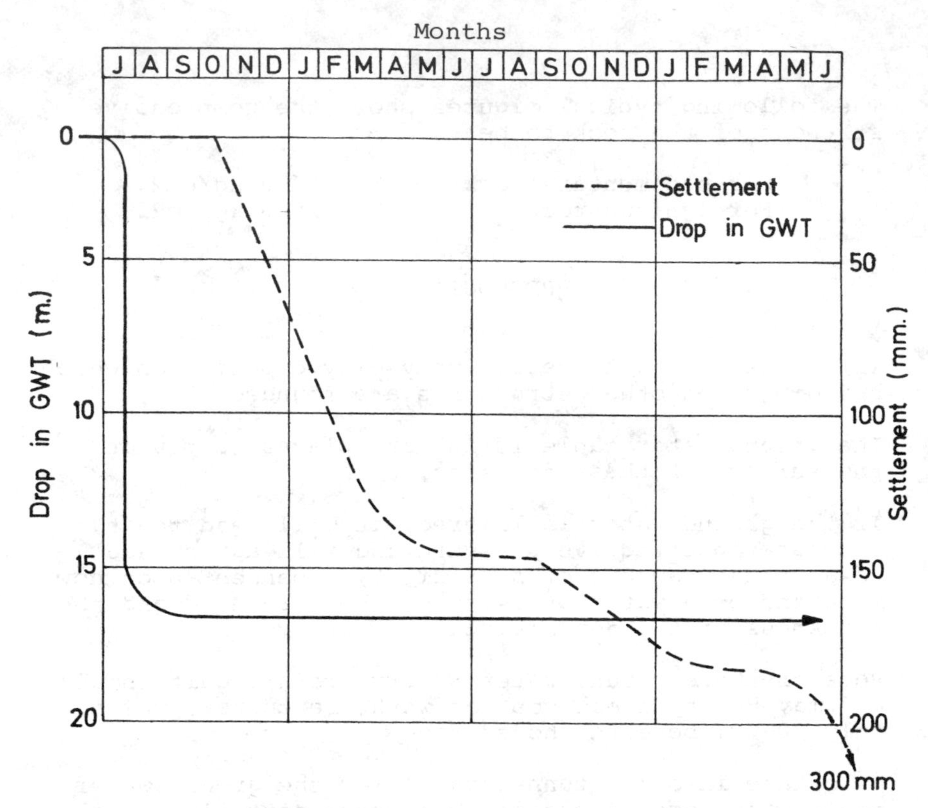

Fig. 1. An example from the Oslo area where no pregrouting was done.

The safest way to prevent these costs is by means of pregrouting. Some secondary effects of grouting are less inleakage of water, i.e. less water at the treatment plant, and it also seams that it has a stabilazing effect of the rockmass, particulary where it is heavily fractured.

In the tendering documents pregrouting was specified quite strictly. If the TBM could not be equipped acording to these special requirements, the tender was rejected.

TBM.

At the tendering time only one tunnel had been mechanically bored in the Oslo area. The pregrouting system failed and the contractor went into bankerupcy. This showed that the problem should be looked upon with great attention. To gain the best experiance, A/S Høyer-Ellefsen went together with the Sviss contracting company Murer AG of Erstfeld. They already had a suitable tunnel boring machine free. Diametre of this machine was 3.0m, but to provide space for the probehole drilling equipment, a new cutterhead of 3.35m was installed. The TBM is of make Wirth TB II H with electric hydraulic drive of the cutterhead.

Just behind the main body of the machine there is placed an Atlas Copco 2 boom jumbo with Cop 1038L hydraulic drills. For this reason the conveyor belts, hoses, etc. had to be extended by 11m.

The first plan was to guide the drillsteel along the TBM, through the cutterhead and into the rock. This was a bad solution, and after some expcrimentation decision was made to force the drill bit into the rock behind the second gripper pads. From these there is 6m to the front of the cutterhead. It was a requirement that the packers should be placed 1.5-2.0m in front of the tunnel face, and therefore each probehole is 6m longer than actually needed. The packer rods are also much longer this way. However, this was found to be the best solution.

Required was also a place for groutpump, mixer, agetator etc. An extra platform was buildt in behind all the main parts of the machine, 45m from the tunnelface and emediately in front of where the rails are placed. Fig. 2 shows how the grouting epuipment is incorporated in the TBM. The dotted lines indicate the placing and direction of the probeholes. In this way the machine got a total length of 90m, 18m more than normal where no pregrouting is done.

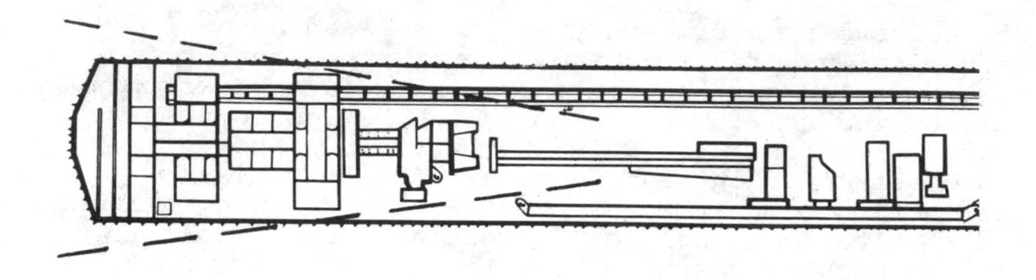

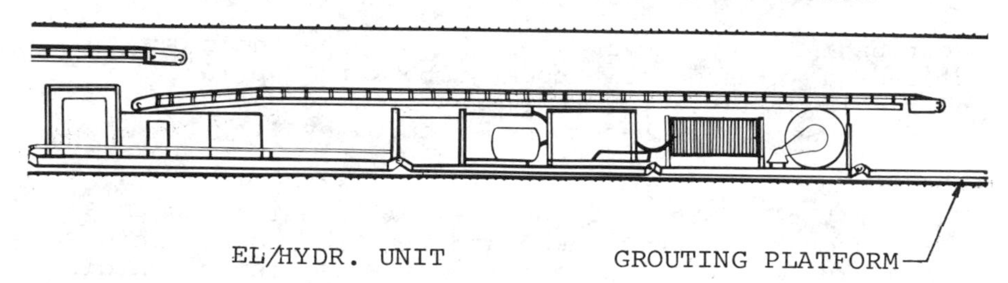

Fig. 2. TBM with grouting equipment incorporated.

GROUTING.

The tendering documents contained a detailed description of how the pregrouting shold be carried out. However, there was possibilities for the contractor to forward new solutions and methods, as long as these could be accepted by the client. This has to some extent been done.

The main grouting material is Rapid Portland Cement. A special cementmixture with less than 30 minutes hardening time is used at the finishing stage of the grouting. This means that tunnel boring can commence as soon as the grouting is finished.

To fill cracks with openings less tha 0.1mm, chemical solutions with viscosities equal to water is pumped in.

These solutions consists of silicates and a hardener called Stabilodur FR from ICI. The gel time of the mixture can be adjusted by the amount of hardener, but lays normally in the region of 30-40 minutes.

In the cement 2% of bentonite is used, and sometimes a special admixture to keep the viscosity of the suspention constant with less use of water.

The normal procedure for a round of grouting is as follows:

1. 6 probeholes (51mm dia.), 30m long (24m in front of the fullfacer) are drilled.

2. These holes are tested for loss of water. The loss is measured in terms of Lugeon (1 Lugeon is the loss of 1 litre of water per minute per meter of probehole at a pressure of 10 bar).

3. If losses exceed a certain Lugeon value in some or all of these holes, additional neighbouring holes are drilled and tested. In probeholes with less than 0.1 Lugeon no grouting is needed.

4. Then grouting can begin. Holes exceeding 1 Lugeon with cement, and holes with less than 1 Lugeon with chemicals. Normally most of the holes are grouted with cement. Firstly with water/cementratio of 3: 1, gradually reduced to 1: 1 as the pressure increases. When the pressure does not drop beneath 20 bar in one minutes time, the grouting of this hole is considered as completed.

   Sometimes both cement and chemical grouting is required in one round. By means of a second groutpump and agetator, the two materials can be pumped at the same time. Normally 3-4 holes are grouted simultaniously.

5. It is now up to the owners supervasory staff to decide whether extra control holes should be drilled. This is often the case, and the procedure has to be repeated once, and sometimes even twice before the grouting can be regarded as good enough.

Fig. 3. TBM and the long packer rods inserted behind the grippers.

Fig. 4. The groutpump, mixer etc. are placed 45m from the tunnel face.

6. The tunnel borer can now advance 20m, i.e. there is an overlap of 4m in each round.

In faultzones our experiance is that 24m is too long for one round. Difficulties araises with drilling of probeholes, placement of packers and grouting materials flows into the tunnel.

Therefore the 24m should be reduced to 10m or even less if the rock is heavily fractured.

This method is very timeconsuming, but it seems to be the only way to get through difficult zones without too much drainage of the ground water.

As earlier mentioned, the packer rods are quite long, 7.5m.
It is important that they are flushed with water emediately after the grouting is finished, and before the material has hardened. A special design with a extra plastc tube and a simple valve in the front of the packer makes it possible to do this and to use the packer rods again and again.

The cement is transported into the tunnel in 50 kg bags and lifted by hand directly into the mixer. Chemicals are pumped directly from a transport tank.

For the grouting a total of 5 men is needed. It is the same workforce that is doing the tunnel boring.

To give an indication of the amount of grouting done until the end of 1980, the following figures can be mentioned:

Total length of probeholes	58.000 m.
Total amount of cement	1.100.000 kg.
Total amount of chemicals	200.000 l.

This gives an average of:

Probeholes	9.5m per metre of tunnel
Cement	164kg per metre of tunnel
Chemicals	31 l per metre of tunnel

All the works in conection with pregrouting represents a value of approx. 40% of the tunnelprice,and it takes up about 50% of total avalable working time.

Postgrouting was also prescribed, but has only been used to a small extent, due to the fact that the result of the pregrouting has been good enough.

RESULTS.

Along the route of the tunnel a lot of gauges for recording pore water pressure are placed.

Readings of these were made once a week already 1-2 years before the excavation started,to get a picture of the natural variation of the ground water table.

During and after excavation of the tunnel so far, only two gauges have showed a drop in pore pressure. In one of these cases infiltration of water was carried out, and in the second case the pressure was restored by means of postgrouting.

This means that so far no damage due to settlements from ground water lowering have occured.

Inleakage of water into the tunnel has been measured to be 6-8 litre per minute per 100m of tunnel.

The maximum permissable value of this figure is assumed to be in the region of 10 litre per minute per

100m of tunnel. However, this figure may vary according to the local circumstances. To get a picture of the amount of water present in the rock, it can be mentioned that a flow of 100-200 litre per minute from a single probehole have been recorded in several occations. As mentioned earlier, pregrouting is very timeconsuming and will lead to a reduced advance rate of the tunnel boring. In spite of this, an average of 55m of tunnel per week (10 shifts a 7.5 h) has been achieved.

When the grouting is carried out, the boring operations must be stopped. It is only possible to do cutter-change, repair and service work on the TBM. This means that the utilization during tunnel boring can be improved by 5-10%.

CONCLUTION.

General development in urban areas will call for more and more excavation of tunnels and other subsurface space. It is very important that this can be made without to much damage to overlaying structures.

A successful pregrouting is one way to prevent settlements in the clay deposits. Pregrouting together with mechanical boring of tunnels is not the most widely used method, but it has proved to be a good alternative both concerning costs and results.

The secondary effects, especially the stabilizing of the rockmass in front of the tunnelface is important, and can secure the advance of the TBM. From the probehole drilling, a good picture of any faultzones can be obtained, and measures can be taken early enough so that the machine does not run into the most serious trouble. One method is then to insert 6-10m long rock bolts in holes already drilled with the incorporated jumbo.

Without the possibility to cope with the ground water problem, many tunnels may not be realized. This will again lead to less work for all the firms involved in the subsurface business.

Chapter 62

THE FEASIBILITY STUDY - SELECTION OF A MINING METHOD INTEGRATING ROCK MECHANICS AND MINE PLANNING

by David E. Nicholas and John M. Marek

Call & Nicholas, Inc.
Tucson, Arizona

Pincock, Allen & Holt, Inc.
Tucson, Arizona

INTRODUCTION

The purpose of this article is to outline the data requirements for selecting a proper underground mining method and to discuss the general steps taken in selecting that method. Determining the appropriate mining method is an iterative process that continues throughout the life of a mineral deposit.

We will discuss the subject from the standpoint of a feasibility study, where a realistic assessment is necessary in order to determine investment merit. The feasibility stage of a project is that point where the drilling program has defined sufficient geologic reserves to consider mining the deposit but little or no underground development has been done.

Primary parameters for consideration in choosing a mining method are

1) geometry of the deposit;
2) distribution of grade;
3) rock mass strength for the deposit, as well as the hanging wall and footwall;
4) mining cost and capitalization requirements;
5) mining rate;
6) type and availability of labor;
7) environmental considerations; and
8) other site-specific conditions.

Of these parameters, the first four have the most impact on determining the general mining method to be employed.

In the past, choosing the type of mining method was based primarily on operating experience at similar type deposits, as well as on methods already tried and proven in the district of the deposit. Modifications to the mining method were then made as ground conditions and ore character were better understood during the early years of mining. And because their years of mining experience taught them what to look for at any deposit, engineers involved in the selection of a mining method probably considered the eight parameters listed above. Although experience and engineering judgment are still useful in choosing the mining method, each deposit has its own characteristics of geometry, grade distribution, and rock mechanics properties, even though they may look surficially similar. Subtle differences in the characteristics of each deposit, which may affect the method chosen or the mine design, can usually be perceived only through analysis of measured parameters.

In a feasibility study, mining method selection should be at least a two-stage affair. The first stage is mainly the elimination of those methods that are not obviously applicable, by using some type of classification system. The remaining possible mining methods can then be ordered, based on general mining cost and other site-specific considerations: environmental conditions, required production rates, and market conditions, for example. With this ranking, we can go on to the second stage. This involves making a preliminary layout of the two most probable mining methods in order to calculate the mining cost and capitalization from what a cut-off grade can be determined and a minable reserve calculated. As part of the mine layout, rock mechanics would be used to evaluate the required size of openings, types and amount of support, caving characteristics, and expected subsidence. During the mine planning stage, problems with the chosen methods might be encountered, at which time modifications could be made. Today the large capital investment required to start a new mine or change a mining system make it imperative that the method selected and the mine design have a high probability of meeting the production requirements. Remember, "Plans are cheap," (Tom Couzens, personal communication) and some creative thought on paper may help in evaluating the true potential of methods under consideration.

DATA REQUIREMENTS FOR METHOD SELECTION

Data required for selection of a mining method and initial mine layout are geologic sections and level maps, a grade block model of the deposit, and rock mechanics characteristics of the deposit, footwall, and hanging wall. Much of this data is obtained from drill core, and, if not collected during the initial core logging or assaying, it will be lost.

Geology

Basic geology interpretation is of major importance in any mineral evaluation. Geologic sections and level maps which show major rock types, alteration zones, and major structures, such as faults, veins, and fold axes, should be prepared. It may be advisable to define the alteration zones on a separate set of maps, which can then be overlain onto the rock type geology maps. These geologic sections and level maps should be prepared at the same scale as will be used for the mine planning. Sections should be drawn to true scale, without any vertical exaggeration, because it makes it easier to visualize the relative layout of mine workings. The area included on the maps should extend horizontally in all directions 1.75 times the depth beyond the limit of the orebody. Although an area this size may seem excessive, it will ensure that there is sufficient information for evaluating the limit of ground surface movement due to mining: this information is needed to locate shafts, adits, buildings, etc.

The importance of a complete set of interpreted sections and levels cannot be overstated. These maps are necessary for defining grade distribution, as well as units of similar rock mechanics characteristics.

Geometry of Deposit and Distribution of Grade

During Stage 1 of the feasibility study, the geometry and grade distribution of the deposit are defined. The geometry of the deposit is defined in terms of depth below surface, ore thickness, plunge, and general shape (Table 1). Grade distribution is defined as uniform, gradational, or erratic (Table 1). During Stage 2, the minable reserves are determined. In order to describe the geometry and grade distribution of the deposit and to calculate an ore reserve, a grade model of the deposit is necessary. The type of model constructed will depend on the complexity of the geology and how well it is understood, as well as on the drill hole spacing.

Current work in geostatistics has resulted in improved grade estimation techniques. In order to make use of these geostatistical estimation methods, the orebody must be understood geologically, and there must be sufficient data within each rock type or statistical population to make an accurate interpolation. If the geology is not well understood or is not complete, or if drilling is wide-spaced, then perhaps one of the more traditional methods, such as inverse distance weighting or polygoning, may be used for developing a model.

TABLE 1: Definition of Deposit Geometry and Grade Distribution

Geometry of Deposit	
1) Depth below surface	
shallow:	<150 m (<500 ft)
intermediate:	150 m - 600 m (500 ft - 2000 ft)
deep:	>600 m (>2000 ft)
2) Ore thickness	
narrow:	<10 m (<30 ft)
intermediate:	10 m - 30 m (30 ft - 100 ft)
thick:	30 m - 100 m (100 ft - 325 ft)
very thick:	>100 m (>325 ft)
3) Plunge	
flat:	<20°
intermediate:	20° - 55°
steep:	>55°
4) General shape	
Massive:	all dimensions are in the thick-to-very thick range
Plate or tabular:	two dimensions are many times the thickness, which does not usually exceed 100 m (325 ft)

Grade Distribution
1) Uniform the grade at any point in the deposit does not vary significantly from the mean grade for that deposit
2) Gradational grade values have zonal characteristics, and the grades change gradually from one to another
3) Erratic grade values change radically over short distances and do not exhibit any discernible pattern in their changes

To define the geometry and grade distribution of a deposit for use in Stage 1, elimination of mining methods, the model should be put on sections and level maps at the same scale as the geology maps and should be contoured by grade, or the blocks should be colored by grade categories. These contoured or colored grade sections and level maps, when overlain on the geologic sections and level maps, will indicate the dominant rock types, as well as their spatial relationships to the orebody.

Rock Mechanics Characterization

The rock mechanics characterization should indicate the rock mass strength and the pre-mine stress field. In a feasibility study, the data is usually taken from drill core samples; so it is important that it be collected prior to core splitting. Strength of the rock mass is a function of the strength of the intact rock, the strength of the geologic structures (joints, faults, etc.), and the characteristics of the geologic structure (orientation, length, spacing, etc.). Once the geologic structure data are available, potential failure geometries can be defined and stability analyses can be made using the strength properties.

In the first stage of the feasibility study, the rock properties need to be classified for an overall rock mechanics picture of the deposit. There are a number of classification systems that have been presented (Deere, 1968; Coates, 1970; Bieniawski, 1973; Barton et al., 1974; and Laubscher, 1977). The basic measurements include rock substance (intact rock) strength, some measurement of the fracture intensity, and some measure of the fracture strength. The classification systems of Bieniawski, Barton et al., and Laubscher use the individual parameters to calculate an overall rock mass quality.

Table 2 presents our definition of rock substance strength, fracture spacing, and fracture shear strength. The rock substance strength is the ratio of the uniaxial compression strength to the overburden stress, which is related to depth. The uniaxial compression strength can be estimated using the method originally presented by Terzaghi and Peck (1967), which was then modified by Deere (1968), Jennings and Robertson (1960), and Piteau (1970) (Table 3). However, a better estimate of the uniaxial compression strength could be obtained relatively inexpensively by using a point load testing machine.

Fracture spacing is defined in terms of fracture per meter and RQD, Rock Quality Designation (Table 2). RQD is the sum length of all pieces greater than or equal to two times the core diameter divided by the total length of a drill run; it has become a fairly common measurement. Although we have used RQD in the past, we are beginning to use the fractures per meter measurement instead because it provides a more quantitative description of the rock fragment size. The fracture shear strength is determined by observation (Table 2).

TABLE 2: Rock Mechanics Characteristics

1) Rock Substance Strength (uniaxial strength [Pa]/overburden pressure [Pa]

weak:	<8
moderate:	8 - 15
strong:	>15

2) Fracture Spacing

	Fractures/m	(ft)	% RQD
very close:	>16	(>5)	0 - 20
close:	10 - 16	(3 - 5)	20 - 40
wide:	3 - 10	(1 - 3)	40 - 70
very wide:	< 3	(< 1)	70 - 100

3) Fracture Shear Strength

weak:	clean joint with a smooth surface or fill with material whose strength is less than rock substance strength
moderate:	clean joint with a rough surface
strong:	joint that is stronger than rock substance strength and is filled with material

As part of the geologic log, one should measure and record an estimate of the fracture per meter or RQD measurement, and the fracture shear strength. This data can then be interpreted on sections and levels at the same scale as the geologic maps. The cumulative sum technique (Piteau and Russell,1972) can be used to help define zones of similar rock substance strength, fracture spacing, and fracture strength. These maps, when overlain onto the geology and grade outline, will spatially define rock mechanics characteristics.

Strength Properties. Basic strength properties needed for Stage 2 of the feasibility study are uniaxial compression strength, stiffness (Young's Modulus), Poisson's ratio, tensile strength, intact rock shear strength, natural fracture shear strength, and fault gouge shear strength. Rock units, such as salt, shales, etc. may require creep testing under controlled temperature and humidity.

All the strength properties can be measured using unsplit drill core specimens except perhaps the fault gouge strength. The number of specimens required for representative testing depends somewhat on variability of the rock unit; however, three to six samples per rock type per test type should be sufficient for the second stage of a feasibility study. Unsplit core samples must be saved for rock testing during the drilling program. We recommend collecting three samples per rock type per test type per drill hole. By sampling each hole, a collection of samples will be built up, from which samples for testing can be selected.

TABLE 3: Relationship Between Hardness or Consistency and Unconfined Compressive Strength

Hardness	Consistency	Field Identification	Approximate Range of Unconfined Compressive Strength MPa X 10^{-2}	(psi)
		SOILS AND FAULT GOUGE		
S1	very soft soil	Easily penetrated several inches by fist	< 2.4	(<3.5)
S2	soft soil	Easily penetrated several inches by thumb	2.4 - 4.8	(3.5 - 7)
S3	firm soil	Can be penetrated several inches by thumb with moderate effort	4.8 - 9.6	(7 - 14)
S4	stiff soil	Readily indented by thumb but penetrated only with great effort	9.6 - 19.3	(14 - 28)
S5	very stiff soil	Readily indented by thumbnail	19.3 - 38.6	(28 - 56)
S6	hard soil	Indented with difficulty by thumbnail	>38.6	(>56)
Hardness	**Consistency**	**Field Identification**	**Approximate Range of Unconfined Compressive Strength MPa**	**(psi)**
		ROCK		
R0	extremely soft rock	Indented by thumbnail	.2 - .7	(28 - 100)
R1	very soft rock	Crumbles under firm blows with point of geologic pick, can be peeled by a pocket knife	.7 - 6.9	(100 - 1000)
R2	soft rock	Can be peeled by a pocket knife with difficulty, shallow indentations made by firm blow of geological pick	6.0 - 27.6	(1000 - 4000)
R3	average rock	Cannot be scraped or peeled with a pocket knife, specimen can be fractured with single firm blow of hammer end of geological pick	27.6 - 55.2	(4000 - 8000)

TABLE 3: (continued)

Hardness	Consistency	Field Identification	Approximate Range of Unconfined Compressive Strength MPa (psi)
		ROCK	
R4	hard rock	Specimen required more than one blow with hammer end of pick to fracture it	55.2 - 110.3 (8000 - 16,000)
R5	very hard rock	Specimen required many flows of hammer end of geological pick to fracture it	110.3 - 220.6 (16,000 - 32,000)
R6	extremely hard rock	Specimen can only be chipped with geological pick	>220.6 (>32,000)

S1 to S6 after Terzaghi and Peck, 1967
R1 to R5 after Deere, 1968, and Jennings and Robertson, 1969
Modified by Piteau, 1970

Geologic Structure. Rock mass strength depends largely on the fracture characteristics, orientation, spacing, length, strength, etc. Fracture shear strength has already been discussed in the rock strength section. For Stage 2 of the feasibility study, areas with similar joint orientations are defined as structural domains; distribution of the fracture set characteristics and potential failure paths are defined for each domain.

Geologic structures are divided into two categories: major structures and rock fabric. Major structures are faults, folds, dikes, etc., which have lengths on the order of the deposit size and are usually considered individually in design. Rock fabric is predominantly joints and faults that have a high frequency of occurrence and are not continuous.

Structural data can be obtained by using detail line mapping (Call et al., 1976) or cell mapping. Detail line mapping is a technique that involves the measurements of fracture characteristics of all joints which intersect a line. This mapping technique is a spot sample within a structural domain; it provides the data for determining distribution of joint set characteristics on a joint-by-joint basis. Cell mapping, which involves measuring the mean orientation and fracture characteristics for each fracture set within a 10 to 15 m (30 to 50 ft) wide cell, can be done by the geologist during his mapping of surface and underground rock exposures. This method provides the data to evaluate variability in geologic structure on an areal basis and is, thus, a means of delineating structural domains.

Cell mapping and detail line mapping are used in those instances where some type of rock exposure exists. However, in any feasibility study in which structure data can be obtained only from drill core, a few oriented core holes should be included in the drilling program. Oriented core holes provide the same information as detail line mapping, except that oriented core data will not provide joint length characteristics. The oriented core data can, however, aid the geologist in his interpretation of the geology.

Pre-Mine Stress. Pre-mine stress is one of the most difficult parameters to determine. Because of the complex tectonics associated with many mineral deposits, the stress field will probably be variable, depending on proximity to the nearest major geologic structure. Techniques such as stress-relief overcoring and hydrofracturing are available, but these methods are generally expensive and difficult to justify until the initial feasibility study has been completed. The pre-mine stress field can be estimated using the geologic history, orientation of geologic structure, and type of fault movement (Abel, personal communication). Although this method is indirect and could be misleading about the pre-mine stress field, it is probably better to use it than to assume the elastic theory.

Hydrology. Hydrologic conditions do not usually play an important role in determining mining method, but they can affect strength properties of the rock, as well as the cost of mining. Basic information needed is a water table map, location of water sources, and potential geologic structures that would be water-bearing. Because a pump test would provide a quantitative estimate of the pumping requirements necessary during mining, one should be made, if possible.

Mining Cost and Capitalization Requirements

In choosing a mining method, one would prefer that method which has the lowest operating cost per ton and provides the highest revenue during the early years of mining. After the first stage of a feasibility study has been completed, where the mining methods that are not possible have been eliminated, the remaining methods should be ordered by increasing mining costs. Morrison (1976) has ranked the mining methods by increasing cost, which we have modified:

block caving,
sublevel stoping,
sublevel caving,
longwall,
room and pillar,

shrinkage stoping,
cut and fill,
top slicing, and
square set.

The effects of capitalization requirements can only be evaluated after the two most likely mining methods have been studied.

Other Parameters Used in Method Selection

After the first stage of the feasibility study has been completed and the two most probable methods are being examined, parameters such as mining rate required, type and availability of labor, environmental considerations, etc. should be taken into account.

Mining rate should be dictated by the mining method chosen. However, in instances where a mill already exists in the area, a production rate that is perhaps higher or lower than that dictated by the least costly mining method may be required. Therefore, a compromise mining method must be chosen.

Other factors affecting the mining rate would be the market for the resource being mined and the available labor pool. If the labor pool is large and unskilled, a method that is highly mechanical or technical and requires skilled personnel should not be chosen.

Today, environmental considerations are more and more becoming a controlling factor in method selection. Whether or not subsidence is permitted can determine what methods are feasible. Also, the environmental conditions underground must be considered.

METHOD SELECTION AND MINE PLANNING

As already discussed, method selection for a feasibility study is at least a two-stage process.

In Stage 1, the deposit is described in terms of geometry, grade distribution, and rock mechanics properties. Once these parameters are defined for the deposit, those mining methods that do not appear feasible are eliminated. The remaining methods are ranked according to general mining cost, required mining rate, type and availability of personnel, environmental considerations, and other site-specific considerations.

In Stage 2, the two most likely mining methods are costed out in some detail, based on a general mine plan. These costs are then used to determine a cut-off grade from which a minable reserve can be calculated. Economic feasibility can then be evaluated.

Stage 1

We have already outlined the basic information needed to describe the deposit. This information should be used in a classification system similar to that presented by Boshkov and Wright (1973) (Table 4). We are in the process of improving this classification, and it will be presented at the International Conference on Caving and Sub-level Stoping to be held in Denver in November, 1981. Morrison (1976) has also presented a classification for defining the conditions needed for the different mining methods.

TABLE 4: Applications of Underground Mining Methods*

Type of Ore Body	Dip	Strength of Ore	Strength of Walls	Commonly Applied Methods of Mining
Thin beds	Flt	Stg	Stg	Open stopes with casual pillars Room-and-pillar Longwall
		Wk/Stg	Wk	Longwall
Thick beds	Flt	Stg	Stg	Open stopes with casual pillars Room-and-pillar
		Wk/Stg	Wk	Top slicing Sublevel caving
		Wk/Stg	Stg	Underground glory hole
Very thick beds				Same as for massive
Very narrow veins	Stp	Stg/Wk	Stg/Wk	Resuing
Narrow veins	Flt			Same as for thin beds
(widths up to economic length of stull)	Stp	Stg	Stg	Open stopes Shrinkage stopes Cut-and-fill stopes
			Wk	Cut-and-fill stopes Square-set stopes
		Wk	Stg	Open underhand stopes Square-set stopes
			Wk	Top slicing Square-set stopes
	Flt			Same as for thick beds or massive

TABLE 4: (continued)

Type of Ore Body	Dip	Strength of Ore	Strength of Walls	Commonly Applied Methods of Mining
	Stp	Stg	Stg	Open underhand stopes Underground glory hole Shrinkage stopes Sublevel stoping
Wide veins				Cut-and-fill stopes Combined methods
			Wk	Cut-and-fill stopes Top slicing Sublevel caving Square-set stopes Combined methods
		Wk	Stg	Open underhand stopes Top slicing Sublevel caving Block caving Square-set stopes Combined methods
			Wk	Top slicing Sublevel caving Square-set stopes Combined methods
		Stg	Stg	Underground glory hole Shrinkage stopes Sublevel stoping Cut-and-fill Combined methods
Massive		Wk	Wk/Stg	Top slicing Sublevel caving Block caving Square-set stopes Combined methods

Wk = weak; Stg = strong; Flt = flat; Stp = steep.
*Modified from Boshkov and Wright, 1973.

Stage 2

The economic feasibility of a deposit is primarily determined by mineral price and minable tons and grade. We have no control over the mineral prices; however, minable tons and grade are determined by the cut-off grade, which is determined as a result of the mine planning and cost estimate. Although determining the cut-off grade is one of the basic starting points of any mine design, few engineers seem to agree on the proper approach. We propose a simplistic method for calculating the cut-off grade: it uses only the direct, indirect, and smelting costs, and will not include the cost of capitalization, as is common with many other methods.

The direct mining cost per ton and direct milling cost per ton can be determined from the preliminary mine planning work. These costs should not include capital equipment but should include replacement equipment and consumables. The supervision, fringe benefits, and other indirect costs should also be included. (Information from other mines with similar operations can be used in determining these costs.) Transportation and smelting or benefaction charges should be calculated at a cost per ton, using a reasonable estimate of mill recovery. The cut-off grade, then, is that grade of material at today's commodity price whose net worth is equal to the total cost.

The difference between this method and other approaches is that there are no costs for capital, such as mining equipment, mill construction, and shaft and underground development. If these costs had been included, the cut-off grade would have been higher and the minable tonnage lower. The argument for not including the cost of capital is that (1) those tons which would be eliminated from the mine plan will pay for the direct, indirect, and smelting costs, as well as having some excess value which could contribute to the loan payment or profitability; and (2) the capital costs are usually carried by the higher grade tons mined early in the life of the property.

With the cut-off grade and the resulting mine plan, the minable ore reserve and cash flows can be estimated on an annual basis to determine if the return is sufficient to capitalize loans and provide an acceptable profitability.

REFERENCES

Barton, N., Lien, R., and Lunde, J., 1974, "Engineering Classification of Rock Masses for the Design of Tunnel Support," Journal of the International Society for Rock Mechanics, vol. 6, no. 4, p. 189-236.

Bieniawski, Z. T., 1973, "Engineering Classification of Jointed Rock Masses," The Civil Engineer in South Africa, December, p. 335-343.

Boshkov, S. H. and Wright, F. D., 1973, "Basic and Parametric Criteria in the Selection, Design and Development of Underground Mining Systems," Chap. 12.1 in SME Mining Engineering Handbook, vol. 1 American Institute of Mining, Metallurgical and Petroleum Engineers, New York, p. 12.2 - 12.13.

Call, R. D., Savely, J. P. and Nicholas, D. E., 1976, "Estimation of Joint Set Characteristics from Surface Mapping Data," 17th U.S. Symposium on Rock Mechanics, p. 282.1 - 282.9.

Coates, D. F., 1970, Rock Mechanics Principles, Queens Printer, Ottawa, Mines Branch Monograph 874, p. 1-46 - 1.50.

Deere, D. U., 1968, "Geological Considerations," Chap. 1 in Rock Mechanics in Engineering Practice, ed., K. G. Stagg and O. G. Zienkiewicz, John Wiley & Sons, London, p. 1-20.

Jennings, J. E. and Robertson, A. M., 1969, "The Stability of Slopes Cut Into Natural Rock," Proceedings, 7th International Conference on Soil Mechanics and Foundation Engineering, Sociedat Mexicana de Mecanica de Suelos, Mexico, vol. 2, p. 585-590.

Laubscher, D. H., 1977, "Geomechanics Classification of Jointed Rock Masses - Mining Applications," Transactions of the Institute of Mining & Metallurgy of South Africa, vol. 86.

Morrison, R. G. K., 1976, A Philosophy of Ground Control, McGill University, Montreal, Canada, p. 125-159.

Piteau, D. R., 1970, Engineering Geology Contribution to the Study of Stability of Slopes in Rock with Particular Reference to DeBeers Mine, vol. 1, Ph.D. thesis, University of Witwatersrand, Johannesburg, p. 114-115.

Piteau, D. R. and Russell, L., 1972, "Cumulative Sums Technique: A New Approach to Analyzing Joints in Rock," Thirteenth U.S. Symposium on Rock Mechanics, p. 1-29.

Terzaghi, K. and Peck, R., 1967, Soil Mechanics in Engineering Practice, John Wiley & Sons, New York, 729 p.

Chapter 63

EFFICACY AND EQUITY OF THE MANAGEMENT OF LARGE UNDERGROUND PROJECTS

Alan M.MUIR WOOD[1] and Gerhard SAUER[2]

1. Sir William Halcrow & Partners, London
2. Consulting Engineer, Salzburg

ABSTRACT

There are two essential features of administrative practices in tunnelling in order to provide proper encouragement to innovative and economic tunnelling: first, that there should be a continuity in the decision making at all stages so that the full implications of decisions in early stages of planning and design are understood; second, that there should be appropriate provision for variation so that the greatest possible benefit can be derived from modifying the working scheme in relation to the characteristics of the ground and from study of its behaviour during execution of the work. Examples are given from the Authors' experience as to the benefits to be derived from the application of such principles.

INTRODUCTION

The technical and organisational aspects of civil engineering projects are too often treated apart and, in the extreme, handled for a single project by different people, with different backgrounds and understanding of the demands for good engineering, who remain inadequately co-ordinated. In tunnelling in particular the only certainty is that the outcome will not correspond to initial expectation; it is imperative, for effective and economic results, that a project must be viewed throughout its evolution and execution as an entity, with full continuity across all its phases of development.

Of course there is a need for particular (and probably specialist) expertise in many respects: for a large underground urban railway project for example, entailing expertise in the fields of transport economics, physical planning and development, geology, geotechnics, probably several different aspects of tunnelling and in railway engineering, operating and maintenance, to name the most significant. It remains essential to ensure a degree of continuity in control throughout so that optimization of the whole may take precedence over optimization of a specific aspect where some degree of compromise is called for. Figure 1 indicates in a simplified way the degree of

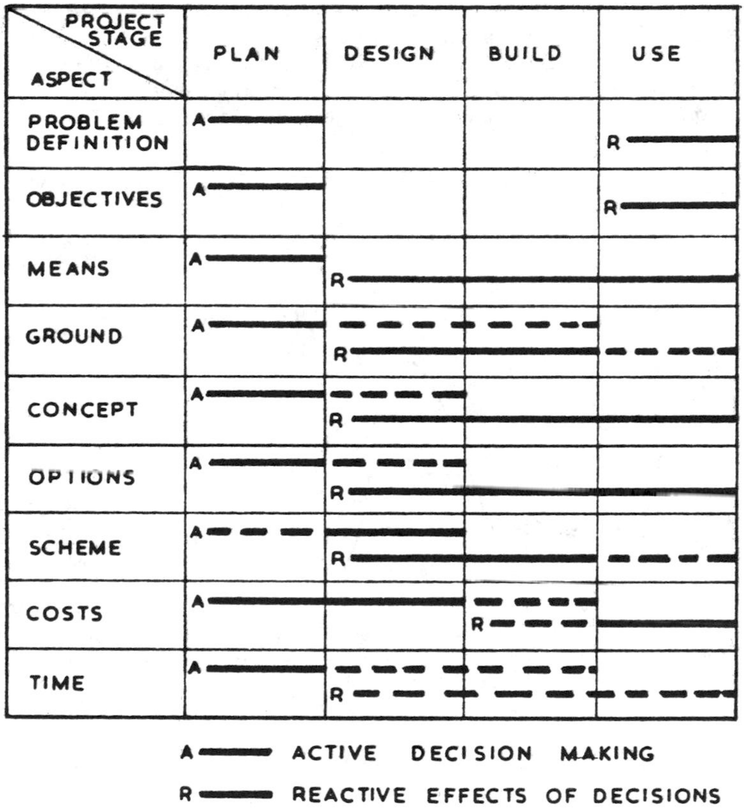

PROJECT STAGE / ASPECT	PLAN	DESIGN	BUILD	USE
PROBLEM DEFINITION	A			R
OBJECTIVES	A			R
MEANS	A	R		
GROUND	A	R		
CONCEPT	A	R		
OPTIONS	A	R		
SCHEME	A	R		
COSTS	A		R	
TIME	A	R		

A ACTIVE DECISION MAKING

R REACTIVE EFFECTS OF DECISIONS

Fig.1 Decision making for underground projects

interaction between decisions made in the initial "upstream" stages of a project and their consequences in subsequent "downstream" phases. The general implication of this diagram is that actions taken and decisions made in early phases must, for successful outcome, take account of their impingement upon actions and decisions at other stages. This entails a degree of awareness of these consequences by no means evident in many recent large underground projects.

In many aspects of engineering the recent trend has been away from a directly deterministic approach towards the introduction, in one of a number of alternative methods, of the notion of uncertainty. Where the engineering can be expressed with complete confidence and certainty, then the contractual relationships may be expressed with a comparable certainty, at least in relation to the engineering concept and work content. As soon as uncertainty is introduced which bears upon the finished project, the nature and extent of the work in its achievement or in its consequential effects, we can apply the same argument towards a flexibility in the contractual basis as we do in the technical response to corresponding uncertainty in engineering terms. This concept may be modelled by the diagram in Figure 2 which

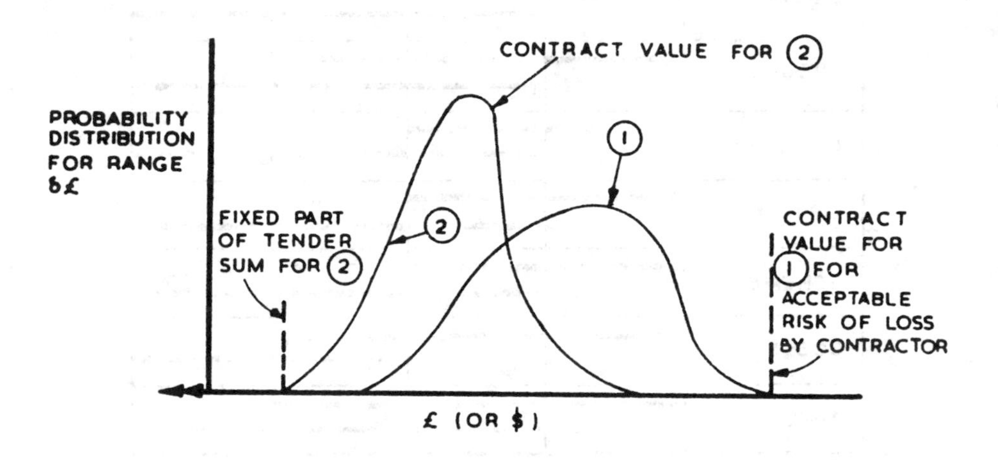

Fig.2 Probability of final cost as assessed at time of Tender:
(1) Fixed price contract
(2) Cost reimbursable contract

considers extreme cases of (1) a fixed price contract and (2) a contract whose value is related to the conditions encountered, for circumstances in which these are uncertain. The shape of curve (1) has to be estimated at the time of Tender and the speculative degree of Tender (1) is incomparably greater than Tender (2). Lucky indeed is the Contractor who has pitched his Tender for (1) as indicated or higher, is reasonably correct in his assumptions and has been awarded the Contract. The Contractor will be disinclined to innovate and he will be tempted, in such uncertainty, to cut corners, often unwittingly, to maximise profit; hence the wide range of possible costs to the Contractor. For Case (2), innovation is favoured with appropriate adaptability to match the conditions encountered so the probable cost to the Contractor is reduced and the range of variability of cost confined; for the extreme case considered, the Contractor is assumed to recover full costs incurred. The skill comes in so devising the contract form and structure, between these two extremes, as to minimise costs for reasonable profit to the Contractor, with appropriate control on behalf of the Promoter (Fig.3). This is the essence of efficacy and equity.

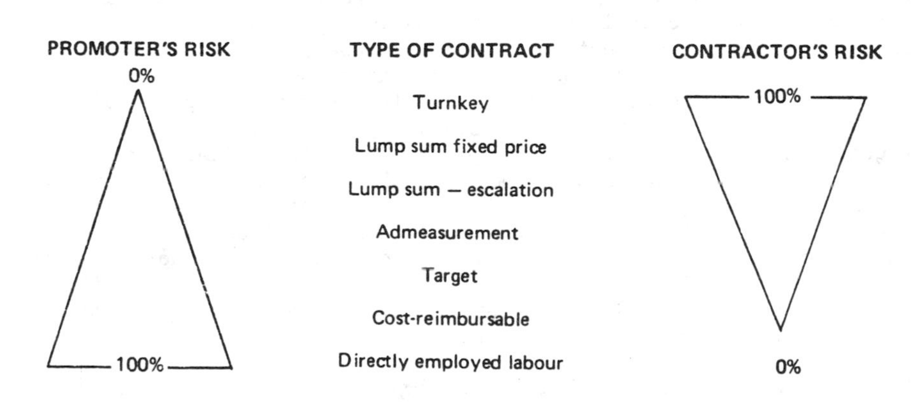

Fig.3 Type of contract related to share of risk (CIRIA 1978)

PROJECT CONTINUITY

The interaction between the several phases of a project is grossly over-simplified by Figure 1. We cannot usually subdivide the work into such neat parcels nor can we state precisely what decisions are taken at each phase. It is the sheer imprecision of the process which helps obscure when and what decisions are taken, and part of the object of this brief paper is to attempt to clarify this state of affairs. Throughout the process the assumption is made that there is a unique decision taker; in fact there is, or should be, a single line of command concerning decisions within expressly stipulated areas of devolution of decision taking, in effect to ensure that no one decision is made without awareness as to how it affects others involved in this process. But too often the time dimension is forgotten so that although contemporaneous decisions may be co-ordinated, effects upon subsequent decisions are obscure. To correct this condition we must consider the nature of the decision maker. Essentially, advice that he receives on every aspect must provide answers to particular questions and one of the arts of decision making lies in correctly framing these same questions, and remaining perceptive to the limitations beyond his own field of expertise. Good engineering entails the ability to make a synthesis between the many aspects of knowledge and expectation. This pre-supposes the ability to ask the right question at the right time. So we can start by establishing that the overall co-ordinating function is appropriate to an engineer. If early decisions are not to introduce subsequent costly consequences then some way must be devised to ensure adequate prescience in this respect. Otherwise we shall find ourselves perpetuating the mistake made, for example, from planning an underground railway on traffic requirements without any thought to the gross geological complications that these, uncorrected, may entail in determining the route. We are concerned here with the difference in results between attempting to optimize, by a continuous process of reduction of options, all the major parameters throughout evolution of the project or the more expensive alternative of attempting to optimize each in turn within the constraints imposed by separate optimization of those already determined.

If we then continue with the oversimplification of Fig.1 and consider the attitudes of the parties concerned with the specific continuation to each of the four stages, we can arrive at a diagram on the lines of Fig.4 in which the ordinate represents depth of understanding and we consider, in gross oversimplification, the roles of Planner, Designer, Builder and User to keep to comparable nomenclature. What springs immediately from this diagram is that if, for example, the designer is not appointed until completion of the planning stage, then the Planner has to have a far deeper understanding of the downstream consequences of his planning since the designer is not there to protect the position of himself and his followers.

There is no single solution to this criterion for continuity but it is the view of the Authors based on their direct experiences in satisfactory (and unsatisfactory) roles that the notion of the Engineer involved and accepting responsibility in defined ways between the concept and the completion of the project provides the most

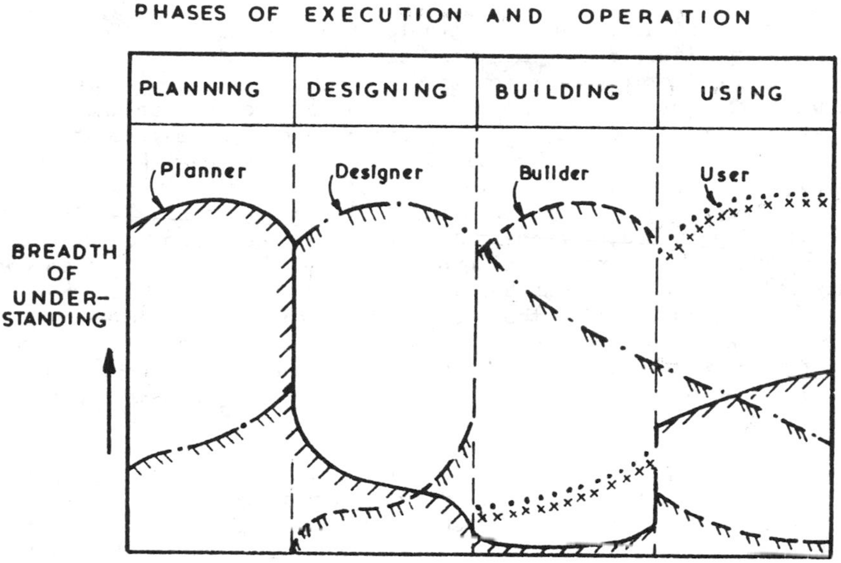

Fig.4 Percipience of the participants

satisfactory means of continuity. The diagram of Fig.4 is drawn around this arrangement and would need recasting for any other acceptable solution.

MANAGEMENT AND ENGINEERING

Our concern here is with the not too well understood inter-relation between management and engineering, (the latter taken here as embracing the technical content, including all aspects of engineering judgement). We cannot consider the relationship without the notion of uncertainty. For example Fig.3 indicates in relation to type of Contract (one only of the several aspects) how different basic types of Contract make different provision for uncertainty in cost to the promoter and the contractor. By far the greatest factor in contractual risk in tunnelling is normally related to the unknown aspects of the ground. A high degree of certainty of cost to the Promoter is a desirable aim but this can only be achieved where conditions permit a lump sum contract (see Fig.2). The Promoter is accepting unnecessarily high costs of adopting such a contract basis when the technical risk is high.

Unless a contractor is a charitable organisation - and few in the Authors' experience are - then the less the provisions for variation and for the objective valuation of such variations, the greater the allowance he must make at the time of tender to cover for uncertainty. The alternative is equally unsatisfactory in that he may be able to establish that information provided at time of tender was such as to mislead a (n experienced) contractor into underestimating the nature of the difficulties. There is nothing clever, or beneficial in the out-turn, in persuading a contractor to undertake a project with an underestimate of the problems involved, where these are known to, or suspected by, the beguiling party. The technique simply leads to the legal profession becoming the one party to profit from tunnelling at a great loss to society and to the construction professionals and work forces engaged in underground construction. Furthermore, such a procedure enhances the probability of hazard during construction (Muir Wood, 1975).

A similar argument may be applied to the contractual arrangements (or Agreements) between other parties concerned in the project. The sharper the definition of the task in planning and in designing (also in supervision and in providing for the optimal arrangements for operation and maintenance) the more reasonable is it to aim towards a lump sum fee and clear cut terms of reference. Only those with experience through such processes know how the unexpected tend to be the rule rather than the exception.

In consequence it is wise always to lean in the direction of excessive scope for variation rather than excessively Procrustean relations. For a professional to be in a position of knowing that he cannot within his fee satisfactorily undertake a service, which has expanded, without personal loss is a position of much disbenefit to all parties concerned.

GOOD TUNNELLING AND CONTRACTUAL RISK

A number of recent contributions have been made nationally and internationally towards the object of defining the sources of risk in a contract and in establishing how best, in the interest of the common good, these are shared among the parties concerned. (ITA report 1979 CIRIA Report 1978). The latter, which builds upon practice in the United Kingdom and nowadays largely accepted in Austria (and certain other European countries), has a number of essential features, the most important of which may be summarised thus:-

a) Generally attribute acceptance of risk to the party best able to control its incidence or, for minor risk, to make reasonable provision for its cost.

b) Provide appropriate encouragement to use methods of construction that show best prospects, in the available knowledge at any time, of an economic result.

c) Provide appropriate flexibility for change in construction methods to follow the range of variation in ground and other conditions foreseeable by a knowledgeable engineer.

d) Simple and equitable arrangements for disposal of disputes.

These different aspects of a single problem cannot be treated in isolation one from the other but need a little amplification in particular respects.

Once we start to attribute risk we identify the common interest (which is always there but often obscured) in the reduction of uncertainty about the ground. It is not good enough to calculate the percentage expected cost of a project spent on site investigation, for example, as if there were some general optimal figure. Experience elsewhere in comparable circumstances may provide some guidance but, in particular and not universally evidenced, site investigation should be designed in relation to the special features and uncertainties of the ground, related to construction as well as design, with incremental costs of extra investigation justified by the expectation of a reasonably high benefit to cost ratio of the results obtained (and of course it is still a benefit to discover more about special problems to be encountered and to be prepared for). We must here repeat that the capacity to vary the scheme of construction in relation to changes in the ground is highly dependent upon the tunnelling technique. Thus, any of the techniques based on the observational method (whereby predictions in ground/support behaviour are constantly monitored by observation and measurement, using usually a calculated or estimated set of alternative schemes of construction in relation to any one range of observations) necessitates considerable foresight into the range of conditions but usually less dependance on limitations of variability than a more specific and perhaps highly mechanised scheme of construction. The New Austrian Tunnelling Method (NATM) is the best known exponent of the observational method in tunnelling although, at the present time, the development of such methods worldwide can be seen against the particular national conditions of tunnelling and, in particular, the extent to which appropriate contract conditions have been adopted. The principles above are illustrated in their effects by Fig.5.

Brief examples of such techniques in the experience of the Authors, with indication of the nature of cost savings and other benefits, are provided at the end of this paper.

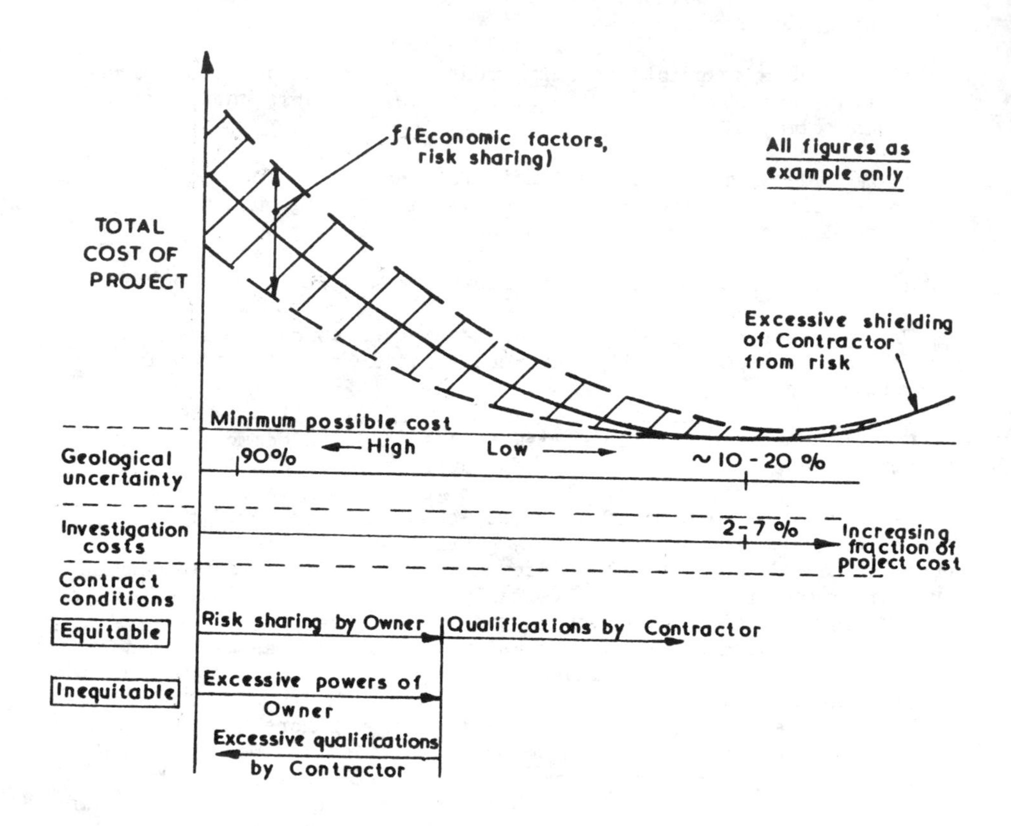

Fig.5 Features of minimising project cost

If the Contractor is to be encouraged to use particular methods of construction which promise economic benefit for expected conditions, then he must be given the answer to the question 'If not, what?'. In its turn this may require the Engineer to go further than simply providing all site investigation data (which clearly should be done and should we repeat be designed as much to answer questions of construction as questions of design) but also to guide the Contractor to the interpretation to put upon them if these are to serve as a basis of reference for variation. Involvement of the Engineer in an overall capacity much enhances the likelihood of sufficient awareness at the investigation stage of the main problems of construction to be investigated. We are here helping to solve two problems at once:

- to provide a set of reference conditions against which the effects of changed conditions can be measured and computed (and it is remarkable how prescient some Engineers expect Contractors to be once all parties are informed by hindsight!).

- to avoid the need for a Contractor to provide in the fixed part of his Tender Sum for the expensive, albeit improbable, circumstances of failure of a method on account of departure of the condition of the ground beyond tolerable characteristics.

We then have to consider, by the means above, how to categorise the ground into grades, normally related to the particular scheme for supports and so forth, so that appropriate prices may be given for each. This is of course nowhere near the end of the road in evaluating variation but it provides a base to remove much of the antagonism and anguish. In general, once a Contractor has no chance of making a profit, the project is likely to be a partial failure - not for the Contractor alone.

However, disputes will arise in the most orderly arrangements and this prospect must be foreseen. The British tradition of its independent Engineer has much to commend it in providing throughout an arbiter on whose judgement depends the interpretation of the contract or on the foreseeability of the unexpected. Even in the United Kingdom, there are ominous trends of encroaching upon the powers (but not usually the concomitant duties!) of the Engineer, by those who appear not to understand the full import of this action in preventing an equitable (and hence efficacious and economic) operation of the Contract. These encroachments take two forms:-

a) a curb on the Engineer's power, with interpretation of the Contract in relation to structure and variation reserved to an employer's Contracts or similar department, a body of legalistic people who are insulated from the salutary effect of bearing responsibility. This results in encouraging a lesser breed of Engineer, inadequately objective.

b) a tendency to oppose reasonable claims by Contractors forcing arbitration, with the associated and sometimes grossly inequitable threat to sue the Engineer if the Employer loses the case; the obverse is an increasingly litigacious attitude among Contractors.

This trend shows total unawareness of the nature of risk and of the Employer's contribution (it is his ground!) to the problems. It should be possible to establish whether or not the Engineer has been negligent in the nature of his undertaking to his Employer. It should not be necessary to debate this from the premise that if he has been in error in his judgement, negligence necessarily follows. On the contrary, if the benefits of the notion of 'reference condition' are to be achievable then the implication is that the Engineer must from time to time be wrong in his initial definition of expectations (or the Contractor would be satisfied to accept his own interpretation of the ground data without the protection of 'reference conditions'). These reference conditions will err towards optimism to avoid need to negotiate 'negative' claims. In fact, for this particular example of a workable system, reliance must be placed on the Engineer's judgement; he should be dealing with engineers who can question his or her judgement but not allowed to be vindictive on every occasion of fallibility of judgement. If he is expected to be infallible then a fixed price contract should be preferred at the acceptance of the high cost to be paid. We are concerned with total systems, not with selecting particular parts that swing the interest unduly in the direction of one party to the Contract only.

The Contract system in Austria, as applied to the operation of the NATM, relates payment for support to geological conditions, the classification system being determined jointly between Employer and Contractor and the method of excavation and means of support being broadly the responsibility of the Contractor. Technical advance and economic costs have been encouraged by this approach; at the present time unit rates for tunnel construction are on average about 20% below costs in Germany and 30% below costs in Switzerland.

Much recent development in tunnelling, development only justified by contributing to reductions in time and cost of construction, could not have been achieved outside a basis of risk-sharing and of variation of the scheme of construction; such variation needs to conform to knowledge of behaviour of the ground, and of its variability, only acquired during the course of construction. Without the protection of a code of conduct on some such lines as those described above, the Engineers for sheer self protection will cling to the traditional, safe approach; the costs of projects will be unnecessarily high (and we are concerned with factors of, say 1.5 to 5 or more) and innovation will be thwarted. Much of innovation is only possible as a result of extending practical experience; its successful adoption in one project may therefore be a necessary concomitant of its adoption in a more testing subsequent project.

EXAMPLES OF APPLICATION OF THE PRINCIPLES

Successful civil engineering must compound theory and practice. It may therefore be instructive to indicate, for those unfamiliar with the principles set out above, four examples of brief accounts of typical applications.

Example 1

A rock tunnel of 100 sq.metres section had to traverse a difficult

200m long zone of quartz-mylonite under a 25m depth of cover. The material was uniform grained (0.02-0.07 mm). Short-term cohesion resulted from the natural moisture content.

After trial excavation at crown level, timber forepoling had to be used to resist heavy ground loading. On resumption of work, after a fortnight's break over Christmas, the rock collapsed into the cavity. Tunnel driving resumed, after considering proposals for remedial work, with future interruptions to progress limited to a maximum period of 7 hours, sidewalls being advanced ahead, subsequently enlarged to full-face without problems. When the rock improved (to weak phyllites and sericite schist) full-face driving was resumed, the face somewhat domed and benched in two steps to improve stability.

Example 2

A three-lane road tunnel had to traverse a talus with internal friction of about 36° and very slight cohesion, the overburden thickness varying between 3-20 metres. Excavation started for a sidewall heading but a fall occurred on account of the low overburden. The Contractor took responsibility of changing to a top heading, accepting local unavoidable falls, the steel arches with mesh being covered in such areas with a bituminous fabric sheet. After shotcreting from within the tunnel the cavity above was refilled. On account of the high angle of friction, the change in overburden weight was accepted by the arch without problem, there being no great restriction on vertical movements of the surface.

Example 3

The 80km Orange-Fish tunnel was known to penetrate a series of sandstone/siltstones and dolomitic dikes and sills with possible problems of gas and of water. The Contract was based upon several alternative forms of ground support which in the event needed to be varied with experience, with the evolution of criteria in monitoring (mainly of rock convergence) to establish the adequacy of that adopted for any particular length of tunnel. Many problems were encountered but ultimately the criterion remained as to the degree of departure from the 'reference conditions' (not in fact so called for this project) and the appropriate adjustment in payment. Initial support was largely based upon different patterns of rock bolts and the general use of shotcrete of different thicknesses and reinforcement.

Example 4

The fundamental basis for the design of the Heathrow Cargo Tunnel, which permitted a cost of probably less than 50% of a more conventional approach, assumed the practicability of:

a) keeping the tunnel near the surface with a total cover of appreciably less than the diameter and the acceptance of a perched water table, locally separated by no more than about 1.2m above the crown of the tunnel

b) adopting a system of tunnelling which required a continuous clay cover

c) constructing the tunnel full-face without pilot.

Unless the responsibility for these criteria had been removed from the Contractor it is certain that the highly economical method proposed would not have been accepted, except at an additional cost which would have eroded much (or even all) of the achieved saving.

CONCLUSIONS

The Authors hope that the principles set out in the paper and the brief account of their applications will help to a more general acceptance of the managerial principles for economic tunnelling, and for relatively prosperous protagonists.

It should be emphasised that the benefits of a more general adoption of these principles fall: upon the Promoter (Owner or Employer) with a cheaper, faster and more reliable project; on the Engineer, with greater scope for his ingenuity and upon the Contractor with greater confidence for a fair return for his skill and resources. The only losers are likely to be the profession's vultures. The alternative is likely to be continuing unnecessary escalation in costs, lack of economic innovation and the increased impregnability of the legal profession as the only beneficiary of the result.

REFERENCES

1. International Tunnelling Association Contractual sharing of risk Bron, May 1979.

2. Construction Industry Research and Information Association Tunnelling - improved contract practices CIRIA Report 79 London, May 1978.

3. Muir Wood, A.M. Tunnel hazards: UK experience Hazards in tunnelling and on Falsework. Inst.C.E.London, 1975, pp 47-59.

Chapter 64

SOLUTION TO PROBLEMS WITH ROADHEADER INSTALLATION IN TUNNELLING PROJECTS

by Karl H. Gehring

Doctor of Mining Engineering
Lecturer on Heading-Technology at Montanuniversität Leoben
Leoben, Austria

Head of Geotechnical Department
VOEST-ALPINE AG, Werk Zeltweg
Zeltweg, Austria

ABSTRACT

According to the increasing importance of boom type roadheaders in tunnelling essential problems occuring in the application of these machines are dealt with.
Based on a chart including the various stages for decicion finding the excavation method of underground cavities, both the technical limits and economic criteria are discussed in order to determine the range of applicability of roadheaders.
Giving examples, the numerous developments in the fields of pick and cutting technology, performance data of boom type roadheaders in hard rock, safety technology and increase in the machines' degree of utilization, research and development of VA is illustrated. Two topic operation examples show partial aspects of the various tendencies of development.

INTRODUCTION

The worldwide increasing number of tunnel kilometers headed for traffic facilities, power plants as well as for supply and sewer installations bring about a lot of problems:
- increasingly cavities are excavated in densly populated areas
- the availability of highly qualified workers decreases with the increase of tunnelling operations

- the up-to-date layout of underground constructions is primarily dependent on how they will be used; very often the rock qualities met require smooth operating methods
- emissions for example due to blasting have to be limited to a great extent or even completely avoided.

All these problems show that there has been an unproportionally high increase in the mechanized excavation. In this connection boom type roadheaders gain more and more importance due to the below mentioned factors:

- as compared to full face boring machines boom type machines have relatively reasonable prices
- boom type roadheaders have quite a flexible working range as far as profile and direction of the cavities are concerned
- in unfavourable rock conditions the higher speed of full facers are no longer an advantage due to the lining measures required. On the other hand when applying roadheaders the actual working area at the face is easily accessible which facilitates rock protection measures.
- the percentage of highly qualified workers in the crew can be reduced.
- installation of a roadheader is simple (no basic drift for machine installation, easy reshifting of the machine) therefore its application is economically feasible even in short tunnels.

Nevertheless, any individual application of a roadheader has to be examined carefully as to whether it is possible at all, and if so, whether is a more economic alternative to other excavation methods.

DEFINITION OF THE RANGE OF APPLICABILITY

Technical aspects:

A technical limitation of the application of roadheaders as compared to TBMs, on the one hand, and to the drill and blast heading, on the other hand can be carried out on the basis of the following scheme including as well the most important economic factors.
As you may see in figure 1 the selection of the right method is quite complex. The basis is formed by geological and technical criteria but the final decision is determined by economic rentability. Only topography, respectively height and strength of overburden in populated areas can have a direct influence on the method to be chosen. Indicative values for a technical limitation are to be seen in Fig. 2 (Gehring 1980)

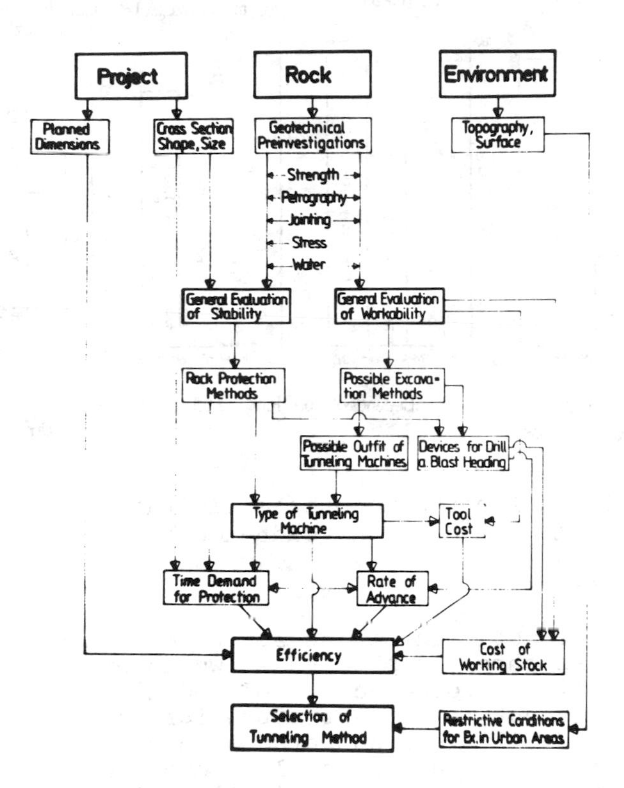

Fig. 1 Scheme for selecting the appropriate method for the excavation of underground cavities.

In this figure you may see that new technologies and heavier machine types have essentially enlarged the range of application.

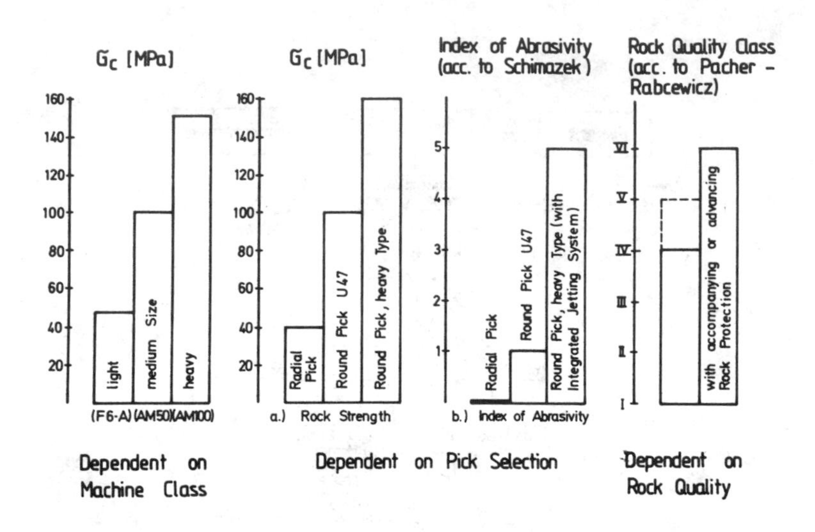

Fig. 2 Criteria for the technical limitation of the range of application of VA roadheaders.

Economic Aspects

The scheme for determining the approximative excavation costs includes three graphs and shows as example a traffic tunnel with a cross-section of 130 m2.
This scheme cannot indicate the precise costs for excavation, yet rentability as compared to other technologies can be determined in a more or less exact way. As the figures show, an extensive examination of the rocklayers to be cut as regards strength, abrasivity, and stability have to be carried out beforehand.
Moreover, organization of the roadheading operations and time spent on rock protection have to be considered as well since they have an influence on the machines degree of utilization.
The determination of the values for rock characterisation has been dealt with in other papers. (Schimazek and Knatz, 1970, Gehring 1975 and 1979)

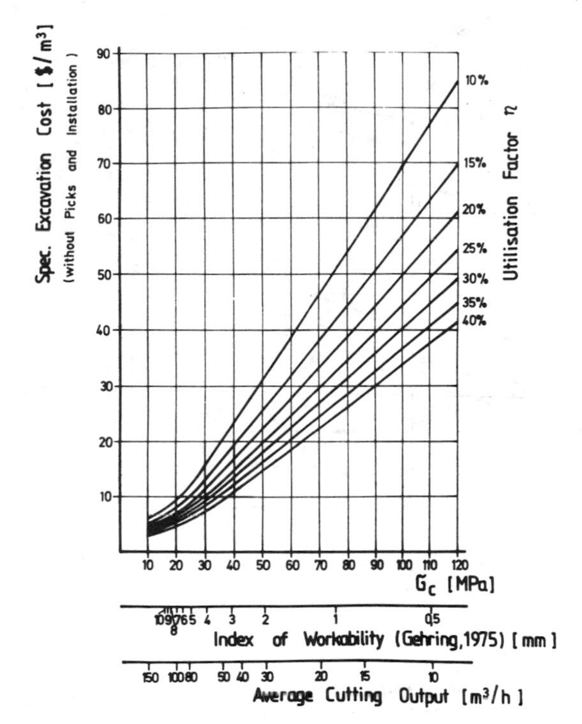

Fig. 3 Specific excavation cost C_E (without installation and picks) dependent on rock strength and degree of utilization (Roadheader AM100)

You may see, that excavation costs as of a strength of 30 MPa are direct proportional to the strength of the rock to be cut. The costs are indicative mean values and include:

- machine costs (depreciation and interests)
- costs for spare and wear parts inclusive costs for repair work
- costs for operating means such as lubricants, hydraulic oil etc.
- energy costs
- labour costs

Moreover pick costs according to Fig. 4 have to be added.

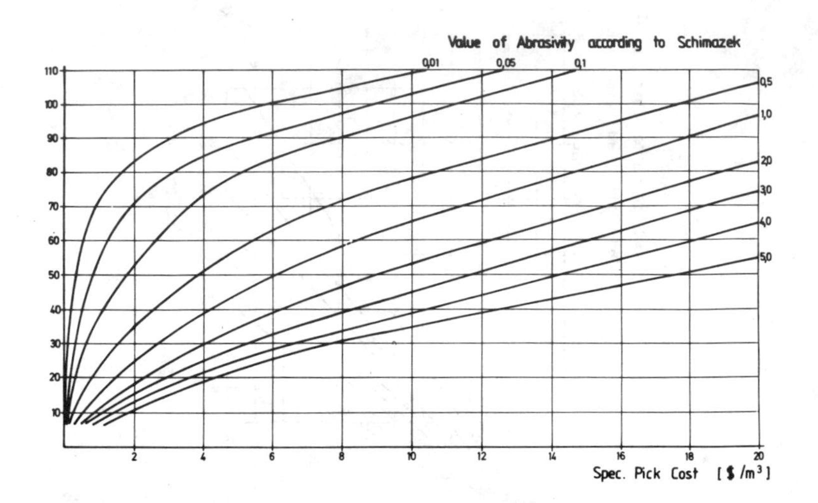

Fig. 4 Specific pick cost C_p (Pick type U 47) dependent on the uniaxial compressive strength and value of abrasivity.

When the abrasivity is low the costs are rising progressively only in rock with relatively high strength values- contrary to conditions where abrasivity is high, then the pick costs are already high in rock with comparatively low strength.
As has been learned from applications in practice, the values for excavation and pick costs determined by rock parameters, are clearly reduced in highly fissured rock. These factors are of consequence in rock quality classes worse than III.
According to Fig. 3,4 and 5 the actual excavation costs (C_{ET}) are determined according to the following formula:

$$C_{ET} = C_E \cdot r_E + C_p \cdot r_p + \frac{C_I}{V}$$

Key: r_E .... reduction factor for excavation cost AM 100
r_p .... reduction factor for pick cost (U 47)
C_I .... cost for machine installation
V ..... total volume of excavation (m3)

When planning the application of roadheaders these costs can only be used as indicative costs since important parameters such as degree of utilization or rock quality class can only be determined quite inexactly even in extensive preinvestigations.

The amount of the expected excavation costs however may be estimated which makes it possible to determine the range of economic machine applications.
yet, the factors for less disturbance of rock have to be considered which result in a reduced destruction of the rock body and less excessive excavation as compared to blasting.
This in turn sharply reduces the costs for lining and support work which can have a strong favourable influence on mechanized roadheading.

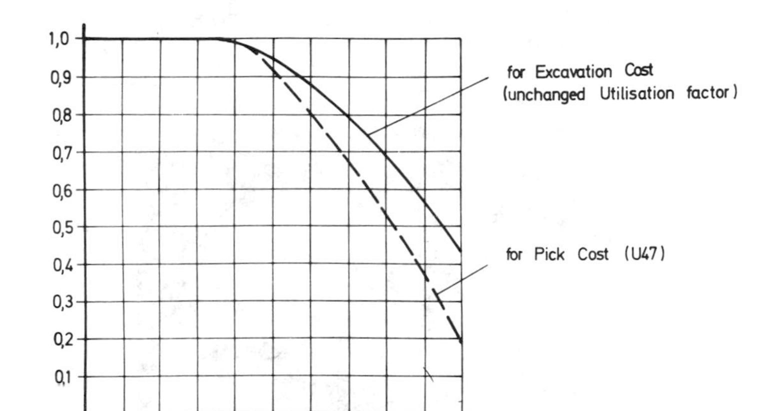

Fig. 5 Reduction factors for excavation and pick cost dependent on rock quality classes according to Rabcewicz - Pacher (Rabcewicz, Pacher, Golser 1974)

SOLUTIONS TO PROBLEMS OF ROADHEADER INSTALLATIONS

In the field of a comparatively high cost level, tunnelling with boom-type roadheaders is only considered when special circumstances are involved such as advance work in areas where blasting is forbidden or must be avoided.
The following paragraphs show which steps VA has taken in order to operate roadheaders in areas in which economic operation has not been possible up to now. Additionally, it is demonstrated by which components of the roadheading system especially developed to meet the requirements of tunnel construction the machine's rentability can be increased.

Cutting of hard, abrasive rock

When operating with the normal version of even the strongest machine on the market at present in rock of uniaxial compressive strength of more thän 70 MPa and of abrasivity values above 1 (according to Schimazek) rentability is no longer given. The reason is that cutting performance is decreasing when, at the same time, pick costs are rising exponentially to strength value.
Thin intercalations of harder rock however, can be cut according to their thicknesseven up to far higher values. In order to pass sections of higher rock strength, a drill rig for blast holes which can be adapted to the machine has been developed and also successfully used in practice (Fig. 6)

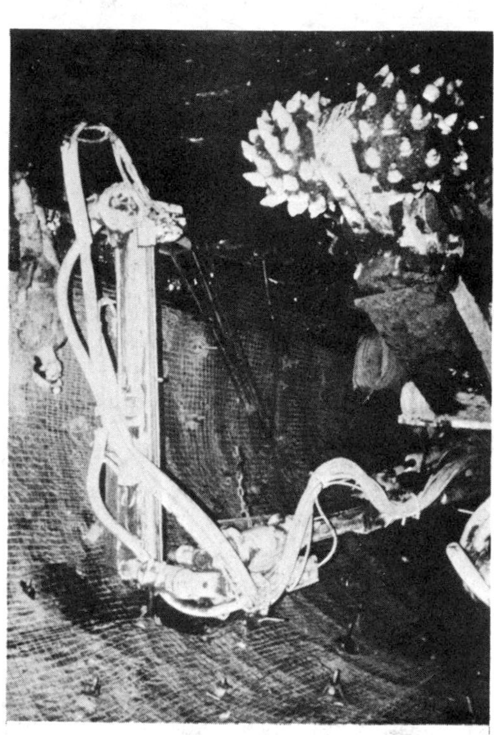

Fig. 6 Blasthole drilling and rock bolting device.

The blasted debris is transported by the gathering arms of the machine to the subsequent means of haulage. This installation is predominantly scheduled for small cross-sections up to abt. 25 m2. It is also suited as a rock bolting device. This is of special importance in rock

formations in which according to NATM bolting has to be carried out as early as possible in order to create a self-bearing ground arch surrounding the cavity.
Even when actually cutting hard abrasive rock layers essential improvements could be achieved.
In the field of pick technology great improvements could be achieved by reinforcing the carbide inserts and base body of the pick (Anon. 1979)

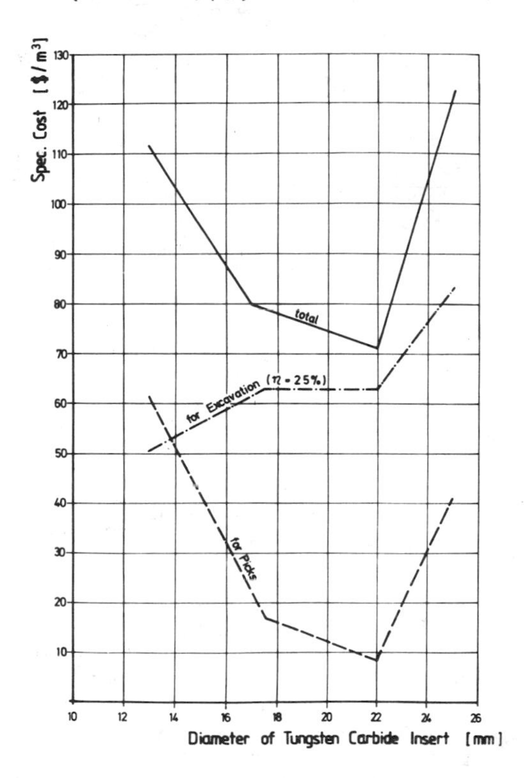

Fig. 7 Optimal selection of the carbide insert diameter in conical picks based on field tests.

As you can see from the figure in connection with σ_c = 100 MPA, σ_t = 12 MPA and an abrasivity value of 1 the optimum cost result was achieved with a carbide insert of 22 mm diameter.
This may be explained by the fact that greater diameters reduce the penetration ability of the pick and consequently the cutting performance without bringing down the specific pick costs. According to tests carried out up to now tough rock results even in a markable increase.
An additional progress in such rock conditions may be

achieved by directing high pressure jets (water pressure 150 - 200 bar) towards the picks in operation. The valves feeding the water to the jet are being opened by the pick itself, when it hits the rock. (Zitz, Sigott 1980)

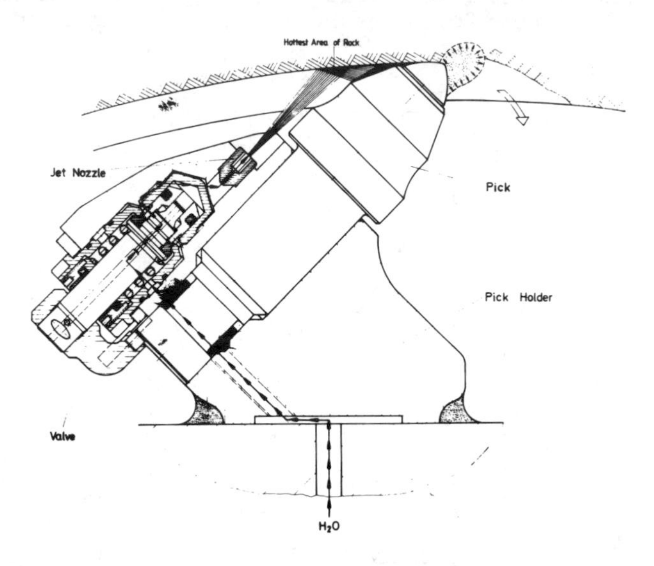

Fig. 8 Pick holder with conical pick and pick controlled high pressure water valve.

The advantage of this system is that water is only sprayed when the picks in contact with rock thus water consumption is limited despite the high pressures involved.
On the test bench pick consumption could be reduced by 1/8 as compared to operations without water jetting.
At present field tests are carried out to determine the degree of maturity and endurance capacity of the system - there are already highly satisfactory results-as well as the actual economic pick cost advantage to be expected.
Reduction of the danger of ignition in methan-air mixtures.

Due to the cooling effect not only the pick itself is effected but also - especially in coal mining - the dangerouslyhigh temperature at the pick tip as well as the formation of red-hot, ignitable sparks is brought down below the dangerous limit.
This factor which is decisive for a safety operation was the incentive for the development of the integrated water jetting system. On the test bench and in field tests it has been clearly proven that this approach is highly efficient.

Reduction of respirable dust content.

Another advantageous effect of the integrated water jetting system with high pressure water is the reduction of dust since by applying the aforementioned system dust is wetted immedeately where it generates and consequently cannot spread.
Results obtained on the test bench are shown in table 1

TABLE 1. Result of comparative dust measurements (test bench)

Operating Condition	fine dust concentration	coarse dust concentration
without integrated waterjetting system (mg/cm3)	70,1	1075,6
with integrated (mg/cm3) water jetting system	11,3	85,2
reduction of dust concentration (%)	83,9	92,1

These resutlts have not yet been analyzed in field tests as regards quantity but have been verified by means of decisevely improved sight conditions (the cutter head is clearly visible from the operator's platform during the whole cutting operation)
This dust combating approch, however, will only be reserved for operations in hard and abrasive rock formations. In many other cases the dust laden air has to be sucked off and cleaned in dust collectors. The best prerequisites for this method have tunnel headings with a drift of small cross section which has been driven before starting the full profile project. The dust laden air can be sucked off via this drift, and, consequently, the working area remains free of dust.
In all other cases one or more dust collectors have to be positioned behind the machine. The machine itself is equipped with integrated exhaust ducts, leading the dust laden air to the dust collector. The dust collectors available on the market at present are limited to an exhaust quantity of max. 800 cubic meters/min. Therefore the cross-sections in which these dust collectors can be applied satisfactorily are also limited.
New tests are aiming at the formation of a stable dust wall immidiately behind the face by applying high quantities of air which are blown in. Laterally located air exhaust ducts, not integrated in the machine, create a crosscurrent in the dust air mixture so that 2 dust

collectors of the present possible capacities are sufficient.
At present this system is tested in practice in Switzerland.

Increase of the machine's degree of utilization

As can be seen from figure 3 excavation costs are highly influenced by the degree of utilization which in turn is determined by the following factors:
- method of operation and construction
- rock quality and rock protection demand
- susceptability tobreakdowns and maintenance work of machine and other components of the roadheading system
- cutting performance of the machine
- organization of roadheading operation

From all these factors, only the reliability of the machine can be directly influenced by the machine itself. All other items are pre-determined by the operating conditions and are therefore more difficult to influence. The solution is the selction and adaptation of the machine to the existing conditions.
The method of construction can be adapted for the machine so that various points of attack are given, especially in large cross-sections. Consequently, cutting and protecting can be carried out alternatively in the various stages of the heading.
In this connection, an early cooperation between planning department, contractor and machine supplier can bring about very positive results.
The rock protection demand has the strongest impact on the degree of utilization. In rock of increasingly worse quality time spent for excavation and time spent for rock protection show an opposite trend (Fig. 9 according to Gehring 1980)
The most important step for improving this disproportion is an increase of the simultaneity factor for excavation and protection work.
On the one hand this can be achieved by temporary protection measures advancing with the machine, yet this method causes considerable rock deformations and is therefore primarily interesting in mining.
In the construction of tunnels and drifts a first step towards an improvement can be taken by reducing the set-up time of the installations for rock protection devices. (e.g.: drilling and bolting device mounted onto the machine)

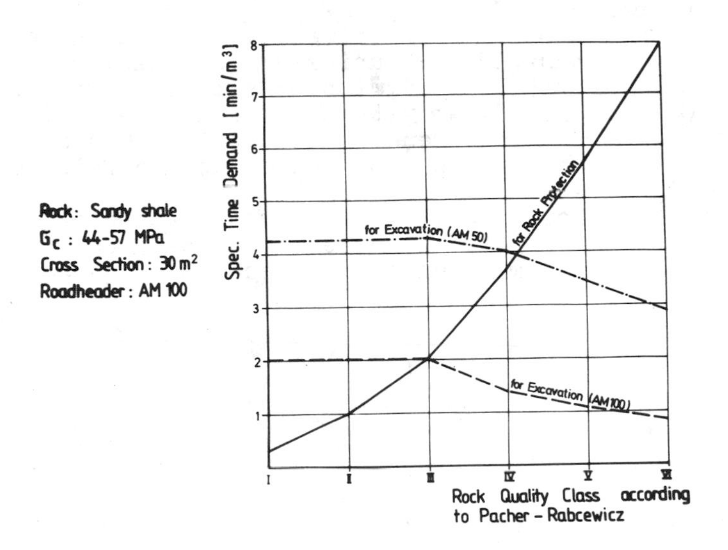

Fig. 9 Specific demand of time for excavation and rock protection in different rock qualities (roadheaders AM 50 and AM 100)

In larger cross sections and provided that dust suction is satisfactory, it is possible to operate a boom type roadheader and a rock bolting jumbo simultaneously. A flexible partition wall carried along with the advancing drivage enables a better separation of excavation and protection area.
The cutting performance of the machine can be adapted to the protection demand by the selection of the right machine version, as can be seen in figure 9.

EXAMPLES FOR SOLUTIONS TAILORED TO THE REQUIRED PROJECT CONDITIONS

By presenting two projects which are carried out at present some aspects shall be discussed again.
Intentionally two projects with extremely different cross-sections have been selected: a sewer tunnel with a cross-section of 6,5 m2 and a road tunnel with a cross-section of 154 m2.

Sewer Tunnel Hürtgen-Kleinhau

This drift is at present driven with an AM 50 near Aachen

(Federal Republic of Germany).
The rock body is formed by an alteration of mudstone, siltstone and sandstone with uniaxial compressive strength values from 20 to 63 MPa and with tensile strengths from 2,6 to 7,0 MPa. Sporadically thin intercalations of sandstone with compressive strengths of about 90 MPa are occurring. Rock abrasivity can be judged as moderate to considerably abrasive.
The drift has a horse-shoe profile, rock protection is carried out with reinforced shotecreteof 3-15 cm and resin roof bolts of 2 m dependent on rock quality.

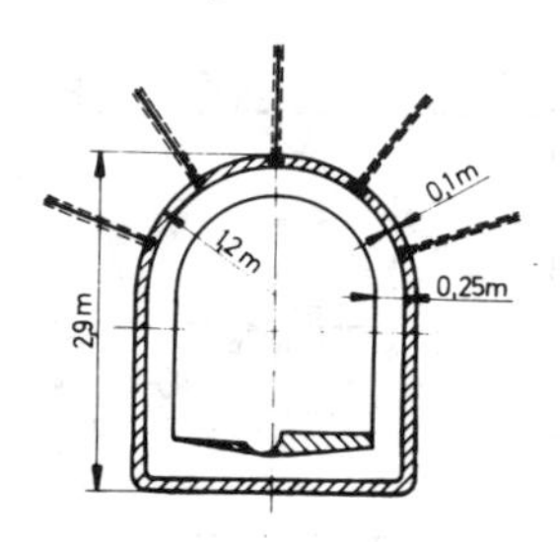

Rock Protection: Resin Roof Bolts, 2 m long
(up to 5, if necessary)
Reinforced Shotcrete, 10 cm

Support: Concrete Shell, 25 cm

Fig. 10 Sewer Tunnel Hürtgen-Kleinhau
Regular profile

Haulage is track-bound employing Mühlhäuser Trams with a capacity of 2.8 m3. A dry dust collector with a capacity of 400 m3 of dust laden air is carried along on a monorail behind the machine.

At a machine availability of 100 %, the degree of utilization is limited to 15 % due to the fact, that on the one hand rock protection is difficult in small space, and on the other hand, that there is partially quite a high water inflow.
Nevertheless a daily rate of advance of 4 m on the average (two shifts of 8 hours each) has been achieved. This corresponds to a cutting performance of 10.8 m3. So far pick consumption has been below 0.01 piece per m3. In the prevailing circumstances these values have to be considered as very good.

Milchbucktunnel
The Milchbucktunnel is part of the Zürich motorway system. On the one hand the rock is a water bearing moraine which had to be passed through by ground freezing. The then following fresh-water molasse consists of an alternative of marl and sandstone with a uniaxial compressive strength from 20 to 82 MPa (tensile strength 2,3 to 5,5 MPa), the rock is considerably abrasive.
At present the roof-section is driven with a remaining cross-section of 40 m2 (3 drifts, each with a diameter of 3 m have been driven by a full facer before the application of the AM 100)
The centre drift serves as duct for dust suction; the dust laden air is passed to a wet-type dust collector located in one of the drifts.
Rock protection is by means of shotcrete of varying thickness and by cemental bolts of 4-8 m.
In areas of bad rock quality steel arches are set.
The final support follows the rock protection work in distance of a few meters.

Fig. 11 Application of AM 100 in the Roof Section of the Milchbucktunnel Project

Haulage behind the machine is carried out by dumpers which are loaded via a swivel belt conveyor connected to the machine. The daily advance rate is about 3-6 m with a working time of 16 hours. At an availability of 94% and a degree of utilization of about 17% the cutting performance (including profiling) reaches values of 35-55 m^3/h. Pick consumption up to now has been 0,08 pieces per m^3. The low degree of utilization is predominantly dependent on the extensive rock protection work which is indispensable when working below populated areas.

CONCLUSIONS

The high availability values of the machines show that the principle seems to be successful not by applying a number of different machine types but by a corresponding adaption of few basic models to the manifold requirements of modern tunnelling in order to find siutable solutions covering the whole method of construction.
The applications reveal at the present moment two weak points in particular:
- too low degree of utilization
- high dust quantity

Since these two factors are mutually influencing each other, further development of the existing solutions presented in this paper is necessary.
Due to the heavily changing conditions which often occur fran project to project, the last step of development has to be taken either in the final planning stage of the project or even at the job-site.
In this connection boom-type roadheaders offer the best pre-requisites due to their flecibility and adaptability

REFERENCES

Gehring, K.H., 1975, "Über den Zusammenhang zwischen Gebirgseigenschaften und Gewinnbarkeit unter besonderer Berücksichtigung der Vortriebstechnik", GHM Springer Verlag Wien.

Gehring, K.H., 1979, ;Anpassung von Teilschnittmaschinen an durch von Gebirge und Bauwerk vorgegebene Bedingungen", Proc. 4th ISRM-Congres, Balkema, Rotterdem.

Gehring, K.H., 1980, "Besonderheiten geologisch-geotechnischer Voruntersuchungen beim Einsatz von Teilschnittmaschinen", paper presented on the 4. Nationalen Tagung über Felsmechanik, Aachen (not published)

Pacher, F., Rabcewicz, L.v., Golser, J1, 1974, Zum derzeitigen Stand der Gebirgsklassifikation im Stollen- und Tunnelbau", Heft 18: Auswirkungen geologischer Faktoren auf Bauabwicklung und Vertrag, Bundesministerium für Bauten und Technik, Straßenforschung, Wien.

Schimazek, W., Knatz, H., 1970, "Der Einfluß des Gesteinsaufbaus auf die Schnittgeschwindigkeit und den Meißelverbrauch von Streckenvortriebsmaschinen" Glückauf 106, Verlag Glückauf, Essen, BRD.

Zitz, A., Sigott, S., 1980, "Increasing of Produktivity by Improved Cutting Technology", Seminar on Improved Techniques for the Extraction on Improved Techniques for the Extraction of Primary Form of Energy, organized by the UN-Economic Commission for Europe, Wien.

Anon,. 1979, Anhebung der schneidbaren Gesteinsfestigkeit bei Verwendung von Teilschnittmaschinen, Teil 1: Verstärkte Meißelausführungen, VOEST-ALPINE research report (not published).

15

Hoisting and Materials Handling Practices

Chairmen: C.D. Mann
G.L. Tiley

Exxon Minerals Co., Houston, TX
G.L. Tiley & Associates Ltd., Hamilton, Ont., Canada

Chapter 65

6100 M (20,000 FT.) SLOPE HOISTS AT DEVCO MINES

By David Martell and Wilf Ingram

Senior Mechanical Project Engineer

Mechanical Technician - Man & Material Transportation

Cape Breton Development Corporation

ABSTRACT

For over 100 years mine hoists have been used in Cape Breton Coal Mines which are situated on the eastern coast of Canada. Most of the coal seams have been inclined and as the mine advanced, longer lengths of haul were required. This paper describes the successful operation of slope hoists with rope capacities of up to 6100 m (20,000 ft.) at Cape Breton Development Corporation.

A general description of the hoists is given. The braking systems, controllers and man riding cars used are discussed. The operational problems of using such long lengths of rope are described.

INTRODUCTION

The coal fields of Cape Breton generally dip seaward at angles of between 3° and 20°. Many of the mines were started at the coal "cropping" and were mined following the dip of the seam. As early as 1874 steam hoists were used to haul coal from the mine and to transport men and material to and from the mine. By the 20th. Century most of the coal under the surface was mined out and the mining developed further out under the sea. Electric hoists replaced steam hoists. In some mines an underground hoist was set up to transfer loads. At Princess Colliery a single drum hoist was set up underground in 1943 for taking men in and out of the mine. As the mining progressed more and more rope was added to the hoist until in 1967, 6400 m (21,000 ft.) of 25 mm (1 in.) rope was coiled onto the drum.

A typical hoist of the 50's and 60's was the "Main Arch Deep Hoist" which is still in use today. It is a 1343 kW (1800 h.p.) double clutched, double drum hoist, which was used to haul coal as well as handle men and materials. Trips of fourteen (14) full 2700 kg. (3-ton) mine cars were hauled at the rate of 7.62 m per sec. at an incline averaging 25% for a distance of up to 2100 m (6900 ft.). Loads of up to 54,426 kg. (6,000 tons) per day were hoisted as well as bringing material into the mine and taking the men to and from their places of work. The practice of hauling coal on slopes at high rates caused frequent derailments and accidents.

A new coal mine was started at Lingan in 1969. This mine was to follow the seam of the coal at an angle averaging 11°. Coal was to be transported by belt conveyor and men and material by slope hoist. Four (4) tunnels were driven and three (3) slope hoists were installed. The engine from #2 slope was purchased new from Markhams and was designed for 4572 m (15,000 ft.) using 32 mm (1¼ in.) rope. The other two hoists were salvaged from existing operations and were each over 50 yrs. old.

DEVCO'S HOIST UPGRADING

Lingan

In early 1977, representatives of John T. Hepburn were requested to make an engineering appraisal of our hoists. All our slope hoists (neglecting the new Markham hoist which was not examined) were judged to have drum barrels of insufficient strength for present and future conditions.

Acting on their recommendation, #4 hoist - Lingan was rehabilitated during our vacation shutdown of 1978 with a new drum and shaft, motor and first motion gearing. A new bedframe was fabricated in our Shops and anti-friction bearings were installed all around. The braking system was installed using parts of a Blacks system which were on hand.

The drum built by John T. Hepburn Limited for this hoist was 2.5 m (8' 4") in diameter by 1.8 m (6') wide with a capacity of 6100 m (20,000 ft.) of 32 mm (1¼") rope coiled in thirteen (13) layers. It was fabircated from 125 mm (5") plate and weighed over 56,363 kg. (62 tons). Two (2) 75 ton cranes were required to install the drum on its bedplate.

No. 3 Hoist, Lingan was replaced during October of 1979 with a new one ordered from G.E.C. This hoist was designed for the same loads as imposed on #4 hoist; i.e. 6100 m (20,000 ft.) of 32 mm

(1¼ in.) rope at a rated pull of 129,920 N (29,000 pounds). The hoist consists of a 550 h.p. motor, a Hansen N.P. 31 gearbox and the drum which measures 2.5 m (8 ft. 4 in.) in diameter by 1.8 m (6 ft.) wide. The braking system is a Blacks System similar to that of #4 hoist. Considerable foundation work was required to mount the hoist in the existing hoist house.

No. 26 Colliery

For the hoists to be installed underground at No. 26 Colliery, specialized help was requested, especially for the design of the drums. The drums had to be in small enough pieces to go through an opening 1.4 m (57 ins.) high by 1.8 m (6 ft.) wide, yet be strong enough to coil 4570 m (15,000 ft.) of 32 mm (1¼ in.) rope at a rope pull of 122,152 N (27,450 pounds). The drums on the Arch Deep Hoist are to be replaced with new ones designed by G.L. Tiley and built by O & K Canada Limited during the August shutdown of 1981. These drums will be in the same location as the existing drums and will coil 4570 m (15,000 ft.) of rope in 15 layers.

A complete new hoist has been ordered for the Arch Deep Man Rake Hoist from O & K Canada Limited. The hoist will fit in the same location as the existing hoist. It will feature a 747 kW (1000 h.p.) motor, a Hansen RDP 31A-F3 gearbox, which will go down in the mine in one piece, 14" Cooper split bearings, and a Blacks braking system. The drum designed by G.L. Tiley will be similar to the others for the Main Arch Deep Hoist with the same design loads. The "man rake" however will be used for hauling men only.

HOIST DRUM DESIGN

Because of the loads imposed from winding 13 to 15 layers of rope on a drum, tremendous stresses are built up on the drum. (1) Hoop stresses which act in a tangential direction are known to crush winding drums while bending stresses which act in an axial direction are known to cause cracks in some drums. As each layer of rope is wound on the drum, the tension is added to the tensions of the layers already wound. The drum contracts slightly in diameter with each turn and the tensions previously in the rope reduce slightly.

For the difficult problem of the underground hoists at No. 26 Colliery, G.L. Tiley used a method of stress analysis which incorporates a mathematical technique that rapidly calculates the deflection caused by winding a single turn of rope on the drum including the effect of tensions already wound. For this calculation, considerable computer time is required.

By G.L. Tiley Limited

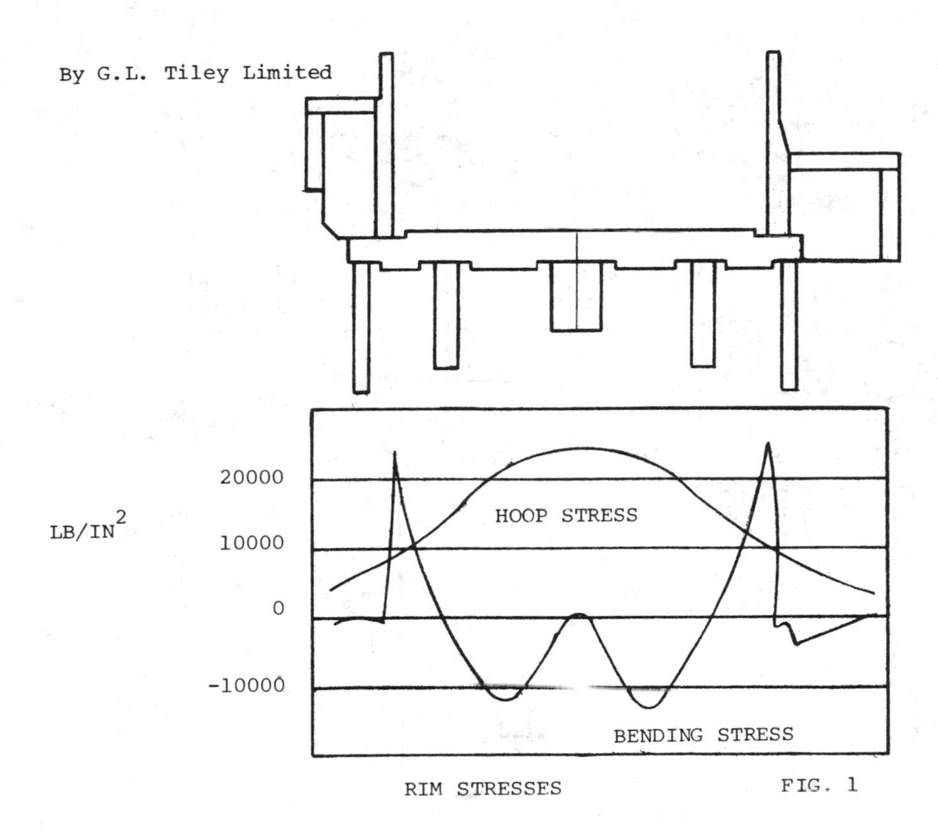

RIM STRESSES FIG. 1

Figure 1 shows the stresses calculated to exist after winding 4570 m (15,000 ft.) of rope in 15½ layers. The bending stresses reach 115,700 N (26,000 pounds) and the hoop stresses nearly the same. Because G.L. Tiley had wisely chosen a high tensile, low alloy steel plate for the drum, these stresses were within acceptable limits.

The parts of the drum were rough machined to achieve close fits prior to welding. Therefore, these fits convey compressive loads and only small welds are needed to hold the parts together and convey torques. The material thickness was limited to 100 mm (4 ins.) and a fairly light, yet effective design was obtained.

BLACKS BRAKES

The braking systems on most of our hoists are high pressure, oil controlled spring brakes using Blacks caliper type brake shoes. A typical circuit for a single drum slope hoist is shown in Figure 2.

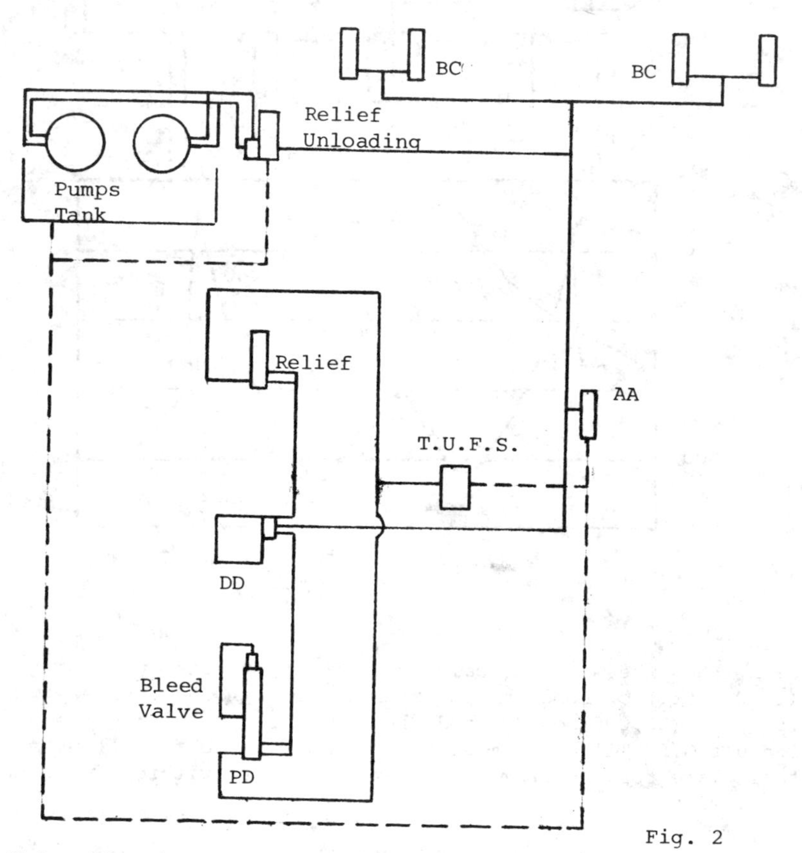

Fig. 2

Hydraulic Circuit for Blacks Brake.

The braking systems are fail-safe type, oil pressure released, spring applied. There is one or more brake cylinders (BC) mounted on each precompressed spring nest capable of exerting their full effort on the brake gear when the oil is at zero pressure. (2)

The pressure control valve (AA) is a seated type, merely acting as a variable choke in the system. By this means the driver is able to vary the pressure in cylinders (BC) with great accuracy.

By lowering the oil pressure below the pressure required to hold the springs at their maximum compression, the brake shoes can be brought into contact with the path and the braking effort at any moment will be that due to the full effort of the spring nests, less the force exerted by the ram of cylinder (BC) under the control of the driver's operating valve (AA). In the event of an emergency trip on overspeed, the power to the trip valve (T.U.F.S.) will be disconnected. The coils will be de-energized opening the valve and releasing the oil from the cylinders (BC) to a predetermined back pressure giving a retardation of approximately 1.2 m/sec.^{2} (4 ft./sec.^{2}) with a descending load. In the case of an ascending load, the oil from the cylinder (BC) is directed to the pause and decay valve (PD) by way of the directional valve (DD). The pause and decay valve (PD) and as its name applies, will allow the braking force to build up rapidly to a predetermined pressure and from that point onward build up a braking effort capable of stopping the inertia of the hoist only, letting the trip stop by its own weight. This type of braking is necessary on slope hoists to avoid the trip over-running the rope.

The brake shoes are designed with 180° of contact and minimum operating movement. 50 mm (2 ins.) moulded brake linings, .6 m (24 ins.) long are used.

Brake rings on the drums built of removable steel segments are preferred over cast iron rings as the mechanical brakes presently provide the only means of stopping the hoist. There are two (2) shoes, each independently capable of stopping the full trip.

CONTROLLER

The hoist control and safety equipment used mostly on our hoists is the Logan Lilly Long Range Controller, Model C. The fundamental principle of operation of the Lilly Controller is based upon the co-ordinated movement of a governor and cams, the governor following the hoist speed and the cams following the relative position of the conveyance, providing a pattern for the correct speeds at all points of travel including retardation.(3)

When the hoist speed slightly exceeds the predetermined safe maximum, or if it is not decreased in conformity with the profile of the retarding cam when approaching the end of travel, an electrical contact closes a circuit to ring a bell or buzzer to warn the hoistman. If he fails to respond promptly and permits a slightly further increase in speed, or if the retarding cam engages the cam roller without the hoist being retarded, the overspeed switch in the Lilly Controller will open the safety circuit thereby cutting off the power to the motor and emergency trip valve which in turn will set the brakes. The long range feature allows protection for the 6100 m (20,000 ft.) of travel and allows the profile of the retarding cam to be relatively long. The dials rotate for only 305 m (1000 ft.) of the top and bottom of the slope. The Lilly Long Range Controller is of particular advantage in our operations because the bottom limits can be easily moved as the slope length increases.

ROPES ON LONG INCLINES

The ropes used on the DEVCO hoists are all flattened strand 6 x 8 construction with a fibre core. The flattened strand gives a better wear in abrasion as it gives a larger bearing area than round strand wire of the same cross-sectional area and the fibre core gives a cushioning action in the rope along with more flexibility. The steel used is 110/120 improved plow steel which gives good breaking strength while retaining flexibility. Conditions which plague the long slope haulage are water on the bottom, bad rollers, chance of stone falling on the rope and heavier wear points due to high spots in the roadway caused by deviation in the coal seam which our slopes follow. Sometimes the seam flattens out to the point where we have difficulties overcoming the friction of the rope when going down while lightly loaded.

Lubrication of the rope is difficult as it is running over hundreds of rollers and the mud and dust tend to keep lubrication out and hold moisture in. The rope tends to corrode in the damp atmosphere of some of our slopes. Initial coiling of the rope is sometimes a problem. The rope is wound from the reel onto the drum, then the end is put through a sheave wheel mounted on a tram and then anchored at the top of the slope. A heavy trip of cars is attached to the tram and the trip lowered and raised under tension. Proper winding is ensured by manually keeping the rope in its proper position if it strays from time to time.

This trip may have to be raised and lowered several times. A swivel is attached to the rope and used for several days to ensure any "life" which is in the rope is taken out through the swivel. If this procedure isn't followed, a danger of the rope spinning and hitting someone or putting itself into a kink which will permanently damage the rope, is very likely when the rope is disconnected from the lead car on the trip.

In past experiences, it has been known for a rope to turn over several cars weighing one ton each when a swivel wasn't applied or seized and failed to allow the spin to come out of the rope.

At Lingan the reel is now placed on a shaft and "braked" so that the rope is now installed under light tension.

It has been found that coiling has been greatly improved with Lebus "soft crossover" grooving. All new hoists have this feature.

It is essential that the rope is no more than 5% oversize as this would prevent the rope from coiling properly.

All ropes are resocketed and tested accourding to the Coal Mines Regulations Act and for our benefit Rotesco do an electro-magnetic inspection of the entire length of the rope.

MAN RIDING CARS

Men are hoisted on slopes with special man riding cars built by Sheepbridge Engineering. These cars have their own hydraulic braking system which can be operated manually by the car attendant (chain runner) or through an overspeed device which is set about 10% above the hoist overspeed limit.

Hydraulic pressure is used to allow diaphragms to lift the cars above the axles. This allows brake friction pads to be lifted free from the rails. When the pressure is released by the brakeman, overspeed device or broken hose, the car bodies are lowered until the weight is on the friction pads and the trip is stopped under its own weight. This type of vehicle can be used on slopes of up to 25% and up to 40% when wheel lifting devices are installed.

ELECTRICS

No. 3 Hoist electrics are that of a conventional A.C. hoist with wound-rotor induction motor and open loop control scheme during 'hoist' and 'lower'. Unlike standard North American practice, a liquid controller is used for secondary resistance. The position of the grids in the liquid controller (and thus the secondary resistance) is controlled by the drivers' control lever via an oil servo unit.

Operators' Console

The operators' console, which was designed and built by DEVCO personnel, includes auxiliary motor control fault indication panel and safety circuit. The entire control circuit is designed to fail to safety.

Main Breaker and Reversing Contactor

A standard stored-energy, air-circuit breaker provides under-voltage, thermal overload, short circuit and ground fault protection for the main motor.

For the first time DEVCO is using vacuum contactors for the main motor reversing switch. Vacuum contactors were chosen for their long electrical and mechanical life as well as the minimal maintenance they require.

Dynamic Brake

Lowering heavy loads for long distances at reduced speeds would stress the thermal capacity of the brakes. The paths on our #4 hoist were permanently damaged after only eighteen (18) months of service. In order to reduce excessive heat build-up at the brake paths and brake wear and to avoid other associated problems, as well as give additional measure of safety, a dynamic braking system was added to the hoist.

During dynamic brake mode, D.C. current is applied to the stator of the main motor which will then behave like a generator. The braking torque thus obtained is used to control the load. The braking torque is controlled by a closed-loop system whereby the D.C. current to the stator is a function of driver's control lever position and the rotor current.

The first system was installed during the vacation period of 1980 at #4 hoist and is working satisfactorily.

SUMMARY

Considerable expertise has been built up at DEVCO mines in the operation of long distance slope hoists. Time and effort qoes into maintaining the ropes. The Blacks braking system is felt to be the best mechanical braking system available. The dynamic braking system should provide relief from brake overheating due to lowering large loads at less than ' line speeds'.

REFERENCES

Galloway, Les, 1980 Hoist Drum Design, G.L. Tiley Report.

G. A. Black, Winder Control and Safety Systems.

Logan, Henry, H., 1944 - The Lilly Hoist Controller, Catalogue C44, Page No. 5.

Chapter 66

MULTI-ROPE HOISTS FOR HEAVY LOADS

by Gerald L. Tiley

Consulting Engineer
Hamilton, Ontario, Canada

ABSTRACT

When payloads and hoisting distances are beyond the capacity of a single headrope, a multi-rope hoist will cost less than, and require less maintenance than, several hoists with one headrope per conveyance.

This paper describes the basic type of multi-rope drum and friction hoists in use today, the types of ropes available, and the essentials of a satisfactory installation.

BASIS OF DESIGN OF A HOISTING SYSTEM

Ropes of very high tensile strength, and of meticulously controlled quality, have been developed to meet the mining industry's requirements of heavier loads and increased depths. In order to exploit the potential capacities of these ropes, equally meticulous attention must be paid to every component of the hoisting system. The basis of design should be a thorough evaluation of the forces that act on, and the subsequent behaviour of, the ropes. Hoisting machinery, headframes, etc. should be sized to accommodate the ropes, not vice versa.

The combined costs of the production and service hoists seldom amount to more than 2% of the capital required to bring a mine into production. They are also the only components for which standbys are not normally provided. Any savings effected by purchasing under-sized or marginal equipment will be insignificant in relation to the over-all capital cost and will almost certainly result in excessive maintenance and down time throughout the life of the mine.

FATIGUE ENDURANCE POTENTIAL OF WIRE ROPES

Steel wire ropes are manufactured from selected carbon steel rods. The required strength and ductility of the wires is obtained by a carefully controlled sequence of cold drawing, normalizing and quenching operations. Breaking strengths of the wires are of the order of 3 to 5 times that of the parent steel rods.

In service, however, ropes fail due to fatigue: when subjected to repeated stress applications during hoisting, minute cracks will start at points of stress concentration (usually at the surface of the wire, and in the form of corrosion pits, or scratches, or where mechanical abuse has resulted in an overhardened, brittle area) and propogate through the wire.

The level of repeatedly applied stress that will lead to failure of the rope in service is called the "fatigue endurance limit". It is considerably lower than the breaking strength obtained by a single application of load in the laboratory and is not directly proportional to this breaking strength; an increase of, say 10% in the breaking strength will result in, at most, a 5% increase in the "fatigue endurance limit" strength of the rope.

On a normal working cycle, hoist ropes are subjected to:

- a direct static load
- transient shock loads when loading, dumping and changing speed
- bending stresses as the rope passes over sheaves or friction wheels or is wound on drums, and
- variations in individual tensions in a multi-rope installation.

In addition, ropes wound on a hoist drum are subjected to crushing and buffetting by adjacent turns, particularly at crossover points.

When the sum of the above stresses exceeds about 25% of the breaking strength of the ropes, small additional loads have disproportionately large effects on potential rope lives.

Wire rope manufacturers' catalogue data is based on breaking strengths; mining codes allow reduced factors of safety with depth. In deep shafts, rope performance is liable to be unsatisfactory if high tensile ropes are stressed to the allowable statutory rope factors of safety.

STATUTORY FACTORS OF SAFETY AND BENDING RATIOS

In general, Federal and State Regulations do not specify minimum rope factors of safety for ore or material loads, but require that, when men are carried, rope factors of safety shall be:

Length of Rope (metres)	Minimum Factors of Safety New Rope	Discard
153 or less	8	6.4
153 to 305	7	5.8
305.5 to 610.5	6	5.0
611 to 916	5	4.3
916.5 or more	4	3.6

The factor of safety is usually defined as the rated breaking strength, divided by the dead suspended load (i.e. payload plus conveyance weight plus suspended rope weight). One exception is New Mexico, where the live suspended load, which includes acceleration forces and friction drag, is used in the formula.

Federal regulations also require that the drum and sheave diameters of personnel hoists shall not be less than

80 times the rope diameter for stranded ropes over 25.4 mm diameter, and
100 times the rope diameter for lock coil ropes.

ROPE CONSTRUCTION AND TYPES

Figure 1 illustrates the various types of ropes commonly used on mines.

A. Round Strand Regular Lay The wires are laid up (i.e. twisted together) to form strands in the opposite sense to which the strands are laid up to form the rope. The wires on the outside surfaces of the strands lie approximately parallel to the axis of the rope.

Under tension, the wires tend to untwist in one direction and the strands tend to untwist in the other direction. With careful design, the rope will show little tendency to twist when loaded.

B. Flattened Strand, Lang Lay The strands are formed around a triangular core and the wires are laid up to form strands in the same sense that the strands are laid up to form the rope. The wires on the outside surfaces of the strands lie at approximately 45° to the axis of the rope.

This construction was developed specifically for multi-layer winding on hoist drums. When compared to a round strand regular lay rope:

- it is more flexible because the wires lie parallel to the rope near the centre, not the surface
- the wires at the outer surface of the rope are less subject to "plucking" by adjacent turns as the rope coils on the drum, and
- contact loads at the surface of the rope and between the strands are distributed among more wires.

The one disadvantage of a Lang Lay rope is that it tends to untwist when loaded.

C. Multiple Strand, Non Spin ropes were developed to overcome the torsion forces developed by Lang Lay ropes. They are more susceptible to the crushing forces associated with multi-layer winding on a drum, and have a lower strength/weight ratio than, Lang Lay Flattened strand ropes.

They are used on drum hoists during shaft sinking, where the required service life is relatively short, and as tailropes for friction hoists.

D. Lock Coil Ropes are built up from concentric layers of wire. The wires in the outer layer are of "Z" cross-section and the wires in the inner strands are either round or of "X" cross-section.

The lay of the various layers can be arranged so that the rope does not have any tendency to untwist when loaded. In addition,

- the structure is compact and stable and better able to withstand crushing stresses than any other rope, and

- the line contact seals between the wires in the outer layer keep lubricant in, and corrosion out, of the rope.

On the debit side, the specially shaped outer wires cannot be made as strong as round wires and the rope is less flexible than a stranded rope. Larger sheaves and drums are required for ropes of equivalent strength.

MULTI-ROPE DRUM HOISTS

EVOLUTION

The "Blair" multi-rope drum hoist was developed some 30 years ago, by engineers of the Anglo American Corporation in South Africa, in order to increase production from the very deep shafts in the Witwatersrand gold mines. It is named after Robert Blair, who was, at that time, their chief Mechanical Engineer.

Two ropes are used per conveyance. Both ropes wind, in the same sense, on a drum which is divided into two compartments. Stages in the evolution of the hoist are illustrated in Figure 2.

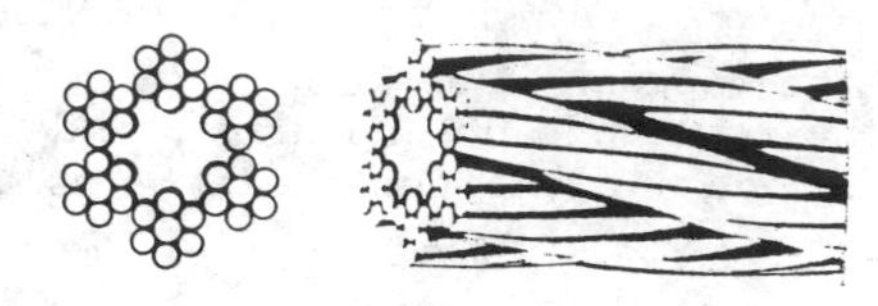

A. ROUND STRAND REGULAR LAY

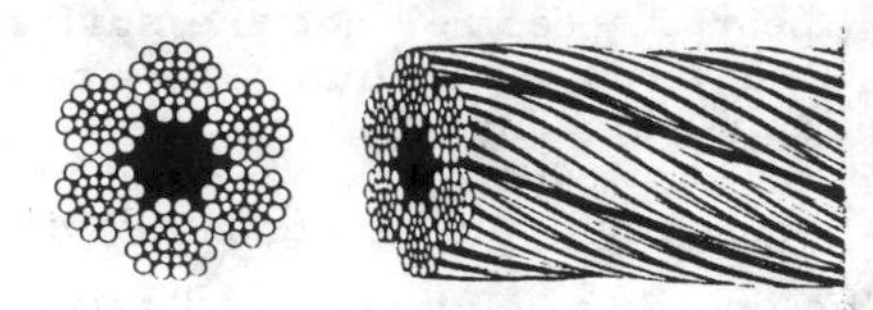

B. FLATTENED STRAND LANG LAY

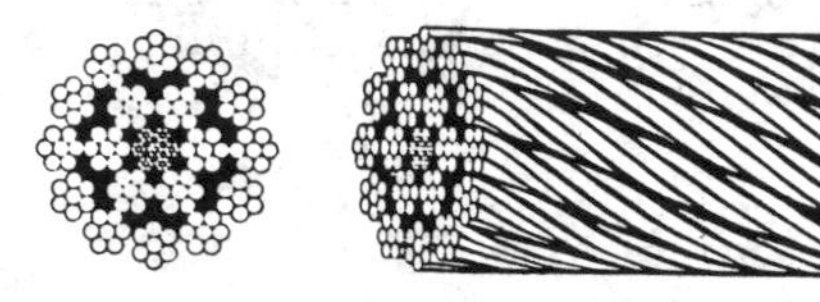

C. NON ROTATING

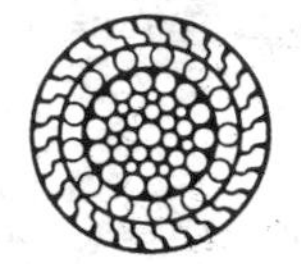

D. LOCK COIL

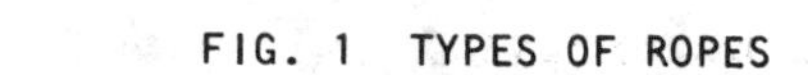

FIG. 1 TYPES OF ROPES

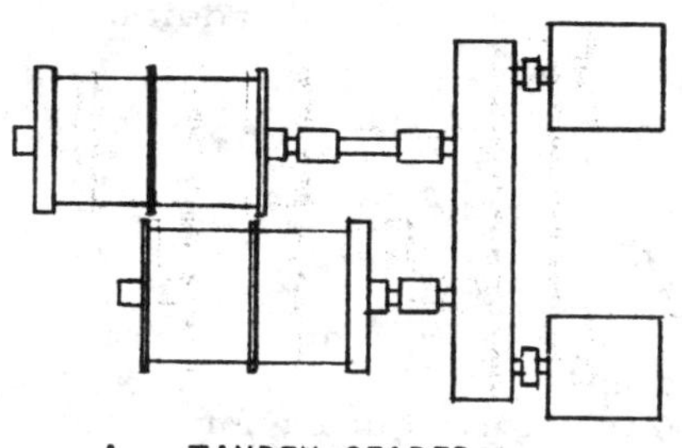

A. TANDEM GEARED

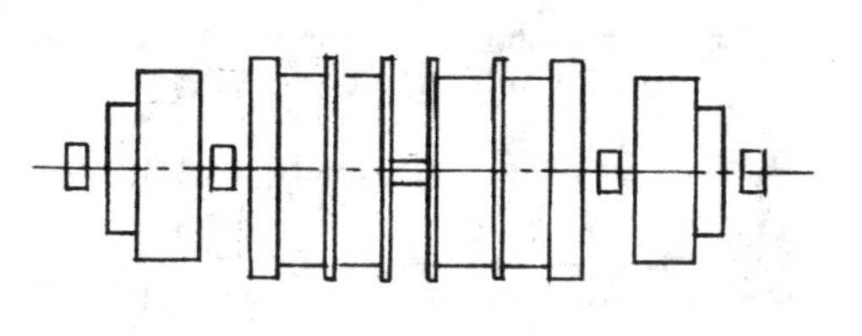

B. IN LINE DIRECT DRIVE

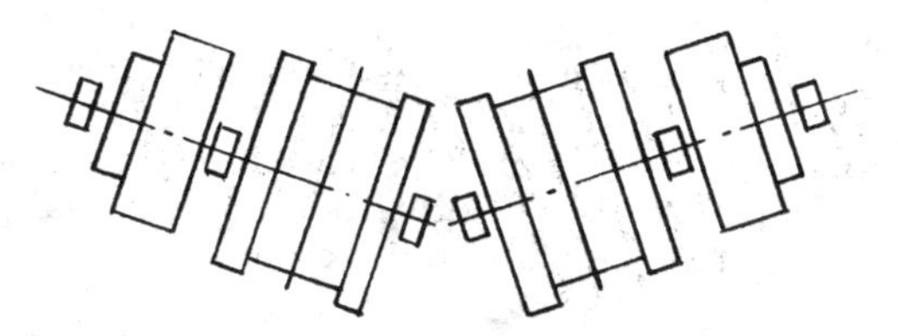

C. GEARLESS

FIG. 2 TYPES OF BLAIR HOISTS

A. Tandem Geared In order to fit the shaft compartment centres, the drums in the first installation were placed one behind the other. The gears have to transmit torques between the drums as well as motor torques, and are large and very expensive.

B. In Line, Direct Drive Both drums are mounted on a common shaft that is supported in two bearings and driven by a direct coupled motor at each end. This is the simplest and most elegant arrangement, but is only possible if the shaft compartments are far enough apart to fit the drum centres.

C. "Gearless" Blair The "Gearless" Blair consists of two single drum hoists, each with two drum compartments and driven by a direct coupled DC motor. Each motor and associated power conversion equipment and the brakes must be designed to handle the unbalance torques of a single drum hoist.

The power equivalent of the difference in torques acting on the drums is transmitted electrically between the drives; the power demands on the utility system approximate those of an in-line Blair. (See Figure 8) Although the electrical drives and brakes are large and expensive, the "Gearless" Blair Hoist imposes no restrictions on shaft layout. Drum centrelines can be offset as shown in Figure 2C to suit the shaft compartment centres.

ROPE TENSION COMPENSATING SYSTEMS

It is impractical to expect that drum compartments and ropes will be of exactly the same diameter, or that exactly the same amount of each rope will be wound in or paid out every revolution of the drum.

Three compensating systems have been developed to ensure that the ropes of a Blair hoist share load reasonably well.

Monitoring of Rope Coiling If the ropes coil on different layers, active lengths will differ by: 5.4 x (rope diameter) each revolution of the drum. Miscoiling is detected by rods located under the drum compartments, parallel to the drumshaft, and just clear of the first layer of rope when the conveyances are at their lowest elevation. These rods are moved out radially, to maintain the small clearance, just before the ropes reach the end of each layer. If a rope miscoils, it will touch the rod and initiate an emergency stop.

Compensating Sheaves on the Conveyances (Figure 3) In early installations, the ends of the ropes were not attached directly to the conveyance; they were wrapped several times around, and then attached to, a spirally grooved sheave.

The ropes were coiled in opposite directions. An increase in tension in one rope would cause the drum to rotate until tensions were equalized.

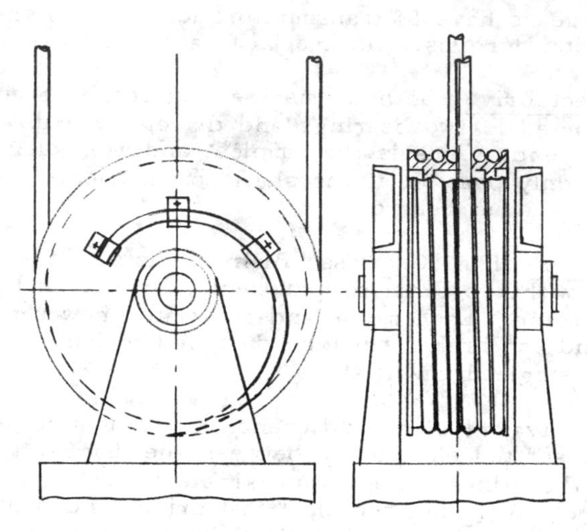

FIG. 3 COMPENSATING PULLEY

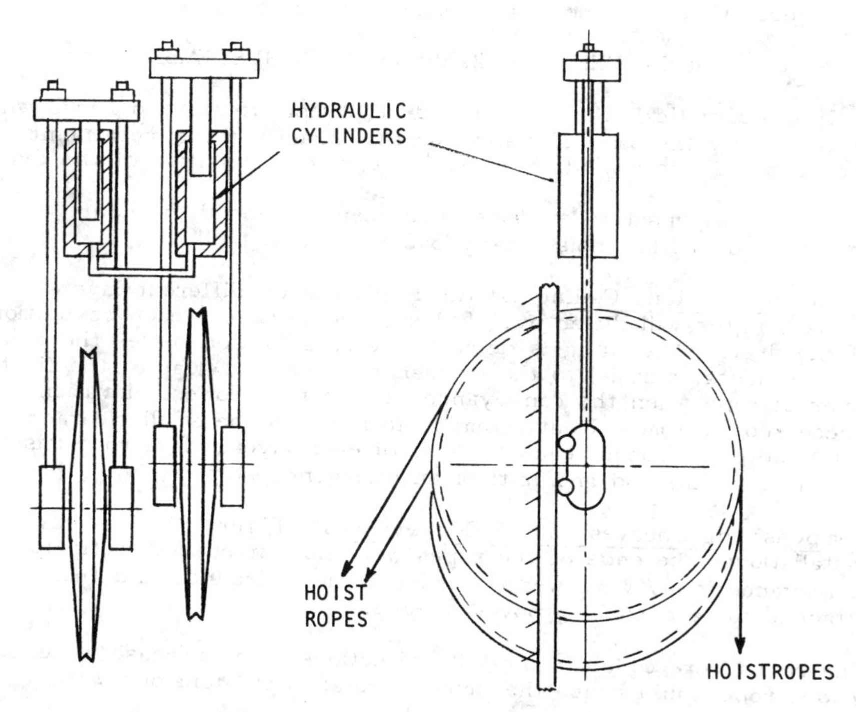

FIG. 4 FLOATING HEADSHEAVES

These devices worked, but had the following disadvantages:

- they added dead weight to the conveyances
- their capacity was limited, and
- a radio link was required to detect when either rope was almost uncoiled.

Floating Headsheaves (Figure 4) A better solution is to suspend pairs of headsheaves from hydraulic cylinders that are connected to a common supply of oil under pressure. The sheaves will move up or down to equalize rope tensions. Miscoiling is detected by limit switches that are actuated by excessive differential movements of the sheaves. The majority of Blair Hoists now work with floating headsheaves.

MULTI-ROPE FRICTION HOISTS

EVOLUTION

The first friction hoist was developed by Dr. Karl Frederich Koepe, and installed in a colliery near Hanover, Germany, in 1877. Figure 5A illustrates the general arrangement:

- the Koepe Pulley, which was lined with timber blocks, was mounted at shaft collar elevation
- a single headrope passed around the pulley, over two headsheaves and was attached to the tops of the two conveyances, and
- a single balance- or tailrope was attached to the bottoms of the conveyances.

By the early 1930's ropes of up to 75 mm diameter were being used to handle the payloads required by mining engineers. Because these ropes tended to be unstable and unreliable in service, twin rope, ground mounted Koepe hoists, employing 4 headsheaves, were developed.

The next step was a 4 rope hoist. If ground mounted, 8 headsheaves would have been required and the hoist was therefore designed for installation in a tower, directly over the shaft, as shown in Figure 5B. The first 4 rope, tower mounted friction hoist was installed at another colliery near Hanover in 1938.

Modern friction hoists employ plastic, rather than wooden treads, and deflector sheaves (one per rope) are often used to bring the headropes into shaft compartment centres (Figure 5C). Deflector sheaves are of lighter construction than headsheaves because they deflect the ropes less than 15° (compared with approximately 150° for headsheaves).

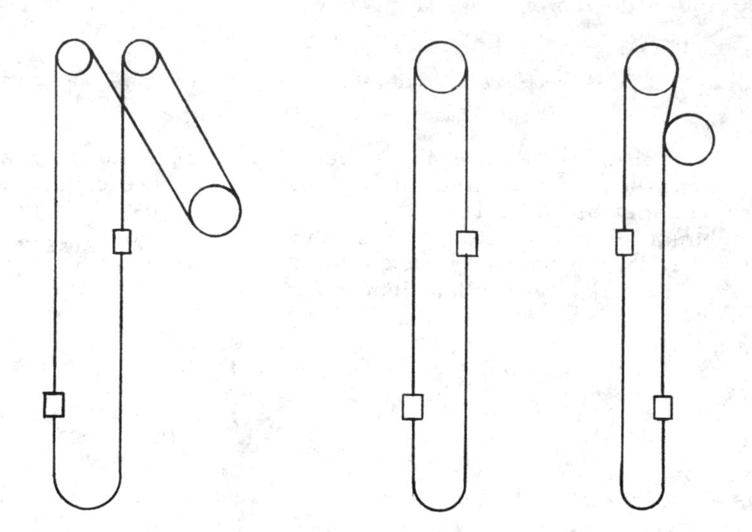

FIG. 5 GROUND & TOWER MOUNTED FRICTION HOISTS

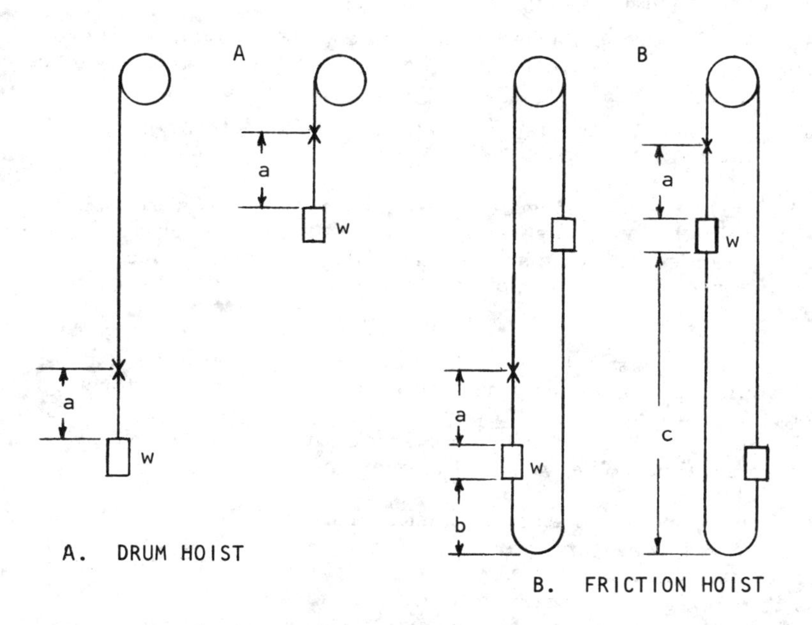

FIG. 6 TENSIONS IN HEADROPES

FACTORS AFFECTING THE PERFORMANCE OF FRICTION HOIST HEADROPES

TAILROPES

Figure 6A represents a conventional drum hoist, rope and conveyance. The tension at any point "X" in the rope is the sum of "a" feet of headrope plus the attached load W. This tension remains constant throughout each hoisting cycle.

Figure 6B represents a friction hoist, ropes and conveyances. When the conveyance is near the bottom of the shaft, the tension at "X" is the sum of "a" feet of headrope, plus the attached load W, plus "b" feet of tailrope.

When the conveyance is near the top of the shaft, the tension at "X" will be greater because the weight of "c" feet of tailrope has to be supported. The tension at any point in a headrope increases continuously as the conveyance ascends and decreases as the conveyance descends.

As already discussed, ropes of Lang Lay construction tend to untwist when tension loads are increased and vice versa; when used on a friction hoist, they tend to spin as they pass over the wheel. The amount of spin, measured in several installations, has been found to be approximately proportional to $(\text{hoisting distance})^{2.3}$. This spin wears away the treads and reduces the fatigue lives of the ropes.

In general, Lang Lay ropes have not been satisfactory in friction hoist installations where the hoisting distance is greater than about 750 m. Lock coil friction hoist headropes have been operating successfully for many years in Canada at depths of up to 1400 m. Several of these hoists are designed for ultimate depths of over 1800 m.

ROPE TENSION VARIATIONS

In a multi-rope friction hoist installation, individual rope tensions are affected by:

- differences in the cut length of the ropes

$$\Delta T = A.E. \frac{\Delta L}{L} \quad \ldots\ldots\ldots\ldots(i)$$

- and differences in the effective rope tread diameters

$$T = \frac{\Delta D}{D} A.E. \text{ Ln} \frac{(L)}{(l)} \quad \ldots(ii)$$

where ΔT = Difference in rope tensions

ΔL = Difference in cut rope lengths

ΔD = Difference in tread diameters

A = Cross-section area of the rope

E = Modulus of Elasticity of the rope

L = Rope length, wheel to conveyance at lowest level

l = Rope length, wheel to conveyance at highest level, and

D = Average tread diameter

Figure 7 is a non-dimensional plot of $\frac{\text{Incremental Rope Tension}}{\text{Area x Modulus}}$

when ΔD = 0.001 inches per inch of tread diameter.

In most installations, a given difference in tread diameter will have more than 1000 times as much effect on rope tensions as the same difference in cut lengths of the ropes.

In addition, differences in the cut lengths of the ropes will tend to be compensated by permanent stretch of the ropes, but differences in tread diameters tend to be aggravated in service because there is a greater tendency for the ropes in the small grooves to surge forward (and scrub off more tread material) than for the ropes in the larger grooves to surge backwards.

Neither compensating sheaves nor floating headsheaves can be used to equalize the headrope tensions of a multi-rope friction hoist. Satisfactory load sharing is, however, possible, providing that:

The wheel is large enough. The accuracy to which treads can be machined is determined by the type of tool and the rigidity of the tool supports. It is independent of the wheel diameter. As shown in Equation (ii), the difference in rope tensions is proportional to:

$$\frac{\text{Difference in Tread Diameters}}{\text{Average Tread Diameter}}$$

If a particular wheel tread is, say 0.01 inch larger in diameter than the others, then the rope in contact with that tread will be stretched 0.0314 inches with every revolution of the wheel. Obviously, a large wheel will make fewer revolutions per trip than a small wheel, and the cumulative rope stretch associated with a particular error in tread diameters will be less.

There are a minimum number of headropes. Less maintenance will be required to keep, say, 4, rather than 8 rope treads equal in diameter. In addition, a larger wheel will be required for 4, rather than, 8 ropes, and machining tolerances will therefore be less critical.

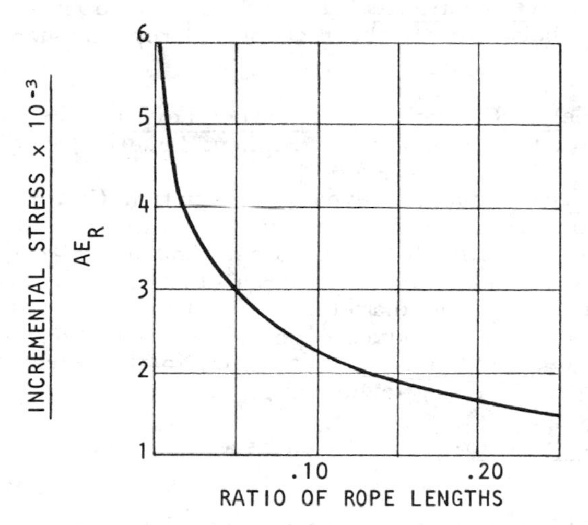

FIG. 7 EFFECT OF UNEQUAL TREAD DIAMETERS

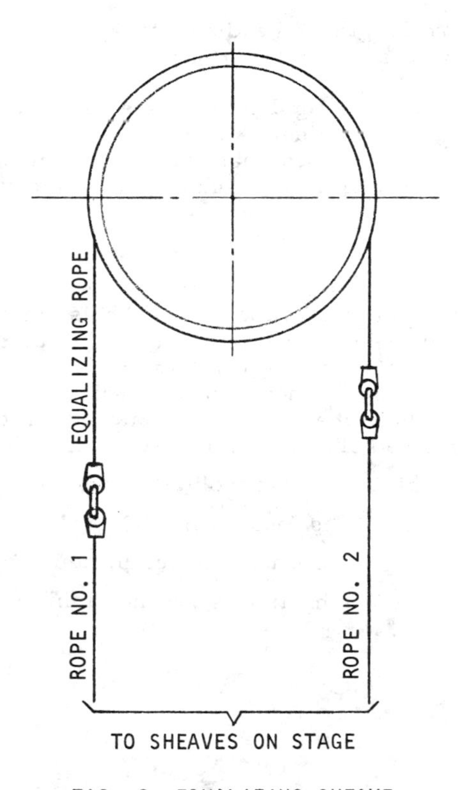

FIG. 9 EQUALIZING SHEAVE

There is adequate overtravel clearance. Refer again to Equation (ii). For a given diameter of hoist wheel, the incremental rope tension is proportional to:

$$\mathrm{Ln}\ \frac{\text{(Rope Length - Wheel to Conveyance at Lowest Level)}}{\text{(Rope Length - Wheel to Conveyance at Highest Level)}}$$

The wheel structure is resilient. In developing equation (ii), the wheel was assumed to be rigid: if the structure is resilient, the tread carrying the rope subjected to the greatest tension will contract as the conveyance ascends, and vice versa, to tend to compensate for initial differences in tread diameters. Plastic rope treads are resilient, but can only act to reduce rope tension variations if they are of adequate cross-section and are secured to the wheel in a manner which allows their elasticity to be effective.

Tailropes are lighter than headropes. As an ascending skip approaches the dump:

- rope tension variations caused by unequal tread diameters increase, and
- there is a minimum length of headrope to absorb the shock loads as the skip enters the dump scrolls.

In addition, tailrope weights tend to increase as they become coated with rope dressing and rock dust. The above effects can be alleviated by specifying tailropes that are lighter than the headropes, so that the average static headrope tension is reduced as the skip ascends.

OPERATING EXPERIENCE

We have observed that in multi-rope friction hoist installations, a trained and competent maintenance crew can maintain rope tensions within 5% of one another when the conveyance is at the lowest level, by equalizing rope lengths. They can also maintain rope tensions within 10% of one another when the conveyance is at the highest level, by equalizing tread diameters, provided that:

- the wheel makes less than 100 revolutions per trip
- the ratio of rope lengths is less than 50/1
- they have precision groove machining equipment, and
- the elastic properties of the treads are not inhibited by the wheel structure.

FEASIBILITY STUDY - HOISTS TO RAISE 1000 TONS/HR. (907.5 TONNES/HR.) THROUGH 1 MILE (1600m) VERTICAL

On this project, the initial milling rate is to be 70,000 tons (63,500 tonnes) per week and ore is to be hoisted on afternoon and night shifts, Monday through Friday. The required hoisting rate, allowing one hour of delays per shift, is therefore 1000 tons (907.5 tonnes) and a maximum speed of 3300 fpm (16.8 m/sec.) were selected as a basis for design.

Data on ropes and suspended loads for alternative multi-rope Friction and "Blair" double drum hoists is listed in Tables 1 and 2. Fatigue Endurance Potential calculations for the ropes in the four cases are summarized in Tables 3 and 4.

Note that the skips for the friction hoists are heavier than for the drum hoists. This is because:

- they have to support the weight of the tailropes, and
- there are more rope attachments.

CASE 1 is a "Blair" double drum hoist that would conform to Federal and most State regulations. Under ideal conditions, the potential life of a set of headropes will be at best 44,000 skips, or 1.6 million tonnes of ore. Broken wires will probably be evident after about 3 months operation.

The ropes will stretch approximately 2.75 m when a skip is loaded. After running through the shaft with empty skips, the drums should be clutched with one skip at the loading pocket and the other skip at least 3 m above the "skip fully dumped" point.

CASES 2A and B are Blair double drum hoist, using the strongest ropes that are currently available. Under ideal conditions, the potential life of a set of headropes will be approximately 335,000 skips in Case 2A, and 450,000 skips in Case 2B. This difference is solely the result of lower bending stresses.

It should be noted that an increase of 5% in maximum stress will approximately halve potential rope life.

Crushing pressures were not considered in these calculations: an increase in drum diameter will reduce both the bending stress and the crushing pressures on the rope. High localized crushing pressures occur at the crossover points during multi-layer winding and result in plastic deformation and a hardened, brittle, surface on wires that have already been heavily cold worked during manufacture. Rope lives can be improved by periodically winding them completely off the drums, and cutting approximately 1/3 turn from the drum ends to move the points of crossover. This procedure is usually scheduled for weekends, in premium time, and can represent a substantial addition to maintenance costs. A larger drum will allow longer intervals between drum end cuts.

CASE 3 is a 4-rope friction hoist which would conform with Federal and most State regulations. As a Production Hoist, however, it would be a disaster

- potential life of a set of headropes would be, at best, 45,000 skips, or 1.65 million tonnes of ore

- tread pressures are about 70% higher than current practice. We have no data on tread life at these pressures, but would be suprised if they lasted more than a week

- rope tension ratios would result in rope slip if the mineshaft is wet and the ropes require lubrication.

CASE 4 is a 6-rope Friction hoist that will perform satisfactorily. Rope lives will be optimum (over 500,000 skips or 18 million tonnes of ore if individual rope tensions can be maintained within 5% of the mean value).

Tread pressures are in line with current practice, and barring accidents, the treads should outlast several sets of headropes.

Rope Tension Ratios are also low enough to permit the headropes to be heavily lubricated if the mineshaft waters are corrosive.

ELECTRICAL DRIVE AND CONTROLS

Cardinal points on equivalent duty cycles, raising 36.3 tonne payloads at a maximum speed of 16.8 m/sec. through a vertical distance of 1600 m, are plotted in Figure 8. Recommended motor ratings would be :

In Line Blair - 10,000 kw, 58 rpm frequent 200% peaks

Gearless Blair - Two 10,000 kw, 58 rpm frequent 200% peaks

Friction - 7000 kw, 60 rpm frequent 175% peaks

TABLE 1 ROPES & SUSPENDED LOADS - BLAIR DOUBLE DRUM HOIST

	CASE 1	CASE 2 A	CASE 2	CASE 2 B
Drum Diameter (m)	3.82	4.58		5.34
Hoisting Distance (m)	1600		1600	
Suspended Rope (m)	1620		1620	
HEADROPES				
Type	LANG LAY FLATTENED STRAND			
Number	2		2	
Diameter (mm)	47.5		57	
Ultimate Strength (kgx10^3)	172 (IHT)[a]		240 (UHT)[b]	
Weight/metre (kg)	9.05		12.97	
Drum/Rope diameter	80/1	80/1		96/1
SUSPENDED LOADS (kgx10^3)				
Headropes	29.25		42.0	
Payload	36.3		36.3	
Skip plus attachments	18.15		18.15	
ROPE TENSIONS (kgx10^3)				
Loaded skip at L.P.	83.7		96.45	
Loaded skip at Dump	54.5		54.5	
ROPE FACTORS OF SAFETY				
Loaded skip at L.P.	4.11		5.0	
Loaded skip at Dump	6.32		8.83	
Statutory	4.0		4.0	
PEAK TREAD PRESSURE (MPa)	4.52	3.62		3.03
ELASTIC ROPE STRETCH (m) (when skip is loaded)	2.7		1.9	

a) Intermediate High Tensile Strength wires.

b) Ultra High Tensile Strength wires.

TABLE 2 ROPES & SUSPENDED LOADS - MULTI-ROPE FRICTION HOIST

	CASE 3		CASE 4	
Wheel Diameter (m)	3.66		5.34	
Hoisting Distance (m)	1600		1600	
Suspended Rope (m)	1635		1650	
HEADROPES				
Type	LOCK COIL			
Number	4		6	
Diameter (mm)	36.5		44.5	
Ultimate Strength ($kgx10^3$)	116 (Std)		179 (Std + 5%)	
Weight/metre (kg/m)	7.21		10.83	
Wheel/Rope diameter	100/1		120/1	
Wheel Revolutions/Trip	139		95	
TAILROPES				
Type	NON ROTATING			
Number	3		4	
Approximate Diameter (mm)	48		61	
Weight/metre (kg)	9.33		14.96	
SUSPENDED LOADS ($kgx10^3$)				
Headropes	47.2		107.3	
Tailropes	45.8		98.7	
Skip Load	36.3		36.3	
Skip plus attachments	27.2		29.5	
ROPE TENSIONS ($kgx10^3$)				
Loaded Skip T1	110.7	109.3	173.1	164.5
Empty Skip T2	73.0	74.4	128.2	136.8
T1/T2	1.52	1.47	1.35	1.2
TOTAL SUSPENDED LOADS ($kgx10^3$)				
Loaded Skip	183.7		301.3	
Empty Skip	147.4		265.0	
TREAD PRESSURE (MPa)				
Peak, Loaded Skip	4.07		2.39	
Average, Loaded Skip	3.37		2.08	
ROPE FACTORS OF SAFETY				
Loaded Skip	4.19	4.24	6.21	6.54
Empty Skip	6.35	6.23	8.39	7.86
Statutory	4.0		4.0	
ELASTIC ROPE STRETCH (m) (when skip is loaded)	1.45		0.65	

TABLE 3 FATIGUE ENDURANCE POTENTIAL - BLAIR HOISTS

LOADS PER ROPE ($kg x 10^3$)	CASE 1		CASE 2A		CASE 2B	
Static Load	41.85		48.21		48.21	
Acceleration Reaction (0.8 m/sec^2)	4.88		5.61		5.61	
Direct Axial Load	46.73		53.82		53.82	
Load Equivalent to Bending Stress	10.0		6.25		5.21	
Total Load	56.73		60.07		59.03	
Tension Variation (%)	0	5	0	5	0	5
Fatigue Stress (%)	33.0	34.65	25.0	26.25	24.5	25.7
FATIGUE ENDURANCE POTENTIAL (per set of ropes)						
- Skips x 1000	44	34	335	190	450	240
- Ore (million tonnes)	1.6	1.25	12.2	6.8	16.25	8.7

TABLE 4 FATIGUE ENDURANCE POTENTIAL - FRICTION HOISTS

LOADS PER ROPE ($kg x 10^3$)	CASE 3			CASE 4		
Static Load	27.68			28.85		
Acceleration Reaction (0.8 m/sec^2)	3.22			3.36		
Direct Axial Load	30.9			32.21		
Load Equivalent to Bending Stress	9.14			10.77		
Total Load	40.04			42.98		
Tension Variation (%)	0	5	10	0	5	10
Fatigue Stress (%)	34.5	36.3	38.0	24.0	25.2	26.4
FATIGUE ENDURANCE POTENTIAL (per set of ropes)						
- Skips x 1000	58	46	37	Optimum (over 500)		420
- Ore (million tonnes)	2.1	1.65	1.35	over 20		15.25

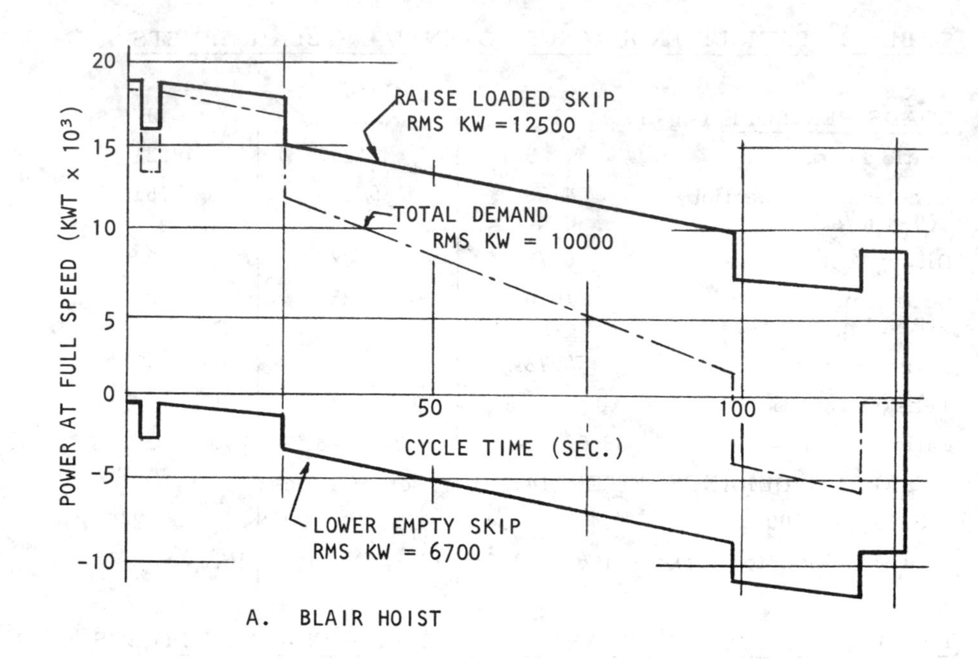

A. BLAIR HOIST

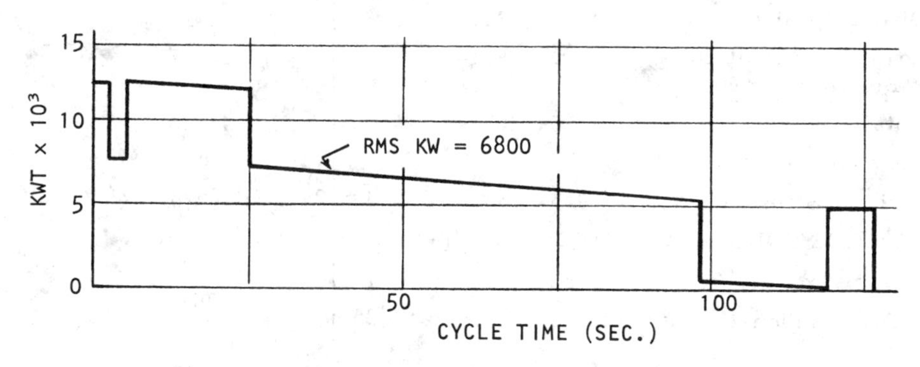

B. FRICTION HOIST

FIG. 8 EQUIVALENT DUTY CYCLES
HOISTING DISTANCE = 1600 M
MAX. SPEED = 16.8 M/SEC
PAYLOAD = 36.3 TONNES

MULTI-ROPE SHAFT SINKING STAGE HOISTS

Drum Type Stage Hoists In modern shaft sinking operations, a movable working platform, called a Galloway stage, is suspended by ropes from surface and is lowered as shaft sinking progresses. This stage carries the shaft mucking equipment and facilities for handling the shaft wall forms, concrete lining, steel sets, guides, pipes, cables, etc. Stages have been built with up to 7 decks and weighing over 110 tonnes. These stages are suspended from two or more ropes. As illustrated in Figure 10, each rope can pass up and down the shaft several times. In the arrangement shown, the stage is suspended by 8 falls of rope. Stage handling equipment may be either a multiple drum, clutched hoist, with the ropes wound in the same sense (eg. overlay) on each drum, or several single drum hoists.

Load sharing between ropes is usually not a problem because the stage is seldom moved more than 50 m at any time and the relative rope lengths can be adjusted after each move by rotating one drum while the other drums are held stationary. If the stage has to be moved greater distances, and is suspended from two ropes, tension variations can be limited by connecting their dead ends to a rope which passes over a sheave in the headframe, as shown in Figure 9. Attached loads and working depths are, in theory, limited only by the weight of rope that can be manufactured in one length and shipped to the site. The largest rope spinning machines in North America can manufacture stranded ropes weighing up to approximately 91 tonnes, i.e. about 7000 m of 88 mm diameter stranded rope. Two such ropes could handle an attached load of 300 tonnes through 1600 m vertical.

Blair Friction Type Stage Hoists Until very recently, when computers became available, hoist drums were designed by "rule of thumb" and extrapolation from previous examples. The effects of multiple layers of rope, wound on at high tensions, were not appreciated and drum failures were fairly common. The engineers under Mr. Blair's direction developed a friction type stage hoist to overcome this problem. Figure 11 illustrates the general arrangement of Blair stage hoist. Each rope passed several times around a capstan, and was stored at a relatively low tension on a drum. The two capstans were driven through dog clutches by a common motor; the two storage drums were driven by separate motors.

Back tensions on the capstans were maintained constant by weights in towers between the capstans and storage drums. Storage drum motors were started and stopped by limit switches that were activated by the rising and falling of the weights. If, for example,

- the coefficient of friction between rope and capstan is 0.1 (a conservative value), and
- there are 3.75 laps of rope around each capstan,

then the capstans could safely support tension ratios of up to 10/1.

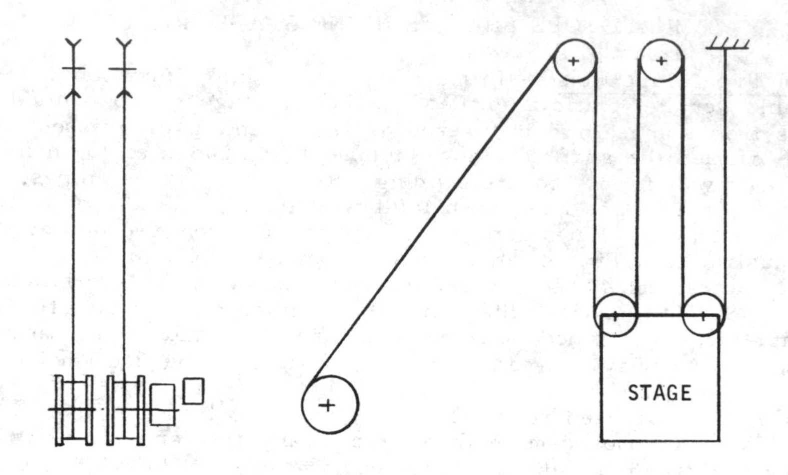

FIG. 10 DRUM STAGE HOIST

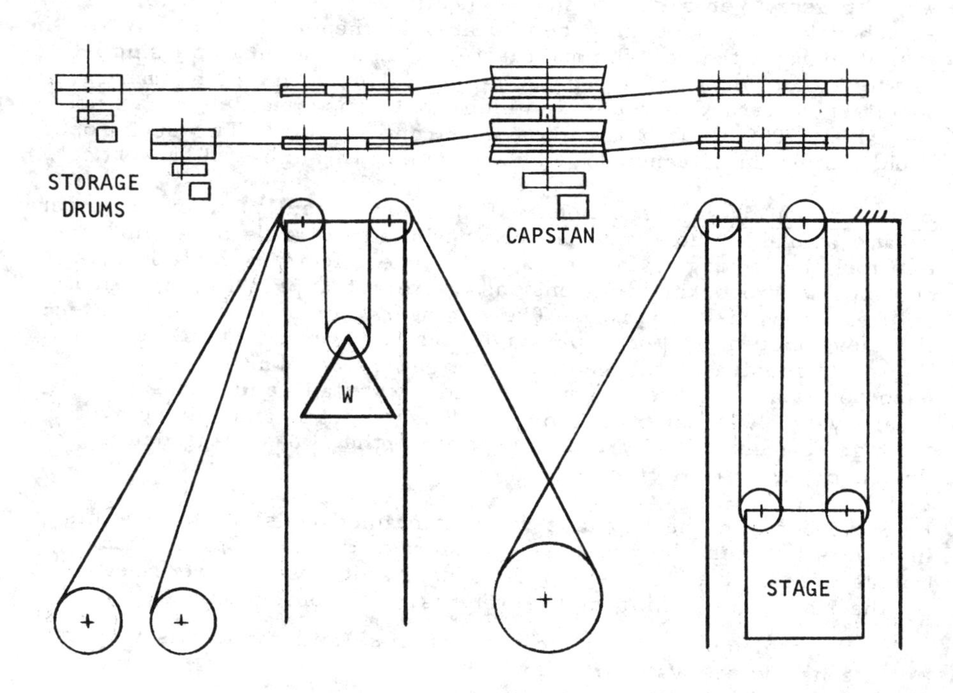

FIG. 11 BLAIR STAGE HOIST

16

Large Underground Openings for Mines

Chairmen: C. Gerity
M. Young

Occidental Minerals Corp., Lakewood, CO
Ozark Lead Co., Sweetwater, MO

Chapter 67

EXCAVATION AND SUPPORT OF UNDERGROUND CRUSHER FACILITY AT CARR FORK MINE

by N.S.P. Kumar

Chief Design and Construction Engineer

Anaconda Copper Company
Carr Fork Mine
Tooele, Utah

INTRODUCTION

Development work at Carr Fork Mine of Anaconda Copper Company in Tooele, Utah commenced in August 1974. A decision to install an underground gyratory crusher for primary crushing run-of-mine ore and waste was made in 1976 Higher throughput rates, larger reduction ratios and greater flexibility in terms of meeting immediate and expanded production needs were the main reasons for selecting the gyratory crusher over the jaw crusher.

UNDERGROUND MATERIALS HANDLING

Underground crushing and conveying system was designed for a capacity of 16,300 mtpd of ore and waste on a 2-shift, 5-day week basis. Engineering and design of crusher complex was performed by Anaconda engineers at Carr Fork.

Figure 1 represents the longitudinal section of mine showing the general materials handling system. Mine area is trackless except for materials and production haulage which is run on rail track on both 1200 and 970 levels. Ore from stopes and waste rock from development headings are handled by 3.8 cu m (5 cu yd) Jarco scoops and dumped into 2.4 m (8 ft) diameter ore and waste passes at the 1200 level. The material gravitates down to the 970 level where it is loaded into 12 cu m (420 cu ft) ASEA mine cars using side loading chutes. The muck train, consisting of 15 to 18 cars and two 27 mt General Electric trolley locomotives, is hauled over a distance of 2,300 m (7,550 ft) to the ASEA train dump under which a 1,000 mt capacity coarse material bin is situated. At the 930 level, the coarse rock is fed to the 1350 mm x 1850 mm (54 in. x 74 in.) Traylor gyratory crusher by a 1.8 m x 6.1 m (6 ft W x 20 ft L) Hewitt-Robins elliptex vibrating feeder at 1800 mtph. Under the crusher, a 1.2 m x 6.1 m (4 ft W x 20 ft L) NICO apron feeder feeds the -150 mm (-6 in) crushed product on to a 1.2 m x 49 m (4 ft W x 161 ft L) inclined belt conveyor. This conveyor discharges ore into crushed ore bin #1 and ore or waste on to a shuttle conveyor. The shuttle conveyor, in turn, discharges ore into #2 crushed ore bin or waste into #3 waste bin. Each bin has a storage capacity of 2500 mt From the bottom of the bins at 870 level, the material is drawn out by 1.2 m x 2.1 m (4 ft W x 7 ft L) Syntron mechanical vibrating feeders. Two 1.2m (48 in) wide belt conveyors with hydraulic drives and a short waste conveyor convey the material to the production shaft skip loading pockets. The production shaft is equipped with four 13.6 ton SALA skips running on rope guides for hoisting the ore and waste 1100 m (3609 ft) up the shaft. Two tower-mounted, 3150 mm (126 in) diam Canadian General Electric friction hoists are used for hoisting ore and waste at a speed of 915 m per minute (3,000 fpm). Figure 2 shows an isometric view of the underground crusher complex including the conveyor system. Figure 3 represents a section through the crusher area indicating the arrangement of equipment.

EXCAVATION AND SUPPORT OF CRUSHER FACILITY

Central focus for the excavation of crusher area including handling of all required materials and equipment was the 5.8 m (19 ft) diameter, concrete-lined service shaft. During the development phase of the mine, the shaft was equipped with loading pockets at 1200 and 870 levels. A double-deck cage and a 15 ton Lakeshore Jeto skip serviced the shaft. All development muck generated from the crusher area excavation was hoisted from the 870 loading pocket.

Two diamond drill holes were drilled in February 1978, from the service shaft 930 level station into the crusher complex area to evaluate the geological features prior to commencing excavation. Results indicated that the openings would predominantly be in competent dark-grey quartzite formations with occasional limestone beds cutting across.

Access drift excavation for the crusher complex on the 930 level commenced from the service shaft station in June 1978. Figure 4 shows the sequence of excavation carried out on the 930 and 910 levels. Drift was excavated using a Joy 3-boom jumbo and a 3.8 cu m Jarco scoop. Muck was transferred to the 870 level shaft load-out system through the 970-870 muck pass with a finger connection at the 930 level. Figure 5 shows the plan view of the 930-910 levels.

The crusher room itself was excavated from the top down. From the intersection on the access drift, a pilot ramp at 20% grade was started up to the crown of the crusher room. At the crusher room, the drive was continued flat across the width of the room. A short raise was driven up to the arch at the center of room and the arch areas on both sides of the raise were slashed. Then the top slice of the room was taken by breasting across the length. The back was supported by bolting and shotcreting. Remaining portion of room and access drift was excavated to the 930 level by benching.

In conjunction with the excavation of the upper crusher room, a decline (up to 15.5% grade) to the 910 conveyor gallery was driven from the 930 level. When the gallery was excavated to below the crusher room, a pilot raise was drilled up to the 930 level and the crusher well area was slashed by benching using a Gardner-Denver air track drill. Excavation and ground support of crusher room and 910 conveyor gallery was completed in April 1979.

During excavation it was observed that the crusher area lies in jointed quartzite formations that are highly fractured especially in fault zones. Perimeter smooth wall blasting technique was employed during the excavation. Access drift and crusher chamber including feeder area were temporarily supported with 1.83 m (6 ft) long split sets (friction rock bolts) on a 1.5 m (5 ft) square pattern. Wire mesh and straps were installed with these bolts. Later on, these areas were shotcreted to provide permanent ground support. In the main chamber, 3 m (10 ft) long Williams grouted rock bolts were installed in addition to the split sets. Rock bolting was followed by the application of 150 mm thick shotcrete. Walls of these excavations were prone to slough especially where the quartzite bedding joints contained clay and shale partings. To control sloughing at the top of crusher well, a concrete wall was poured around the perimeter of the well. This wall was further reinforced with post-tensioned, high-strength Dywidag rods to provide adequate bearing strength for the bridge crane support column footings. Ground movement in the chamber is being monitored with rod extensometers and convergence meters. Movement to date has been negligible.

The conveyor gallery was supported by pattern bolting and shotcreted later. In order to meet the scheduled mine production start-up date of September 1, 1979, it was planned to bypass the crusher initially. However, this plan still needed the excavation of the crushed ore bin #2 and equipping of the conveyor #2 on the 870 level. In January 1979, excavation of bin #2 was given high priority. An Ingersoll-Rand RBM-7 raise borer was set up on the 970 level and a .28 m (11 in) diam, 84 m (275 ft) long vertical pilot hole was drilled through the 910 conveyor gallery into the 870 loading drift. The hole was reamed up from 870 to the 910 level using a 1.83 m (6 ft) diam reamer bit. The bin was then excavated by slashing the reamed hole to 7.3 m (24 ft) diameter by benching using Gardner-Denver sinker drills. Broken rock was handled at the 870 level by a 3.8 cu m (5 cu yd) Jarco scoop through 870 loading pocket at service shaft. During excavation of the bin, ground support was provided by bolting and wire meshing as required. Later, the bin was intermittently lined with 1.5 m (5 ft) high concrete bands to give a finished inside diameter of 6.7 m (22 ft). The #2 bin was ready for handling muck by July 1, 1979.

Excavation of #3 and #1 bins was similarly performed and completed in August 1979, and September 1980, respectively.

For excavating the ASEA train dump on the 970 level and the coarse material bin below the dump, a 24.4 m (80 ft) pilot raise was driven from the 930 to the 970 level. The dump was then excavated by benching into the raise. After concreting the dump, the coarse bin was slashed to 6.4 m (21 ft) diam and later lined with concrete with a facing of 41 kg (90 lbs) relay rail liners. All muck from this excavation was handled on the 930 level.

TABLE I

NO.	AREA	EXCAVATION VOLUME (cu m)	START DATE	COMPLETION DATE
1.	930 Access Drift	4300	May '78	Aug '78
2.	Crusher Room	5550	Aug '78	March '79
3.	Electrical Room	450	Oct '78	Oct '78
4.	930-910 Ramp	1950	Aug '78	Oct '78
5.	910 Conveyor Gallery	1700	Oct '78	Nov '78
6.	#1 Bin	1500	Jan '79	Sept '80
7.	#2 Bin	1500	Jan '79	May '79
8.	#3 Bin	1500	Feb '79	Aug '79
9.	ASEA Dump	400	Apr '79	May '79
10.	Coarse Bin	400	Aug '79	Oct '79
	Total	19,250 cu m (25,180 cu yds)		

Table I summarizes the crusher complex excavation project. All excavation was performed by Carr Fork Mine Department crews. The entire project performance was closely monitored for quality control and timely completion by the Engineering and Project Control Departments using CPM scheduling.

CONCRETE HANDLING

Concrete for the crusher room and auxilliary facilities was handled through a 150 mm (6 in) diam slick line in the production shaft. At the 970 level station, a Conspray pump was used to remix and pump the concrete through a 125 mm (5 in) diam pipe line on the level and then through a 125 mm (5 in) diam cased borehole at about 45° into the crusher room at the 930 level. To minimize segregation in concrete because of the 915 m (3002 ft) drop through the slick line and to increase slump, plasticity and workability of concrete, an additive called Melment was added to the concrete during batching at the production shaft collar. A total of 1750 cu m (2289 cu yd) for foundations, floor slabs and concrete lining was handled through this system for the crusher complex. About 800 cu m (1046 cu yd) of shotcrete was also used for ground support purposes.

ACKNOWLEDGMENT

The author is indebted to the Anaconda Copper Company for permission to present this paper and to the Engineering staff at Carr Fork for assistance with drawings and illustrations.

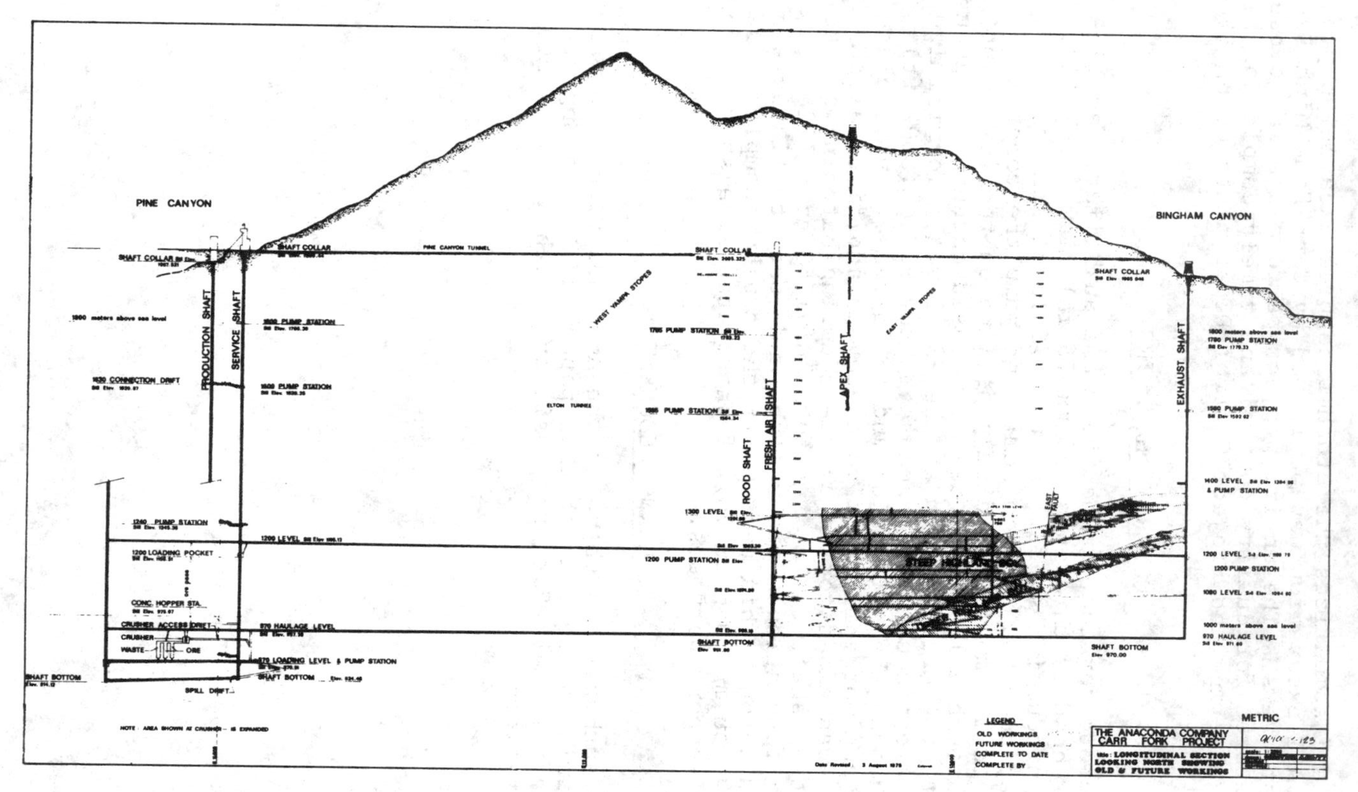

Fig. 1. Longitudinal Section

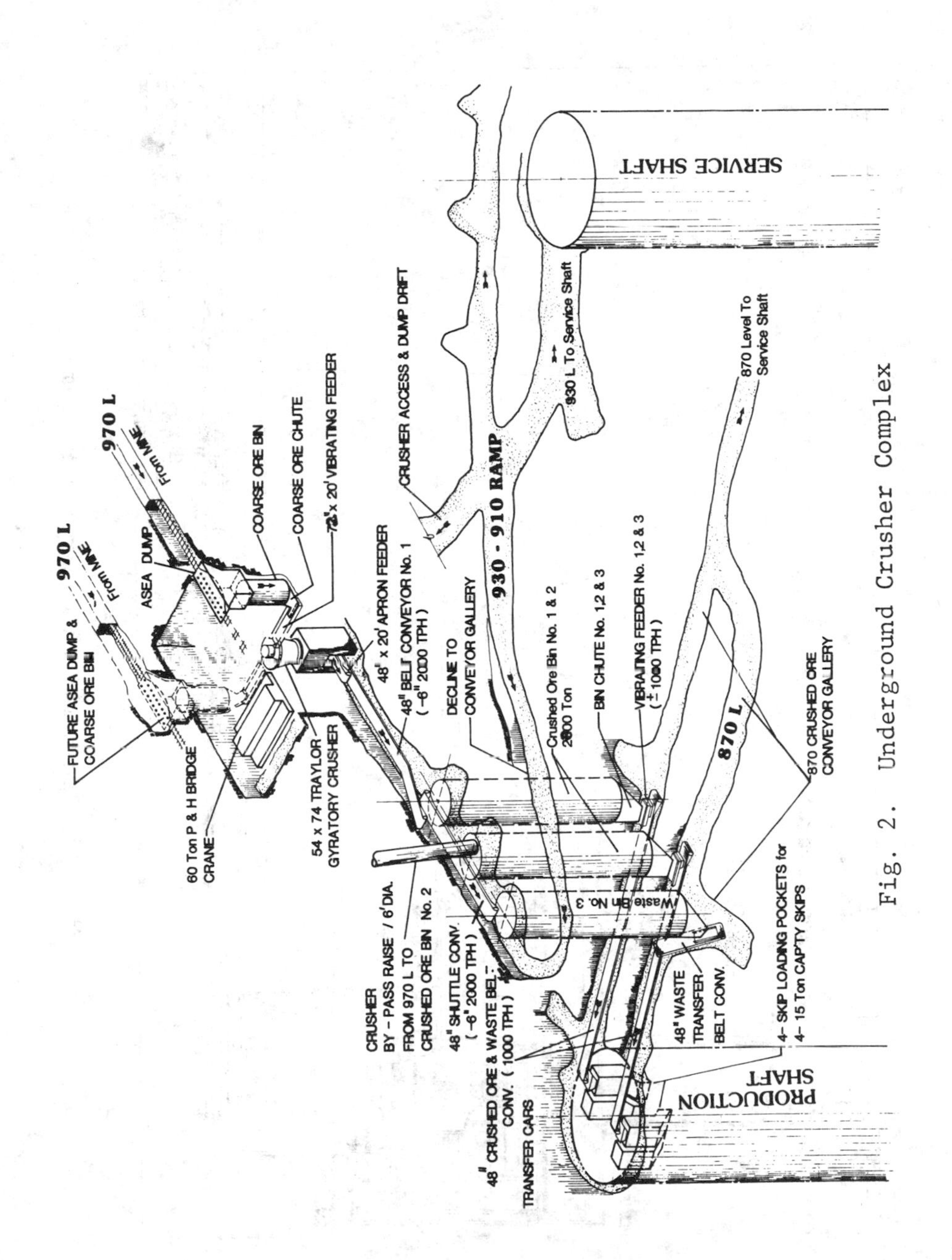

Fig. 2. Underground Crusher Complex

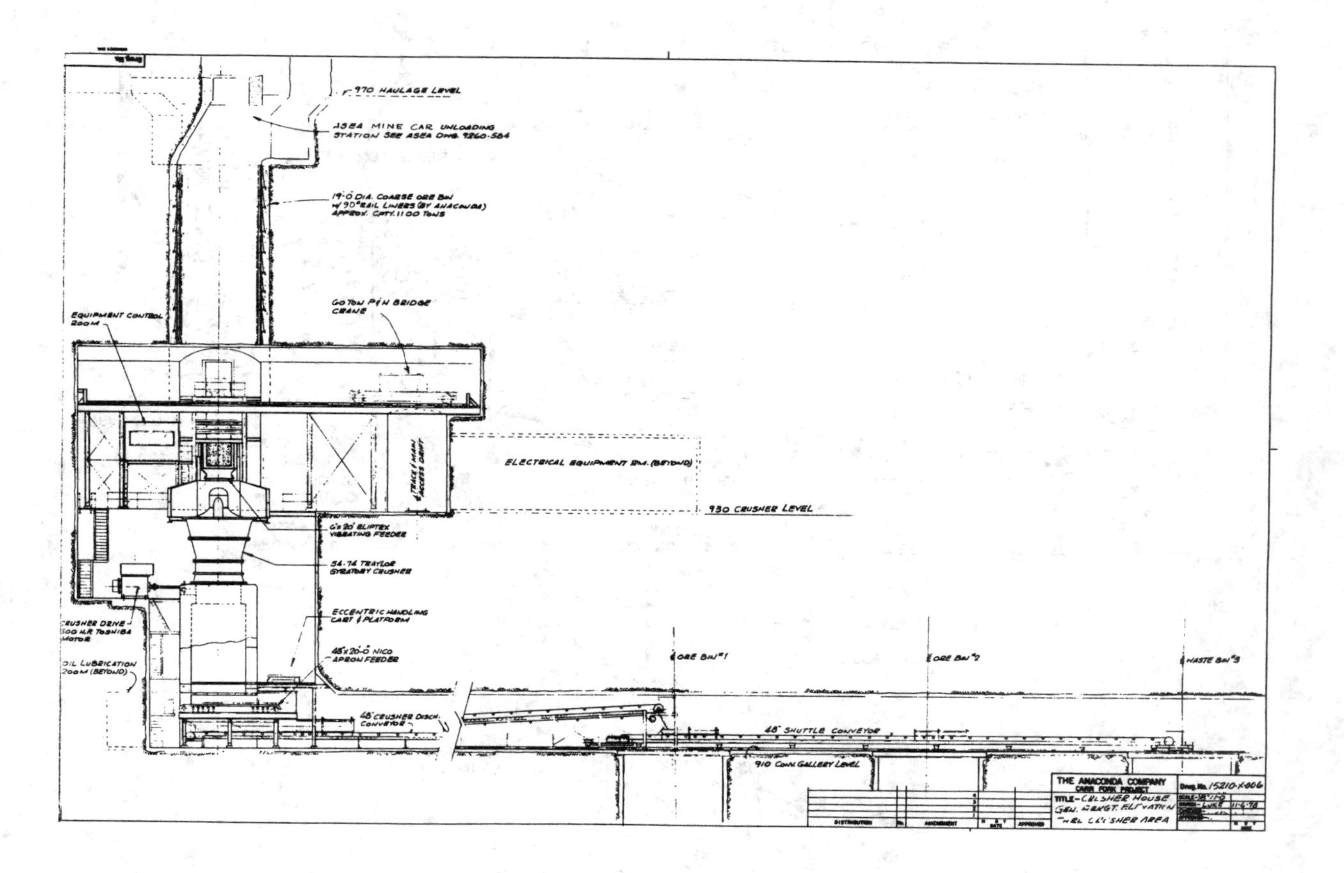

Fig. 3. Crusher Area General Arrangement

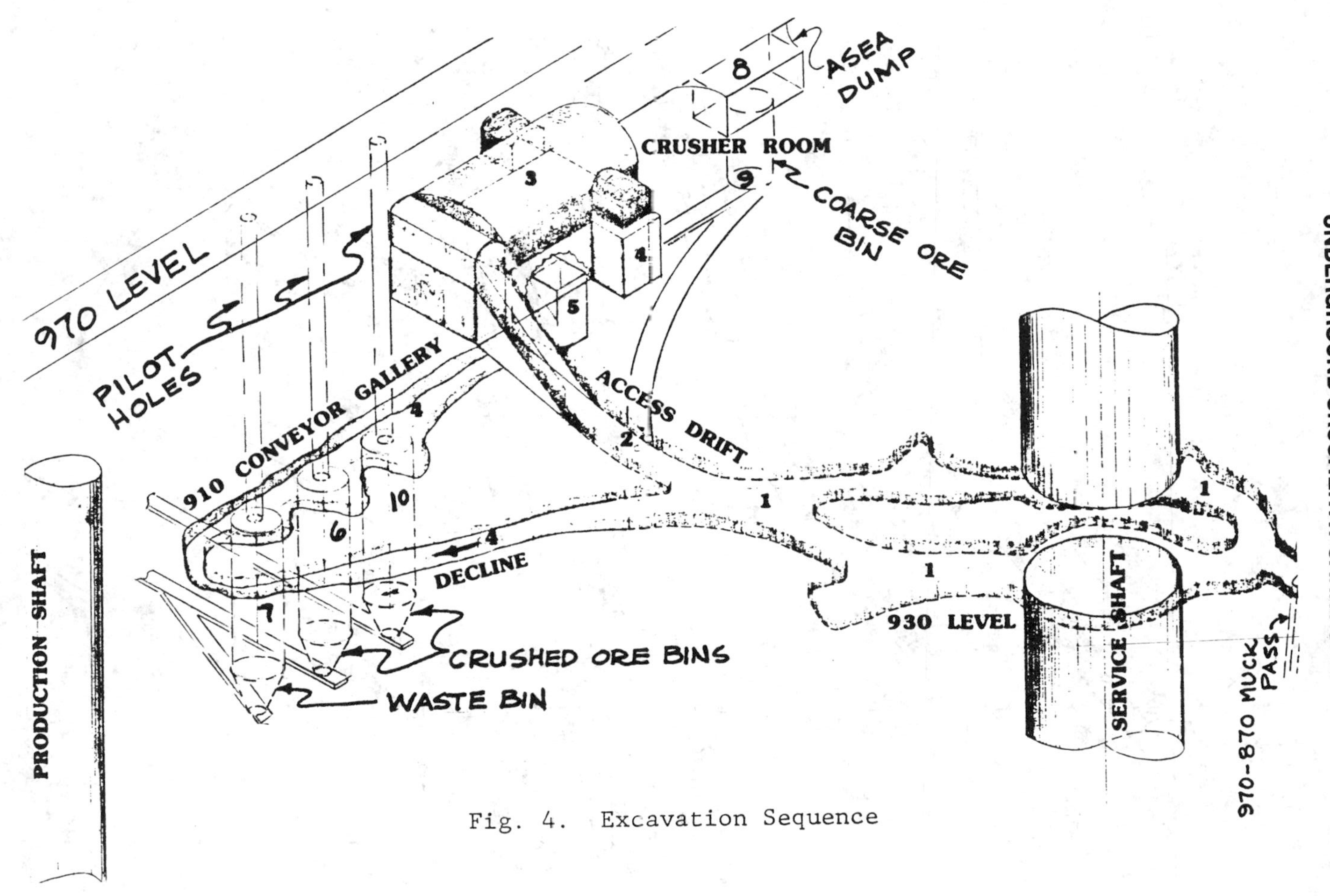

Fig. 4. Excavation Sequence

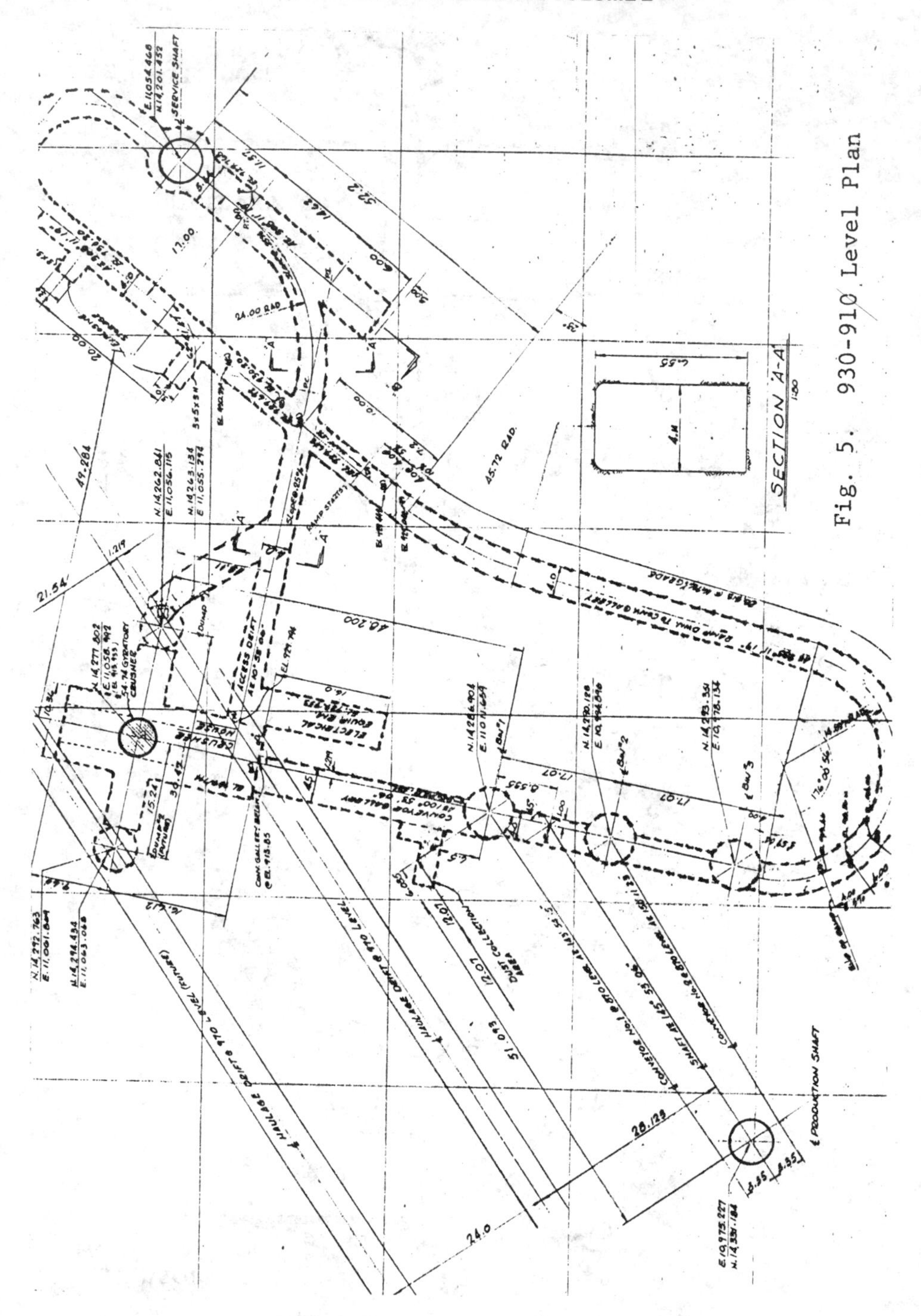

Fig. 5. 930-910 Level Plan

Chapter 68

VERTICAL RETREAT MINING

J.D. SCOTT

ONTARIO DIVISION OF INCO METALS COMPANY

This paper consists of a review of the development and application of spherical charge blasting at Inco Metals Company. Topics will include the Livingston Strain Equation, the field data required for its use in full scale operation, the type of ground in which mining has been carried out, explosives in use and their characteristics and finally, an overview of actual production applications. These applications include Primary Stope Mining, Secondary Mining Against Fill, Mining a Faulted Ore Zone and Drop Raise Blasting.

INTRODUCTION

Crater blasting in itself has been in use for over twenty years, but only recently has the technique been combined with a spherical size charge to form the Vertical Retreat Mining Method. This article endeavours to put the Livingston Strain Equation in a practical light, to describe several actual hard rock applications, and the results achieved in each case.

THE LIVINGSTON STRAIN ENERGY EQUATION

C.W. Livingston put forward the following equation as a standard means of determining the optimum burden required for full crater production blasting. The constant "E" is included in an attempt to recognize secondary breakage caused by strain waves.

The Formula Is Expressed As

$$d = \frac{d}{N} E \sqrt[3]{W} \qquad \text{or} \qquad d = \Delta E \sqrt[3]{W}$$

Where: d = depth to the center of gravity of charge in feet

N = the critical depth, the deepest point at which ground failure occurs and its value is estimated from field test results

$$\Delta = \frac{d}{N}$$

E = the strain energy factor and is calculated based on the estimated value of N

When: d = N

$$E = \frac{N}{\sqrt[3]{W}} \qquad (1)$$

In our original work with CIL, the field data was charted graphically after estimating the value of N from test blast results. The graph (Figure I), is required to confirm the optimum depth ratios and inturn d_o.

From experience we have come to believe that a graph of V/W VS d/W 1/3 will give good results, more directly in determining d_o and d_c for production use. Normally this graph takes the form as illustrated in Figure II.

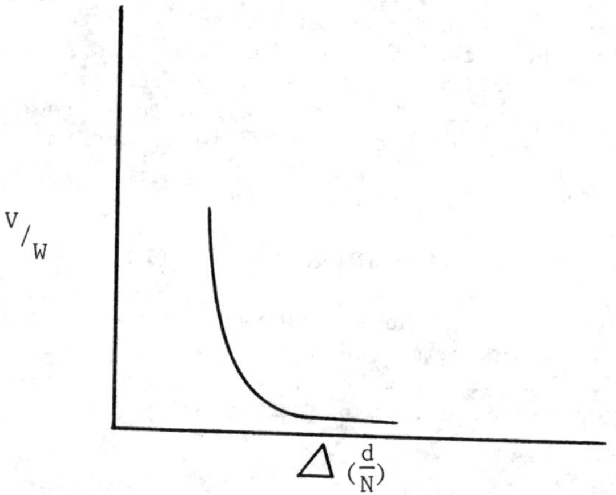

FIGURE I GRAPH BASED ON ORIGINAL TEST

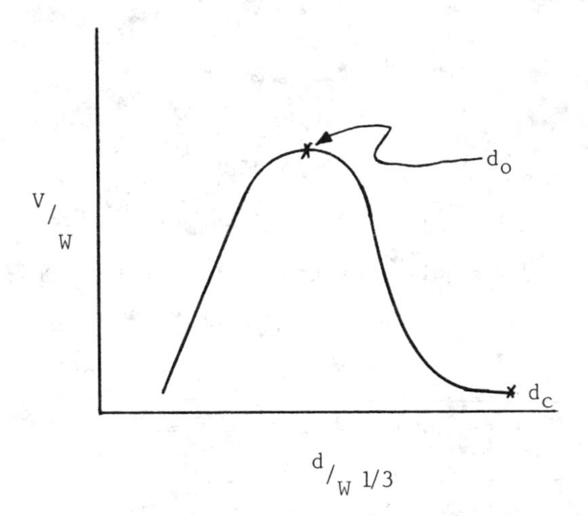

FIGURE II PLOT OF IDEAL TEST BLAST RESULTS

Charge weight in all of our applications has been sized at six times the hole diameter in order to retain spherical charge dimensions. This is not a requirement of Livingston's Equation.
Example: .9m (3 ft.) of M210 in a 165 mm (6½ in.) diameter hole equals 34 kg (75 lbs.)

THE FIELD DATA

Ideally, cratering tests should be carried out in a location that is representative of your proposed production area. The surface area must be large enough to accommodate a crater 3.35 m (10-12 ft.) in diameter, when using 5 kg (11 lbs.) of explosive in a 70 mm (2 3/4 in.) diameter hole.

Example A is a typical record of field results for 70 mm (2 3/4 in.) diameter holes blasted with 5.8 kg (12.8 lbs.) of explosive. The data recorded is depth to bottom of charge, depth to center of charge, average radius of cone base, depth of crater, the calculated crater volume and the values of V/W and $d/W^{1/3}$. A section drawing of the face to be blasted, recording the geology, is also useful when reviewing crater results for the causes of abnormal cone volumes, thus allowing knowledgeable adjustments to be made to the final graph. From the plot of V/W, $d/W^{1/3}$ we determine d_o and d_c, with the value of d_o and the full size charge weight we can now scale up to a production blast using the formula: -

$$d_p = Wp^{1/3} \frac{d_o}{W^{1/3}}$$

Wp = Production Charge

d_p = Distance to Center of Production Charge

d_o = Distance to Center of Test Charge

W = Test Charge Weight

EXAMPLE A. Typical Record Of Field Results

Hole Number	Depth To Bottom Of Hole	Depth To Center	Depth To Crater	Average Radius Crater	Crater Volume	V/W	$d/W^{1/3}$
1	8.75	7.75	0.92	2.22	4.75	0.37	3.3
2	8.00	7.00	1.10	1.56	2.80	0.22	3.0
3	7.50	6.25	0.50	2.94	4.52	0.35	2.7

EXPLOSIVE - HYDROMEX M210-U 12.8 Lbs.

Compressive And Tensile Strengths Of The Various Mined Material

	Greenstone	Norite	Sulphide	Quartz Diorite
Compressive	33,000 Pa* (48,000 psi)	17,250 Pa* (25,000 psi)	14,130 Pa* (20,500 psi)	22,475 Pa* (32,600 psi)
Tensile	1,170 Pa* (1,700 psi)	1,100 Pa* (1,600 psi)	895 Pa* (1,300 psi)	

* Pa x 10^4

EXPLOSIVES AND THEIR CHARACTERISTICS

Product	Velocity Of Detonation M/Sec. (Ft./Sec.)	Relative Bulk[1] Strength	Average Density
CIL Hydromex M-210	4,900 (16,200)	217	1.52
CIL Aquamex	4,600 (15,100)	178	1.56
CIL Procore III Primer	7,600 (25,000)		2
CIL Toe-Det Primer	7,300 (24,000)		2

1 These values are related to a standard AN/FO formula which has an assigned RWS and RDS value of 100 units. Standard AN/FO is defined as a mixture of prilled ammonium nitrate having 1% inert coating and 5.7% diesel oil resulting in a product with a density of 0.84 and an oxygen balance of -0.5% (½% by weight oxygen deficient).

2 454 g (1 pound) primers used

GEOLOGY OF THE NICKEL IRRUPTIVE

The examples of Vertical Retreat Mining described in this paper are all taken from the North Range of the Sudbury Nickel Irruptive, a unigue elliptically shaped layered intrusive with dimensions approximately 60 km by 25 km. The origin of this structure, although problematical, has been attributed to a large metecrite impact almost 2 billion years ago.

The economic Copper-Nickel mineralization in the areas described by this paper is restricted to the common sulphide assemblage pyrrhotite - pentlandite - chalcopyrite, although the relative quantities of Copper with respect to Nickel can vary significantly.

Two distinct sulphide environments are represented by the mining described herein. The first of these, "Granite Breccia" ore, is a local term applied to a leuocratic inclusion-bearing and metamorphic textured breccia containing variable quantities of the common sulphides as disseminations, blebs, "fragments", and stringers. Rock inclusions in this breccia range from very angular locally derived granite and mafic gneisses to well rounded "exotic" ultramafics. "Granite Breccia", located immediately below the norite of the Nickel Irruptive, is considered to be a member of the "sublayer" of the irruptive. The second ore type encountered consists of irregular and variably sized stringers of massive sulphide contained within the apparently fractured or fragmental local country rocks found immediately to the footwall of the "Granite Breccia" ore. Majority of such footwall rock in the mine environments is an irregularly banded feldspathic or granite gneiss. The sulphide stringers vary in composition from pyrrhotite - pentlandite to relatively pure chalcopyrite.

Structure was not a major consideration or influence in most of the VRM examples cited in this paper. Jointing, although common, had little significance. Minor slips and shears were also encountered. The one exception was 28 Stope on 1600 Level at Levack Mine, where the ore zone sat immediately to the hangingwall of the Fecunis Lake Fault, a major transverse fault with apparent horizontal displacement in the order of 488 m (1600 ft.). Because of the influence of this structure, the ore in 28 Stope was characterized by chlorite and quartz-carbonate filled fracturing and shearing.

PRODUCTION APPLICATIONS

Approximately 7% of the ore produced at the Levack Complex, is mined by the Vertical Retreat Mining Method. All blasting is under the control of the Engineering Department to ensure consistent quality.

The following examples show how the technique has been applied selectively to mine ore safely, and profitably in some cases where economics were questionable.

Coleman Mine - 1380 Stope

The block of ore in 1380 Stope, containing 43,265 tons of low grade material, was converted to Vertical Retreat Mining as it was considered uneconomic to mine by conventional Cut and Fill methods. The ore consists of pyrrhotite - pentlandite - chalcopyrite mineralization occurring as sulphide blebs, stringers and inclusion massive sulphide in a granite gneiss complex. Ground conditions in the development of this stope were good, with no major geological structures observed.

The drill sill was developed to 12.2 m x 4.6 m x 42.7 m, and three drawpoints were driven on the extraction level. Drilling consisted of 71 holes, only 11 of which were drilled to breakthrough. Breakage was slow at first, but once enough holes were slashed in, break averaged about 2.1 m per hole with a powder factor of .45 kg per ton.

The last 9.1 m of ground in the stope was loaded in 3 decks and blasted in one shot. Each deck consisted of three 140 mm diameter sacks of Aquamex and a slider primer for initiation (on a downline), with two 22.7 kg bags of mortar sand for stemming. All of the bottom charges were timed to ignite first, with #17 nonel caps placed in the sliders. The middle deck and top decks were delayed with #18 and #19 nonels respectively. Anodets, series 0-16 were attached to the downline at the collar of each hole, increasing in delay from the centre to both ends of the stope. The 0-16 collar delays and 17-19 deck delays were set so that when the first deck shot went off, all other holes were in the delay stage.

Approximately 10 tons of explosives were used in the crown blast. By having both horizontal and vertical delays, only 295 kg of explosives detonated at any one time. There was no damage to the underground installations from the blast and a blast vibration survey showed peak particle velocities (ppv's) of 30 mm per second, 28 m away and 11 mm per second, 152.4 m away.

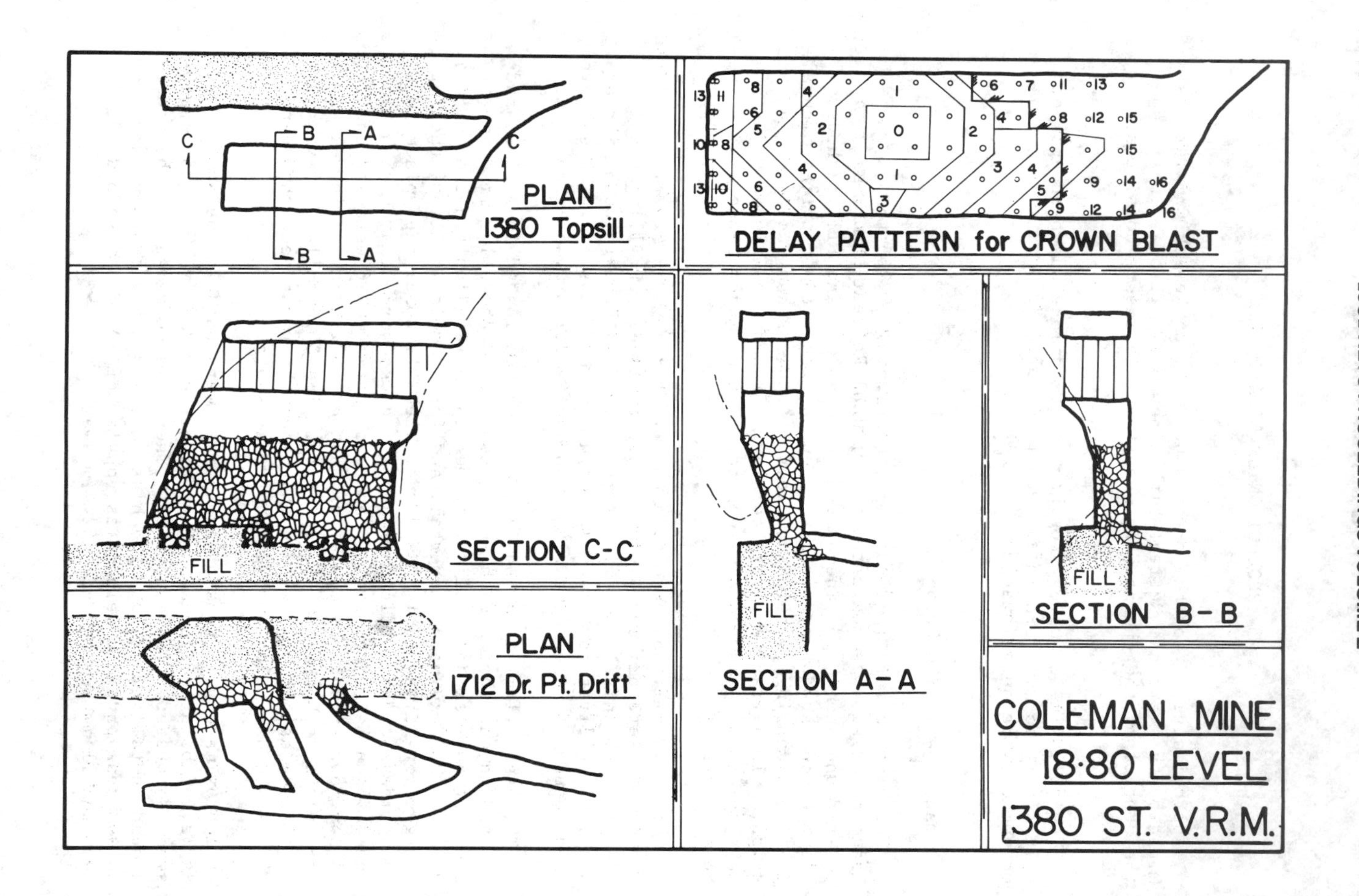
PLAN
1380 Topsill
DELAY PATTERN for CROWN BLAST
SECTION C-C
FILL
SECTION A-A
FILL
SECTION B-B
FILL
PLAN
1712 Dr. Pt. Drift
COLEMAN MINE
18·80 LEVEL
1380 ST. V.R.M.

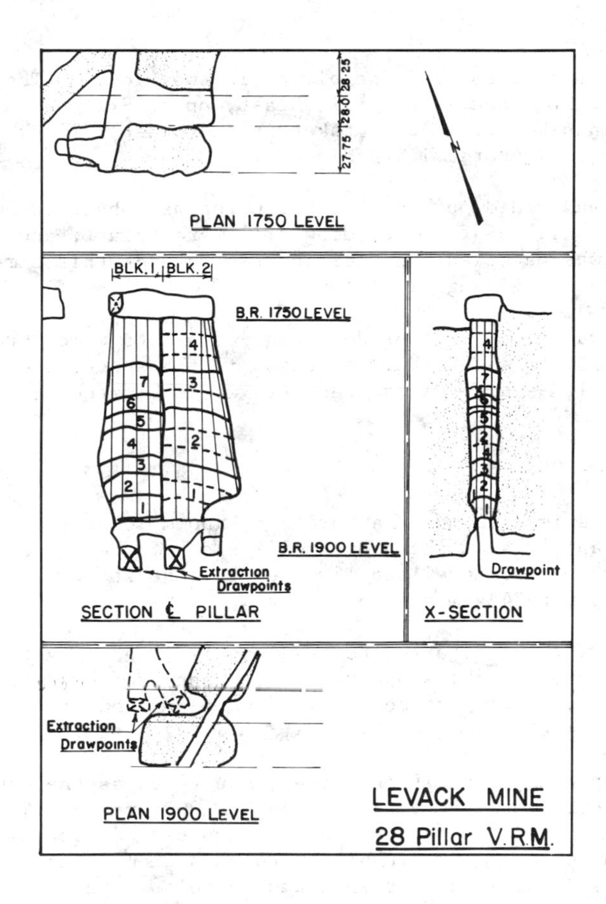

Levack Mine - 28 Pillar

28 Pillar measured 4.9 m x 24.4 m x 40.2 m and was situated between two mined out cut and fill stopes located on 1900 Level. The stopes had been filled with 30:1 cemented mill tailings with a high pyrrhotite content. The walls of the pillar were irregular, and the ground was badly fractured.

In all previous mining of Vertical Retreat pillars between stopes with cemented sandfill, the greatest vertical height mined was 24.4 m. Since 28 Pillar was 40.2 m high, the free standing fill left in this pillar after mining would be higher than in any previous Vertical Retreat Mining pillar.

Plans were made to mine the pillar in two blocks. The first block was to be mined in a single blast, up to 9.1 m from 1750 Level, and the remaining 9.1 m crown taken in one blast. Block 1 would then be filled, before mining block 2.

Block 1 was mined out, no fill dilution was observed in the draw-points, the walls of free standing fill were intact, and no heating of Po fill was detected. A decision was made at this time, to mine Block 2 without filling Block 1.

Block 2 was mined in four deck-charged blasts which broke an average of 10.1 m each. Fill dilution in the second block was approximately 12% and final ore recovery was estimated at 95%.

Levack Mine - 28.0 Stope

28.0 Stope is located in an ore zone known locally as "Bouclin's Ore Body", and lies on the hangingwall side of the Fecunis Lake fault, between 1500 Level and 1600 Level. The stope measures approximately 15.2 m x 24.4 m x 30.5 m.

In 1975, work was started to develop the area for Vertical Retreat Mining. Mucking of the stope was to be done by a captive scooptram, which would muck from drawpoints into cars in a haulage drift on 1600 Level.

Very poor ground conditions were encountered as the haulage drifts advanced into the faulted area on 1500 and 1600 Levels. Due to the poor ground conditions, the plan to use scooptrams for mucking was changed in favour of slushing into cars from a slusher trench and boxholes. The slusher trench and boxholes were driven, bolted and screened, and reinforced with 2.1 m rebar and resin.

Bottom silling was started on 1600 Level, and had to be stopped due to dangerous ground conditions. The mining plan was reviewed again and plans were made to open up the bottom sill by crater blasting.

The bottom sill was opened up at the centre boxhole by cratering to a height of 3 m above the boxhole and then slashing into the opening on each side until the other two boxholes were reached. Blasting was then continued in single deck charges up to 9.1 m from 1500 Level. The remaining 9.1 m was triple-deck charged and taken in one blast.

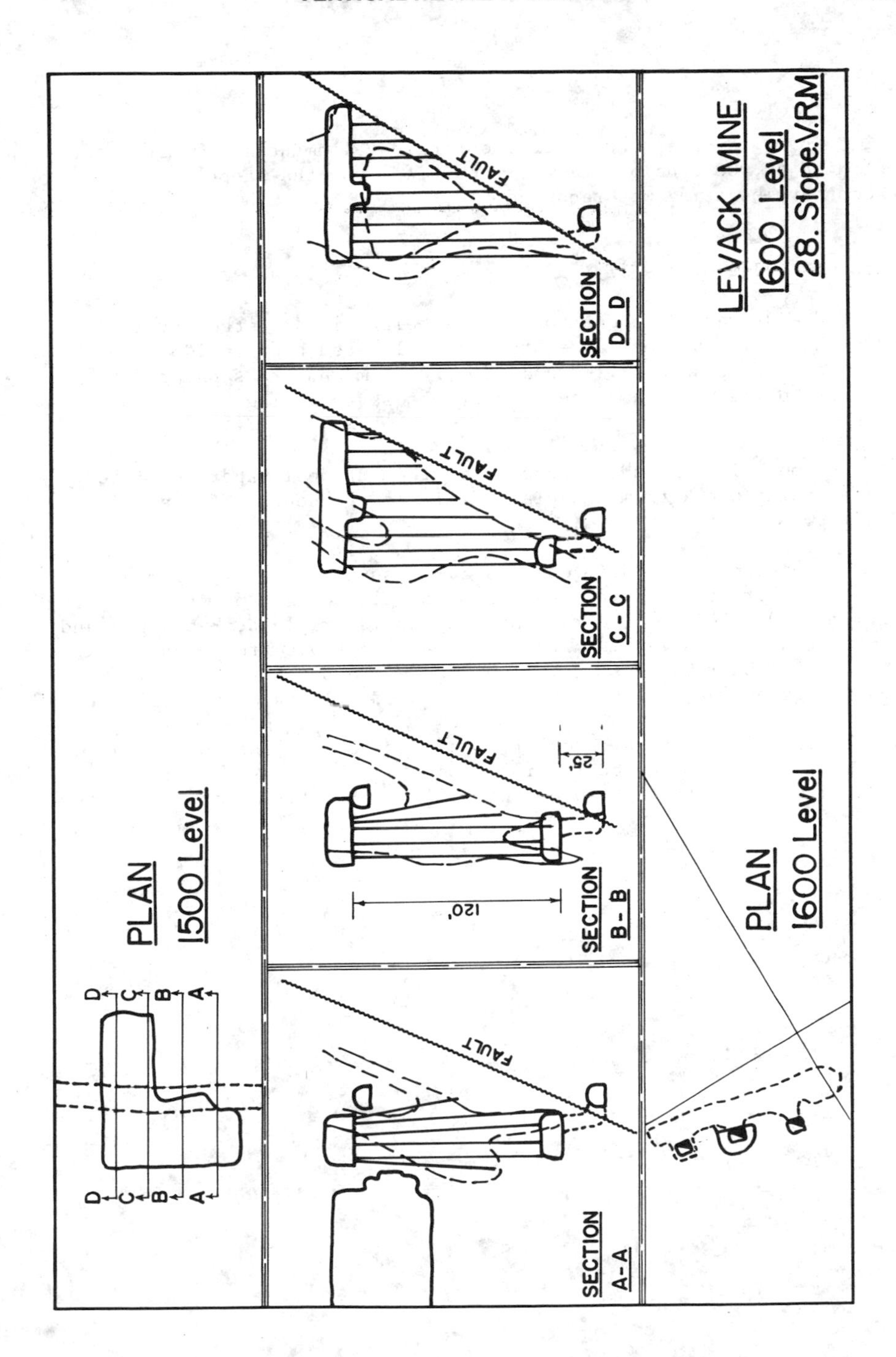
LEVACK MINE
1600 Level
28. Stope.V.R.M.
PLAN
1500 Level
PLAN
1600 Level
SECTION A-A
SECTION B-B
SECTION C-C
SECTION D-D
FAULT
FAULT
FAULT
FAULT
120'
25'
A
B
C
D

Despite reverses encountered during development and mining, the planned 40,000 tons of ore was recovered from the stope, and no secondary blasting was required.

McCreedy West Mine - 51 & 52 Stopes

McCreedy West Mine has two stopes being mined by the Vertical Retreat Mining Method. The stopes are located between 1080 and 950 Levels, measure 12.2 m x 33.5 m x 122 m and are separated by a 9.1 m pillar. Each stope consists of seven mining blocks 18.2 m long.

The muck is removed by scooptrams from drawpoints driven into each mining block from a haulage drift in the centre of the pillar on 1080 Level.

Mining blocks are drilled on a 3.0 m square pattern, from 950 Level and are blasted in a series of single charged blasts to within 9.1 m of 950 Level. The remaining crown is triple-deck-charged and detonated as one blast. After the ore is removed from each block, a sandfill barricade is installed in the drawpoint and the block is filled hydraulically with 23:1 cemented alluvial sand fill.

In the first blocks, some ore loss occurred in the form of a skin of ore alongside previously filled blocks. This was remedied by reducing the distance between the fill and the first line of holes to 1.5 m.

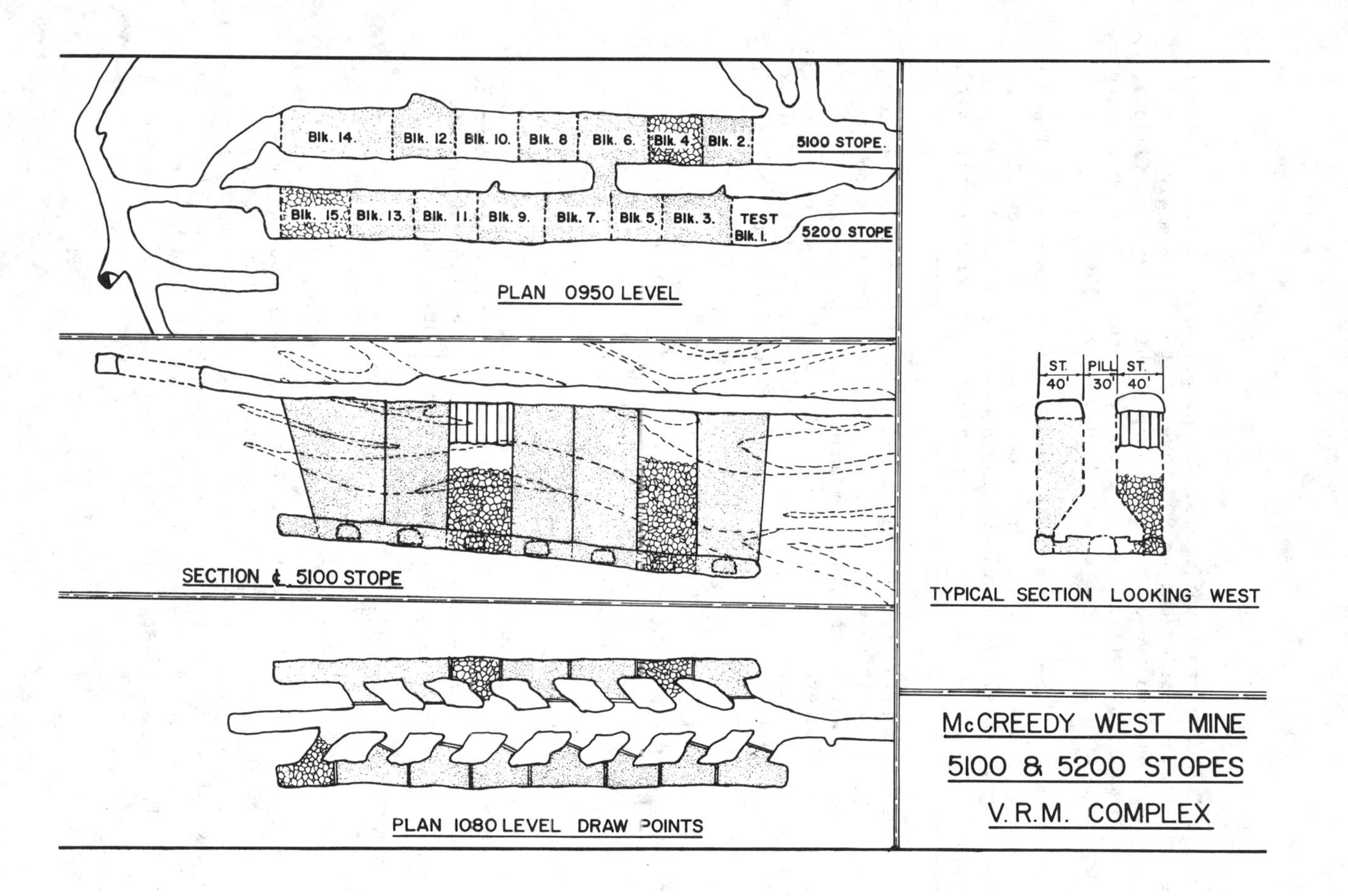
Blk. 14.
Blk. 12.
Blk. 10.
Blk. 8
Blk. 6.
Blk. 4
Blk. 2.
5100 STOPE.
Blk. 15.
Blk. 13.
Blk. 11.
Blk. 9.
Blk. 7.
Blk. 5
Blk. 3.
TEST
Blk. 1.
5200 STOPE
PLAN 0950 LEVEL
SECTION ℄ 5100 STOPE
PLAN 1080 LEVEL DRAW POINTS
ST.
40'
PILL
30'
ST.
40'
TYPICAL SECTION LOOKING WEST
McCREEDY WEST MINE
5100 & 5200 STOPES
V.R.M. COMPLEX

Levack Mine - No. 2 Pillar

No. 2 Pillar is an experimental V.R.M. pillar recovery application presently being carried out on 900 Level. It is 12.2 m wide and is situated between two 30.5 m wide stopes which have been filled with rock and gravel fill. It is typical of the pillars which make up the remaining ore in the Levack Main Ore Body.

Drifts were driven in the center of the pillar on 700 Level and 900 Level. A 6.1 m block was drilled off at the hangingwall in three rings, spaced 3.0 m apart. The holes were drilled on a pattern designed to leave a 2.1 m skin of ore against the gravel fill, after blasting.

If the 2.1 m skin of ore fails during blasting, any fill running into the pillar will show up as dilution at the drawpoint on 900 Level. Mining will be stopped immediately and the block will be filled from 700 Level, through the drill holes, with cement sandfill. Upon successful mining of block 1, the block will be filled. Block 2 will then be drilled off so that a 1.5 m skin of ore will be left against the gravel.

This is the first time that Vertical Retreat Mining has been carried out in a pillar between gravel filled stopes and at this time Block 1 has been successfully mined out.

Levack Mine - 0231 Drop Raise

In order to carry out the development of the previously mentioned No. 2 Pillar, a finger raise from 900 Level was required to connect into the existing 2.1 m diameter bored raise. A plan was devised to apply our knowledge of Vertical Retreat Blasting Methods.

Using a 100 mm diameter I.T.H. drill, six 113 mm diameter holes were drilled within a 1.5 m square. The average hole depth was 12.8m, the total length of hole drilled was 765 m.

The five holes to be blasted were blocked with wooden plugs, the top of each plug being located .78 m from the bottom of the hole. Four 89 mm cartridges of Aquamex, 14.5 kg were placed in five of the six holes. Each blast consisted of a total of 72 kg of blasting agent where at the 6:1 ratio the minimum charge could have been 52 kg. The center of each charge was located 1.4 m from the bottom of the hole. The raise was blasted seven times advancing 1.8 m per blast.

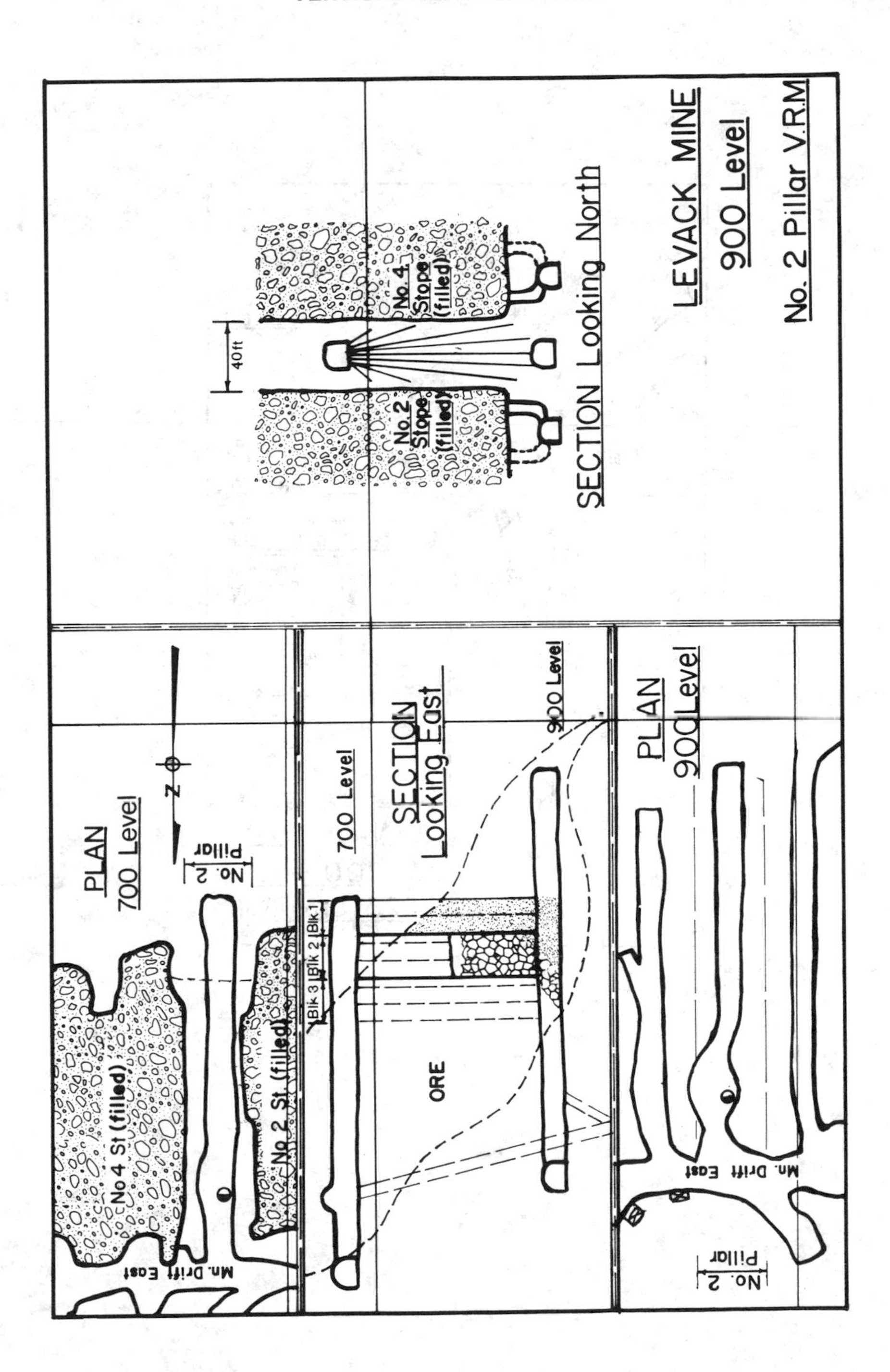
LEVACK MINE
900 Level
No. 2 Pillar V.R.M
SECTION Looking North
No. 4 Stope (filled)
No. 2 Stope (filled)
40ft
PLAN
700 Level
N
No. 2 Pillar
No 4 St (filled)
No 2 St (filled)
Mn. Drift East
Blk 3
Blk 2
Blk 1
700 Level
SECTION
Looking East
900 Level
ORE
PLAN
900 Level
Mn. Drift East
No. 2 Pillar

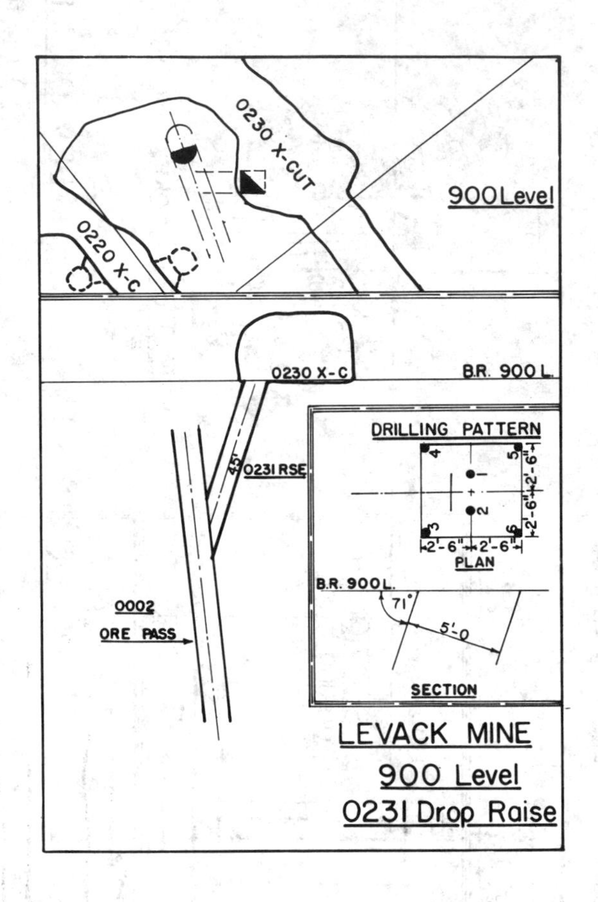
0230 X-CUT
900 Level
0220 X-C
0230 X-C
B.R. 900 L.
DRILLING PATTERN
0231 RSE
45°
2'-6"
2'-6"
PLAN
B.R. 900 L.
71°
5'-0
0002
ORE PASS
SECTION
LEVACK MINE
900 Level
0231 Drop Raise

REFERENCES

Bauer, A., January, 1961, "Application of the Livingston Theory" QUARTERLY OF THE COLORADO SCHOOL OF MINES, Volume 56, No. 1.

Grant, C.H., November, 1964, "Simplified Explanation of Crater Method", ENGINEERING AND MINING JOURNAL, Volume 165, No. 11, pp. 86-89.

Lang, L.C., "The Basic Principles of Cratering and the Results of Spherical Charge Blasting at Levack Mine", CANADIAN PATENT APPLICATION, Serial No. 231, 434.

Pfleider, E.P., 1968, "Surface Mining" First Edition by THE AMERICAN INSTITUTE OF MINING, METALLURGICAL, AND PETROLEUM ENGINEERS, INC.

Starfield, A.M., "Strain Wave Theory In Rock Blasting", EIGHTH SYMPOSIUM ON ROCK MECHANICS, FAILURE & BREAKAGE OF ROCK.

Chapter 69

STABILITY ASSESSMENT OF A WIDE STOPE EXCAVATION IN A LEAD-ZINC MINE

by P. R. Sheorey, D. Barat & B. Singh

Central Mining Research Station
Dhanbad, Bihar, India

ABSTRACT

Presented is a stability analysis for a trial stope in a lead-zinc mine. The trial stope would have an excavation width of 20 m with an initial height of 3 m. Filling would commence when the stope was heightened to 6 m. A two-pronged approach to predict the stability of such an opening was used viz. the finite element method and the rock mass classification method. Corroboration is shown to exist between the two methods. Deep borehole extensometer observations during stope extraction have been compared with predicted displacements.

INTRODUCTION

A trial stope was proposed by the Hindusthan Zinc Ltd. at their Rajpura Dariba Mine. The orebody consists of zinc, lead and copper mineralisation, the hangwall is graphite mica schist and the footwall is made up of calcareous biotite schist. The dip of the orebody is 50°-80° due East and there is a major thrust above the working area.

The proposed trial stope is located between 400 and 444 MRL with an excavation width of 20 m and an initial height of 3 m. After heightening the stope of 6 m, the first 3 m would be filled. A section of the proposed workings is shown in Fig. 1.

It was decided to use a two-pronged method for estimating the stability of the 20-m wide opening at two differ-

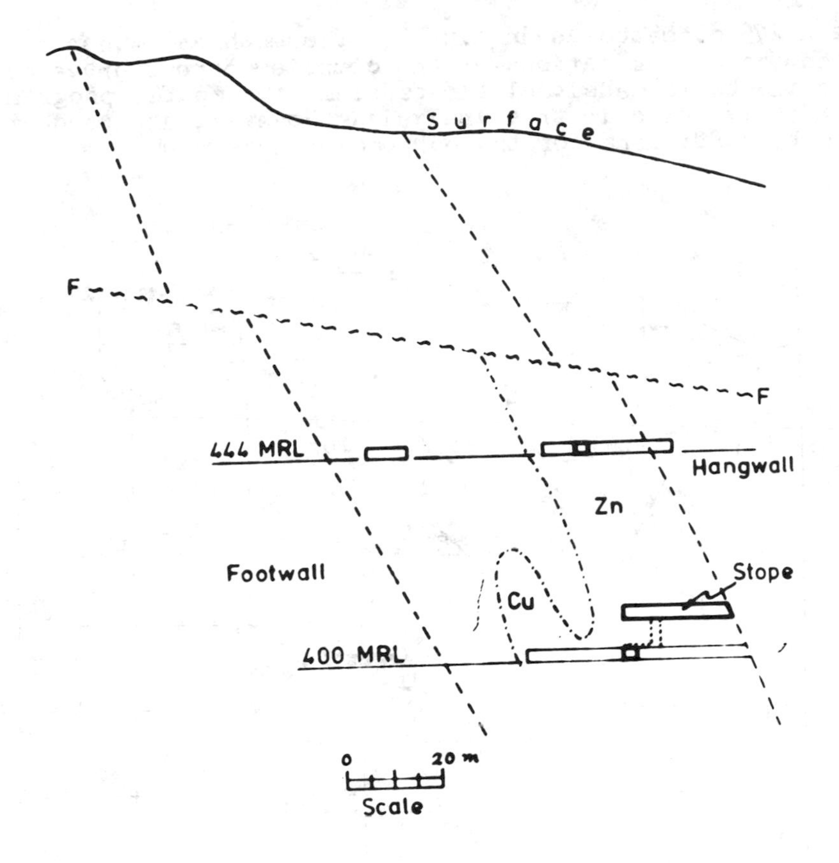

Fig. 1. A section of the proposed workings of trial stope at Rajpura Dariba.

ent heights, 3 m and 6 m. Firstly, the stresses in the stope back would be estimated using the two-dimensional finite element method, giving the safety factor of the stope back. Secondly, the method of rock classification would be applied determining the distribution and nature of joints in the area and the R.Q.D. (rock quality designation) of the rock.

ANALYSIS BY THE FINITE ELEMENT METHOD

The area under consideration was discretised into triangular and quadrilateral elements, giving 149 nodes and 175 elements as in Fig. 2. The mesh is rather coarse because of limitations on the computer core storage due to the two-dimensional finite element computer program which was used in this analysis. However, it was deemed to be sufficient for the purpose of this work.

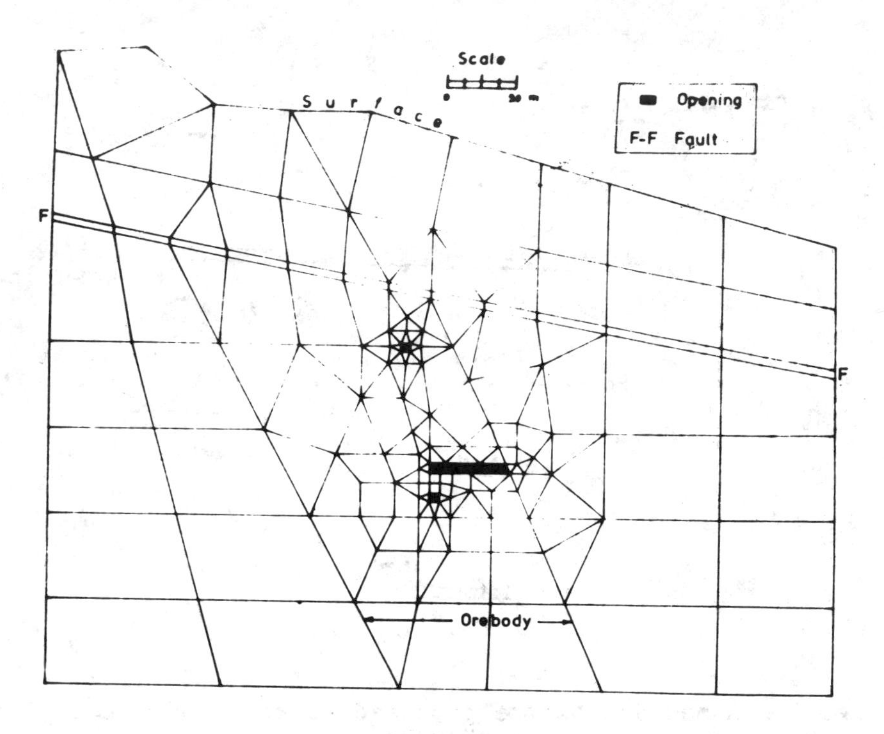

Fig. 2. Finite element model of the workings in Fig. 1.

For gravity and virgin stresses, the "Gravity turn-on" analysis was used in which the gravitation is due to the weight of the rock mass itself and the virgin stress field at a point is given by

$$\sigma_x = \frac{\mu}{1-\mu}\rho h \ , \quad \sigma_y = \rho h$$

where σ_x, σ_y are horizontal and vertical virgin stresses, μ is Poisson's ratio, ρ is the pressure per unit depth and h is the depth of the element centroid.

ESTIMATION OF MATERIAL PROPERTIES FOR THE ANALYSIS

The finite element model of Fig. 2 includes four different material types:

1. Footwall rock
2. Lode
3. Hangwall rock
4. Fault material

The laboratory values of elastic modulus and compressive strength for the four material types were reduced to estimated in situ rock mass properties by the following procedure.

(A) From the geological plan of 444 M.R.L. the joints could be grouped as

Joint spacing	% of total No. of joints
0.1 m to 1 m	21
1 m to 10 m	72
Greater than 10 m	7

It is seen that a majority fall in the group 1 m to 10 m which shows that the rock mass is not highly jointed. Fig. 3A (C.S.I.R. Report, 1971) shows that the reduction in compressive strength from laboratory to in situ will be 20-40% (say, 30%).

(B) The average RQD values obtained from the logs of two boreholes drilled in the stope area were:

Hole	RQD
BH-1	73.7
BH-2	70.6

For these RQD values (which are more or less the same) Fig. 3B (Deere et al, 1966) gives the reduction in the elastic moduli from laboratory to in situ values as about 70%.

The fault material has been simulated as softer than the other three rock types. For this the average of the elastic moduli of the three rock types was reduced by 10 times to give the value for the fault material. The fault has not been simulated as a series of shearing Goodman elements (Goodman et al, 1968) but as a meterial significantly softer than the parent rock (Zienkiewicz, 1977).

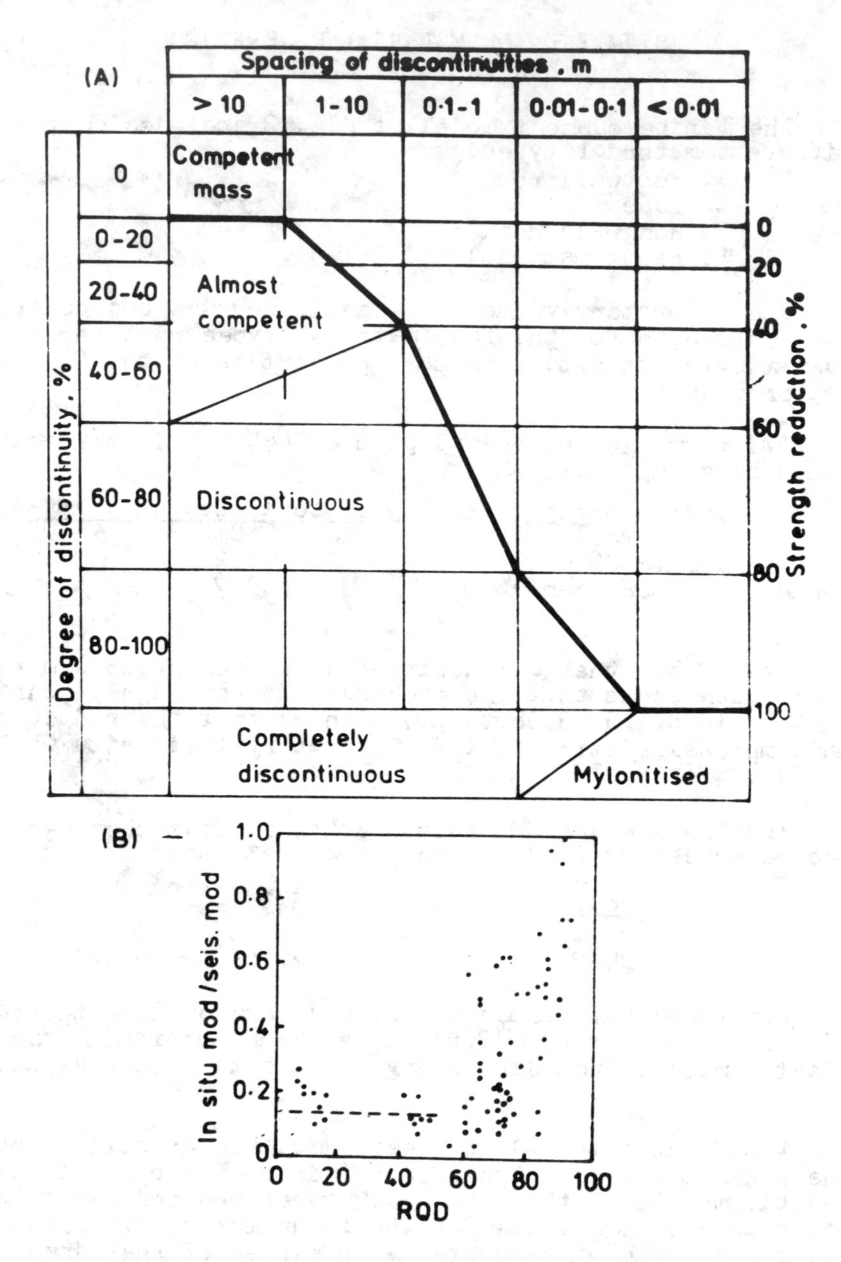

Fig. 3. Influence of (A) joint spacing on compressive strength, (B) RQD on elastic modulus of a rock mass.

The original laboratory and estimated in situ rock mass properties are given in Table 1.

TABLE 1. Lab and in situ properties of four material types.

Material type	Lab. value x10^5 kN/m^2		In situ value x10^4 kN/m^2	
	Compressive strength	Elastic modulus	Compressive strength	Elastic modulus
1. Footwall	1.173	260	8.21	780
2. Lode	1.500	342	10.50	1030
3. Hangwall	1.008	297	7.05	891
4. Fault zone	-	-	-	90

ANALYSIS OF COMPUTER RESULTS

The principal stresses obtained from the computer results are shown plotted in Fig. 4. Heightening of the roof from 3 m to 6 m reduces the oblongness of the opening, causing an overall reduction of the stress levels but stope sides have less confinement. This indicates the need for filling (though not at the stage of 6 m) as heightening further would further weaken the sides.

Some of the critical elements of Fig. 4 (numbered 64, 67,70,76) were considered for stability analysis as given below. The principal stresses were plotted as Mohr circles (Fig. 5). The failure envelops for orebody and hangwall were obtained from the in situ compressive and tensile strength values. Because of insufficiency of core samples only a few scanty tensile tests were done. These indicated that the ratio of compressive to tensile strength could be roughly taken as 6.

The ordinate intercept of the failure envelop gives the cohesive strength. Its ratio to the intercept obtained from parallel envelops drawn tangential to the principal stress circle of an element gives the safety factor of that element (Sheorey and Dunham, 1978). When the safety factor is negative, i.e. when an envelop has a negative intercept, or when it is greater than 3.0, the

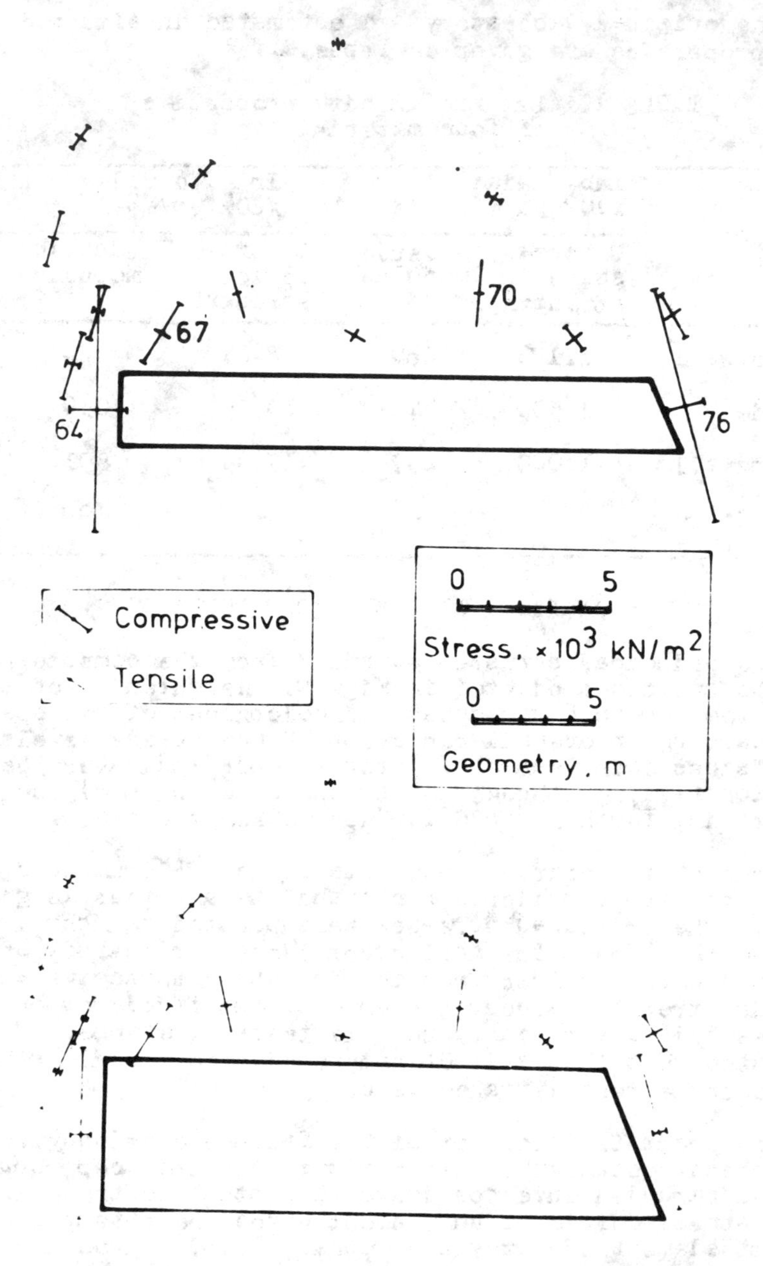

Fig. 4. Principal stresses in the stope back and sides.

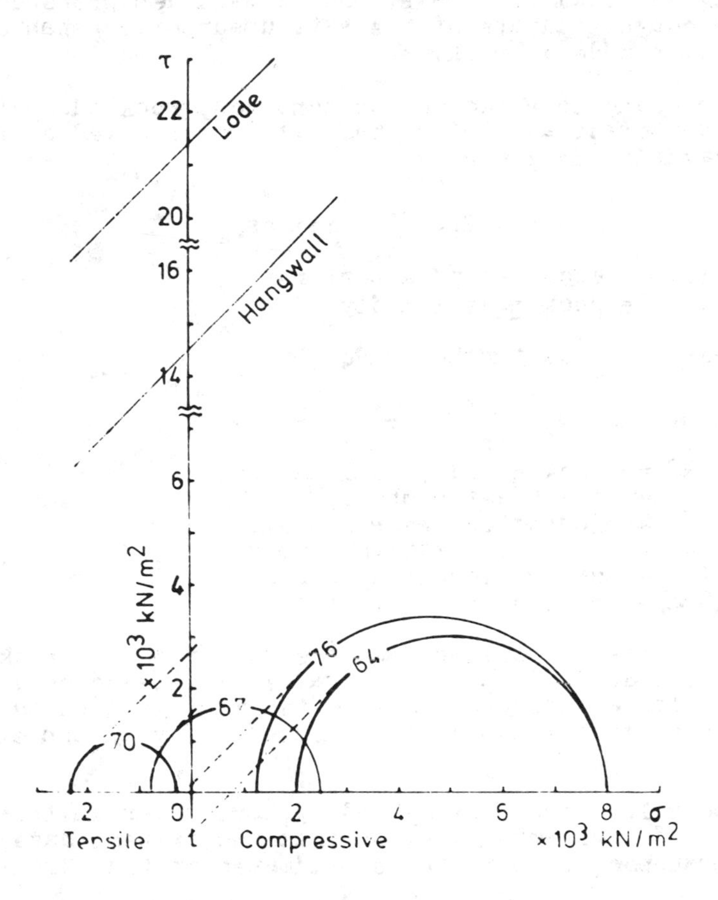

Fig. 5. Safety factor estimation from element stresses using the Mohr-Coulomb failure criterion.

element can be considered stable. This procedure gave a safety factor value of about 8 as the lowest, all other values being higher. This high safety factor is due to the high strength of the rock mass and low stress levels.

ESTIMATION OF SAFE STOPE WIDTH BY ROCK MASS CLASSIFICATION

A geological rock mass, when classified properly, can give a rough estimate of the safe unsupported span of an excavation made in rock.

According to a recent geomechanical rock classification (Barton et al, 1974), the safe unsupported span W of an excavation is given by

$$W = 2\ E_{sr} Q^{0.4} \text{ metres}$$

where E_{sr} = excavation support ratio,
and Q = rock mass quality.

The latter is further given by

$$Q = \frac{RQD}{J_n} \cdot \frac{J_r}{J_a} \cdot \frac{J_w}{SRF}$$

where RQD = rock quality designation,
J_n = joint set number,
J_r = joint roughness number,
J_a = joint alteration number,
J_w = water reduction number
and SRF = stress reduction factor.

These six factors and E_{sr} are given for the rock in this stope in Table 2. These values are based on visual observation and discussion with the mine geologists, and correspond to the table of values given by Barton et al (1974).

Two values each for J_r and E_{sr} are given in this table because of some ambiguity, so that two extreme cases of safe unsupported span can be estimated in this instance:

(1) $$Q = \frac{70}{1.0} \times \frac{3.0}{2.0} \times \frac{1.0}{1.0} = 105$$

$$W = 2 \times 5\ (105)^{0.4} = 64 \text{ metres}$$

(2) $$Q = \frac{70}{1.0} \times \frac{2.0}{2.0} \times \frac{1.0}{1.0} = 70$$

$$W = 2 \times 3\ (70)^{0.4} = 33 \text{ metres}$$

TABLE 2. Factors for estimating rock mass quality and safe unsupported span of stope.

Factor	Description for rock	Value	
RQD	Rock quality designation (obtained from boreholes)	70	
J_n	Sparse jointing	1.0	
J_r	(a) Rough undulating joints (b) Smooth undulating joints	3.0 2.0	
J_a	Slightly altered joint walls, non-softening mineral coating, sandy particles, clay-free disintegrated rock etc.	2.0	
J_w	Dry excavation or minor inflow of water, less than 5 litres/min. locally	1.0	
SRF	(a) High stress (b) Medium stress	0.5-2.0 1.0	1.0
E_{sr}	Temporary mine openings in rock	3 - 5	

The formula given for the safe unsupported span is based on a large number of observations on tunnels of circular and arch-shaped sections, so the estimate for oblong rectangular openings like this stope can only be accepted with reserve. However, the estimated values do support the high element safety factor for the stope back obtained earlier by the finite element analysis, when the stope width is 20 m.

COMPARISON WITH EXTENSOMETER OBSERVATIONS

Multipoint borehole extensometers with four anchors each were installed from the levels at 444 M.R.L. to the proposed stope back to a depth of about 30 m. Observations for displacements were taken for about a year. The maximum displacements obtained were only about 0.6 mm when the stope reached the width of 20 m. The displacements were measured with respect to the collar at the borehole mouth.

The maximum displacements predicted by the finite element run came out to be 1.95 mm. The predicted values are somewhat on a higher side, probably because of the approximate method used for estimating rock mass properties and a few scanty pillars being left in the stope. The movements are, however, too small to make a proper comparison.

It must be mentioned here that finite element runs with time-dependent properties could not be undertaken, so that the displacements predicted are only first approximations. But since the values are quite small, because of the low stress levels, it was felt that time-dependence could be neglected.

CONCLUSION

The finite element analysis was done neglecting planar anisotropy if any in the rock mass and assuming horizontal and vertical virgin stresses. The analysis was, therefore, only a first approximation. The in situ moduli and strength were estimated considering the RQD and joint spacing of the rock mass. In situ testing to determine these properties would have yielded more realistic values, but could not be undertaken for several reasons. The method of rock classification, nevertheless, gives the safe unsupported span as 33 m to 64 m, which confirms the high safety factor for the 20-m stope obtained by the finite element method.

REFERENCES

Anon, 1971, "Properties and Classification of Rock with Reference to Tunneling", MEG 1020, National Mechanical Engineering Research Institute, Pretoria, South Africa.

Barton, N., Lien, R., and Lunde, J., 1974, "Engineering Classification of Rock Masses for the Design of Tunnel Support", Rock Mechanics, Vol. 6, pp.189-236.

Deere, D.U., et al., 1966, "Design of Surface and Near Surface Construction in Rock", Proceedings, 8th Symposium on Rock Mechanics, Minnesota.

Goodman, R.E., et al., 1968, " A Model for the Mechanics of Jointed Rock", Proceedings, American Society of Civil Engineers, Vol. 94, SM3, pp. 637-659.

Sheorey, P.R., and Dunham, R.K., 1978, "An Approximate Analysis of Floor Heave Occurring in Roadways behind Advancing Longwall Faces", International Journal of Rock Mechanics and Mining Sciences and Geomechanics Abstracts, Vol. 15, pp. 277-288.

Zienkiewicz, O.C., 1977. The Finite Element Method, McGraw Hill, p. 490.

Chapter 70

PILLAR RECOVERY AT OZARK LEAD COMPANY

By Jack Bradbury

Production Engineer, Ozark Lead Company

Sweetwater, Missouri

ABSTRACT

The open stope room and pillar method of mining is used throughout Ozark Lead Company's underground mine located at Sweetwater, Missouri. This method of mining produces an approximate overall ore extraction of 80%. Pillar recovery, on a limited and experimental basis, was started in January of 1979 to determine the maximum size underground opening that could be mined safely. Monitoring the roof and surrounding pillars for potential failure during this pillar recovery process was accomplished by utilizing a simple rod extensometer to measure roof sag. Boreholes 7.5cm in diameter were drilled 3.5m into the roof to spot any separations or cracks that might have propagated between the bedded layers of rock. Underground openings 85m in length by 46m in width have been mined successfully without roof or surrounding pillar failure. Continued measurements to establish long term results will be necessary.

INTRODUCTION

Ozark Lead Company (OLC) is located near Bunker in southeast Missouri. Lead, zinc, and copper ores are mined within the Bonne-Terre formation in several different mining levels with lead ore being the most significant product. Room and pillar mining is the method that is used at OLC. Standard pillars are 8.5m square and mining drifts are 9.8m wide. Mining heights vary from 4.5m to over 16m. The mine workings are about 305m deep in undulating multiple level mining zones. Overall mine production is scheduled for 6000-6500 TPD. Many times the ore that is left in these pillars is higher grade than the overall mine grade, which is approximately

4.7% lead. When these pillars can be salvaged safely, they are extremely profitable. Basically, the reasons for initiating the pillar robbing project, other than the economic aspects, include determining the maximum size underground opening that could be mined safely and whether or not this could be accomplished under the normal production routine.

W-1 PILLAR RECOVERY TEST AREA

The first pillar recovery project was located in the mined out W-1 area referred to as the 65 zone, approximately 21m (65 ft) below the overlying Davis shale. The rock consists of mostly thin bedded dolomite with good partings between bedded layers. The mining height ranged from about 5m on the upper level to 10m on the lower level where it was partly benched out. The idea was to completely remove three pillars in succession but not all at the same time as seen in Figure 1.

If this was successful, an opening 30m wide and 67m long would be left without any pillar support and 100% of the ore extracted. The 65 zone had previously been mined in some areas as wide as 15m during its normal mining cycle, so in effect, the span would be doubled in the experimental area with the pillars gone. The project was completely controlled, however, and was not a normal production situation. One miner did the drilling and blasting under strict supervision on a specific but slow schedule. In order to determine what was happening to the back or roof as the pillars were being removed, several convergence stations were installed, as shown in Figure 1. To install these stations, holes 15cm deep were drilled into the back and floor and the measuring plugs were resin grouted in place. An original reading was taken with a mechanical rod extensometer before any blasting occurred. The extensometer is capable of measuring convergence to the nearest 0.0025cm. After each blast, the stations were measured to see how much convergence had taken place. Since this was an experimental project, the area was roped off after every blast until it was checked to see if the rate of convergence seemed normal. It took three blasts to completely remove each pillar. Once the pillars had been shot twice, it was observed that the convergence associated with pillar No. 1 was unusually high compared to the convergence associated with either of the other two pillars, as seen in Figure 1. At that time, the non-rock bolted area around pillar No. 1 was bolted. The sequence of blasts are also shown in Figure 1. Basically, part of one pillar would be shot on one day and several days later, after taking daily measurements, part of the next pillar would be shot out. Finally, all three pillars were gone. Only a part of any one pillar was ever shot at one time. As shown in Figure 1, a large convergence was measured after each blast, followed by a decreasing rate of convergence until the next blast occurred. This indicated a normal and stable situation. The

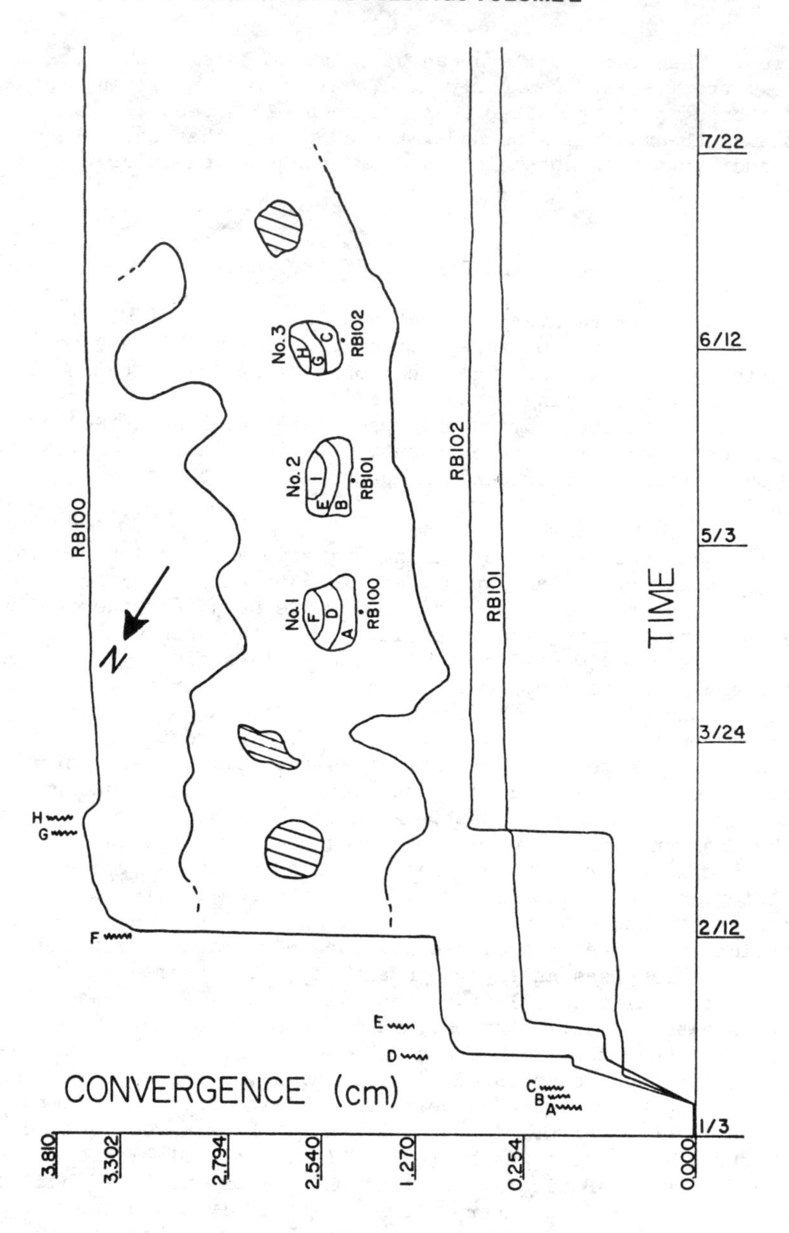

Fig. 1. Plan map of W-1 area and convergence graph. A = blast. RB 100-102 are measuring stations.

length of time between blasts was directly related to the time it took for roof stabilization to occur. The first blast on pillar No. 1 was on January 9, 1979. As can be seen in Figure 1, the only thing remaining after March 8, 1979, was a very small part of pillar No. 2. Measurements continued to be taken, and are still taken, on a monthly basis. On December 18, 1979, the final stub that remained was blasted out. Several things were learned during this first pillar removal project that would become beneficial to the success of the second pillar recovery project. It was learned that the back should be totally roof bolted in thin bedded ground before pillar recovery commences. This opinion is based upon the rather large total convergence (about 4.3cm) associated with the removal of pillar No. 1 which is the area that was not bolted originally. The total convergence associated with the removal of pillar No. 1 was about 3-1/2 times the total convergence associated with either of the other two pillars. Their average convergence was about 1.3cm. The large convergence that was observed with the removal of pillar No. 1 was the result of a bed separation within the first meter of the roof rather than an overall roof sag as reflected by the area surrounding the other two pillars. This suggested that in subsequent testing areas, the installation of deeper sag measuring stations would be necessary to eliminate the question of where the movement was coming from. Observation holes drilled into the back 3-4m would also be necessary to determine if the convergence reflected total roof sag or just a shallow bedding separation. The results of the initial pillar removal project in the W 1 area were generally good. The project was successful in that there have not been any roof falls or surrounding pillar failures and 100% of the ore was extracted for that particular area. Approximately 4800 tons of 15 to 20% lead ore that otherwise would have been left behind was recovered. Based upon current measurements, the area is stable, but it is still converging at a very slow rate which would indicate that some time in the future the roof may fail unless convergence stops.

J-2 PILLAR RECOVERY TEST AREA

Considering the first project to be a success, another test area for pillar robbing got underway; this time in another mining zone. The plans for the new test area were modified considerably. The mining was going to be accomplished by a regular production crew and at a much faster rate. The experiment this time was only partially controlled instead of completely controlled. The original plan was to remove 8 pillars, two rows of four each as seen in Figure 2. If successful, this would leave an unsupported opening that would measure 46m wide and 82m long. This project was located in the J-2 mining area which incorporated the 175 mining zone, approximately 57m (175 ft) below the Davis shale. The back was mostly made up of a much more massive dolomite which was expected to make a stronger roof than the thin bedded dolomite layers that made up the roof

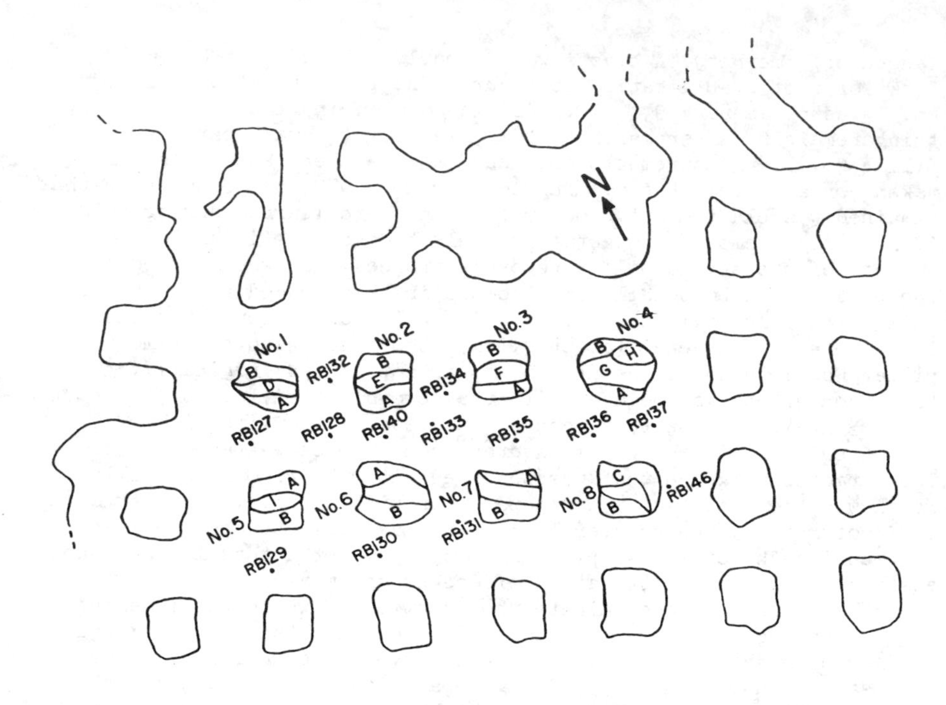

Fig. 2. Plan map J-2 area. Letters A-I designate order of blasts. RB 127-146 designate measuring stations.

in the W-1 test area. The average mining height was about 4.5m. The average grade of the 8 pillars ran about 9% lead. The W-1 pillar removal area had two massive barrier pillars; one in the north and the other on the south side of the mining area. The J-2 mining area had a massive barrier pillar on the north side of the mining front, but all other sides of the J-2 area were surrounded by normal room and pillar conditions. This time 13 monitoring stations were installed as shown in Figure 2. The installations were quite different, however. Boreholes were drilled into the back and the floor measuring 1.2m deep. The measuring stations were then point anchored at that depth by the use of rock bolt resin. With the stations being anchored 1.2m deep, any surficial movement within the back up to about one meter would not show up in the closure measurements, thus a better feel for the overall roof stability could be determined. Two verticle boreholes 7.5cm in diameter and 3.5m deep were drilled into the roof as inspection holes to check for any bedding separations that might occur as the pillars were being removed. The mining was also different. The pillars were all drilled out at one time on two sides of each pillar. The first blast occurred on December 27, 1979. It consisted of shooting the inside ribs of 7 of the pillars all at all at the same time as seen in Figure 2. Following the blast, the stations were measured as usual. The roof in the J-2 area behaved similarly to the roof in the W-1 area as seen in Figure 3.

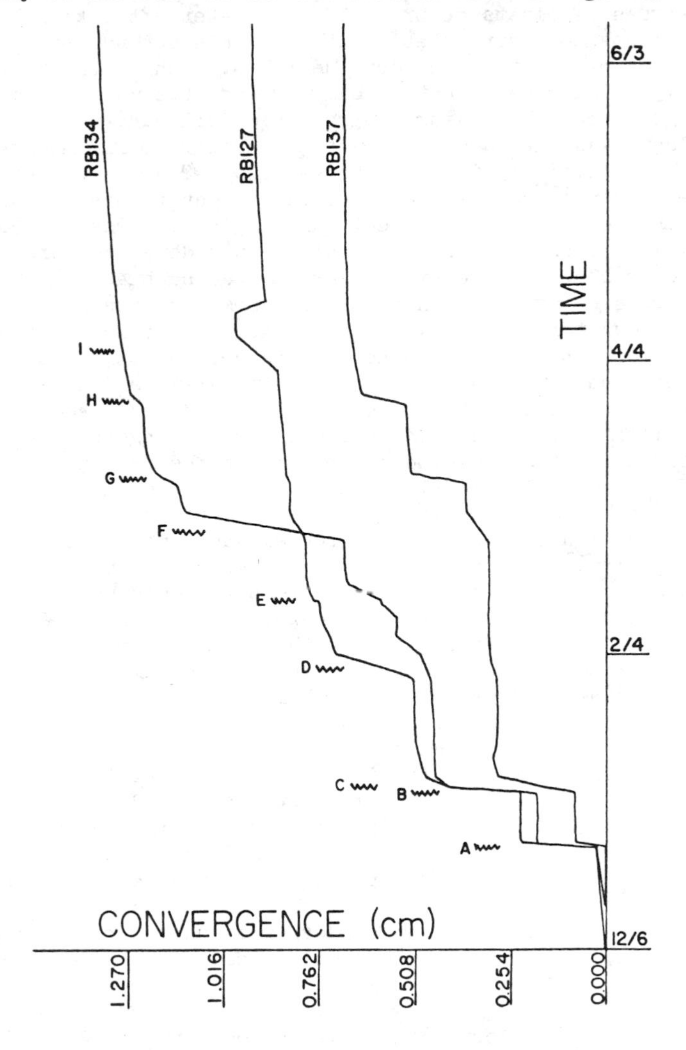

Fig. 3. Convergence graph of J-2 area shows results at 3 different locations. ≀ = Blast

After each blast, there was a significant immediate convergence, which was followed by a rapid decrease in the rate of closure indicating stabilization. This was a normal and expected situation. The second series of blasts occurred 10 days later after taking daily measurements to insure stabilization. This second series of blasts consisted of shooting the outside rib of each of the 8 pillars simultaneously. This meant that in only 10 days the majority of the 8 pillars were gone. The measuring procedure following the second series of blasts was the same as were the results. Daily measurements were taken initially in both the W-1 and J-2 areas to establish a daily rate of convergence since the rate of convergence is more important than the total convergence. As long as the rate of convergence remained constant, or preferably slowed down, the area was determined to be stable. One time after the second blast in the J-2 area the rate of movement increased for some unknown reason. The area was shut down for about a week until the rate of movement started decreasing again. At this time, the pillars were whittled down to the point where one more blast would completely remove them in most cases. Pillar No. 1 was shot out and closure readings were taken for two weeks. Pillar No. 2 was then shot out and convergence readings were again taken for two weeks, etc. up through the removal of pillar No. 5. The final removal of the 5 pillars was an extremely slow process, not because it was necessary for safety, but because it created production problems. The problem was a matter of time versus productivity. In order to shoot out the remaining small stubs which only amounted to 150 tons each, the miners would have to come in and do an extensive amount of work to get the area ready for drilling. The time and effort spent on the final stages of the project did not seem worthwhile as compared to the initial series of blasts where a relatively few number of holes and a small amount of scaling produced large tonnages. It was during the final stages of removal that a convergence warning light was used for added safety. At this point, there was no indication of any roof problems, but the miners wanted a warning device of some sort that would tell them if any problems should occur. A warning light was devised which consisted of a spring loaded extensometer with a flashlight attached. An arm on the extensometer would depress the switch on the flashlight and activate the device. The warning light could be set as sensative as desired so that a predetermined convergence would turn the light on and signal the miner that it was time to leave until the area could be checked.

The total convergence for the area was normal, but it was noticed that some of the pillars that bordered the south side of the removal area showed some signs of taking weight; therefore, the three remaining stub pillars No.'s 6, 7, and 8 were left for what little support they might provide. Since that time, no further deterioration of those surrounding pillars has occurred. Approximately 7000 tons of 9% lead ore was obtained to benefit the overall production output that once again could have been left behind. There are many more relatively high grade selected pillars remaining to be mined as supplemental tonnage and grade to normal production activities. As was the case for the W-1 area, the J-2 pillar project was also successful . Roof conditions are stable and the surrounding pillars have stabilized. The area does continue to exhibit a very slow convergence rate which again would indicate that at some time in the future a roof failure could occur unless the convergence stops completely.

CONCLUSION

The two pillar projects that have been carried out thus far have been successful and beneficial to OLC in many ways. The total number of available mining places was increased by the simple action of starting up a pillar removal area which is much easier and faster than developing a new ore block. This in turn led to increased tonnage and grade with no extra development costs. By adding pillar removal areas, the total extraction ratio has also been increased. An important part of pillar robbing at OLC is selecting high grade areas that are easily accessible. Several potential pillar robbing areas are full of stockpiled development waste rock which, without double handling of the waste, would greatly limit the accessibility to the pillars. Another factor in selecting a pillar removal area deals with the aspect of pillar support between pillar removal areas. Currently, in these early stages of pillar removal at OLC, there is very little feel for how far the removal areas should be located from one another. As a result, the two areas that have been mined thus far are in different ends of the mine and are at different mining levels. Further study and measurements are needed to predict any long term results.

17

Underground Caverns for Civil Projects

Chairmen: J.G. Warnock
R.J. Redmond

Acres American Inc., Columbia, MD
MacLean Grove & Co., Inc., Greenwich, CT

Chapter 71

HIGH-HEAD UNDERGROUND POWER PROJECT
PRESENTS DESIGN/CONSTRUCTION CHALLENGES

Arthur G. Strassburger

Manager, Civil-Hydro Construction
Pacific Gas and Electric Company
San Francisco, California

INTRODUCTION

High in the Sierra Nevada Mountains of California, some 50 air-line miles (80 km) northeast of Fresno, and near the John Muir Wilderness and Kings Canyon National Park, a large underground hydroelectric project is under construction. Pacific Gas & Electric (PG&E) Company's 1,125 MW Helms Pumped Storage Project exhibits a number of impressive statistics, unusual features, and other characteristics of interest to the tunneling or power plant designer and construction contractor.

The most significant underground facilities include almost 20,000 ft (6,096 m) of 27-ft (8.2 m) diam concrete-lined pressure tunnel; 3,700 ft (1,128 m) of access tunnel; 1,600 ft (488 m) of steel-lined high-pressure conduit, 2 major underground chambers more than 1,000 ft (305 m) below ground; 3 deep vertical shafts, and one steep inclined shaft. Maximum static pressures within the conduits range from 200 ft (61 m) to 1,744 ft (532 m), with hydraulic transients that increase pressure to 2,500 ft (762 m). The purpose of these underground works is to provide 475,000 hp (354,350 KW) of water power to each of the 3 reversible pump-turbines, each connected to a 375 MW generator motor. The units, rated at 1,744 ft (532 m) maximum static head, are among the world's front-runners, considering the size-head combination.

The Helms Project develops the existing power drop between two of PG&E's reservoirs, Courtright Lake and Lake Wishon. These reservoirs are retained by two concrete-faced rockfill dams completed in 1958, each storing approximately 125,000 acre ft (154×10^6 m^3) of water. Although the project is intended to operate on a typical daily and weekly peaking/pump-back cycle, this large reservoir capacity will permit operation at peak load for several days, the actual time depending upon antecedent conditions. When this project is completed in 1982, it will complete a total power drop of almost 7,300 ft (2,225 m) between Courtright Lake and Pine Flat Reservoir. Pine Flat Reservoir is owned by the Corps of Engineers and operated by the Water & Power Resource Service. Between the lake and the reservoir are two of the highest-head hydroelectric power plants in the United States: Haas at 2,445 ft (745 m) and Balch at 2,390 ft (728 m). The Kings River plant at 800 ft (244 m) completes the development.

The combinations of high hydraulic pressures including transients, size and depth of excavations, number of deep shafts, and difficult weather conditions, all combined to present some real engineering and construction challenges.

GEOLOGY

The project is situated in granitic terrain of the Central Sierra Nevada Mountains. The dominant rocks, comprising a large batholith, are plutonic of Mesozoic age with some areas of glacial deposits. The pressure tunnel runs through granodiorite, quartz monzonite, and quartzite, as well as small areas of quartz diorite and aplitic dikes. The powerhouse area is granodiorite. The rock generally has the following properties:

Mohr Hardness = 5-6
Compressive Strength = 15,000 - 20,000 psi (103 - 138 MPa)
Pulse Velocity = 14,000 - 25,000 ft/sec (4,267 - 7,620 m/s)
Tensile Strength = 1,450 - 2,340 psi (10 - 16 MPa)
Specific Gravity = 2.64 - 2.88

Geological investigation consisted of the following:

- The surface between the two lakes was mapped in detail and the major joint sets were determined in the areas of major construction.

- A total of 7,750 ft (2,362 m) of NX core was taken from 13 holes, some vertical and some inclined, using Longear 38, Chicago Pneumatic-8, and Chicago Pneumatic-15 drill rigs. Men and equipment were transported by helicopter to a number of the remote drill sites. After cores were logged, photographed, and stored, the water level in the holes was monitored to determine the fluctuation of the groundwater.

- Downhole seismic measurements were made in the powerhouse area to determine the modulus of the rock and whether it varied with depth. The average value of Young's Modulus was

1,060,000 psi (7,303 MPa).

Hydrofracturing stress measurements were taken at different depths in two holes in the powerhouse area. The minimum horizontal stress was 775 ± 100 psi (5,340 ± 690 kPa), the maximum was 1,400 ± 400 psi (9,650 ± 2,760 kPa). The direction of the stresses was also determined by using a rubber packer. The minimum stress was less than the maximum static pressure in the tunnel; therefore, a few changes were made in the powerhouse area. The stresses were also used in a finite-element analysis of the rock around the powerhouse chamber in the "during" and "after" excavation conditions.

MAJOR FEATURES

A plan and profile of the project are shown in Figure 1. A submerged, large, but rather conventional intake-discharge structure will start the water under way for generation. Water will then flow through 13,446 ft (4,098 m) of 27-ft (8.2 m)-I.D reinforced concrete tunnel and 22-ft (6.7 m)-diam steel-lined tunnel and surface pipe before dropping down a steeply inclined penstock shaft. The contractor drove a 30-ft (9.1 m) straight-walled horseshoe section (Figure 2) using conventional driving methods. Two bulkhead gates at the Courtright Lake intake provide conventional shutoff, and a 21-1/2 x 32-ft (6.6 x 9.8 m) wheel gate located in a gate shaft 1,343 ft (409 m) from the intake provides emergency shutoff.

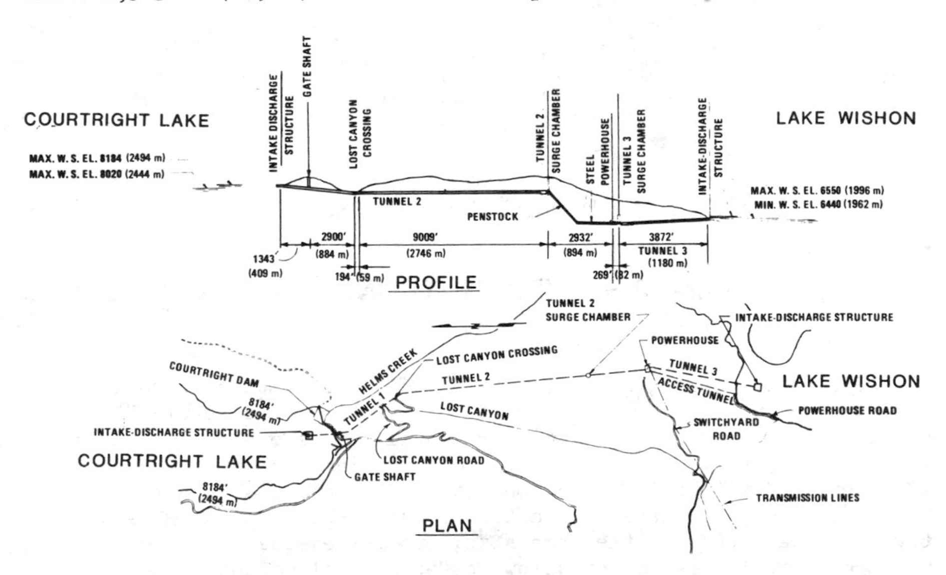

Figure 1 - HELMS PUMPED STORAGE PROJECT

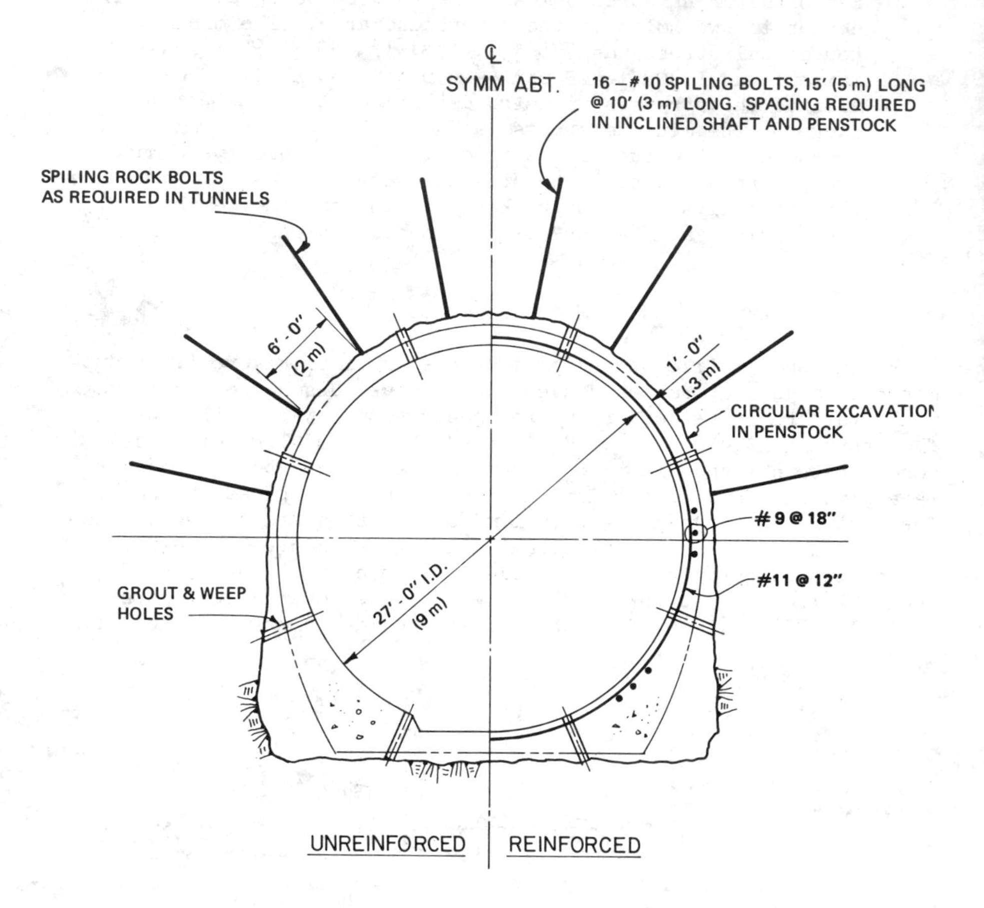

Figure 2 – TYPICAL TUNNEL SECTION

The penstock shaft, inclined at 55° to accommodate self-mucking during construction, drops 1,430 ft (436 m) (measured vertically), and connects to a 300-ft (91 m) horizontal run before connecting to the penstock manifold. This 27-ft (8.2 m)-diam high-pressure shaft will be lined with reinforced concrete to a minimum thickness of 27 in. (0.7 m). Bidders were asked to submit bids for an alternative vertical shaft of the same size; but the evaluation of costs and hydraulic losses, after allowing for a total conduit length, favored the inclined shaft.

The penstock manifold consists of two non-symmetrical reinforced-concrete bifurcations (see Figure 3). Eventually, each of the three legs terminates in a 500-ft (152 m)-long steel-lined conduit before entering the powerhouse chamber. The portion of the steel lining from under the transformer chamber and into the powerhouse is designed for full internal pressure. The upstream 410 ft (125 m) of the conduit is designed to transfer a portion of the load into the surrounding concrete and rock.

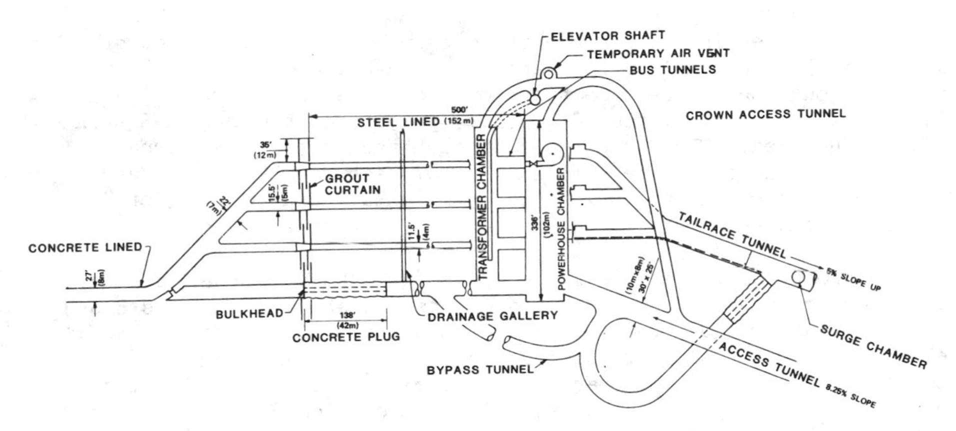

Figure 3 - EXCAVATION POWERHOUSE COMPLEX

Downstream from the powerhouse chamber, steel-lined draft tube extensions combine via two reverse bifurcations into Tunnel 3. All bifurcations are in the concrete section. This tunnel, identical in section to Tunnel 2, rises almost 200 ft (61 m) along its 3,872-ft (1,180 m) length to the Lake Wishon Intake-Discharge Structure, which is similar to the structure at Courtright Lake.

Tunnels 2 and 3 were originally bid with alternative designs: as 27-ft (8.2 m)-diam concrete lined tunnels, and as 38-ft (11.6 m) horseshoe-shaped, unlined tunnels with paved invert. Evaluation of bids resulted in selection of the smaller concrete-lined section. The reason for the large difference in size between the lined and unlined tunnels was that a maximum permissible velocity of ± 8 ft/sec (2.4 m/s) was established for the unlined tunnel. The concrete-lined diameter was an "economic diameter," and velocities will be about 16-1/2 ft/sec (5 m/s). Because the rock in the area of Tunnel 1 was believed to be relatively blocky, the unlined alternative was not bid for that tunnel.

The portion of Tunnel 1 upstream from the gate shaft, and situated underneath Courtright Lake, was designed to be reinforced, as was the concrete-lined penstock. Rock quality under the reservoir however was found, upon excavation, to be of such high quality and so watertight that the reinforcement was deleted. Spiling bolting is required in the penstock and is an alternate means of support elsewhere in all pressure tunnels. The tunnel concrete lining is provided with weep holes to permit rapid pressure response across the concrete. All tunnel linings require backfill grout. Reinforcement is designed to resist buckling due to external loading equal to 30 percent of static, and to prevent concrete fallout in the event of cracking.

Two concrete-lined surge shafts, one in Tunnel 2 and the other in Tunnel 3, are provided for rapid load on-off and for emergency unit tripout conditions. Sections of these shafts are shown in Figures 4 and 5. Only the 10-ft (3 m) portion of the Tunnel 3 tank will be unlined. The top portion of each tank consists of true structural concrete. The main chamber of each will be weeped and reinforced to withstand 30 ft (9.1 m) of unbalanced (non-uniform) external loading.

The two principal chambers are the powerhouse cavern and the transformer chamber. Layout and sections are shown in Figures 3 and 6. The chambers, although not large when compared to some excavated elsewhere, potentially are subject to extremely high water pressures. Four major design parameters were: (1) the exceptionally high upstream conduit pressures, (2) consideration of the deep submergence (the powerhouse crown is 200 ft [61] below maximum tailwater elevation, 110 ft [33.5 m] below minimum tailwater) and depth within the mountain, (3) simplicity of layout and design, and (4) consideration of the *in situ* rock-stress ratios.

High upstream pressures are mitigated first with the 500 ft. (152 m) of steel-lined penstock discussed earlier. A long concrete plug, complete with contact grouting, shuts off the penstock access tunnel. High-pressure grout rings at the upstream end of the plug and at the steel-lined sections will increase the path of percolation and reduce the hydrostatic level. A transverse drainage gallery, along with a drainage curtain, downstream from the plug will provide relief and monitoring of groundwater seepage. A second drainage curtain inclined toward the high pressure source is located at the upstream springline of the transformer chamber.

Pressures originating from the tailwater side are being relieved by a curtain of drain holes, drilled upward and inclined toward the tail tunnel, from the powerhouse crown access tunnel. Another row of drains will be drilled from the powerhouse turbine floor and inclined downward toward the steel-lined draft tube extensions. A grout curtain is being provided at the downstream end of these steel liners. Three 4,000 gal/min (0.25 m^3/s) dewatering pumps, which discharge into Tunnel 3, will keep the powerhouse chamber dry in the event of unexpected moderate leaks or seepage.

The long conduit and high head necessitated deep submergence of the pump turbines to provide adequate suction head during pumping. The submergence, and consequent increase in conduit pressures on both sides of the chamber, in turn required that the number of openings for control conduits, pipes, valves, or other projections through rock or steel barriers be kept to an absolute minimum. In addition, plugs, gates, penstock and steel liners were designed very conservatively. Simple fail-safe methods of operation were designed.

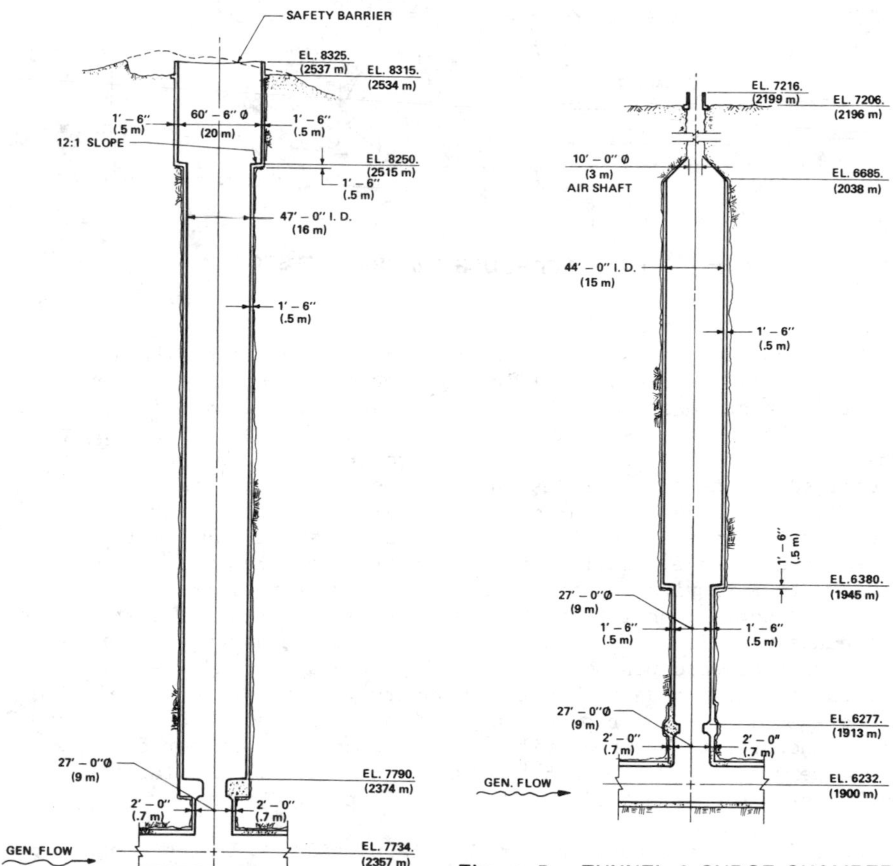

Figure 5 - TUNNEL 3 SURGE CHAMBER

Figure 4 - TUNNEL 2 SURGE CHAMBER

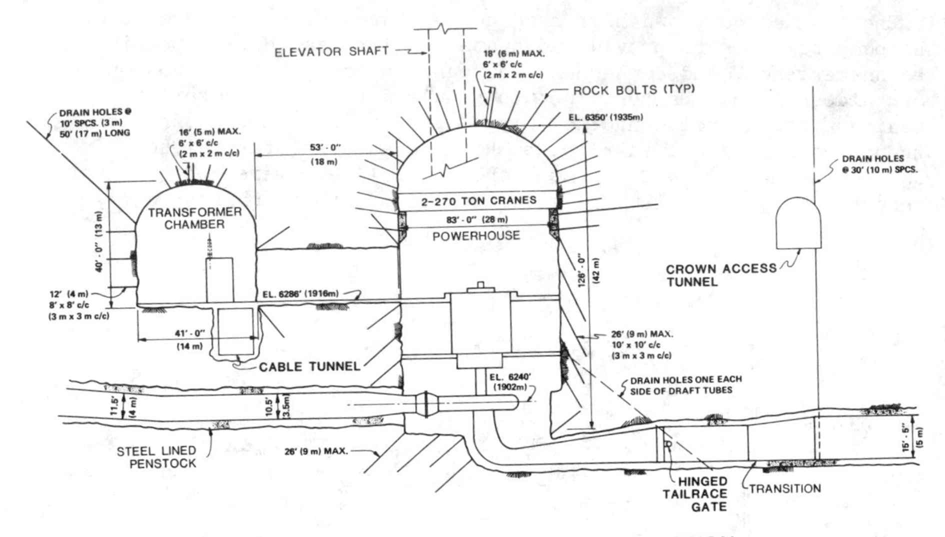

Figure 6 - POWERHOUSE TRANSVERSE SECTION

Space utilization studies were conducted on a systems basis to assure that any excavation ultimately would be used as efficiently or as often as possible. Thus, the elevator, stairway, high-voltage leads, other utilities, and ventilation are combined in one shaft. The contractor chose to add a powerhouse crown access tunnel, not specified in the original design, for access to the chamber arches and for early access to the elevator shaft for ventilating purposes. The penstock access tunnel will also provide space for compressors, tanks, and storage. Well into the construction phase, the Company decided to authorize construction of a bypass tunnel from the Tunnel 3 access tunnel to the penstock access tunnel. This was done to reduce traffic congestion in the powerhouse chamber while the inclined shaft and penstocks were being excavated, and the concrete and electrical-mechanical work was underway in the powerhouse. The two cranes in the powerhouse chamber run on two reinforced-concrete beams anchored to the rock with a prestressed rock-anchor system. These permanent 260-ton (235,868-kg) cranes will be available very early for the contractor's use in installing equipment.

No tailrace gate-handling chamber is provided. Instead, hinged, hydraulically operated gates with simple fail-safe controls are provided. Only man and tool access is provided into the penstock from the powerhouse side. Heavy equipment for any future major repairs of the penstock will be lowered down the inclined shaft.

Radial resin-grouted bolts combined with shotcrete provide the roof-support systems for both chambers. Sidewall excavation required spiling bolting. Smooth-wall blasting, required in the powerhouse chamber, met with limited success. Pre-bolting around portals of interconnecting tunnels was also required. Figure 7 shows a longitudinal cross-section of the powerhouse chamber and basic rock bolting equipments.

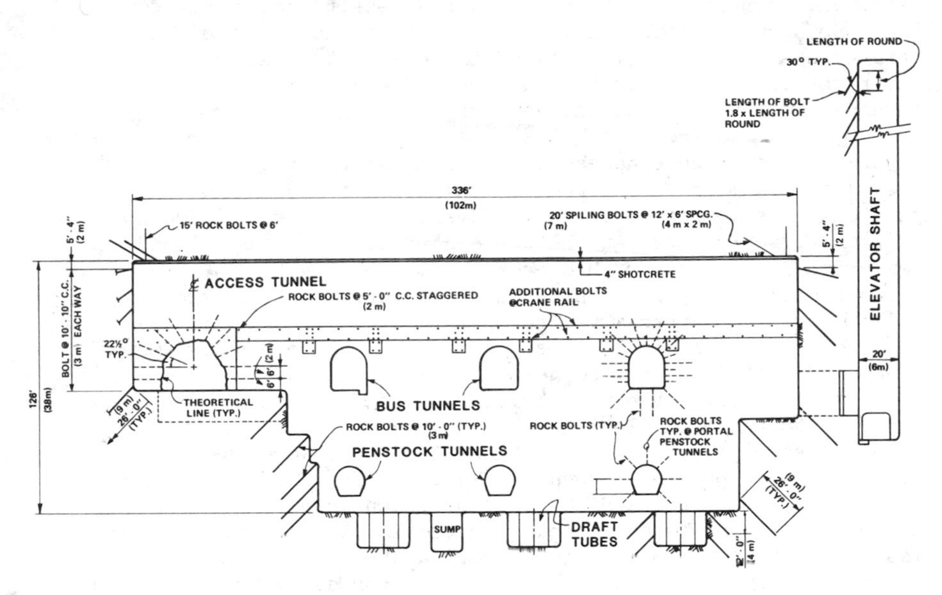

Figure 7 - POWERHOUSE LONGITUDINAL SECTION

The powerhouse access tunnel, 3,700 ft (1,128 m) long and at an 8.25 percent slope, is 30 x 25 ft (9.1 x 7.6 m) and mostly unlined, except for a paved (originally specified as concrete but since revised to A.C. in order to reduce costs and save construction time) invert. Spiling bolting was also required. The 20-ft (6.1 m)-diam, 1,012-ft (308 m)-deep elevator shaft is partially lined with reinforced concrete to a finished diameter of 18 ft (5.5 m). No weep holes were provided.

CONSTRUCTION PROGRESS AND PROBLEMS

Construction of the project started in 1976 with improvement of approximately 26 miles of County and Forest Service roads, construction of about 5 miles of new road, and of camps, water and sewage treatment systems and construction power. In 1977 a contract for all civil work was awarded to the joint venture of Granite-Ball-Groves, with Granite Construction Company of Watsonville, California being the sponsor.

Tunnel excavation progressed almost simultaneously in 3 headings: upstream in Tunnel 1 from Lost Canyon to Courtright Lake, downstream in Tunnel 2 from Lost Canyon to the head of the inclined penstock shaft; and downslope in the powerhouse access tunnel from Lake Wishon to the powerhouse chamber. Courtright Lake was drained during the summer of 1977 to allow the open-cut excavation for the Courtright Intake-Discharge Structure and excavation of a portion of Tunnel 1 downstream to the gate shaft.

When the powerhouse access tunnel reached the vicinity of the power plant chamber, a powerhouse crown access tunnel was driven upslope to the east (elevator shaft) end of the power plant and to the transformer chamber at the top center of each chamber arch, from which each arch was then excavated. See Figure 3. This crown access tunnel, not part of bid plans, was driven at the contractor's option with owner approval. The crown excavation was completed in 3 headings due to limitations specified. Only one heading could be opened and bolted before the next one was permitted to be excavated. Shotcreting followed the rock bolting. Excavation and bolting was completed to the main floor level, at which step the reinforced concrete crane girders and post-tensioned bolts were installed. Excavation then proceeded downward in benches to complete the chambers. The 2 - 270 ton (245 kg) permanent cranes were installed before excavation was completed. Protection of the cranes during blasting consisted essentially of moving them to the far end of the chamber away from the blast area. Only minor damage occurred consisting mostly of chipped paint and dirt accumulation. This early installation of the cranes made them available for civil construction, as well as setting of draft tube and turbine scroll case sections, saving significant time in the construction schedule.

An access tunnel to Tunnel 3 was driven off the main powerhouse access tunnel to the west and looped back on a downslope to pass under the powerhouse access tunnel to reach Tunnel 3 in the vicinity of the Tunnel 3 surge chamber. Tunnel 3 was driven upstream through the Unit 3 draft-tube extension to the center-line of Unit 3 (west unit), from which a raise into the chamber above allowed removal of spoil from the lower portions of the powerhouse chamber. At the same time, excavation proceeded into Units 2 and 1 draft-tube extensions. Later, Tunnel 3 was driven downstream to the Wishon Intake-Discharge Structure.

The main powerhouse access tunnel was continued through the west end of the power plant chamber at the main-floor level, past the transformer chamber, and upstream to the lower end of the inclined penstock shaft. From this penstock access tunnel, the three individual penstock tunnels to the power plant were driven.

All tunnel headings were driven full face using 10- to 12-ft (3- to 3.6 m) rounds. Two drill jumbos were used in parallel in each of the three main tunnel headings (Tunnels 1 and 2 and the powerhouse access tunnel, and later Tunnel 3). There were six drill jumbos, each with four hydraulic, electric drill booms (two on top deck and two below deck). Due to the steep invert grades of the majority of the tunnels, rubber-tired rolling equipment was chosen. Five jumbos were an Atlas Copco design and the other a Gardner-Denver, all mounted on Cat 769 B carriers. Heading muckers were Jarvis Clark JS 800, 8 yd^3 (6 m^3) with ejector bucket, which loaded into Jarvis Clark UDT 426 26-ton (23,582 kg) trucks, were later changed to 988 Cat loaders. All equipment was diesel-powered with water bath scrubbers.

The five shafts totaled 4,655 ft (1,419 m). Each shaft was initially excavated using an Ingersoll-Rand RBM 78 P raise-bore machine. (See Photo 1) The procedure consisted of drilling a 12-in. (0.3 m) pilot hole which was back-reamed to either an 8- or 10-ft (2.4- or 3 m) diam, followed by slashing down to final shaft size using the reamed hole for gravity muck disposal.

PHOTO 1 - RAISE-BORE MACHINE

Following excavation, the concrete tunnel linings are being placed in two lifts: a flat invert followed by the arch, placed continuously with movable steel forms and pump-placed concrete. Steel penstock, and tunnel liners at the Lost Canyon portals, will be placed in sections and joined by welding, followed by pumped concrete backfill. The structural concrete in the power plant, now completed, was placed conventionally and included concrete encasement of pump-turbine scroll cases and draft tube liners. Concrete was delivered into the west end of the powerhouse via the access tunnel and conveyed to the forms by a truck mounted pumper which was lifted to the placement area. There were no unusual problems encountered in placing the powerhouse concrete. Photo 2 shows the powerhouse excavation nearing completion and Photo 3 shows each nearly ready for the Electrical-Mechanical contractor.

PHOTO 2 - POWERHOUSE CHAMBER EXCAVATION

PHOTO 3 - POWERHOUSE CHAMBER MAIN DECK

Concrete in the elevator shaft and Tunnel 2 Surge Tank was slip-formed with excellent progress being made and high quality concrete being placed. Concrete for the lower large diameter Tunnel 3 Surge Tank will be placed using similar slip forming procedures. There was some difficulty in placing the arch concrete in Tunnel 3. The tunnel has a slope of 5%. Concreting started at the Wishon, or discharge, end. Thus concrete had to be pumped uphill and tended to run back down the tunnel. The problem was aggravated by the harsh aggregate made from the crushed tunnel spoil and by the large concrete volume required between the circular form and the vertical sided excavation with rather high overbreak. It was difficult to prevent voids along concrete flow lines. Careful concrete control and partial bulkheading of the lower end of the forms proved to be the answer. To avoid the slope problem during concreting of Tunnel 1, also at a relatively steep slope, it is planned to concrete that tunnel going uphill.

Excavation of Tunnel 2, beneath the Tunnel 2 Surge Tank, revealed about an 80 ft (25 m)-wide shear zone, almost vertically oriented and immediately upstream and perhaps intersecting the future surge chamber excavation. The raised bore hole at the surge chamber center-line had given no evidence of intersecting this shear. Geologic evidence at the ground surface however implied the potential for the zone impinging into the 50 ft (15 m)-diam tank excavation. Early exploratory drilling intersecting the sheared area had been inconclusive. This situation resulted in two concerns: (1) the potential of a large wedge slipping into the enlarged chamber as excavation proceeded downward, and (2) of greater concern was the potential of high unbalanced rock loading such a wedge could place upon one side of the relatively thin concrete lining. Because of the extremely rapid fluctuation in hydraulic loads to which the lining will be subjected during operation, it was considered imprudent to permit any additional eccentric rock loading. Consideration was given to relocating the partially excavated surge chamber, but finally a carefully blocked steel ring support system was used. The shear zone never caused any problems. Excavation and support proceeded without significant incidents, and the entire surge tank is now safely concreted.

One of the more difficult tunnel driving programs occurred in Tunnel 1 upstream of Lost Canyon where the tunnel crosses through an old streambed. Geologic and topographic features suggested that the tunnel might intersect this ancient streambed or possibly sheared materials. Exploratory drilling, which it was believed would confirm discontinuities, indicated excellent rock instead. Actual driving conditions however encountered about 140 ft (42 m) of mixed fine-grained, decomposed granite and varied-size loose rounded stone and rock.

These conditions first required steel supports, then jump sets. Finally, after twice losing supports, the contractor partially refilled the area and proceeded with partial face excavations using a crown drift and wall plate drifts followed by top heading and bench. Grouting of the overlying formation was only partially successful. Final steel sets were supplemented with complete shotcreting between sets. This section of tunnel will eventually be steel lined in accordance with initial plans.

Generally ground conditions, except locally in a few areas, have been about as expected. Short sections of blocky formations and water bearing seams were encountered in the Powerhouse Access Tunnel, the Tunnel 3 Access Tunnel, and the Penstock Bypass Tunnel. Some rock "popping" due to stress relief occurred in Tunnel 2, and in the Powerhouse Chamber as well as surrounding excavations.

In the Powerhouse Chamber, significant overbreak occurred on the north wall, resulting in the need for concrete portal structures at the bus tunnel entrances to support crane guides. (Photo 3). It also required more than expected concrete volume in the post-tensioned concrete crane rail. Overbreak was probably the result of a combination of factors, including in situ stress conditions, rock joint orientation and blasting techniques. These problems extended the required construction time for the crane rails and increased costs over those originally expected. Nevertheless the writer still believes that the decision to use this type of rail support system was a good one. This is confirmed by the Company's decision to again use this post-tensioned concrete system at its Kerckhoff 2 underground powerhouse which is presently being excavated near Millérton Lake some 50 miles (85 km) west of Helms.

One of the most challenging construction problems on the job has been the excavation of the inclined penstock shaft which at this writing is about two-thirds complete. As stated earlier, the inclined shaft was chosen over the vertical alternative for overall economic reasons. A combination of rock joint orientation, the 30 ft (9 m)-diam size, blocky rock in some reaches and the awkwardness associated with the 55 slope have resulted in very slow progress. A 12 inch (1/3 m)-diam pilot bore was first sunk from the upper end. Keeping this bore on line was a problem in itself, but its final hole-through location at the bottom was well within acceptable tolerances. The Ingersoll-Rand raise-bore machine, previously used for the vertial shafts, was then used to ream a 10 ft (3 m) bore and performed well. Deviations from a straight line however later caused problems in the slashing operation. Although alignment tolerances of the slashing operation are not restrictive, drilling crews found it difficult to align themselves. Rock fallouts from the reamed hole also made aligning the drill jumbo difficult. Certain design and operating problems with the jumbo and its machinery resulted in weeks of delay. The jumbo is illustrated in Figure 8. The jumbo could not conveniently accommodate placing of steel ring supports. Safety requirements necessitated continuous installation of wire mesh in the excavated crown and ribs. The writer, given the opportunity again, would in the case of a deep shaft be more favorably inclined toward a vertical configuration for economic reasons.

Use of pneumatic drills on most of the project excavation had many advantages including high speed, reduction of crew size, and reduction in noise. Among the disadvantages were: difficulty of adaptation of the drills to meet requirements that the resin grouted rock bolts be spun into their holes, increased waste water quality problems, and weight. The latter was a factor in the design of the inclined shaft drill jumbo.

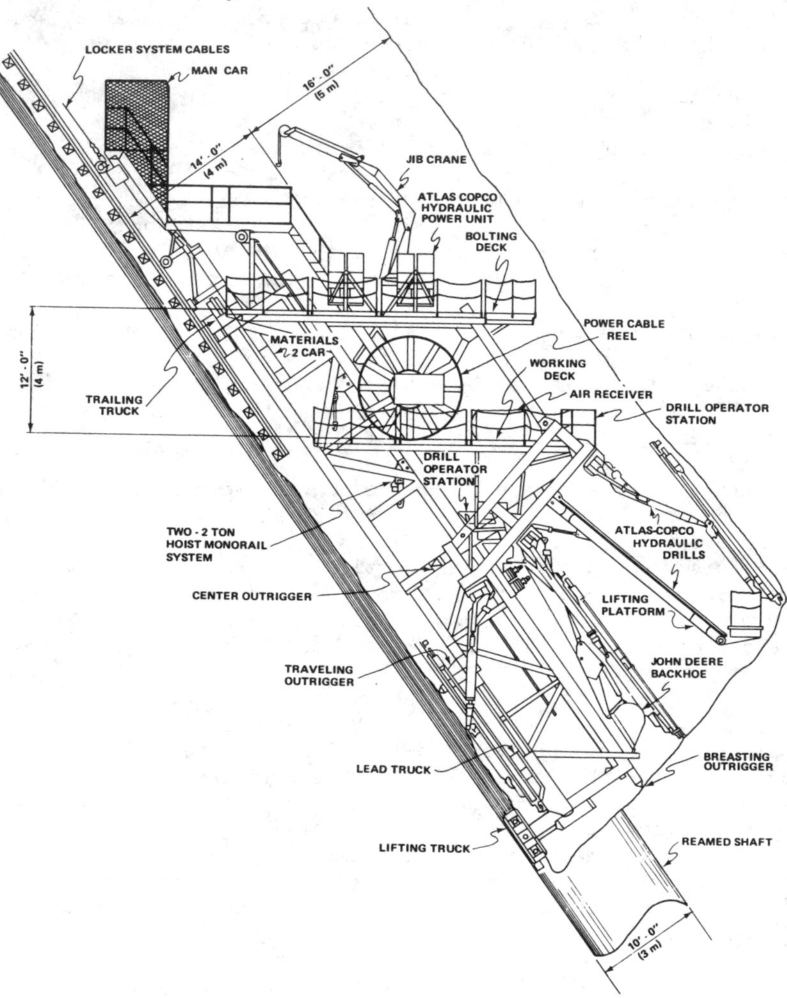

Figure 8 - INCLINED SHAFT DRILLING JUMBO

As of this writing the concrete form jumbo for lining the inclined shaft is being designed. The proposed scheme is quite similar to that used at Churchill Falls.[1]

[1] "Construction of the Inclined Penstocks at Churchill Falls Power Station, Labrador", H. J. Dawson and R. P. T. Lytle, The Institution of Civil Engineers, Proc. Part I, Design and Construction, Nov. '72.

OTHER CHALLENGES

Among the factors which increased construction challenges were difficult winter weather conditions and very limited construction seasons for the intake-discharge structures.

The Courtright intake-discharge structure is located near the very bottom of Courtright Lake. This necessitated drawing down the lake some 200 ft (61 m) and required virtually complete evacuation of the 122,000 acre-foot (151 x 10^6 m^3) reservoir. Lake Wishon had to be drawn down about 140 ft (43 m) to evacuate about 100,000 (124 x 10^6) of its 128,000 acre-foot (158 x 10^6 m^3) of storage. Because of the very high power value of this water (it develops over 1 mile [1600 m] of head below Lake Wishon) water could not be wasted. Thus Courtright has been drained 3 times and Wishon twice during construction. This also limited construction to the late fall and winter months.

The project's location in California notwithstanding, weather conditions encountered can be among the most difficult in the lower United States. As much as 15 ft (5 m) of snow lay on the ground in the 1978-1979 winter. Temperatures dipped to the minus 20s °F (-30° C) at Courtright. Icicles 10 ft (3 m) long and well over a foot (1/3 m) in diameter hung from the crown of Tunnel 1 near the Courtright intake. Snow at the contractors' trailer camp was so deep there was no longer space to store the snow shoveled off the trailer roofs. At one point the entire job was shut down in order to clear snow from the camp. In 1979-80 the headquarters camp roof, designed for a smow load of 250 psf (.012 MPa) began to sag under its load and had to be manually cleared of snow.

Such conditions did little to encourage workers to seek employment at the project from the nearest major labor pool at Fresno, 2 hours driving time away in good weather. As a result the job has, through much of its construction, suffered from a surfeit of good qualified craftsmen as well as some levels of supervision.

JOB STATUS

The Helms Project was first conceived in 1970. The Company filed for an FERC License late in 1973. The License was received in spring of 1976. Original project completion was scheduled for 1980. Delays in licensing deferred the expected completion date to 1981, with the last unit coming on line in June. Subsequent delays have resulted in a scheduled operating date of June 1982 for the first unit.

The project cost in early 1973 was estimated at $212 million. This was revised to $385 million in 1977. Final completed cost is now estimated at over $600 million, including all overheads.

Electrical-Mechanical installation is being done by Wismer & Becker of Sacramento, California. Principal suppliers are Hitachi Ltd. (pump-turbines), Westinghouse Electric (generator-motors), American Bridge (steel penstocks and tunnel liners), Kaiser Steel (gates and draft tube extensions), Landel (powerhouse cranes).

CREDITS

The author wishes to thank Messrs. Roy R. Friedrichs and Jerry A. Davis, both of Pacific Gas and Electric Company for their significant contributions to this paper by virtue of their co-authoring with me a previous paper [2] which served as a basis for much of this work. Mr. Friedrichs also reviewed and edited this paper.

(2) "California Pumped-Storage Project Advances State of the Art in High-Head Tunneling", A. G. Strassburger, R. R. Friedrichs, J. A. Davis, U. S. Committee on Tunneling Technology Newsletter, June 1978.

Chapter 72

GEOTECHNICAL DESIGN OF LARGE OPENINGS AT DEPTH

by Evert Hoek

Principal, Golder Associates,
Vancouver, Canada

ABSTRACT

Two types of failure have to be considered in designing large openings:

(a) Structurally controlled failure caused by discontinuity intersections,

(b) Stress induced instability which occurs when induced stresses exceed the rock mass strength.

Structurally controlled failures, which occur in hard jointed rock masses at relatively shallow depth, are briefly reviewed. This paper is primarily concerned with stress induced instability at greater depths and with the problem of estimating the strength of a rock mass surrounding an underground opening. Some of the practical aspects of support design for large openings are discussed.

INTRODUCTION

Structurally controlled failures occur in the roof and sidewalls of underground excavations when blocks or wedges are released by intersecting structural features such as faults, joints and bedding planes. These types of failures are common in excavations in hard rock at depths of less than about 500 m below surface but they do occur at greater depths in the mining of orebodies which are associated with faults. In general, these failures do not involve fracture of the intact rock and are simply gravity falls or the sliding of wedges or blocks on inclined planes.

Stress induced failures occur when the stresses induced around an excavation exceed the strength of the rock mass in which the opening is mined. In general, these types of failures occur in hard strong rocks at depths in excess of 1,000 m below surface but they can also be induced at shallower depth in weak rocks or in zones of exceptionally high stress such as slender pillars between large openings.

Obviously there are situations in which both structural and stress controlled failures can occur in the same excavation but these are relatively rare and generally one or other mode tends to be dominant in any particular excavation.

In order to analyze these failures, the following information is required:

(a) The virgin stress conditions which exist in the rock mass before the excavation is mined,

(b) The stresses induced in the rock by the creation of the excavation,

(c) The mechanical properties of the intact rock material,

(d) The inclination and orientation of significant structural features (faults, joints, bedding planes etc.) in the rock mass in which the excavation is to be mined,

(e) The characteristics of any fault gouge or joint infillings which may be encountered during the excavation of the openings,

(f) The ground water conditions in the rock mass in which the excavation is to be mined.

Virgin Stresses in Rock

Brown and Hoek (1978) have summarized the results of 116 in situ stress measurements carried out in different parts of the world. Linear regression analyses have been performed on data sets from each country and the results are presented in Figure 1. Unfortunately insufficient data are available to permit a detailed analysis of individual horizontal stresses and Figure 1 gives plots of average horizontal stresses against depth below surface.

In spite of the wide variations in the results presented in Figure 1, the following general trends are evident.

(a) Vertical stresses increase approximately linearly with depth, with stresses at depths in excess of 1,000 m being reasonably well predicted by equation 1:

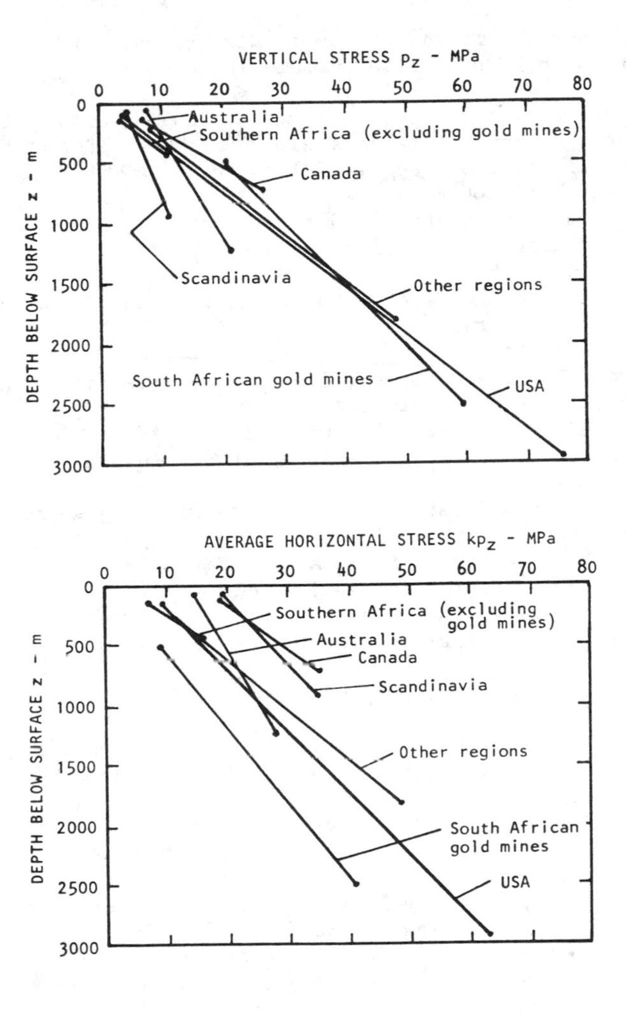

Figure 1. Trends of vertical and average horizontal stress with depth in different parts of the world.

$$p_z = 0.026z \quad (1)$$

where: p_z is the vertical stress in Mega Pascals and
z is the depth below surface in meters.

(b) With the exception of deep level South African gold mines, average horizontal stresses are generally higher than vertical stresses for depths of less than 1,000 m below surface. At a depth of 500 m below surface, the average horizontal stress is approximately 1.5 times the vertical stress with higher ratios being evident at shallower depths.

(c) For depths in excess of 1,000 m below surface, the horizontal and vertical stresses tend to equalize.

(d) Horizontal stresses measured in the massive strong quartzites in which most South African gold is mined are generally less than the vertical stress. On average, the ratio of average horizontal to vertical stress in these mines is 0.75.

Figure 1 provides a first estimate of the stresses which are likely to be encountered at depth and this estimate may be adequate for a preliminary analysis of excavation stability. In critical cases or in cases where the rock mass has been subjected to recent tectonic activity, it is strongly recommended that in situ measurement of rock stress be carried out as early in the project as possible.

Stresses Induced Around an Excavation

When an excavation is mined in a rock mass, the in situ stresses which acted upon the rock which is removed are redistributed in the remaining rock mass. This results in local increases in the stresses in the immediate vicinity of the excavation and, in some cases, these induced stresses can cause local failure of the rock mass.

Figure 2 gives a plot of the maximum roof and sidewall stresses induced in the rock surrounding excavations of various shapes for different ratios of horizontal to vertical stress. These results have been derived from a large number of detailed elastic stress analyses carried out by means of the boundary element technique (Hoek and Brown, 1980a). The application of the results presented in Figure 2 will be illustrated by means of a practical example at the end of this paper.

Mechanical Properties of Intact Rock

When the strength of the intact rock is lower than the stress induced at the boundary of an excavation, failure of the rock will occur. This type of failure can take place in weak rocks such as mudstones and shales at relatively shallow depth or in hard strong rocks

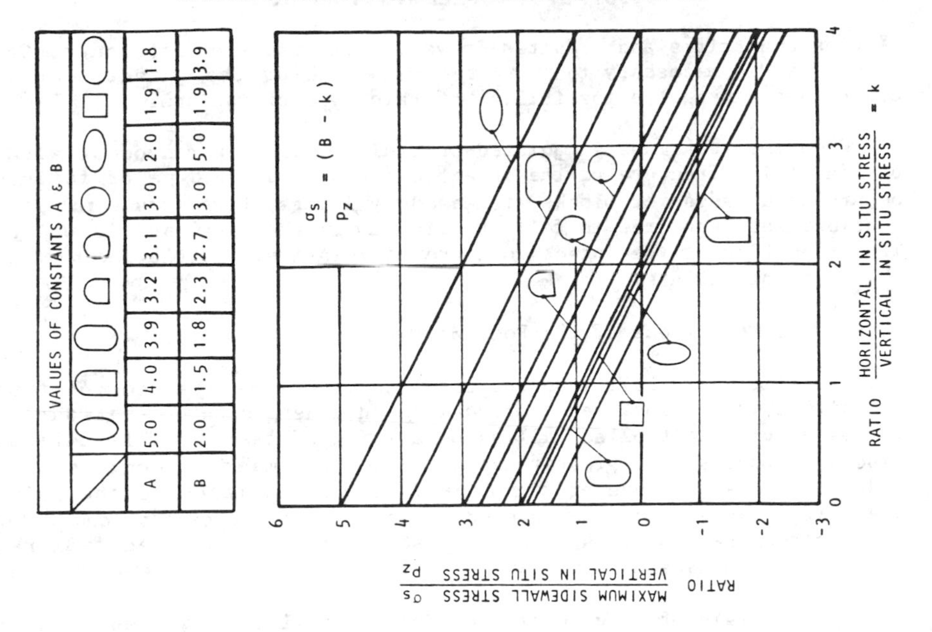

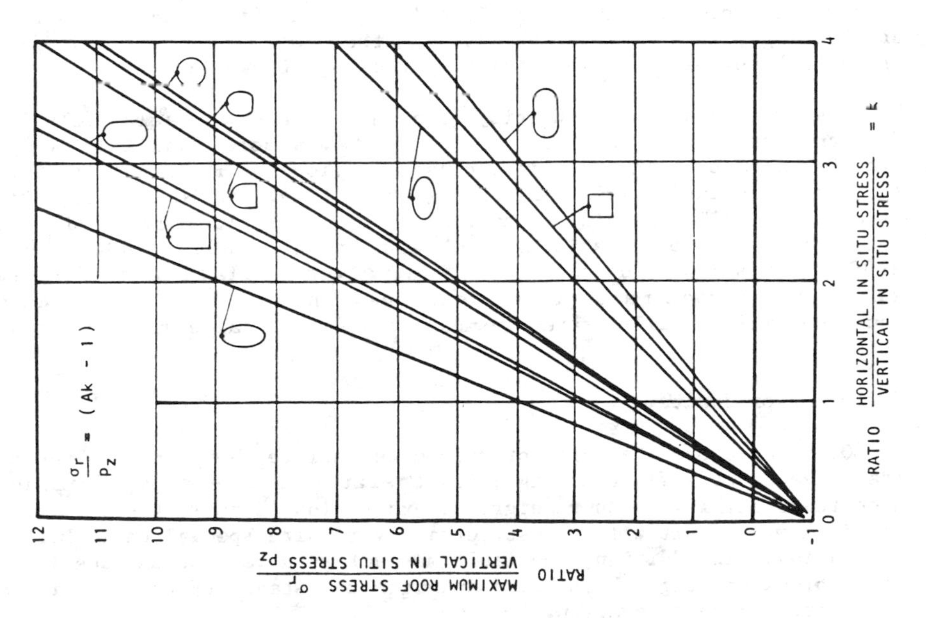

Figure 2. Maximum roof and sidewall stresses induced in the rock surrounding excavations of various shapes for different ratios of horizontal to vertial stress.

such as quartzites and granites in very high stress environments. Obviously it is necessary to know the strength of the intact rock in order to evaluate the possibility of this type of failure.

When the rock mass is jointed or faulted, failure can occur without involving fracture of the intact material. This type of failure occurs when wedges or blocks, released by intersecting structural discontinuities, are free to fall or slide from the roof or sidewalls. The properties of the intact rock are of relatively little interest in this type of failure.

Structural Conditions of the Rock Mass

At relatively shallow depths below surface, the most common type of failure in the rock mass surrounding an underground excavation involves gravity controlled falling or sliding of structurally defined blocks or wedges. At greater depths, the rock mass strength may be reduced by the presence of structural discontinuities to the point where it is lower than the induced stress around the excavation. Under these circumstances, both stress and structurally controlled failures may occur simultaneously.

The analysis of structurally controlled failure requires a knowledge of the orientation and inclination of significant faults, joints and bedding planes in the rock mass. Methods of data collection and analysis have been described fully by Hoek and Brown (1980a).

When the rock mass is heavily jointed but there are relatively few dominant structural features such as faults, a more qualitative approach, based upon the rock mass classifications of Barton et al (Barton, Lien and Lunde, 1974) and Bieniawski (1974), can be used to estimate the overall strength of the rock mass. Table I, summarized from Hoek and Brown's publications (Hoek and Brown, 1980a, 1980b, Hoek, 1980), gives a set of approximate equations relating rock mass strength and rock mass classifications. The application of these equations will be illustrated by means of a practical example later in this paper.

Influence of Faults

Over and above the types of rock mass failure described earlier, the presence of a fault of significant size can have a major impact upon the stability of an underground excavation. The soft gouge filling in a wide fault will almost certainly require special care during excavation. In addition, the fault may act as a release surface for a major block or wedge which could endanger the stability of a significant part of the excavation.

When it is impossible to avoid a fault or faults, it is essential that as much information as possible be gathered before the fault is

TABLE 1 - APPROXIMATE RELATIONSHIP BETWEEN ROCK MASS QUALITY AND CONSTANTS

Empirical failure criterion $\sigma_1 = \sigma_3 + \sqrt{m\sigma_c\sigma_3 + s\sigma_c^2}$ σ_1 = major principal stress σ_3 = minor principal stress σ_c = uniaxial compressive strength of intact rock, and m, s = empirical constants.	CARBONATE ROCKS WITH WELL DEVELOPED CRYSTAL CLEAVAGE *dolomite, limestone and marble*	LITHIFIED ARGILLACEOUS ROCKS *mudstone, siltstone, shale and slate (normal to cleavage)*	ARENACEOUS ROCKS WITH STRONG CRYSTALS AND POORLY DEVELOPED CRYSTAL CLEAVAGE *sandstone and quartzite*	FINE GRAINED POLYMINERALLIC IGNEOUS CRYSTALLINE ROCKS *andesite, dolerite, diabase and rhyolite*	COARSE GRAINED POLYMINERALLIC IGNEOUS AND METAMORPHIC CRYSTALLINE ROCKS *amphibolite, gabbro, gneiss, granite, norite and quartz-diorite*
INTACT ROCK SAMPLES *Laboratory size specimens free from joints* CSIR rating 100 NGI rating 500	m = 7.0 s = 1.0	m = 10.0 s = 1.0	m = 15.0 s = 1.0	m = 17.0 s = 1.0	m = 25.0 s = 1.0
VERY GOOD QUALITY ROCK MASS *Tightly interlocking undisturbed rock with unweathered joints at 1 to 3m.* CSIR rating 85 NGI rating 100	m = 3.5 s = 0.1	m = 5.0 s = 0.1	m = 7.5 s = 0.1	m = 8.5 s = 0.1	m = 12.5 s = 0.1
GOOD QUALITY ROCK MASS *Fresh to slightly weathered rock, slightly disturbed with joints at 1 to 3m.* CSIR rating 65 NGI rating 10	m = 0.7 s = 0.004	m = 1.0 s = 0.004	m = 1.5 s = 0.004	m = 1.7 s = 0.004	m = 2.5 s = 0.004
FAIR QUALITY ROCK MASS *Several sets of moderately weathered joints spaced at 0.3 to 1m.* CSIR rating 44 NGI rating 1	m = 0.14 s = 0.0001	m = 0.20 s = 0.0001	m = 0.30 s = 0.0001	m = 0.34 s = 0.0001	m = 0.50 s = 0.0001
POOR QUALITY ROCK MASS *Numerous weathered joints at 30 to 500mm with some gouge. Clean compacted waste rock.* CSIR rating 23 NGI rating 0.1	m = 0.04 s = 0.00001	m = 0.05 s = 0.00001	m = 0.08 s = 0.00001	m = 0.09 s = 0.00001	m = 0.13 s = 0.00001
VERY POOR QUALITY ROCK MASS *Numerous heavily weathered joints spaced < 50mm with gouge. Waste rock with fines.* CSIR rating 3 NGI rating 0.01	m = 0.007 s = 0	m = 0.010 s = 0	m = 0.015 s = 0	m = 0.017 s = 0	m = 0.025 s = 0

exposed in the excavation. Drilling from surface or probing ahead of an advancing heading is the most effective means of collecting this information and it should be used whenever a significant fault is anticipated.

Ground Water Conditions

Ground water pressure will seldom induce serious instability in underground excavations but the presence of significant quantities of ground water can cause disruption in the excavation process.

The most serious problems with ground water occur when it is encountered unexpectedly and it is essential that, whenever possible, the presence of significant amounts of ground water should be anticipated. As in the case of faults, drilling from surface or probing ahead of advancing headings is an effective method for evaluating ground water conditions.

ANALYSIS OF UNDERGROUND EXCAVATION STABILITY

One of the most effective times for a geotechnical engineer to become involved in a large underground excavation project is during the very early feasibility studies. Sound geotechnical advice given at this stage can minimize difficulties and disagreements later in the project.

Unfortunately, during the early feasibility stage, very little information is available and the geotechnical engineer has to base his advice upon experience and upon engineering or geological judgement. In an attempt to summarize his own experience, the author has compiled the crude correlation between rock mass quality and maximum excavation boundary stress presented in Figure 3. This graph may be used to obtain an initial evalation of excavation stability as follows.

Suppose that an underground powerhouse cavern is to be constructed in massive gneiss at a depth of 300 m below surface. A geotechnical engineer asked to comment on the proposal finds that the only information available consists of the logs of some diamond drilled holes around the proposed site.

On the basis of the information contained in these logs and from his own examination of the core, the following estimates are made by the geotechnical engineer:

Unconfined compressive strength of intact gneiss	150 MPa
Rock mass quality - "Good"	
CSIR Rock Mass Rating	65 - 75
NGI Tunnelling Quality Index Q	10 - 40

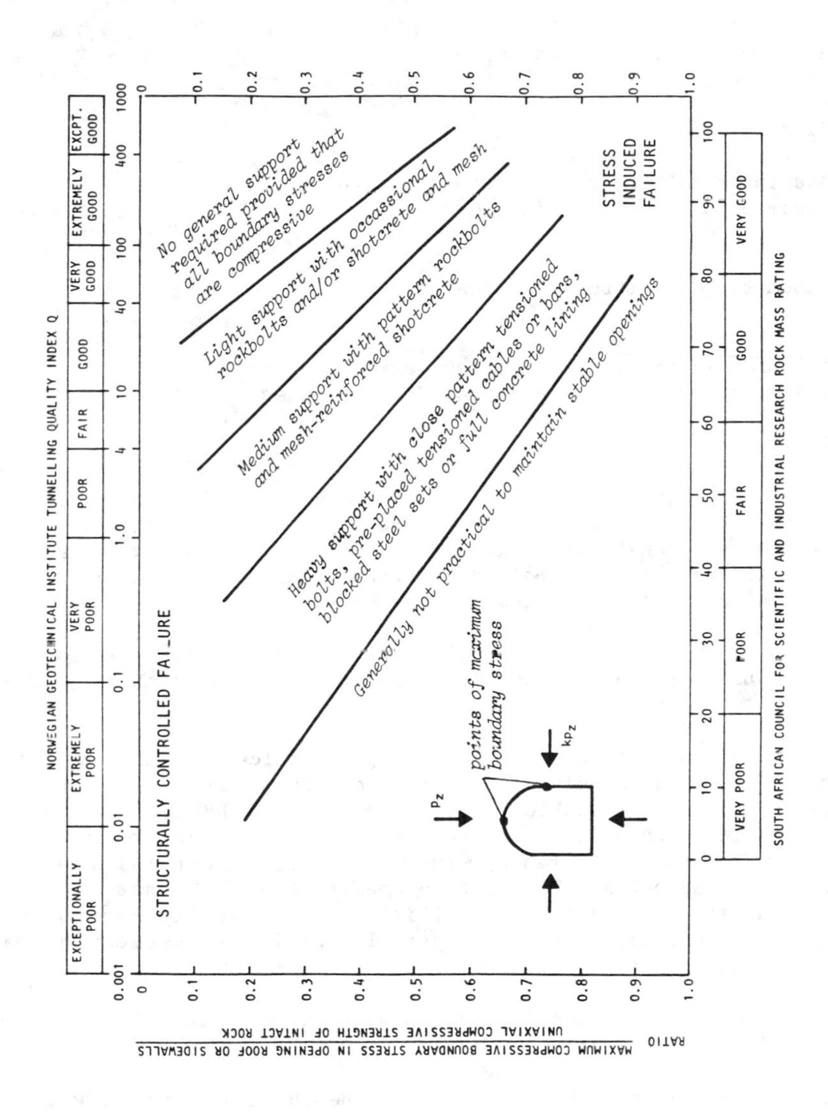

Figure 3. Approximate relationship between excavation stability, rock mass quality and maximum compressive boundary stress.

From Figure 1:

Vertical stress p_z at 300 m	8 MPa
Average horizontal stress kp_z at 300 m	12 - 24 MPa
Ratio of horizontal to vertical stress k	1.5 to 3

From Figure 2:

(Assuming a tall horseshoe shaped cavern)	
Maximum boundary stress in roof	5 p_z (40 MPa) to 11 p_z (88 MPa)
Maximum boundary stress in sidewall	0 to -1.5 p_z (-12 MPa)
Ratio of maximum compressive boundary stress to uniaxial compressive strength of intact gneiss	0.27 to 0.59

From Figure 3:

For good rock mass quality (CSIR rating 65-75 NGI rating 10-40) and for ratios of maximum compressive boundary stress to uniaxial compressive strength of intact rock of 0.27 to 0.59, the use of medium to heavy pattern bolting with mesh reinforced shotcrete appears to be necessary to ensure stability.

Note that the presence of tensile stresses in the cavern sidewalls is also undesirable and may give rise to additional stability problems.

On the basis of this assessment, the geotechnical engineer advises the owner that, even assuming the worst conditions, it appears to be feasible to construct a stable cavern at a depth of 300 m in this rock mass. It is recommended that in situ stress measurements be carried out in an exploration adit being mined and that structural geology mapping be carried out in this adit to confirm the rock mass quality estimates and to evaluate the possibility of structurally controlled failures as opposed to the stress controlled failures assumed in the preliminary analysis.

Once these further investigations have been completed, the following conclusions are drawn:

The quality of the rock mass at cavern depth is confirmed with a best estimate of the CSIR rock mass rating = 65 and the NGI tunnelling quality index Q = 12. The vertical stress at cavern depth is measured at 8.1 MPa and the horizontal stress acting normal to the axis of the cavern is 16.2 MPa.

From Table 1, the failure criterion for the rock mass is estimated as:

$$\sigma_1 = \sigma_3 + \sqrt{m\sigma_c\sigma_3 + s\sigma_c^2} \qquad (2)$$

where

σ_1 = major principal stress,
σ_3 = minor principal stress,
σ_c = 150 MPa is the uniaxial compressive strength of the intact gneiss,
m = 2.5 is an empirical constant and
s = 0.004 is a second empirical constant.

The original proposal for the cavern design visualized a 26 m span by 41 m high horseshoe shaped excavation which would house valves, turbines and transformers. An analysis of the stresses induced around this cavern in terms of the failure criterion defined by equation 2 results in the stress/strength ratio contours illustrated in Figure 4.

Although these contours do not give a precise indication of the quantity of rock which is likely to fail, experience suggests that unstable excavation conditions are likely to occur when the volume of overstressed material (shown by the shaded region contained within the contour marked 1 in Figure 4) is substantial in relation to the volume of the excavation. In the case of this particular cavern, shear failure would occur to depths of 3 to 5 m in both roof and floor and tensile failure would occur to a depth of about 8 m in the sidewalls. The volume of overstressed material indicated in Figure 4 suggests that it may be both difficult and expensive to stabilize this cavern.

At this point, the geotechnical engineer is authorized to examine a number of alternative solutions. The design finally adopted is illustrated in Figure 5 which shows three smaller excavations. The penstock valves have been moved upstream into a small gallery with a span of approximately 15 m and a height of about 20 m. The transformers are housed in a similar gallery downstream of the machine hall. The machine hall has been reduced to a shaped cavern of 20 m span and 30 m height. By carefully optimizing the shapes of the three excavations and the distances between them, the zone of potentially overstressed rock has been reduced to about 1 to 1.5 m which is uniformly distributed around all the openings.

It is recommended that each excavation be excavated by means of a central 8 m x 8 m pilot heading at roof level, side slashing to open the full cavern roof and then benching down in a series of 8 to 10 m high benches. At each excavation stage, a pattern of 3 m long 25 mm diameter reinforcing bars are installed on a 1.5 m x 1.5 m grid. The

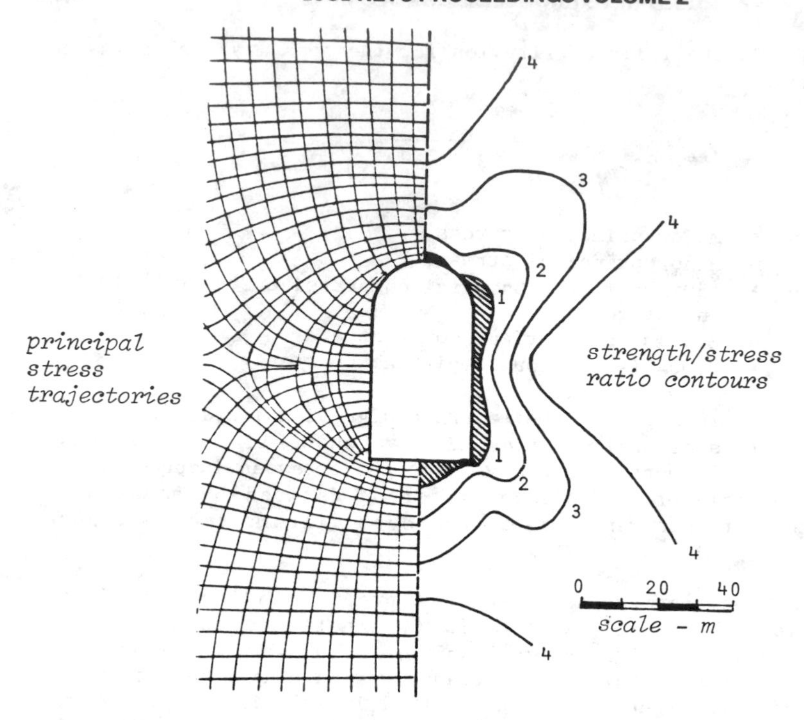

Figure 4. Principal stress trajectories and strength/stress contours surrounding a 26m span cavern in good quality gneiss at a depth of 300m below surface.

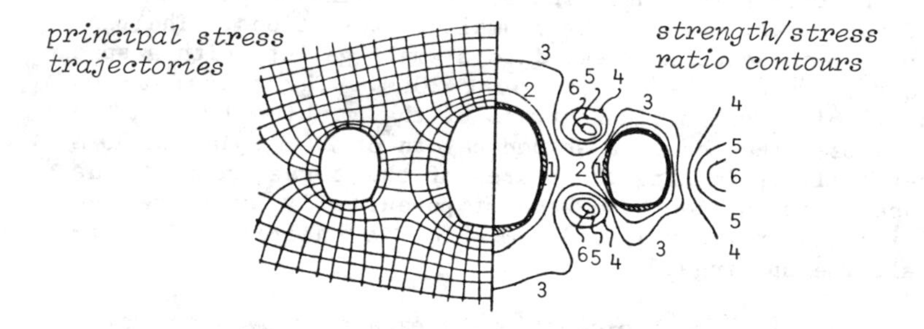

Figure 5. Principal stress trajectories and strength/stress contours surrounding a 20m span cavern with adjacent valve and transformer galleries in good quality gneiss at a depth of 300m below surface.

ends of the bars are threaded to allow for the attachment of a face plate and nut and the bars are anchored into the holes by means of a fast-setting resin cartridge. The remainder of the hole is filled by means of resin from a series of slow-setting cartridges and these bond the reinforcing bar into the hole after it has been tensioned to about 10 tonnes load. A 50 mm layer of shotcrete is applied to any areas of the roof or sidewall which exhibit close jointing and the tendency to ravel between rock bolt face plates.

Cast in situ concrete crane beams are anchored to the cavern sidewalls and a light gantry provides full access to the cavern roof while the final benching of the lower part of the cavern is being completed and while the main crane is being assembled. Final treatment of the cavern roof and sidewalls is carried out from this gantry and consists of attaching a 100 x 100 x 4.2 mm weldmesh to the bolts by means of a second washer and nut. Intermediate mesh fixing is by means of short grouted pins. Once the mesh has been attached and pulled tight to the rock, a layer of 50 mm of shotcrete is placed over the entire area.

CONCLUSION

The hypothetical example described above illustrates one of several approaches which may be adopted in designing large underground openings. In this example, stress induced instability was considered to be the dominant design problem and the excavation shape and the support system was chosen to deal with this problem. In excavations in which structurally controlled failures are considered to control stability, the optimum shape and support system may be entirely different from that arrived at in this example.

In most underground excavation engineering, the dominant problem is generally that of construction schedule and very large cost penalties are associated with the non-availability of the power (or other product) if start-up target dates are not met. The geotechnical engineer who is responsible for the design of support for large underground excavations should keep this construction schedule in mind at all times. His support design should aim not only at eliminating potential instability but should be capable of rapid and efficient installation. If possible, support installation should be integrated into the drill-blast-muck cycle and systems such as "one-shot" resin anchored and grouted bolts are preferable to support systems for which second and sometimes third access must be made available. For the same reason, the use of steel sets or full concrete linings should be avoided unless the ground conditions are such that grouted rock bolts are ineffective.

REFERENCES

Barton, N.R., Lien, R., and Lunde, J., 1974, "Engineering Classification of Rock Masses for the Design of Tunnel Support", Rock Mechanics, Vol. 6, No. 4, pages 189-236.

Bieniawski, Z.T., 1974, "Geomechanics Classification of Rock Masses and its Application in Tunnelling", Proc. Third Intnl. Congress on Rock Mechanics, ISRM, Denver, Vol. 11A, pages 27-32.

Brown, E.T., and Hoek, E., 1978, "Trends in Relationships between Measured in situ Stresses and Depth", Intnl. J. Rock Mech. Min. Sci. and Geomech. Abstracts, Vol. 15, pages 211-215.

Hoek, E., and Brown, E.T., 1980, "Underground Excavations in Rock", Inst. Min. Metall., London, 527 pages.

Hoek, E., and Brown, E.T., 1980, "Empirical Strength Criterion for Rock Masses", J. Geotechnical Eng. Div., ASCE, Vol. 106, No. GT9, pages 1013-1035.

Hoek, E., 1980, "An Empirical Strength Criterion and its use in Designing Slopes and Tunnels in Heavily Jointed Weathered Rock", Proc. Sixth Southeast Asian Conference on Soil Engineering, Taiwan, Vol. 11, in press.

Chapter 73

REPORT ON THE SYMPOSIUM ON THE
DEVELOPMENT OF UNDERGROUND SPACE

D.C. Willett

Acres American, Incorporated

INTRODUCTION

The Symposium on the Development of Underground Space, held in Seattle, Washington, from October 1 through 3, 1980, was organized by the "Deep Space" subcommittee of the ASCE's Underground Research Technology Council. The primary objective of the symposium was the exploration of the interfaces between the investigation, design and construction of large underground facilities in "deep space" which, for the purposes of the committee, has been defined as starting at 100m below ground surface. The meeting focussed primarily on tunnels, caverns and shafts in hard rock; the meeting format comprised a number of brief presentations concerned with the technical aspects of investigation, design and construction, followed by an open discussion, and concluded with the assembly of recommendations regarding the interface problem by the symposium participants. The principal considerations brought out during the symposium, and a general review of the conclusions, are briefly presented in the following paragraphs.

INVESTIGATION

The sessions dealing with "Investigation" were chaired by Dr. H. Pratt. Presentations were made by Dr. D.C. Banks, Dr. W.A. Hustrulid and Dr. Pratt. The extent of the interface of the investigation phase with the other (design and construction) phases of an underground facility will depend in large measure upon the nature of the facility; at one end of the spectrum, the investigation must be in continuous and closely coupled relationship with the design of a radwaste facility. At the other end of the spectrum, for (say) a small mining operation, the interface is largely associated with the initial development, with only minor on-going involvement.

The investigation interfaces are concerned primarily with (a) site evaluation - can the site meet the required technical, environmental and economic criteria; (b) design - identification and measurement of the properties of the rock mass in relation to the required function of the facility; and (c) construction - evaluation of the effect of the rock mass properties on (i) the performance of construction equipment, (ii) the provision of temporary support, and (iii) the requirement for special measures during the construction phase.

As the location of the proposed facility below the ground surface becomes deeper, not only does the cost of investigation increase but also the actual feasibility of obtaining useful data diminishes rapidly requiring a significant degree of extrapolation from the small amount of direct measurement. There develops, therefore, a philosophy which directs the selection of the site in such a way, and to such a location that this extrapolation can be undertaken with a reasonable degree of confidence, as can be seen from the radwaste siting programs in which attention tends to be focussed on large monolithic bodies of rock.

Unfortunately, as the proposed facility location gets deeper, so the investigation interfaces with the subsequent phases become more critical and more significant. Combining this factor with an assessment of the cost-risk trade-off associated with the potential effects of failure of the facility, it is not difficult to see where many of the current problems in the nuclear radwaste field arise.

Interface improvement will come from the development of techniques better able to provide more data about a greater volume of subsurface space at lower cost. There is obviously value in examining carefully just what needs to be measured.

DESIGN

This session was chaired by Dr. Norman Owen, with presentations made by Dr. E. Hoek, Dr. G. Hocking and Dr. A.J. Hendron. The two current approaches to design - one largely empirical, the other principally deterministic - were reviewed in relation to the investigation and construction interfaces: both methods require an appreciation of several common factors, including:

Investigation - nature and frequency of discontinuities
- orientation of discontinuities
- magnitude and direction of in-situ stresses

Construction - sequence
- methods
- engineering/construction interface.

The two primary modes of failure in underground openings - structurally-controlled failure, in which blocks or wedges are released along existing structural discontinuities, such as joints or shears, and stress-related failure in which stresses induced in the rock mass by excavation of the opening exceed the strength of the rock - can be identified, the former generally occurring at relatively shallow depths (less than 300m), the latter at greater depths.

As rock mass quality tends to improve with depth, the situation is that in hard rock, for a zone extending perhaps from 300m to 1000m below surface, neither structurally-controlled nor stress-induced problems are particularly serious, and many caverns have been successfully excavated at these depths.

From the design standpoint, therefore, there are some particularly significant interfaces both with the investigation and construction phases of underground work which mean that neither can be undertaken without reference to the other two, and there will be a continuous cross-feed between the three phases. In the investigation/design interface, both the proposed design procedure and the anticipated failure mode will have a very significant interface with the extent and subjects of the exploration: for instance, there is little point in expending large amounts of money attempting to undertake joint surveys for caverns to be located at great depths, any more than there is in undertaking extensive rock strength testing for caverns at shallow depths. However, in both cases, a thorough appreciation of the rock mass modulus can be essential in establishing the required characteristics and arrangement of the support systems.

At the design/construction interface, there is of course always the classic "who's responsible for safety" problem, particularly in the civil engineering industry, a problem exacerbated by traditional U.S. contractual arrangements. Elsewhere and more recently in the U.S., a very real effort has been made to provide for a close working relationship between the designer and the construction team to provide "instant" review and assessment of geotechnical conditions at the advancing face, and the provision of support required related directly to conditions actually encountered within the context of the overall design.

With regard to the design and excavations for containment or exclusion of fluids or gases, a number of numerical models exist, but these are currently somewhat limited in their scope. Knowledge of the permeability and hydrological regime are critical in relation to the design of such projects as compressed air storage and nuclear waste disposal. Current investigative methods provide data on only small volumes of rock; little reliable information is obtainable without major expenditures for techniques which carry the danger of influencing the actual groundwater regime itself.

CONSTRUCTION

This session was chaired by Mr. L. Jones, with presentations by Mr. T. McCusker, Mr. A.G. Provost, and M. deG. Salter. In both the mining and civil engineering branches of the industry, construction technology has advanced to the point at which tunnel or cavern excavation can be undertaken at great depths in adverse rock conditions. Costs for mining work have been significantly less than for civil engineered projects because of (a) different union practices - mining unions in general tolerate a wide range of duties and hence a smaller workplace than the civil engineering unions; (b) different approaches to rock support - many mines follow a "rob and run" approach, allowing the roof to collapse after the ore has been extracted, while civil engineered projects normally have to provide for essentially permanent support of the roof and walls; (c) different schedules - mines are often excavated over many years, allowing a more detailed knowledge of the material characteristics and a more effective use of equipment than for civil engineered caverns in which schedules are short and production rates high.

None the less, civil engineers are beginning to use many techniques, such as large diameter blast holes and multi-face operation, hitherto considered the province of the miner, in an effort to keep costs down.

Beyond 100m below ground surface (except for side-hill locations) access to underground works is gained almost exclusively by vertical shafts. Conventional drill and blast methods for shaft sinking are slow and costly, with the result that major efforts are being made to develop large diameter boring techniques, with varying degrees of success. At least one manufacturer now offers a machine designed to drill an 8m shaft to a depth of 1000m, using a two-pass system.

Cavern excavation techniques range from conventional heading and benching to increasing use of road-header equipment in smaller tunnels where rock conditions are appropriate. Little use is made in civil engineering work of mining techniques such as stoping and block caving, principally because of concern both as to long-term roof and wall stability and also in regard to maintaining accurate wall profiles.

Principal interfaces with the investigation phase relate to establishing the feasibility of the various methods of excavation through the assessment of the key material properties. This is particularly significant in relation to the use of drilling, milling and boring machines where not only a knowledge of the properties of the intact rock, but also of the behavior of the rock mass during and after excavation, are critical to the successful application of excavating equipment.

GENERAL CONCLUSIONS

The general mood of the symposium seemed to be that there has been sufficient development of design technology and construction equipment to allow virtually any cavern to be constructed in any geological regime, although economy may preclude some solutions.

However, it has to be recognized that current investigation technology cannot, even under the most favorable conditions, provide sufficient data to designers and contractors to allow the preparation of a final and definitive design prior to start of construction. This lack of definition can, for many projects, be reduced to a level at which the risk which must be carried by the owner is small enough to be acceptable and negotiable through appropriate flexibility built into the contracting process. It is only in the more critical areas of nuclear and toxic waste disposal, and perhaps in compressed air storage, that the margin of residual risk at the start of construction must be reduced to a level which places very stringent demands upon both the investigation and design processes, and it is in this area that undoubtedly more development is required.

Chapter 74

METRORAIL'S DUAL CHAMBER ROCK TUNNEL
STATION--TWO CAN BE SIMPLER THAN ONE

by Charles W. Daugherty

Chief, Geology Section
De Leuw, Cather & Company
Washington, D. C.

INTRODUCTION

The Washington Metropolitan Area Transit Authority's (WMATA's) rapid transit system, Metro, ultimately will comprise 162.5 km (101 miles) of line divided among 10 routes. As shown in Figure 1, about 24 km (15 miles) of the system will consist of mined rock tunnels distributed along the A, B, C and K Routes. The structural construction contracts for all of the A, C and K Route rock tunnels are complete and trains are running in about one-third of them. A contract for construction of rock tunnel section B-9, the southernmost third of the B Route, was awarded on June 27, 1980. The final design of Sections B-10 and B-11a, the remainder of the rock tunnel portions of the B Route and the Metro system, are well advanced and should be under construction by 1982.

Of Metro's 87 stations, 11 will have been constructed by mining in solid rock, a not inconsiderable achievement, since each structure must be over 183 m (600 feet) long, wide enough to accommodate two trains and one or two passenger platforms, and high enough to achieve a stable arching action without encumbering columns. With the passage of years, some original priorities have been reordered, and ways have been sought to streamline and simplify this most complex of Metro structures without grossly violating the architectural standards that make it unique. This paper will summarize that search, and describe the design and construction aspects of the resulting product, the dual chamber rock tunnel station.

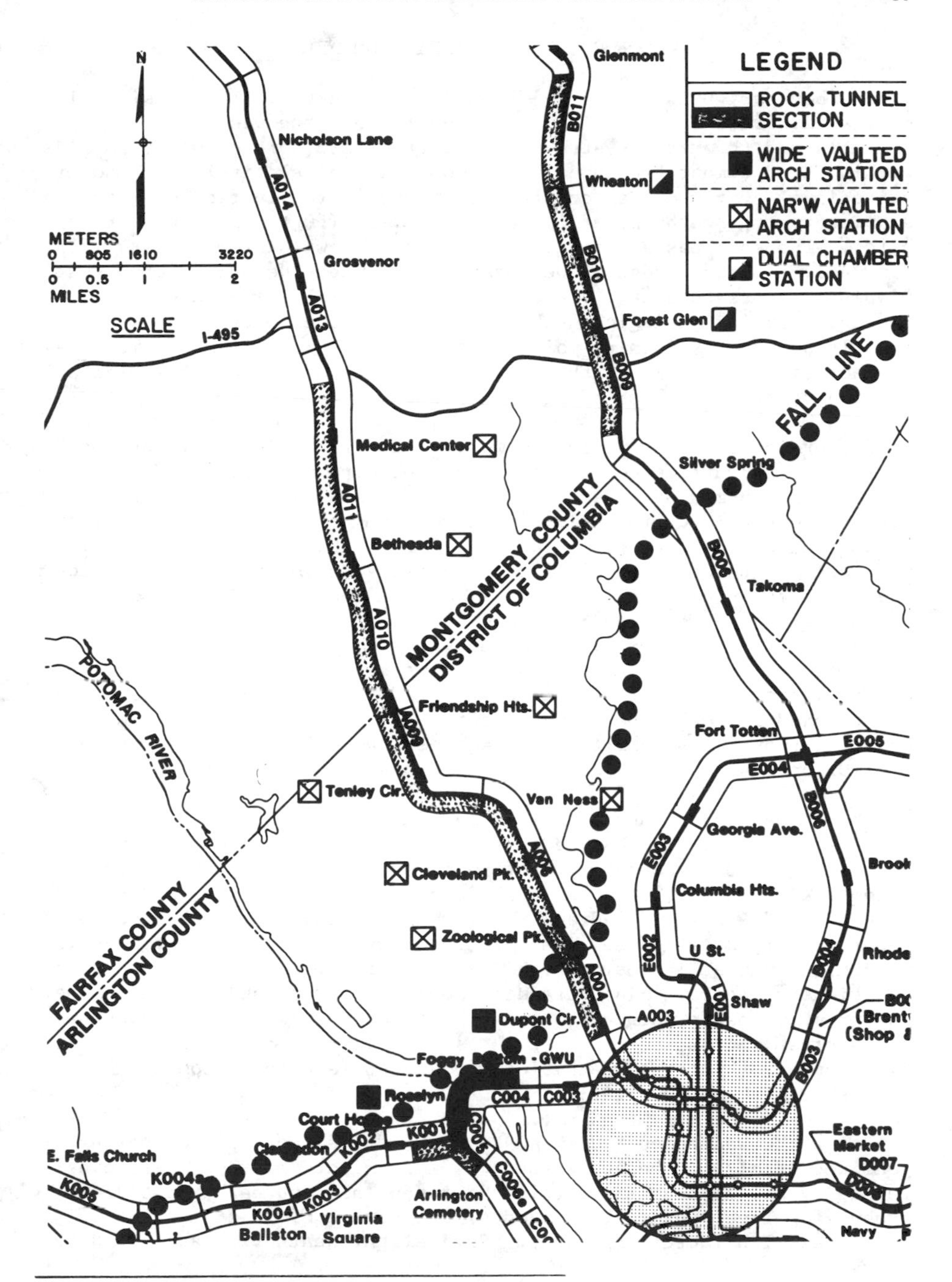

FIGURE 1: METRO GENERAL LOCATION PLAN

GEOLOGY OF THE WASHINGTON AREA

The boundary between two major physiographic provinces of significantly different characteristics passes through the District of Columbia and the Metro system. The northwestern portion of Metro lies within the Piedmont Province, which comprises a relatively thin cover of residual overburden on crystalline bedrock, the surface of which is sloping to the southeast at 11 to 24 m per km (60 to 125 feet per mile). The southeastern portion of Metro lies within the Coastal Plain Province, a broad, wedge-shaped mass of sediments deposited atop that sloping bedrock surface. The NE-SW trending "Fall Line" separating these dissimilar geologic environments is so named because it was originally defined by joining points where rivers grade from the more resistant Piedmont rocks to the softer sediments of the Coastal Plains, leading to the formation of falls or rapids.

For projects to the north and west of the Fall Line, all but the shallowest subsurface construction must be within bedrock. Much of the bedrock was formed by metamorphism of sandy and clayey sediments to form the Wissahickon formation, which is one of the family of similar metamorphics extending from New England to Alabama. For Metro designers, one of the most significant characteristics of the schistose-to-gneissic Wissahickon and some of its associated units is the foliation, which strikes N5°W to N30°E and dips 40° to 80° to the west. The foliation imparts a distinct plane of weakness to the rock, and is associated with numerous shear zones of varying size. Since the strike of the foliation is subparallel to the alignments of the two longest lines constructed in rock, the A and B Routes, it has tended to be a major cause of tunnel instability as blocks of rock relax in a westward direction once some of the confining mass has been excavated.

The second major tunnel-influencing characteristic of the bedrock is the degree to which it has been affected by weathering. In Metro geologic logging the weathering profile is subdivided into the upper Decomposed Rock (D), the mid level Transition Zone (D-WR), and the lower Weathered & Jointed Bedrock (WR). WR material is true bedrock which generally yields at least some core recovery, sometimes as high as 100 percent. Even at its hardest, however, it is highly jointed and the constituent minerals' intergranular bonding so weakened by the weathering process that prudence requires the placement of tunnel crowns below it if other factors permit. It is not uncommon in the Metro system to find depths of intense weathering (ground surface to bottom of WR) that exceed 30 m (100 feet).

Below the Weathered & Jointed Bedrock, the effects of weathering are confined mainly to the joint surfaces and affect the rock mass to a generally slight degree. Within the essentially unweathered bedrock, except for localized fracture zones, the amount of jointing generally decreases with increasing depth. Some slight weathering and the Rock

Quality Designation (RQD)* determine whether such rock is classified as Highly Jointed, Moderately Jointed, or Relatively Sound. The changes from one weathering or jointing zone to another are quite gradational and irregular, notwithstanding any apparently definite "contacts" shown on geologic profiles.

GENERAL HISTORY OF ROCK TUNNEL STATION DEVELOPMENT

Vaulted Arch Station. Early in the planning of Metro it was decided that the inside configuration of the underground cut-and-cover stations would be large, free span coffered vaults approximately 9 m (30 feet) high and more than 15 m (50 feet) wide in order for them to harmonize with the monumental architecture of the Nation's Capital. When constructed by mining in solid rock, these same stations were to have an excavated height of more than 12 m (40 feet). The added height was necessary for two reasons. First, it created the arch size necessary for stability in an extremely wide opening. Second, the space between the excavation support and an inner architectural shell (the latter being constructed of precast concrete panels and providing the desired 9x15 m dimensions) was necessary for air conditioning ducts because it was not possible to create the dome relief shafts used over cut-and-cover stations. Mining of these large cavities in rock at the relatively shallow depths required for passenger access was unprecedented. Within 30 to 60 m (100 to 200 feet) of the surface, the effects of rock weathering and jointing can be pronounced, and the depth-induced ground stresses are not high enough to assure a natural arching over the mined opening. Heavy support and very careful construction procedures are necessary to assure the integrity of the excavation.

Metro's first rock running tunnel, Section A-4a, was constructed as a double track horseshoe. The resultant narrow track centers mandated side platforms for Section A-4b, DuPont Circle Station, Metro's first rock tunnel station. This resulted in a very large station excavation that was 13.4 m (44 feet) high and 21 m (69 feet) from wall to wall (Figure 2). To insure the integrity of this opening in rock of relatively low quality, the arch above the 5.5 m (18-foot) high vertical portion of the station walls was widened to 23.8 m (78 feet). This made it possible to pre-excavate and stabilize an "umbrella" under which the lower bench could be constructed with greater ease. The

*Rock Quality Designation (RQD) is a parameter which reflects the intensity of jointing in a recovered rock core run. For any particular core run, the RQD equals the sum of the lengths of pieces of core longer than 10.2 cm (4 in) divided by the total length of core run, expressed as a percentage. "Quality" designations are assigned to the rock cores according to the computed figures as follows:
RQD 0-25% = very poor; 25%-50% = poor; 50%-75% = fair; 75%-90% = good; 90%-100% = excellent.

cross sectional area of the station cavity was about 242 sq m (2600 sq ft), a size that requires excavation in many small increments or multiple drifts. DuPont Circle Station was constructed in eight different drifts (not counting the pilot tunnel excavated by the A-4a running tunnel contractor) between June, 1971, and September, 1974.

After DuPont Circle, the remainder of the rock tunnel stations on the A Route were slimmed down by some degree. The desire to promote use of Tunnel Boring Machines (TBMs) led to a move to design only single track running tunnels on 11.23 m (36 ft - 10 in) track centers, which meant that trains would run close to the walls rather than through the centers of the stations. The station centers were reserved for passenger platforms, and the new configuration (Figure 2) made it possible to decrease the wall-to-wall widths by as much as 3 m (10 feet). Although the excavation heights were kept to about 13.4 m (44 feet) for assured arching effect and for dome relief, the cross sectional areas were as much as 51 sq m (550 sq ft) smaller than DuPont Circle. Such a difference would perhaps not be so important in deep, sound rock, but in the relatively shallow Metro stations, any substantial reduction in size means the need for less support and a simplification in the construction procedures that may be very worthwhile.

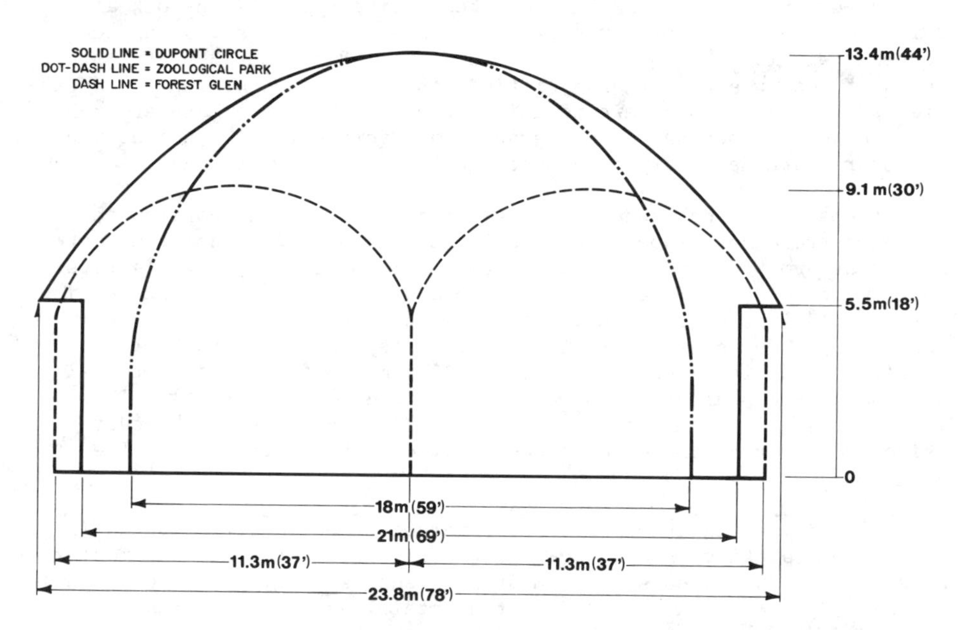

FIGURE 2: DRAWING SHOWING THE EXCAVATION OUTLINES OF METRO'S OLDEST (DUPONT CIRCLE), INTERMEDIATE (ZOOLOGICAL PART) AND NEWEST (FOREST GLEN) ROCK TUNNEL STATION TYPES. IN THIS FIGURE, THE TWO FOREST GLEN TRAINROOMS, ACTUALLY WIDELY SEPARATED, ARE SHOWN IN CONTIGUITY FOR A BETTER INDICATION OF TOTAL CROSS SECTIONAL AREA.

For example, the A-6b contractor constructed Zoological Park Station in only four basic drifts, not counting the pilot tunnel and running tunnels already excavated through the station by the A-6a running tunnel contractor.

Dual Chamber Station. When the design of the A Route was in its final stages, design of the B Route began, with the slimmed down vaulted arch still the rock tunnel station of choice. However, weathering on the B Route extended much deeper than on the A, and tunnels were driven to great depths to achieve rock sound enough for safe construction. (Note: The geology was not conducive to shallow soft ground tunnels with cut-and-cover stations; nor would community impact permit long stretches of cut-and-cover or aerial structure.) This was particularly true at the Forest Glen site in Section B-9, where a vaulted arch station would have had to be placed at the unprecedented depth of 64 m (210 feet) to T/R (top of rail), contrasted with the previous deepest station at 41 m (135 feet). This was so deep that access could not be provided by the standard escalator system. Instead, designers provided for six high speed elevators to be constructed inside a 17 m (56-foot) diam shaft. In spite of its depth, the station was not in any sounder rock than many previous ones, and would have had to be constructed with the usual system of multiple drifts. The large size of the elevator shaft and the depth of it and the two standard vent shafts meant that these structures would be unusually difficult to construct. It was decided to relax some of the architectural criteria in use until that time, and turn the station into a smaller, simpler structure.

The rock tunnel station that resulted from this effort at simplification will be used for both Forest Glen and for the shallower Wheaton Station in Section B-10. Called the dual chamber concept, it has two separate trainrooms rather than one, with the passengers entering and exiting from facilities excavated from the intervening pillar of rock. A plan view of Forest Glen Station is shown in Figure 3. Each trainroom is a horseshoe about 11.3 m (37 feet) wide by 9.1 m (30 feet) high in excavation dimensions, not much larger than a double track running tunnel. This creates a cross sectional area of about 92 sq m (990 sq ft), which when doubled to include both trainrooms, is still smaller than the approximate 200 sq m (2150 sq ft) of previous stations. The two halves of Forest Glen Station are spaced to provide at the entrance an extraordinary 47.2 m (155 feet) between track centers, and create the necessary space for elevator facilities as well as an adequately thick mass of rock between the elevator shaft and the inside wall of each trainroom. This spacing also provides a minimum of 32 m (105 feet) of rock between inbound and outbound chambers in the remainder of the station, a pillar to tunnel width ratio of at least 2.8 to 1. Except for areas of cross adits, the chambers can be considered essentially independent. Because of its smaller and less critical entrance configuration, Wheaton Station has closer 26.8 m (88-foot) track centers, but the generally sound rock will still insure little interaction between the two trainrooms during construction. In

Figure 2 the two trainrooms of a dual chamber station have been pulled together and superimposed over DuPont Circle and Zoological Park in order to show the relative excavation size of this newest station type.

In extremely sound rock where large openings can be excavated without the need to work with numerous multiple drifts, the vaulted arch station might be less difficult to construct than the dual chamber.

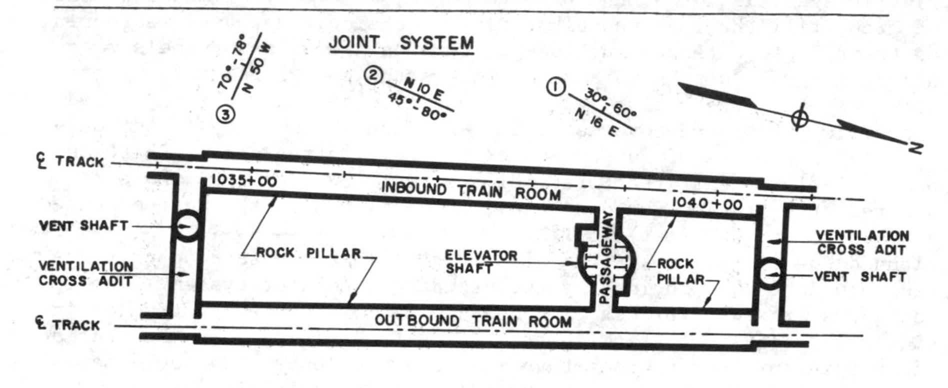

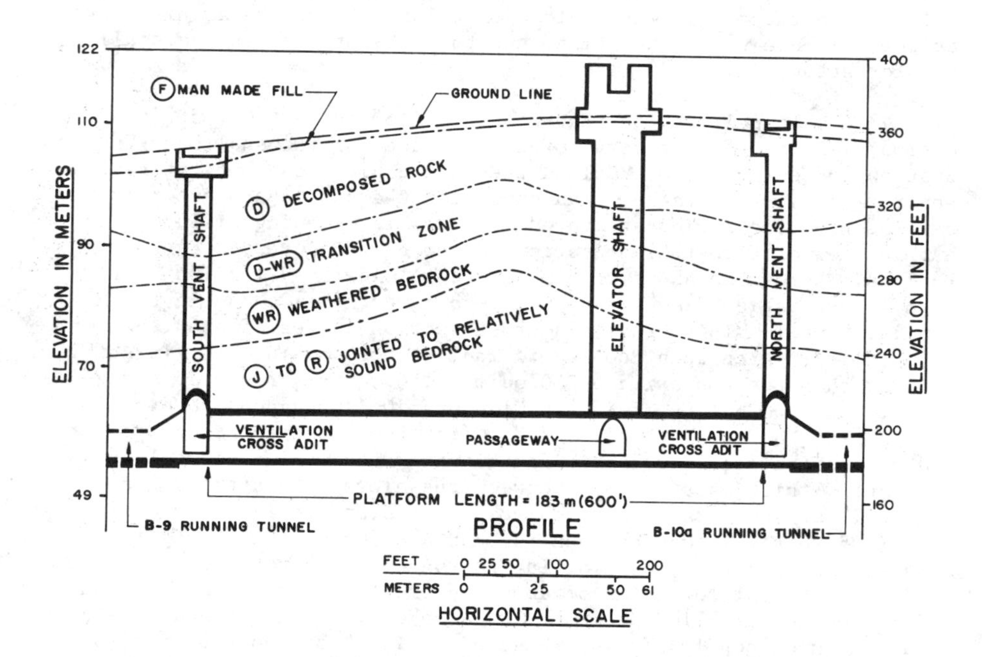

FIGURE 3. FOREST GLEN STATION, GENERAL CONFIGURATION AND GEOLOGY

However, this does not hold true in the rock that characterizes Metro station locations. In the blocky rock of Forest Glen, heavy support would have been required for the original large station. More importantly, the small openings of the dual chamber configuration do not require excavation in many small increments. The worst to be expected is a heading and bench scheme that comprises two drifts per opening, much simpler than the six to eight drifts required of the larger station. This lessened criticality of the excavation operation has the added effect of eliminating the need for expensive pilot tunnels, since the need to know exact crown geology is greatly reduced.

DETAILS OF FOREST GLEN STATION

Station Layout and Alignment. As shown in Figure 3, the Forest Glen entrance intersects the station within the northern one-third of its length. For passenger circulation a central intersection is preferred, but other considerations caused the station to be moved south of its ideal siting location. Land use aspects of the site would not permit that southward move for the entrance facility. The entrance shaft requires an internal diameter of 15.8 m (52 feet) to accommodate an emergency stairwell and the six passenger elevators. Structural walls that are 0.6 m (2 feet) thick result in an excavation diameter of 17 m (56 feet) or more, depending upon the exact construction method and amount of overbreak. Architectural and mechanical considerations would permit a square shaft, but it was given a circular shape to increase its structural stability. Fare gates are located in a below grade passenger facility that feeds directly into the two banks of elevators, which travel vertically from entrance level at elevation +109.4 m (+359 feet) to platform level at +56.1 m (+184 feet).

The lengths of vertical shafts and rise of elevators have been advantageously shortened by the change to a dual chamber structure. The smaller station can be set somewhat higher in the geologic profile than the larger station because it does not require as much cover for stability, a fact which permitted raising the overall vertical alignment at Forest Glen by about 3 m (10 feet). But even if the crown elevation had remained the same as it would have been for the large station, all shafts would still be 4.3 m (14 feet) shorter because the dual chamber has that much less height from invert to crown. This constitutes an important consideration in the case of the large elevator shaft because the combination of smaller station and shallower alignment has resulted in a lessening of shaft length by about 7.3 m (24 feet). The maximum depth of the station, measured from the highest point of ground to the bottom of the invert slab, is now approximately 58 m (190 feet).

At platform level the connection between elevators and trainrooms is provided by a horseshoe shaped passageway that has an excavation width of about 9 m (30 feet) and a height that roughly matches that of the station. With the entrance shaft set precisely half way between the two trainrooms, spacing is such that at least 7.6 m (25 feet) of rock is provided between the excavation outline of the shaft and the closest excavation outline of either chamber. Without such rock masses, the large shaft adjacent to two 11.3 m (37-foot) wide tunnels would have created in effect an extremely wide mined opening with almost no crown cover at that spot. An arching effect to permit the rock to help support itself could not have been achieved.

Ordinarily, trainrooms spread to a particular spacing would maintain that spacing and be parallel for the entire length of the station. In this case, however, the picture is complicated by the need for a double crossover at Forest Glen. Construction of such a facility, which permits trains to cross between outbound and inbound tracks, is achieved by eliminating the intervening pillar of rock from between running tunnels. Crossovers need to be as close as possible to their associated station, and are generally appended to the station. At Forest Glen the wide tunnel spacing made this impossible, so the crossover was moved northward to the point where the spread tunnels converge to their normal track center spacing of 11.23 m (36 ft - 10 in). By skewing the station trainrooms, this convergence was achieved within 427 m (1400 feet) of the northern end of the passenger platforms, but the realignment does cause track centers to vary from 51.8 m (170 feet) at the south end of the station to 45.7 m (150 feet) at the north.

As with any Metro station, the Forest Glen vent shafts are there primarily to relieve the pressure from the "piston effect"--the mass of air piled up and pushed along in front of a train speeding through a small tunnel. A second purpose for the shafts is to serve as housing for stairways required for emergency situations. Their internal diameters at Forest Glen average about 8.2 m (27 feet) in order to accommodate the stairs and the volumes of air involved. The air enters the shafts from the tunnels and trainrooms through the ventilation cross adits with horseshoe cross sections that average 8.7 m (28.5 feet) in width by 12.8 m (42 feet) in height. This great height is mandated by the adits' secondary purpose of providing space for mechanical rooms, with the upper half alone being suffucient to vent the quantities of moving air involved.

The flared tunnels at the ends of the station are transitions where the structure decreases from trainroom height to running tunnel height. The northern flared sections are designed and built as part of the station contract. Hence, the northern ends of the flared sections will eventually mate with the southern ends of the still-under-design running tunnels of the B-10a contract. Since contractors are given the option of building either machine bored circular running tunnels or drill-and-shoot horseshoe running tunnels, and we cannot know what will be chosen by B-10a, both types are shown in Figure 4.

Figure 4 shows that between the 9.1 m (30-foot) wide by 6.4 m (21-foot) high precast concrete architectural shell, which encloses the "users" area of the station, and the ground-supporting structural shell, there is an annular space that reaches a maximum height of

1.4 m (4.5 feet). This space provides the working room necessary to assemble the separate 2.54 m (8 ft - 4 in) wide curved precast panels, four of which must be connected to complete a section. The space also makes it possible to add more waterproofing compound during erection should it be necessary to augment the two layers of cementitious waterproofing applied at the factory. It is necessary to have such a "waterproofable" surface not subjected to the direct pressure of groundwater seeping through the cracks in the structural lining. With this system, the seeping and dripping water falls onto the architectural shell and runs down to the 0.6 m (2-foot) wide space atop the invert slab, where it is fed by gravity into the track drain system. The annular space will also provide access (however cramped) for post construction maintenance.

Site Specific Geology. During design subsurface conditions were delineated through the drilling of 21 bore holes, in conjunction with examination of scattered rock outcrops and aerial photographs. The bedrock at the site is categorized as Quartz Mica Schist to Gneiss exhibiting fairly typical characteristics of the Wissahickon Formation. It is fine to medium grained, occasionally with augens of quartz or plagioclase. Quartz veins ranging up to several cm (several inches) in thickness are common. The joints in Figure 3 are labeled Nos. 1, 2 and 3 to denote what appear to be the primary, secondary and tertiary sets. Although five sets have been identified, it is believed that these three will dominantly govern the rock mass behavior.

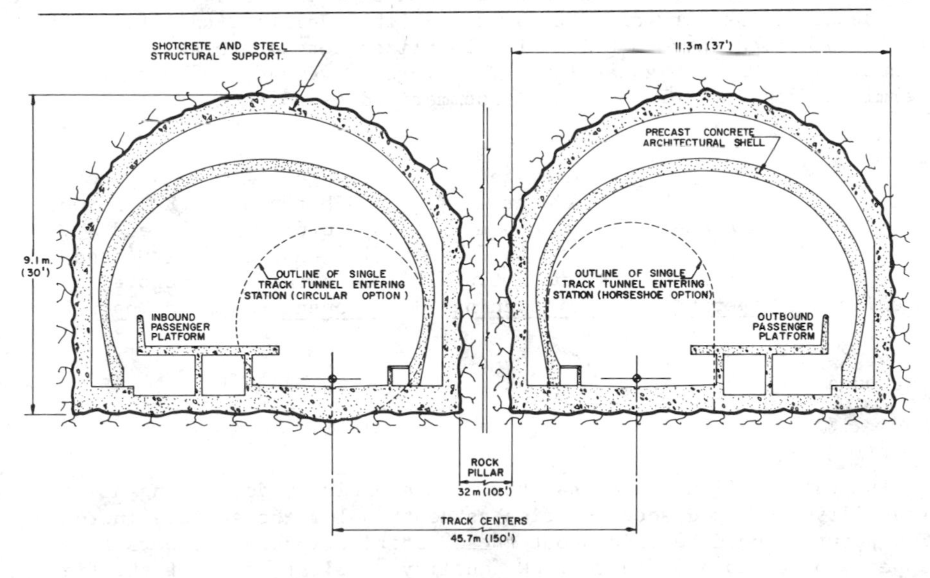

FIGURE 4: CROSS SECTION THROUGH NORTHERN END OF FOREST GLEN STATION (VENTILATION CROSS ADIT NOT SHOWN)

The longitudinal profile in Figure 3 illustrates the extreme depth of weathering at the Forest Glen site. Since the two station trainrooms are so widely separated, conditions were delineated with two lines of borings, but the weathering zones in Figure 3 represent an average of the two original profiles, with the lines projected to an imaginary axis half way between the openings. (Note: In order to furthur simplify the drawing, the groundwater table is not shown, but it lies at an average elevation of +105 m [+345 feet].) The total amount of overburden over the crowns of the trainrooms, flared tunnels, and cross passages reaches a maximum of 48.5 m (159 feet) and averages about 46 m (152 feet). In spite of this great depth, the mass of essentially unweathered bedrock over the structure has an average thickness of only 13.7 m (45 feet), with a respectable maximum of 27.4 m (90 feet) but thinning to a known minimum of only 2.7 m (9 feet) over the inbound side of the southern ventilation cross adit. The actual maximum and minimum cannot be seen in Figure 3 because those division lines are already averages projected to a hypothetical centerline. Recognizing the small percentage of the cover rock revealed by the borings, it seems highly likely that weathered material, particularly at either end of the station, will intrude into the openings.

Even the mass of essentially unweathered bedrock does contain zones of poor quality material. In detailed boring logs and geologic profiles it can be seen that numerous shears, some paralleling foliation, will be encountered. It can also be seen that the individual rock core run descriptions vary all the way from Highly Jointed, with RQD down to 15 (and even down to 0 in a few localized zones), to Relatively Sound, with RQD as high as 100. The overall average rock quality determined from the core borings is summarized as follows:

Opening	Average RQD within opening	Average RQD from 0 to 3 m (0' to 10') above top of opening	Average RQD between 3 and 6 m (10' and 20') above top of opening	Average RQD between 6 and 9 m (20' and 30') above top of opening
Inbound	69	60	46	41
Outbound	77	65	66	45

The numbers illustrate that the rock exhibits a decreasing number of stability-robbing discontinuities as depth below the surface increases. Two points should be made about these positive looking numbers that appear to sum up a definite rock "quality." First, some of the figures may be slightly higher than would be computed by the originator and some users of the RQD concept. In the originator's definition, only "hard and sound" pieces of core longer than 10.2 cm (4 in) would count toward RQD, whereas the variability of rock conditions caused by weathering in the Washington area has led Metro's General Soils Consultant to count all intact core pieces over that length. In Metro design core logging, even Highly Weathered Bedrock may be assigned an RQD higher than 0, thus elevating some of the above figures where the averaged areas extend above the top of essentially unweathered bedrock. The second point is that the micaceous schist-to-gneiss bedrock is highly foliated, which means that the stress release inherent in the process of excavation may cause the opening of latent joints within the rock and may actually produce a fragmented material where the original coring indicates a fairly intact and homogeneous rock mass.

Overall, the prevalence of foliation, shears and cross cutting joint sets means that the rock must be classified as "blocky" even in its unweathered state. Nevertheless, with all qualifications duly considered, it is assessed that the general rock quality at the site ranges from fair to good at the depth planned for excavation.

Design of Ground Support. Test data indicate that the rock at Forest Glen weighs 2726 kg per cu m (170 lb per cu ft), and that a residual angle of friction of 15 degrees can be assumed for sliding surfaces (joints & shears) bounding rock blocks that try to move subsequent to excavation. These data, in combination with the orientation of the geologic discontinuities and subway structures, form the basis for Metro's standard loading conditions upon which rock station permanent lining design is based. Specific point loads can be estimated by superimposing plots of the dips and strikes of shears and jointing systems over the trainroom vault, and determining the apparent dips in a plane perpendicular to the vault axis for each system of discontinuities. The most disadvantageous apparent dips drawn on a sketch in the most disadvantageous location above the vault crown determine the boundaries of rock blocks that could loosen when undermined. The volume of rock between the apparent dip lines and the crown represents the maximum volume of rock that must be supported if the blocks are permitted to move and develop their full potential load. Although a large number of different point loadings may thus be computed, variations in geology over the length of the station will not warrent varying the permanent lining design, so the most unfavorable rock wedges in the entire station are used as the basis for estimating the average rock load. (As will shortly be explained, lining design does vary where vault geometry varies.)

In the case of Forest Glen Station, the load actually used to design the lining was chosen at an average level that would encompass the worst likely case of point loading. The rock mass obtained was converted into a symmetrical, tent shaped vertical load whose peak value is 1.5 times the average vertical load and whose end values are one-half times the average vertical load. Only a portion of the rock mass to the side of the station vault was included when converting to the tent shaped load. The rock mass to the side was considered to be separated from the rock directly above the station vault by a vertical frictionless plane. The rock to the side was then considered as a freebody. Only that portion of the rock mass not supported directly by the rock beneath or by sliding resistence was included in the lining loading.

An average vertical pressure of 96 Kpa (2.0 kips per sq ft) was used for the typical station cavity. This includes, in addition to the rock load, a value representing 25 percent of full hydrostatic head at the crown and 10 percent at the base. A check was also made for full hydrostatic head at crown and 10 percent at base with safety factor of more than one at the ultimate stress. The 25/10 percent values are predicated on the fact that, although no hydrostatic pressure relief pipes are included in the lining, partial relief is obtained through a gravel blanket (not shown in Figure 4) between the concrete invert slab and the rock. Studies have shown that the flow net set up as groundwater seeps into this pervious layer should keep the hydrostatic pressures to the stated levels.

Computer program "STRUDL" was applied to analyze the combination of loading conditions and rock modulus. The design composite section for station support consists of W10 x 60 steel arch ribs and W10 x 88 steel posts at 1.5 m (5 feet) on center encased in 34 500 Kpa (5000 psi) shotcrete, with load distribution supplied by a pattern of radial rock bolts and reinforcing steel bars angled in the direction of advance at approximately 30 degrees from the horizontal (Figure 5). An ultimate behavior of the lining was also investigated. The moment-thrust envelope was constructed using shotcrete strength of 0.67f'c and steel yield strength of 0.9fy. The results indicated that a safety factor of 2 was achieved in the design. Although an alternative lining permitted the contractor to replace the Stage III shotcrete with cast in place concrete, he has chosen the all shotcrete option. The only significant change made to the details of Figure 5 is the result of an approved VECP (Value Engineering Change Proposal) to replace the tensioned, fully grouted rock bolts with tensioned, resin anchored, fully resin encapsulated bolts.

An increased rock loading factor of two was incorporated in the design at the intersection of station vaults with the passageway and cross adits. The rock load decreases linearly to the normal design load at a clear distance of one diameter from the intersection. This results in the support in about 30 m (100 feet) of each trainroom's length being increased to W10 x 60 steel arch ribs and W10 x 112 steel posts at 1.2 to 1.4 m (4 to 4.5 feet) on center.

The Forest Glen ground support was designed in full accordance with WMATA criteria and philosophy of controlling rock loads. The full significance of the design features shown in Figure 5 will become apparent after the next section on construction sequence has been covered. The paramount fact about the permanent structural lining is that it consists basically of a composite section of shotcrete and steel sets designed to carry the thrust and moment generated by the loads from the rock wedges that might reasonably be expected to move against the lining. Those loads are kept to a reasonable level (under the maximum level that could develop) by the proper use of construction headings and the timely installation of earlier elements of support: forward driven steel bars, Stage I shotcrete, and rock bolts. Although the capacity of the early reinforced rock arch is not quantified, the contribution to rock stability is added as the safety factor in the design of the composite steel set-shotcrete structure. In this way all of the elements shown in Figure 5 are a part of the permanent lining even if they cease to play an active support role once the lin-

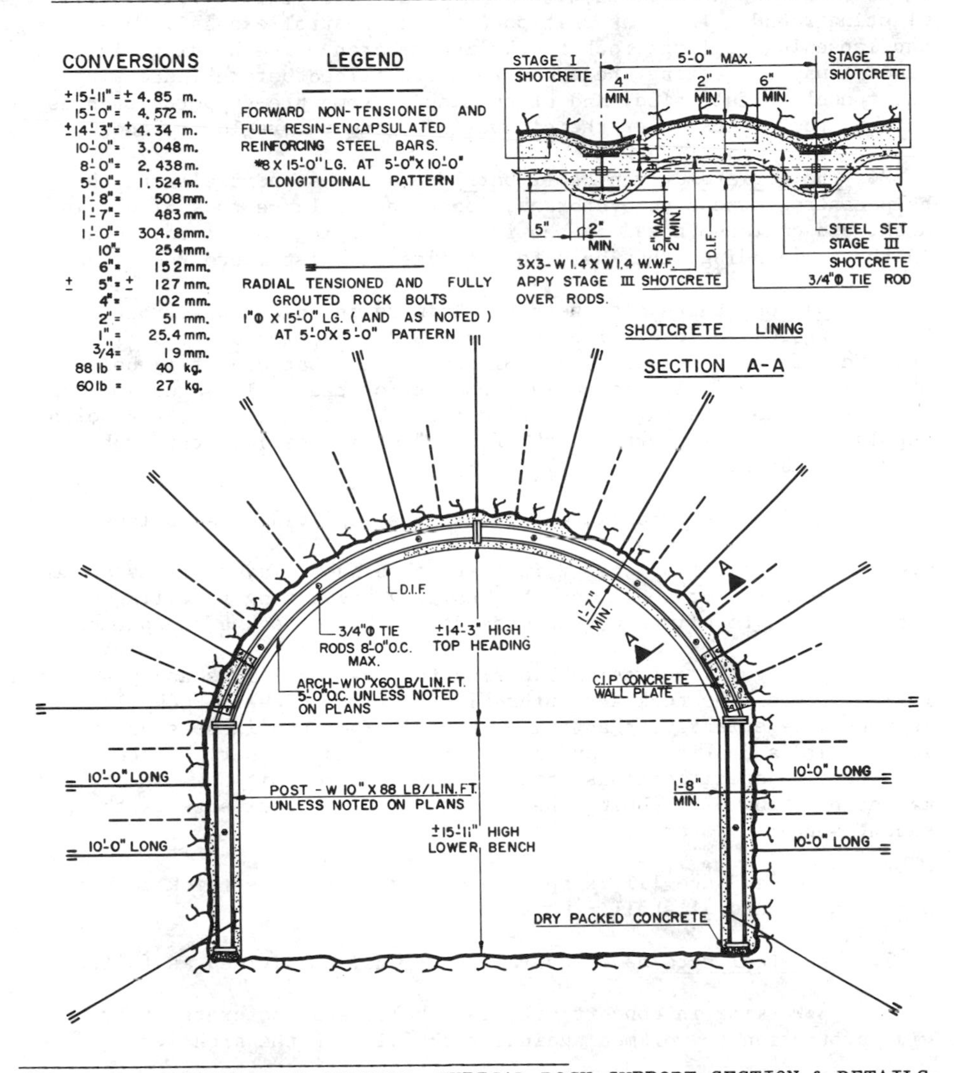

FIGURE 5: FOREST GLEN STATION, TYPICAL ROCK SUPPORT SECTION & DETAILS

ing is completely installed. If the early support were not installed according to specification, then the relatively light final lining might not function as it should because greater than anticipated loads could begin to mobilize with the first blasting round.

A brief description of the functions of the various support elements follows:

1. The top heading constitutes less than half of the tunnel cross section and can be removed with much less powder than a full face blasting round. This makes it possible to control excessive overbreak and loosening of large rock blocks in the arch. The heading also provides a way of getting the crown rock stabilized before increasing the tunnel to full size, and of putting in some pre-support (such as lateral rock bolts) over the sidewalls of the future lower bench.

2. The forward driven steel bars are a pre-support element that help control excessive overbreak, loosening of large rock blocks in the arch, and collapse ahead of the face. By helping to control conditions in the top heading, they help to minimize and distribute rock loads.

3. The rock bolts also help to minimize and distribute rock loads by helping control excessive overbreak and loosening of rock blocks in the arch, face, and sidewalls. Six out of the pattern of 17 bolts shown in Figure 6 also serve as tiebacks for the wall plates and vertical posts. Working in concert with the Stage I shotcrete, the bolts supply the early support for the first 3 m (10 feet) of the arch behind the heading.

4. The shotcrete has several functions subdivided as follows:

- The first 5.1 cm (2-inch) thick Stage I layer serves as immediate support for small rock blocks. By preventing ravelling of the rock it helps to maintain rock mass strength and rock arch continuity.

- Stage II serves as blocking for the steel ribs and posts when filled between the rock and outer flange of the steel. Such blocking is much more effective than timber blocking because it does not deteriorate, it is continuous, and it is stiffer than timber. (Note: The construction specifications for Contract B-9 prohibit the use of "permanent blocking or cribbing where shotcrete and steel sets is the permanent support system.")

- Once Stage III is applied, the shotcrete is thick enough to act as a structural shell.

5. The steel sets have several functions, subdivided as follows:

- Working in concert with rock bolts and shotcrete, they provide protection to workmen against rock falls in the arch.

•They provide a guide that assures placement of a sufficient thickness of shotcrete in a continuous arch.

•They provide a portion of the ultimate thrust and moment capacity of the composite lining.

6. The wall plate, by being cast around the lower 1.1 m (3 ft-8 in) of the arch ribs, becomes their temporary, continuous footing. Then, as each increment of the lower bench is shot out, this footing bridges the gap and transfers the load from each undermined rib to the unexcavated bench in front and to the completed steel sets in back. Once shotcreting is completed, the wallplates will have been incorporated into the permanent lining.

It may appear from Figure 5 and the preceding discussion that the engineer has taken the responsibility for designing the safety oriented short term or "initial" support that is normally within the contractor's domain. However, this is not the case. The construction specifications for Section B-9 (in fact, for all Metro rock tunnel jobs) make it clear that initial support consists of those elements designed, furnished, and installed by the contractor for stability and safety during construction, and are not shown on the drawings. To the extent that the elements of permanent lining shown on the drawings are effective in providing initial support, the contractor may utilize them in meeting his responsibility for providing it. The additional elements may consist of rock bolts, shotcrete, concrete, steel or timber, which may be installed either on a temporary basis or may be left permanently in place if compatible with the permanent lining shown on the drawings. In short, the early support elements shown on the drawings do minimize and distribute the average rock loads sufficiently to assure the adequacy of the final design composite steel and shotcrete lining, but constant control of all rock blocks that may try to slip out requires inspection and decision making on a round-by-round basis.

The Excavation Sequence. Since the adequacy of the permanent ground support system does depend upon preventing the first small rock movements from developing into larger movements, the contractor's order of operations have to be guided somewhat by the design documents. The mandatory minimum early support is one form of guidance; a sequencing of the basic construction operation is another. Of course, the design features shown in Figure 5 already imply a certain degree of order. However, it was necessary to go beyond that design drawing, and to make explicit a sequence of construction actions required in order for the final structure to meet design requirements. Refer to Figure 6 for the general station excavation sequence.

The first prominent impact on the order of excavation results, not from design requirements, but from the fact that surface access will permit no muck to go out through the vent shafts, except for muck from excavation of the shafts themselves. Hence, the excavation and mucking of the trainrooms and the ventilation cross adits must be pursued through the elevator shaft. The first operation has to be the sinking of this large shaft down to at least the level of the passageway springline.

The designer's overall excavation scheme is spelled out in a document called the "Geotechnical Report," which is shorthand for a description of the geotechnical basis of design and of construction specifications. The report is included as an appendix in the specifications, and its directions are considered contract requirements. The Geotechnical Report describes two overall stages of construction.

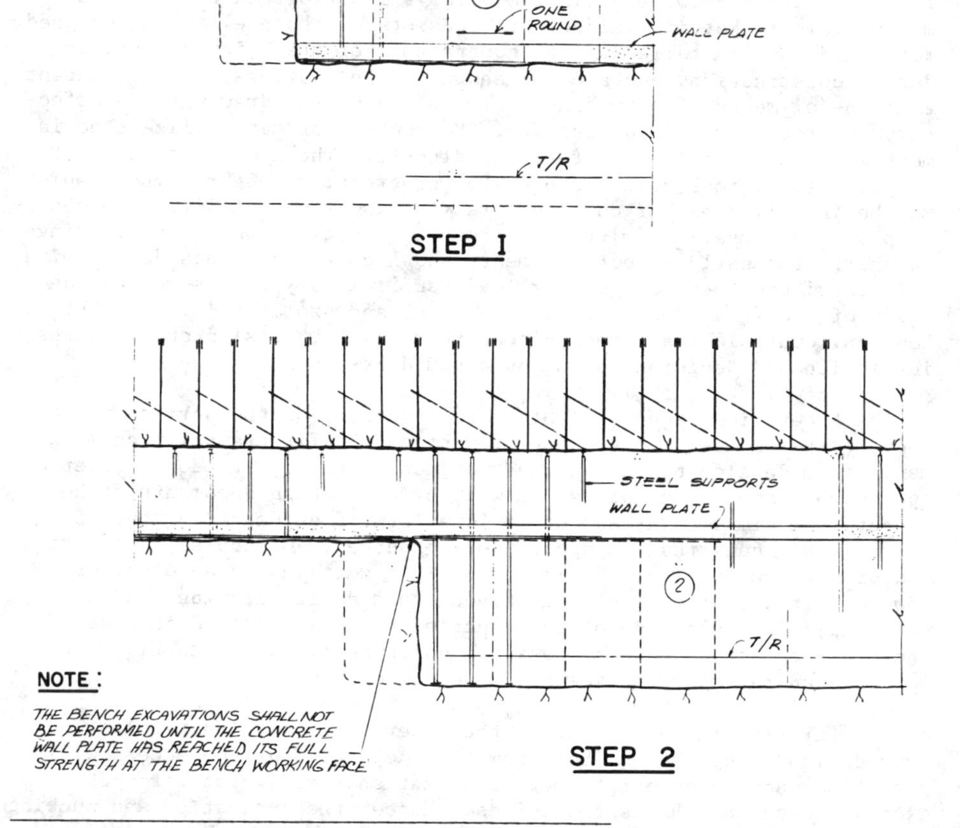

FIGURE 6: FOREST GLEN STATION, REQUIRED EXCAVATION SEQUENCE

In the first stage, the top heading for the passageway is excavated into the trainroom areas in each direction (east and west) to the same invert level as top heading for the trainrooms, about 4.3 m (14 ft - 3 in) below station crown. It is continued laterally across the trainroom areas, with crown following station crown contour. The top heading continues longitudinally in both directions (north and south) along the centerline of each trainroom, and then continues into and through the two ventilation cross adits. Crown steel is placed and the concrete wall plates cast in place to complete the top headings.

In the second stage, the bench excavation is completed in the passageway, the trainrooms, and the cross adits. The passageway is first excavated to station invert to facilitate mucking operations. Trainroom bench excavation can then proceed in both directions, to be followed by bench excavation in the cross adits.

The other part of the excavation scheme provides more round-by-round detail, and is covered in a general fashion by a three-step plan labeled on the drawings as a suggested excavation sequence. In the following list of procedures, the suggestions are supplemented by absolute requirements (underlined) from the drawings, specifications, and the approved rock bolt VECP.

Step 1

- Prior to excavation install steel bars driven ahead of the excavation as pre-reinforcement.
- Excavate one round of top heading and apply Stage I shotcrete. Apply the first layer to the surface of the excavation exposed by blasting and complete within 3 hours after the blast is fired.
- Install radial rock bolts, plus forward driven steel bars ahead of advancing face. Install the rock bolts within 0.9 m (3 feet) of the heading and within 8 hours after blasting and prior to the next shot. Tension to 80 percent of the bolts' guaranteed minimum yield strength before the encapsulating resin hardens.
- Place permanent crown steel supports. Install supports as soon as possible after initial layer of shotcrete is placed and as close to the heading as the work will permit.
- Apply Stage II shotcrete. The Stage II shotcrete must be in place prior to the next advance of the heading.
- Construct wall plates between the crown steel supports.

Step 2

- Remove bench.
- Apply Stage I shotcrete.
- Install radial rock bolts and forward driven steel bars.

•Install permanent steel posts. Steel sets are to be completed to station invert level within 3.7 to 4.6 m (12 to 15 feet) of bench removal.

•Apply Stage II shotcrete.

Step 3

•Apply Stage III shotcrete when heading progresses more than 15 m (50 feet) but less than 23 m (75 feet) from working face. Stage III is to be built up in individual layers not more than 10 cm (4 in) thick. The complete thickness of shotcrete lining must be placed within 15 to 23 m (50 to 75 feet) behind bench excavation, but is not required to be placed during top heading excavation.

Of course, the requirements for contractor designed initial support must be observed at all times during the critical stages of excavation. In regard to this, the specifications state in part, "After each exposure of the final rock surface, examine the surface and confirm that the rock bolt pattern to be installed will be adequate. Provide rock reinforcement that is adequate at all times to ensure the safety of personnel and the construction operations. If initial support is required, keep its installation within 3 feet of the excavated face and do not leave the tunnel unsupported without full initial support for longer than three hours after excavation. Stabilize the face if required."

WHEATON STATION

A detailed discussion of the structural and construction aspects of Wheaton is not appropriate at this time because final design is still short of the 50 percent stage of completion. In general terms the B-10 station can best be described by comparing it with Forest Glen, since many aspects of the latter structure have just been documented. Although there are differences in detail between the two stations, the basic functions and dimensions of the final structures will be similar. For example, the trainroom and adit excavation dimensions for both stations will be almost exactly the same, as will the precast concrete architectural shells and the crawl space above those shells. Wheaton's 26.8 m (88-foot) track centers between trainrooms (narrow compared with Forest Glen) are made possible by the more conventional entrance facility, a 8.2 m (27-foot) wide by 9.8 m (32-foot) high O.D horseshoe shaped escalator tunnel that slants down through the ground at a 30 degree angle to intercept the trainrooms just slightly north of the station midpoint. Because Wheaton sits in the center of a knob of hard rock that is relatively high for the B Route, it was possible to raise the alignment sufficiently to achieve an average depth of 30 m (100 feet) to trainroom crown and 39 m (127 feet) to T/R. For passengers, the depth will still seem large because the vertical rise of the escalator is about 34.7 m (114 feet), greater than any other single escalator rise in the Metro system. The disadvantage is slight when compared with the possible alternatives. Before the advent of the dual chamber concept, a tunneled station had been ruled out for Wheaton because the vaulted arch configuration would, in order to achieve stability, have been driven to depths beyond the normally accepted reach of rapid transit escalators. This had led to Wheaton originally being planned as a 35 m (115-foot) deep open cut structure, which would have resulted in not inconsiderable escalator depths as well as undesirable construction impacts upon a thriving business center. All things considered, the structure that will be built (and this applies to Forest Glen as well as Wheaton) is the best choice among several less than ideal alternatives.

ACKNOWLEDGMENTS

The Washington Metropolitan Area Transit Authority (WMATA) is the owner of Metro, with ultimate responsibility for the planning, design, construction, and operation of the system. Other organizations with direct input into one or more aspects of Metro include the following: DeLeuw, Cather & Company--WMATA's General Engineering Consultant; Harry Weese & Associates--General Architectural Consultant; Mueser, Rutledge, Johnston & DeSimone--General Soils Consultant; Bechtel Associates--General Construction Consultant; the Ralph M. Parsons Company--final designer of Section B-9; a joint venture of Peter Kiewit & Sons Company and J.F. Shea Company, Inc.--prime contractor on Section B-9.

The source of materials presented in this paper include the author's personal experiences and observations, as well as information that originated with the above organizations.

Chapter 75

EXPERIENCE IN THE CONSTRUCTION AND THE USE OF ROCK CAVERNS FOR OIL STORAGE

by Claes G. Björk

SKANSKA (U.S.A.), INC.

ABSTRACT

Over the past decade mined unlined rock cavern storage for crude oil and refined products has become economically more attractive. This trend is likely to continue, primarily due to advances in excavation methods, rising steel costs for above ground tanks and larger capacity requirements.

The construction experience related in this paper comprises the excavation of more than 80 storage facilities (total capacity 90 million bbl) for crude and refined products ranging from propane to heavy fuel oil.

This paper also deals with the experience gained as well as the problems derived from the utilization of these oil storage facilities.

BACKGROUND

One of the world's first and largest underground oil storage facilities still in operation is the U.S. Navy's Red Hill Storage in Hawaii. This 6 million bbl facility was completed in 1943 and contains 20 concrete lined vaults. The underground location was chosen primarily due to the security of fuel oil storage at Pearl Harbor.

About the same time that the Red Hill facility was being planned, research in Sweden showed that a concrete lined vault was impervious to petroleum only when water filled the pores of the concrete. From this knowledge came the idea to store petroleum in unlined caverns, in which all the pores in the surrounding rock are filled with water.

GEOPHYSICAL CONDITIONS

The geophysical conditions in Scandinavian countries are, in general, favorable for subsurface constructions. Most of the bedrock consists of very competent granite gneiss. Decomposed and weathered rock was removed during the last big ice age, which means it is easy to reach the bedrock without major excavation of overburden. However, it should not be assumed that all rock in these countries is of good quality. Bad rock conditions are encountered now and then. Special methods and equipment have been developed to be used in such cases and the projects can still be completed on a sound and economic base. The groundwater situation is also favorable and it is usually easy to find a stable groundwater table.

It is quite obvious that it is not possible to find places all over the world with this favorable combination of conditions. However, there are several places with similar good conditions in many areas of the world. Considerable economic advantages can be gained in constructing storage facilities even in less favorable rock masses. Such plants are still able to compete on an economic basis with steel tank storage systems. Suitable locations for caverns might be found in areas where granite, gneiss, limestone, sandstone, schist and similar types of rock are located. During 10 years of experience in underground construction in the United States, the author has learned of a multitude of locations suitable for underground oil storage. As far as seismic activities are concerned, it is well known that a subsurface structure is safer than a surface structure. Obviously plants should not be located in or very close to an active zone.

BASIC PRINCIPLES FOR STORAGE

Storing oil in unlined rock caverns works on the same principle that nature itself has arranged. It takes advantage of the fact that oil is lighter than water and does not mix with it. A cavern is blasted out so that its roof lies under the groundwater table in the rock. Through the fissures which permeate every type of rock, groundwater percolates into the cavern where it is pumped out. In this way, a so-called cone of depression is formed around the storage cavern. When oil is stored in the cavern, it floats on the water in the cone of depression and is thereby prevented from penetrating the surrounding rock.

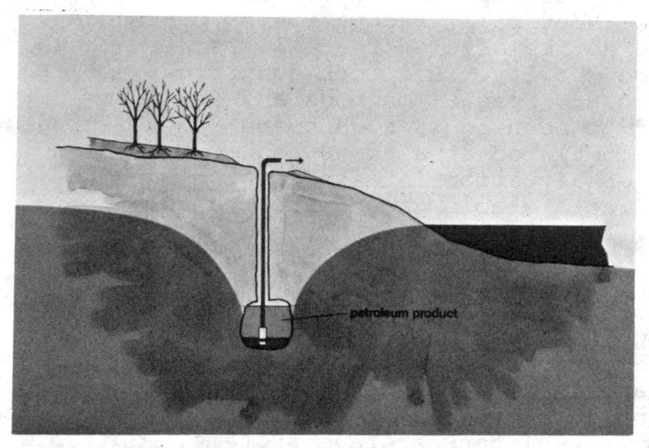

Fig. 1 Principle of underground oil storage

The method for storing crude oil and refined products in mined unlined caverns is, in Scandinavia, the cheapest and safest way provided the quantity is adequate. This is confirmed by the fact that during the last two decades nearly all new storage facilities, both commercial and strategic, have been constructed underground. More than 100 plants with a total storage capacity in excess of 160 million bbl have been completed. See Fig. 2.

An artist's rendering of a complete oil storage facility is shown in Fig. 3.

Fig. 3. Complete underground oil storage facility.

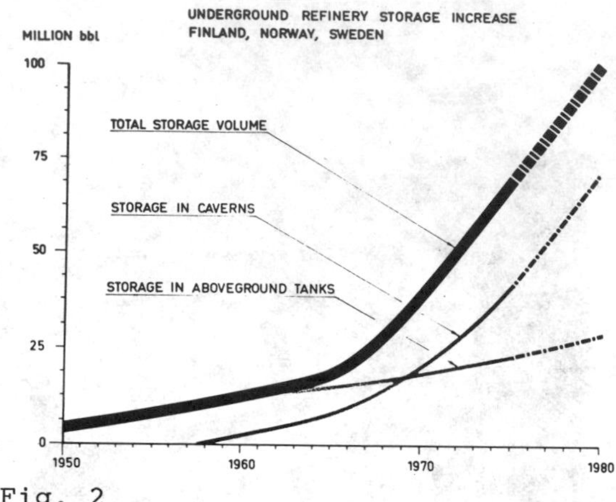

Fig. 2

The general principles governing storage are first described with reference to the storage of products such as gas-oil, which are of low viscosity and non explosive at normal temperatures. The modifications necessary for the storage of heavy fuel oil, petrol, crude oil, LP gas and high viscosity oils are described later.

Storage Over a Fixed Water Bed

Storage over a fixed water bed implies that the water is maintained at the level of the bottom of the cavern and its upper surface is determined by means of a dam around a pump pit in the floor of the cavern. Ground water which seeps in collects in the pit from which it is removed by a water pump. The product floats on the bed and its upper surface varies from top to bed level according to the amount present. The space above the upper product level is filled with a mixture of air and petroleum gas. See Fig. 4.

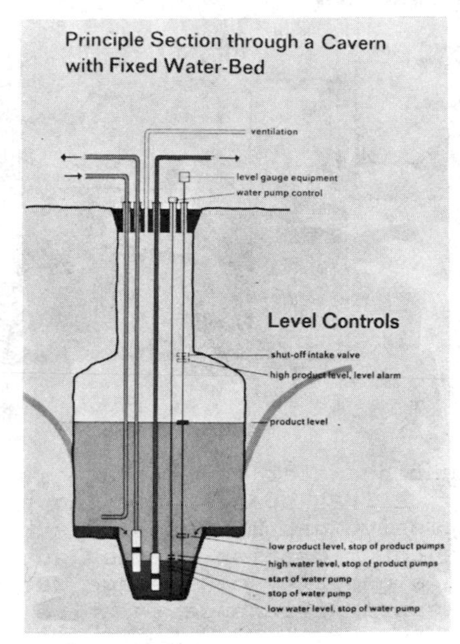

Fig. 4.

Storage over a fixed water bed is the method most commonly used today. It is not necessary to handle large quantities of water whenever the product is pumped in and out. Only seepage water needs removing; and, therefore, the water pumps and the oil separator for the purification of the seepage water can be small. The amount of water seepage is normally quite small, 800 to 4000 liters per hour for a 600,000 bbl storage cavern.

Storage Over a Fluctuating Water Bed

Storage over a fluctuating or mobile water bed also implies that the product is stored floating on a water bed. The upper surface level of the product is maintained substantially constant and at ceiling height. In order to achieve this, the volume of the water bed must be variable. This is done by adding or removing water as the product is pumped in or out. Seepage water is pumped out as required. The free volume above the upper product surface will be small. Refer to Fig. 5.

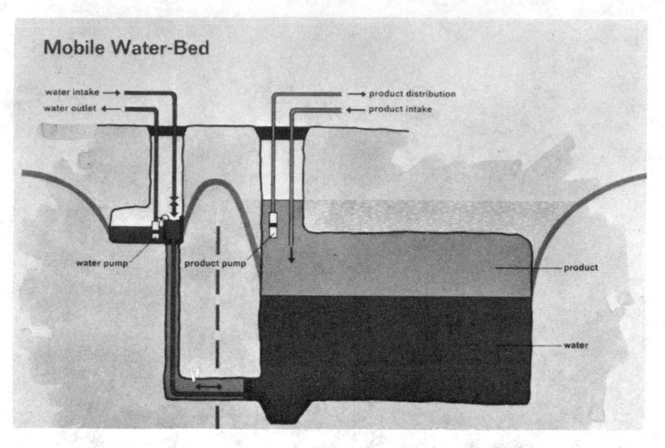

Fig. 5

A fluctuating water bed storage is used principally for petrol. A free space above the product which may contain explosive gas mixtures is substantially less. A risk of product migration between adjacent chambers is reduced and a quantity of seepage water is also less because pressure difference relative to the groundwater is less.

Product Migration

In the case of an isolated cavern, the question of product migration does not arise. The water lies floating in the sump formed by the lower groundwater level. If, however, a number of caverns are constructed adjacent to each other it may be difficult to maintain an isolating groundwater barrier between adjacent caverns. In such a case an artificial barrier may be arranged by constructing a small tunnel furnished with a curtain of bore holes between the two caverns. The tunnel and its bore holes are then put under water pressure with a static height greater than the highest product surface in the caverns. Refer to Fig. 6.

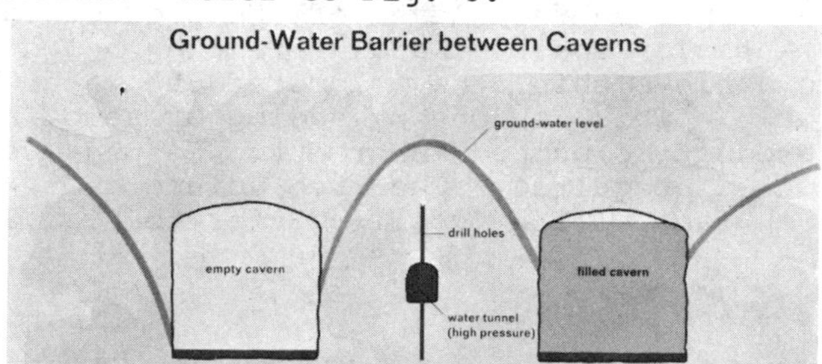

Fig. 6

PRELIMINARY INVESTIGATIONS

The geological survey is designed to answer the following questions concerning the geologic conditions involved (See Fig. 7):

- Suitable geographic siting
- Suitable direction of the storage cavern
- Suitable depth in the rock mass
- Possible cavern parameters (height, span, shape of cross section)
- Forecast of necessary rock reinforcements
- Forecast of water seepage and necessary ceiling work
- Documentation for material selection according to groundwater properties
- Documentation for cost estimates

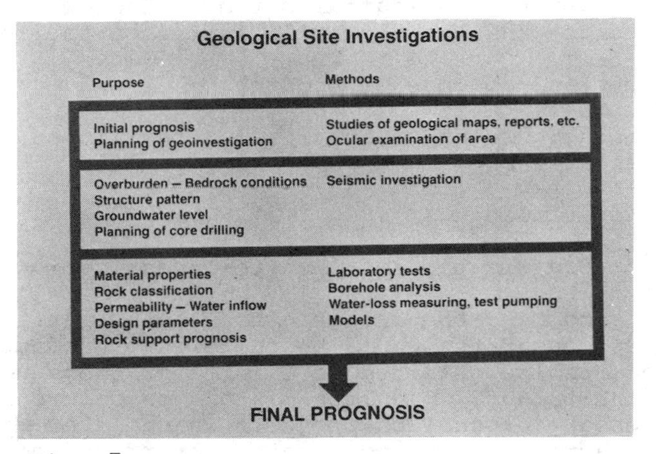

Fig. 7

Basic Technical Requirements

The geological survey must be planned with due regard to the fundamental principles of storage in unlined rock caverns. There are two main types of storage:

Storage At Atmospheric Pressure. This type is applicable to products which are in the liquid phase at atmospheric pressure.

A certain lowering of the water table above the rock cavern is acceptable.

Storage At Over Pressure. This type is applicable to gases in liquid and gas phase. No lowering of the water table above the rock cavern is acceptable, consequently an artificial water barrier is created by constructing a small tunnel furnished with horizontal bore holes. The tunnel is filled with water and put under pressure.

The depth at which the plant is to be located depends not only on pure rock mechanical factors but also on the kind of product, the type of storage and the level of the water table in the rock.

The Owner's Requirements

The Owner's requirements must also be taken into account at the very outset and they, too, influence the planning of the geological survey. The Owner/User's preferences and know-how will influence the following:

- Types and volumes of product

- Siting in relation to existing facilities and installations

- Land available

General Organization of the Pre-Investigation

We recommend the investigation to be carried out step by step; each step would be followed by a decision based on the results obtained as to whether the study is to continue or not. The idea of this procedure is to avoid unnecessary expense on projects which later may prove to be impractical owing to unsatisfactory geological conditions. The various steps may turn out to comprise the following:

- Establishing a basic technical requirement and of the siting preferred

- Studying of maps, both geological and topographical and of any survey material which may be available

- Ocular inspections of conceivable sites and geographical mapping of the same
- Seismic survey
- Core drilling, logging of samples and RQD assessments
- Water loss measurements and water table observations
- Laboratory tests

CONSTRUCTION

Rock Excavation

One of the conditions for low excavation costs is a design which makes it possible to use heavy modern mobile equipment for drilling, loading, mucking and hauling. A sloping access tunnel is always driven from the ground surface to the storage caverns so that the excavated rock can easily be brought up and all necessary equipment in the cavern can be utilized without any difficulty.

The access tunnel is between 20 and 60 sq m (square meters) in cross section area and the inclination is 1:7. When operations are completed the access tunnel is closed with a concrete plug flooded with water and abandoned.

Cost due to the existence of bad rock will increase if the span of the cavern is too large and if the cavern walls are too high. The heights of caverns in good rock will be approximately 20 - 35m (meters) and in poor rock 15 - 20 m. The length of the cavern is, in principle, unlimited.

The rock caverns are excavated in horizontal stages. First a roof gallery is excavated to a height of 6 - 8m where each round has an advance of 4 - 4.5m. Specific drilling is approximately 0.8m per cu m (cubic meter) with contour holes at 0.9m spacing. The hole diameter is 45 mm (millimeters). Drilling is performed using an electro-hydraulic drilling rig with two to four hydraulically operated booms. The specific charge is normally 1.2 to 1.4 kg (kilos) per cu m and the explosive used is ANFO. The loading is done from a special loading truck equipped with a pneumatic charger and a hydraulically operated sky lift.

Two or more benches are excavated after the gallery is completed. Drilling is carried out either horizontally or vertically. When drilling horizontally the bench height is 8 - 9m maximum and the advance is 5m using the same equipment as for the top gallery. When drilling vertically the bench can be 12 - 15m high and the drilling can be performed with air tracs.

Mucking and hauling is carried out with "optimum equipment" which means heavy rubber-wheel front end loaders with a bucket volume of 5 - 8 cu m and 35 - 50 ton trucks.

Disposal of the rock spoil is very important for the total cost of the project. Rock spoil can either be crushed and used for construction purposes or be used for land reclamation.

When poor rock quality is encountered, rock support forms an integral part in the underground works. The site must maintain a high state of alert so that support works can be done rapidly and in short notice in order to avoid any loss of progress or reduced rock output. The rock support is normally rockbolts or shotcrete or a combination of the two methods.

Shotcrete is performed using a remote controlled Robot so that the operator can remain in a safe area while shotcreting of the poor rock is carried out. See Fig. 8.

Cracks with heavy water inflow are cement grouted. If water is revealed while drilling probe holes, grouting is carried out as pre-grouting which gives a far better result.

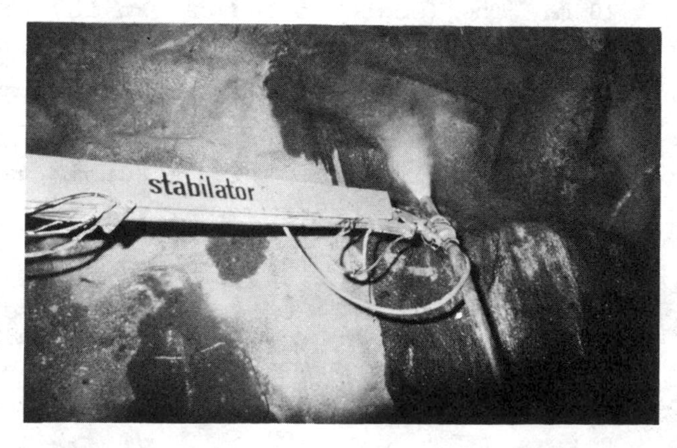

Fig. 8.

Interior Building Work

When blasting is completed, the interior building work is carried out. The cavern floor is leveled, the pump pit lined with concrete and provided with a dam which determines the water level. The storage cavern is closed off from the access tunnel by a concrete wall 1 - 2m thick. The surface between concrete and rock is completely sealed off by grouting and subsequent shotcrete. Refer. Fig. 9

Fig. 9

The upper ends of the pump shaft are covered by a concrete deck in which are cast the necessary apertures for filling pipe, vent pipe, product pumps, seepage water pumps, manholes, and the necessary level control equipment. The shaft to the surface is usually covered and connected to a building which may in some cases house a switch gear, control room and oil separators.

EQUIPMENT

Pumps

The installation is equipped with product pumps for distributing the product, with water pumps for removing seepage water, and, in the case of a mobile water bed, for pumping the bed water in and out.

These pumps hang in their riser pipes from apertures in the concrete deck above the shaft leading down to the cavern. The pump and its motor form a single unit with the motor below. See Fig. 10.

Fig. 10 Product pumps

The product pumps normally have a capacity of 2000 - 3500 liters per minute. It may, on occasion, be advantageous to use a smaller pump which continuously transfers product to a cistern above ground from which distribution can be arranged at higher rates.

Pump Control

The water which seeps into the installation runs down to the bottom and is pumped out automatically. In the case of the fixed water bed control is usually achieved by means of a set of sounds which is hung down from the deck above the shaft. The set may comprise four capacitative or conductive probes which are sited at various levels and which give different signals depending on whether they are in water or in product. The highest and lowest probes serve as alarms while the two medial probes start and stop the seepage water pump.

Level Gauging

Gauges are installed to measure the product level. The gauges consist of a float, running in guides or displacer suspended by a line from a level indicator situated on the deck above the shaft. The indicator is read at the deck but may also be fitted with arrangements to transmit the reading elsewhere. It may also be provided with switches which operate an alarm if high or low levels are recorded.

Volume Measurement

The photogrammetric method is often used. This method is in principle a copying of human stereoscopic vision. Simultaneous pictures of the storage cavern are taken by two cameras in proximity. The pairs of pictures are fed to a stereoscopic instrument which gives a stereo model. It is then possible to calculate, for example, the volume between two horizontal levels. The accuracy of the method is very high.

Pipe Lines

In the fixed water bed installation, the intake line is taken to the floor of the cavern whereas it ends at top level in the mobile water bed caverns.

The cavern is provided with vent pipes through which air may pass as the air pressure in the cavern alters.

Oil Separators

Water which is pumped out of the installation may contain oil particles, and must, therefore, pass an oil separator before discharged to a recipient.

Supervision

Usually an underground oil storage installation is operated by remote control, which is supervised from a control center in an office in the neighborhood. The control center comprises instruments showing product levels, temperatures, start-stop and signal lamps for pumps, indication valves, tell tale lamps for normal and abnormal levels of water and product.

STORAGE OF SPECIAL PRODUCTS

Heavy Fuel Oil

Heavy fuel oil is defined here as products which must be heated in order to be pumped economically.

The heat necessary for temperature maintenance may be furnished by circulating the oil through a heat exchanger. To heat the oil in bulk, it must, after passing through the heat exchanger, be distributed throughout the cavern in such a way that satisfactory circulation is achieved. In such cases it is not necessary to provide a water bed on the floor of the cavern which is instead sloped down to the pump pit so that all seepage water runs down into the pit. See Fig. 11.

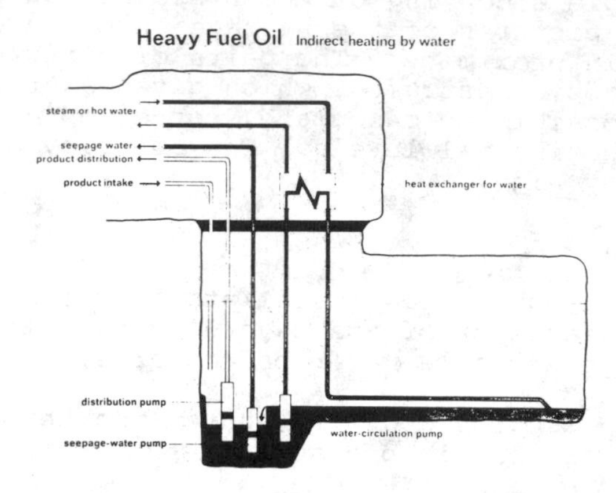

Fig. 11

The heat requirements are considerably smaller than for corresponding tanks above ground with normal insulation. Heat requirements are biggest during the first years of use until the surrounding rock is warmed up. After two or three years the heat has penetrated the rock to a depth of 10 - 15m.

If the temperature is high (more than 60°C) motor requirements change, which might necessitate the use of hydraulic pumps or turbine pumps where the motor is above the deck to avoid cooling problems.

Petrol

When petrol is stored underground over a fluctuating water bed, losses are practically eliminated, since the product surface is always at ceiling height in the cavern.

Storage over a fixed water bed underground does not eliminate losses but reduces them considerably, since the temperature in a rock cavern is almost constant at the yearly average level. "Breathing" on account of daily temperature variations does not occur.

"Breathing" on account of pressure variations may be reduced by fitting pressure vacuum valves in the vent pipes. The over and under pressures which arise on this account may be allowed to reach much higher values than are permissible in tanks above ground.

Crude Oil

In designing an installation for crude oil it is necessary to take into account the sludge which accompanies the oil and the volatile fractions it contains; the latter often makes it necessary to store the oil under pressure.

The amount of sludge accompanying the oil varies with the source and to a certain extent determines the design of the installation. If the sludge is in the form of wax it can be taken care of by heating the wax and mix it with the oil. When the sludge is in the form of particles it is recommended to allow the particles to sediment on the floor. See Fig. 12.

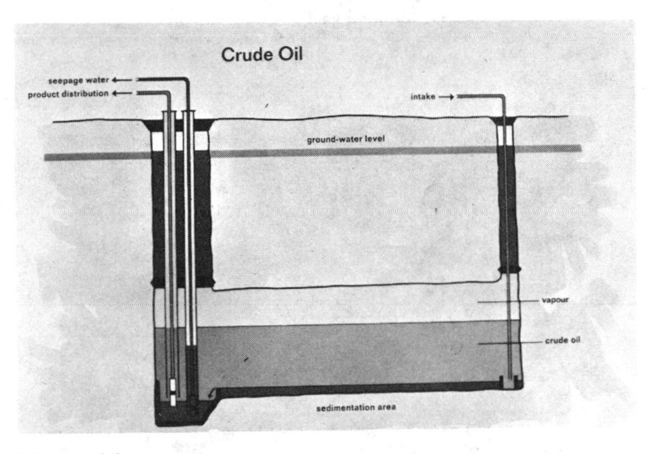

Fig. 12

Particular attention must be paid to the light fractions in the raw oil which are evolved as gas at atmospheric pressure. Storage caverns are sometimes designed to stand the pressure exerted by the lighter fractions.

LPG

Storage of LPG in unlined rock caverns may take place at depth under hydraulic pressure corresponding to the pressure of the gas in the cavern at actual temperature, or at shallower levels at atmospheric pressure with the gas cooled to subnormal temperature. Combinations of the two methods are in use.

The gas is retained in the cavern during storage by placing the cavern at such a level that the pressure of the ground water above the cavern is always higher than the gas pressure. In this case it is also essential that the hydraulic pressure gradient is such that the gas cannot force its way past the water and up through the rock. See Fig. 13.

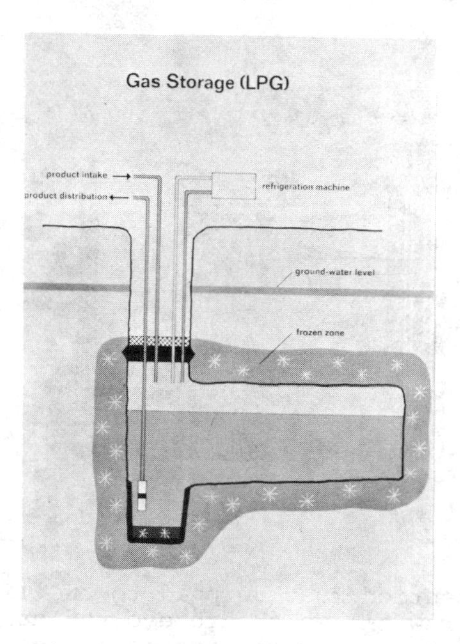

Fig. 13

Water which seeps into the cavern dissolves a certain quantity of gas. The solubility depends on such factors e.g., the pressure which means that the water which is pumped out of the cavern to a lower pressure region, gives off a certain amount of gas. If the water seepage is significant, this fact must be considered from both a safety and an economical point of view.

When LPG is stored in rock caverns where water seepage occurs, it must be remembered that at low temperatures the gas may form hydrates which can obstruct pipes and valves.

EXPERIENCE GAINED FROM THREE DECADES OF UNDER-GROUND OIL STORAGE

As an example we can mention that the Swedish State Power Board has successively extended and utilized the system of cavern storage facilities to stock heavy fuel oil for the last three decades. Their reasons have been based on economy, defense, environment and operation.

The oldest plant was put into use as early as 1948 and this was the first time that the principle of storing oil directly in an unlined rock cavern was applied. The principle of storage was on a moving water bed. Oil storage on a fixed water bed was introduced for the first time toward the end of the 1950's.

The Power Board's latest plants came into operation in 1974. It consists of 9 large rock caverns. These caverns constitute a joint facility for a number of State municipal and privately owned companies who have cooper-ated to take advantage of the benefits resulting from large scale techniques.

The experience acquired by the Swedish State Power Board and other companies has been evaluated, taken into account both older plants that have been in operation for many years and newer plants giving more up to date in-formation. This experience was recently summarized by Mr. Moberg with the Swedish State Power Board as follows:

The long term stability in rock caverns is good. The possibility of rock falls cannot be excluded, but these can be accepted if the storage plant is constructed so that installations inside the cavern can be maintained from the outside. The rock should be reinforced by means of bolts and shotcrete.

Piping inside a cavern should be constructed with due attention to the risk of corrosion, and it should be positioned so that it is protected from rock falls.

If surrounding areas are sensitive to drops in the groundwater table, this should be checked continuously, and measures should be taken when necessary.

A fixed, heated water bed should be avoided in view of the risk of emulsion formation and corrosion problems if high storage temperatures (>35 to 40 ^{o}C) are required. If this principle is adopted, then circulation pumping of the oil will increase operational safety.

Rock caverns should, if possible, be constructed so that sludge can be removed without entering the cavern.

Rock cavern plants for storage of heavy fuel oil have been shown to cause extremely little environmental disturbance. However, the risk of odor problems should be noted, particularly with sensitive sitings near built up areas. Oil filters of the gravimetric type have proved to be very reliable.

Submersible product pumps and seepage water pumps have several advantages. Attention should be paid to the cooling problems and corrosion risks, particularly if high storage temperatures are required.

Storage in unlined rock caverns has proved so successful, both technically and economically, that this form of storage normally ought to be adopted whenever new storage plants are to be constructed.

Fig. 14. Testing of heating system before fill.

CONCLUSION

Oil storage in underground unlined rock caverns has a number of advantages compared to an installation above ground. Maintenance costs are one-third of those to be expected for steel tanks above ground. The product temperature is more even and the breathing losses are less. The risk of fire or other difficulties associated with leakage and accidental discharge of product decreases. The amenities of the countryside are not destroyed by bulky tanks above ground. Underground storage also gives much better protection against attack and observation.

An oil storage facility with tanks above ground may often fully occupy the site and there may be difficulty in acquiring further land. If the site is based on rock the installation may be complemented by an underground installation and the receiving and distribution facilities already in use will serve the extra capacity.

ACKNOWLEDGMENTS

The author wishes to thank Lars Söderberg, Skånska Cementgjuteriet, Stockholm for his help in the preparation of this paper. Appreciation is also expressed to Nancy Cholis, Kanu Desai and Liz McMahon.

REFERENCES

Jansson, G. "Storage of Petroleum Products in Unlined Caverns", Proceedings, Swedish Underground Construction Mission, New York, October 1976.

Moberg, S.H., "Storage of Heavy Fuel Oil in Rock Caverns During Three Decades", Proceedings, Rock Store -77, Stockholm, September 1977.

18

Underground Waste Storage

Chairmen: S.C. Matthews
P. Uertmann

Battelle Memorial Institute, Columbus, OH
Institut fur Tieflagerung, Braunschweig, W. Germany

Chapter 76

DESIGN PROBLEMS FOR

UNDERGROUND NUCLEAR WASTE DISPOSAL IN BASALT

by Birger Schmidt

Senior Professional Associate, Parsons Brinckerhoff
San Francisco, California

Deputy Project Manager, Nuclear Waste Repository in Basalt
Kaiser Engineers/Parsons Brinckerhoff, Oakland, California

ABSTRACT

The design of underground nuclear waste disposal facilities poses new problems related to the requirement of long term safety against radionuclide migration. The degree and effects of rock disturbance caused by construction and by the long term thermal effects from the hot waste must be predicted with confidence.

Computer modeling can, to an extent, be verified by accelerated near-surface tests. Credible extrapolation to deep, long-term conditions requires successful near-surface modeling verification, proper characterization of near-surface and deep rocks, and successful determination of in-situ stresses. Excavation induced disturbance may be assessed primarily by empirical evidence.

ACKNOWLEDGEMENTS

Kaiser Engineers/Parsons Brinckerhoff in joint venture are preparing the conceptual design of a Nuclear Waste Repository in Basalt (NWRB) under contract with the U. S. Department of Energy. D. J. Squires monitors this work for DOE, and D. A. Turner of Rockwell Hanford Operations coordinates this work with other work on the NWRB carried out under Rockwell auspices. Though the concepts and results presented here are derived in part from work for the NWRB, the opinions presented are those of the author and do not purport to reflect policies of Rockwell, DOE or any other organization or authority. Permission by DOE to publish this paper is appreciated.

INTRODUCTION

Nuclear power reactors, the defense program and other users of radioactive materials have over the last 35 years produced large quantities of nuclear waste. This waste is now in temporary storage and it must, sooner or later, be permanently disposed of. More nuclear waste is being produced, but even if all waste production were ended today, the waste already produced would still have to be permanently disposed of. Fortunately, solutions to the nuclear waste problem appear to be at hand. Safe disposal in deep, impervious geologic strata is feasible, and work is underway to enable the construction of such nuclear waste repositories in one or several locations in different geologic media.

From an engineering and construction point of view, an underground repository could be designed and built now. The principal obstacle is the need to show that underground disposal would be safe with adequate margins for the time spans to be considered, and the need to obtain political and public acceptance.

Some radionuclides would be unsafe if released to the biosphere in quantity even after thousands of years. Can it be shown with assurance that the geologic formation will isolate the waste for such periods? Can man-made isolation barriers be counted on for thousands of years? Man's direct experience cannot be called upon to demonstrate assurance that the waste would be isolated for these lengths of time; extrapolations of known behavior, even prediction of future geologic events, must be employed.

Long term isolation is principally a hydrologic problem, because the primary potential migration of radionuclides would be through moving groundwaters, but rock mechanics and other geotechnical issues to a large measure affect probabilities of radionuclide migration.

LONG TERM ISOLATION

Most places in the United States, a deep repository would be below the groundwater table, and the repository would eventually be saturated. The original hydrologic regime would be restored, modified by the presence of the repository and the waste.

The ideal host rock for a repository would be nearly impervious; water in pores and fissures would have been essentially stagnant for millions of years and under very small driving gradients; the host rock formation would be thick and deep; and the site would be distant from recharge and discharge areas. No faults or shear zones would traverse the host rock nearby. Sites can be found which reasonably satisfy these requirements. However, indication of present and past behavior is insufficient. Construction of the repository, and the temperature effects emanating from the hot wastes, permanently alter the local characteristics of the host rock. Some key concerns are the following:

- To what extent is rock permeability increased locally by the creation of underground chambers; will such rock mass alteration affect isolation

- o Is groundwater movement and radionuclide migration predictable to the confidence level required

- o Can the effect of heat on stress levels and room stability be predicted; will increased horizontal stresses produce rock bursts or zones of tensile stresses that may affect isolation?

These are only some of a multitude of concerns related to the design of a repository but they represent the most significant concerns to be dealt with from a rock mechanics standpoint. Before discussing these concerns, the NWRB conceptual design is briefly described.

NUCLEAR WASTE REPOSITORY IN BASALT

The reference location on the Hanford site is underlain by about 700 feet of poorly consolidated granular overburden, followed by a deep series of basalt flows, typical of the Columbia Plateau. These flows are often separated by interbeds consisting of sedimentary rock.

A typical basalt flow has a low-density vesicular or brecciated flow top followed by a thick central entablature, a dense, impervious basalt, fractured by cooling joints and secondary joints in varying patterns. Beneath the entablature follows the colonnade, similar in density to the entablature but with predominantly vertical cooling joints in typical hexagonal patterns. Colonnade joints tend to be continuous; joints in the entablature are more likely to be discontinuous. Variations to this sequence are common, but the central portion of a flow is almost invariably dense, hard and impervious. The present candidate repository basalt flow is the Umtanum Flow at a depth of about 3,700 feet (1,130 m); it is between 200 and 300 feet (60-90m) thick.

The proposed repository is shown in a cut-away perspective on Figure 1. It has five access shafts, shown in order from left, serving the following primary functions:

- o Confinement air exhaust
- o Nuclear waste hoisting
- o Confinement air intake
- o Personnel and materials hoisting, and mine air intake
- o Basalt hoisting and mine air exhaust.

Ventilation is handled by two separate systems, independent of each other, one serving the repository development (mining), the other servicing areas containing nuclear waste (the confinement area).

The shaft pillar area is extensive and complex (see Figure 2) because of the requirement to isolate the confinement and development areas from each other. The layout of the repository is shown in Figure 3. Five central accessways are provided, one for basalt hauling and mine air exhaust, two for mine air intake, personnel and materials, and two for confinement air intake and nuclear waste hauling. The confinement exhaust airways are at the outer extremities of the repository.

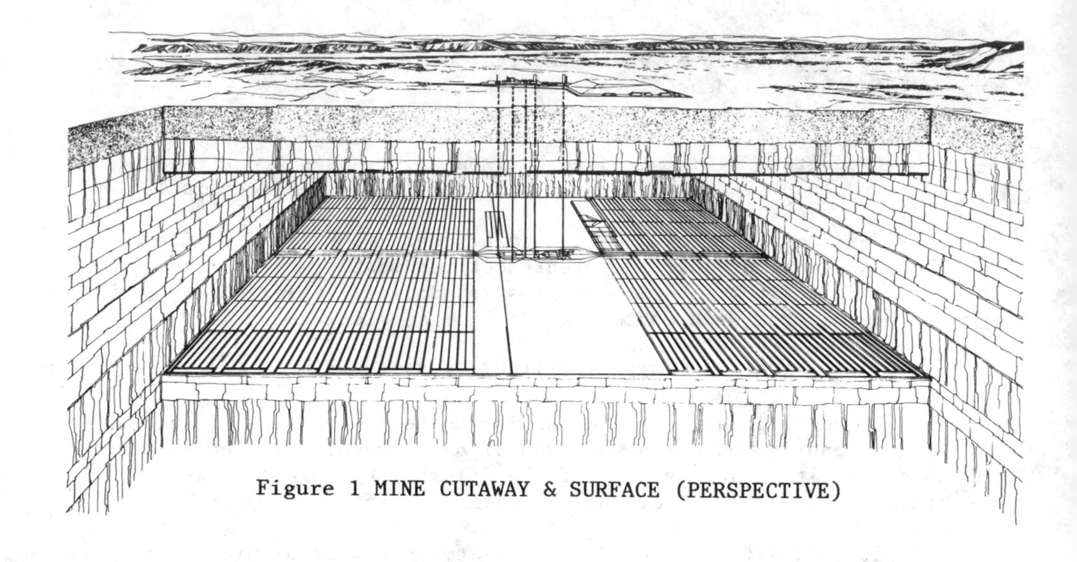

Figure 1 MINE CUTAWAY & SURFACE (PERSPECTIVE)

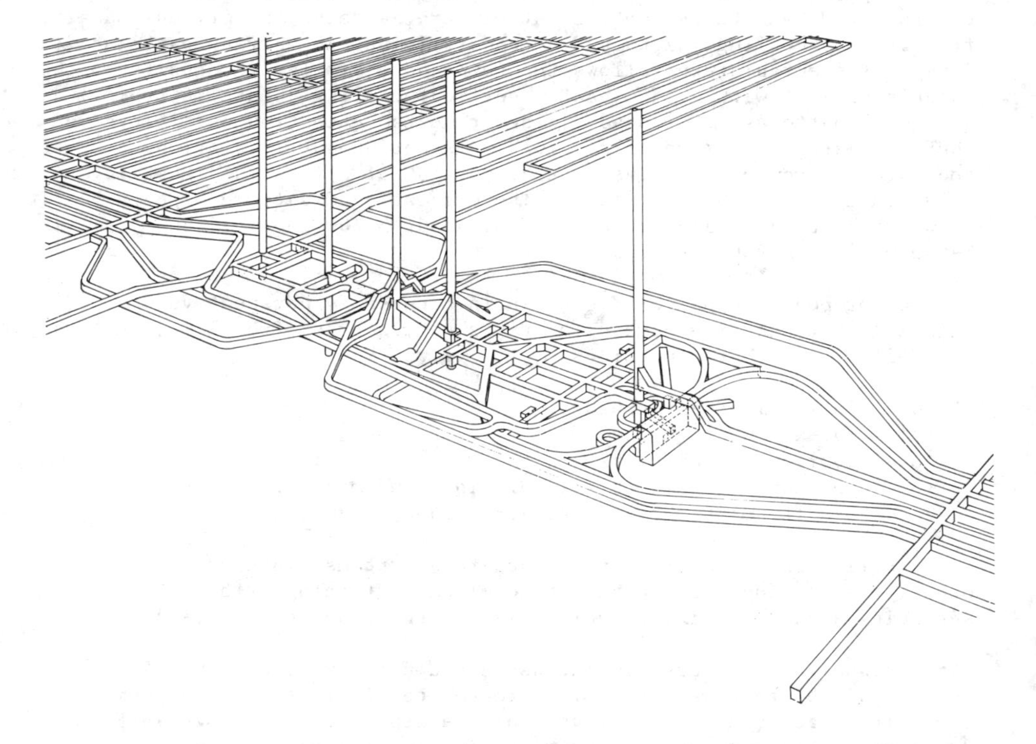

Figure 2 SHAFT PILLAR

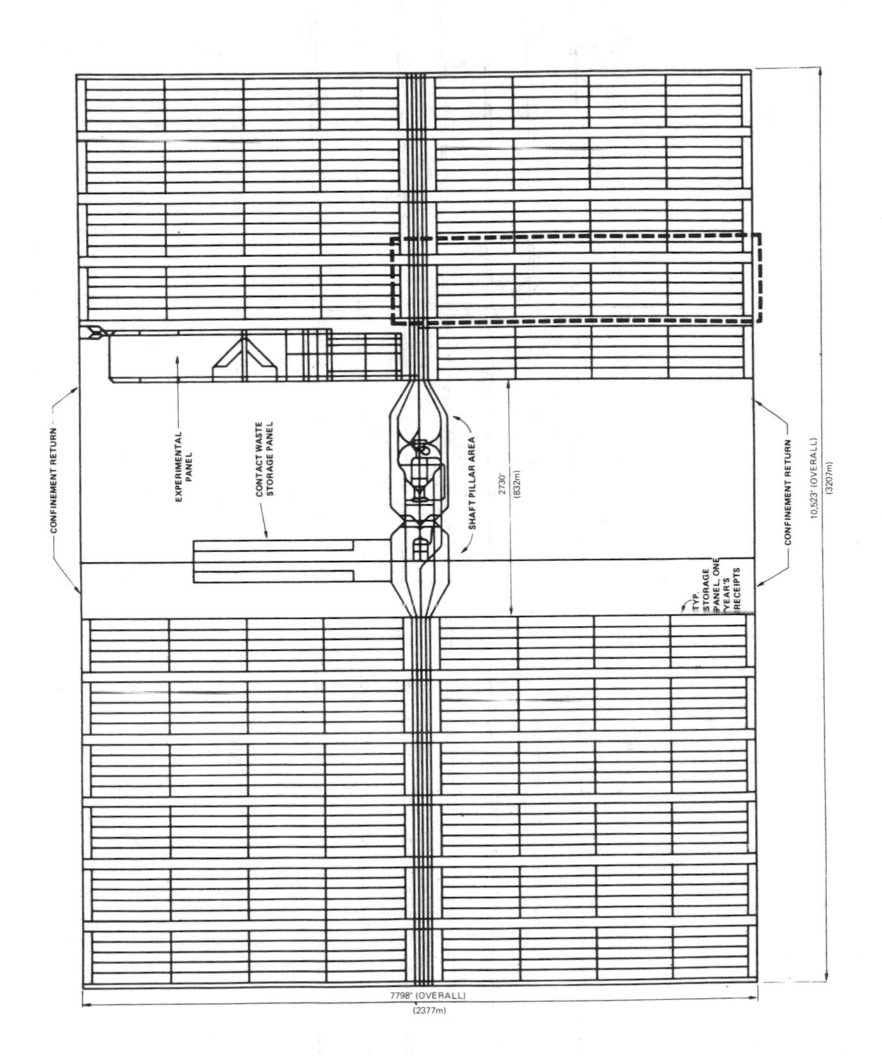

Figure 3 UNDERGROUND FACILITIES LAYOUT

The storage rooms are laid out in panels, each designed to store one year's receipts and isolated from adjacent panels. Each panel has six rooms, about 3,600 feet (1,100 m) long, connected by safety crosscuts, as shown in Figure 4. The rooms are 14 feet (4.3 m) wide and spaced 120 feet, (37 m) center to center for an extraction ratio of about 8 percent.

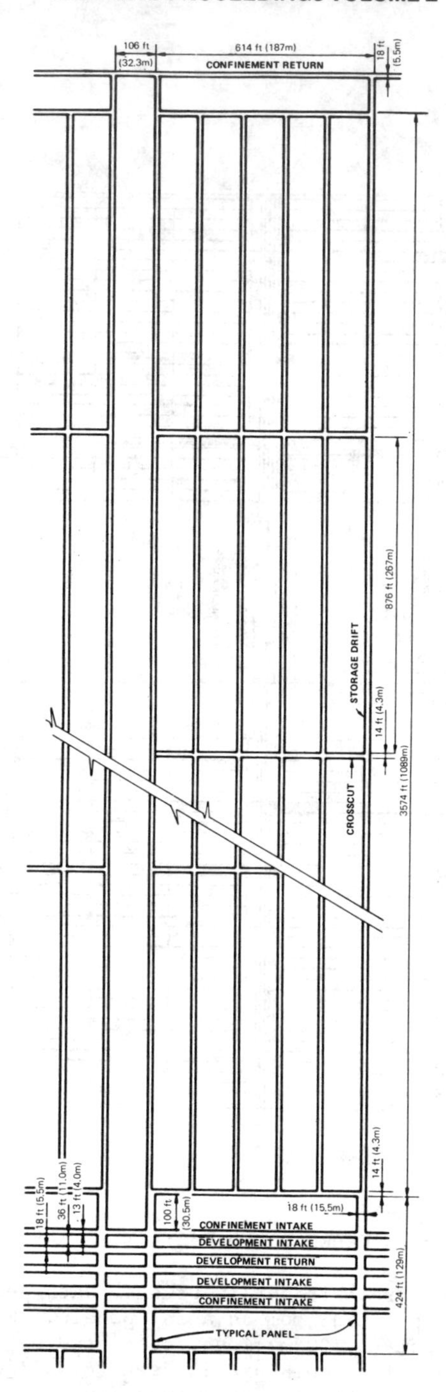

Figure 4 TYPICAL STORAGE PANEL

Nuclear waste is placed in vertical holes drilled in the floor of the repository rooms. The room cross section, showing the position of the waste package, is illustrated in Figure 5. The present concept incorporates a lining placed before the waste package, consisting of a compacted bentonite-crushed rock mixture surrounding a mullite sleeve. To allow easy installation, the bentonite mix is enclosed in an aluminum container so that the sleeve can be prefabricated. The entire sleeve unit is lowered into the hole and packed with a thin annulus of bentonite. Details of the waste package, including the mild steel cannister surrounded by a graphite buffer and a titanium container, are shown together with the sleeve configuration on Figure 6.

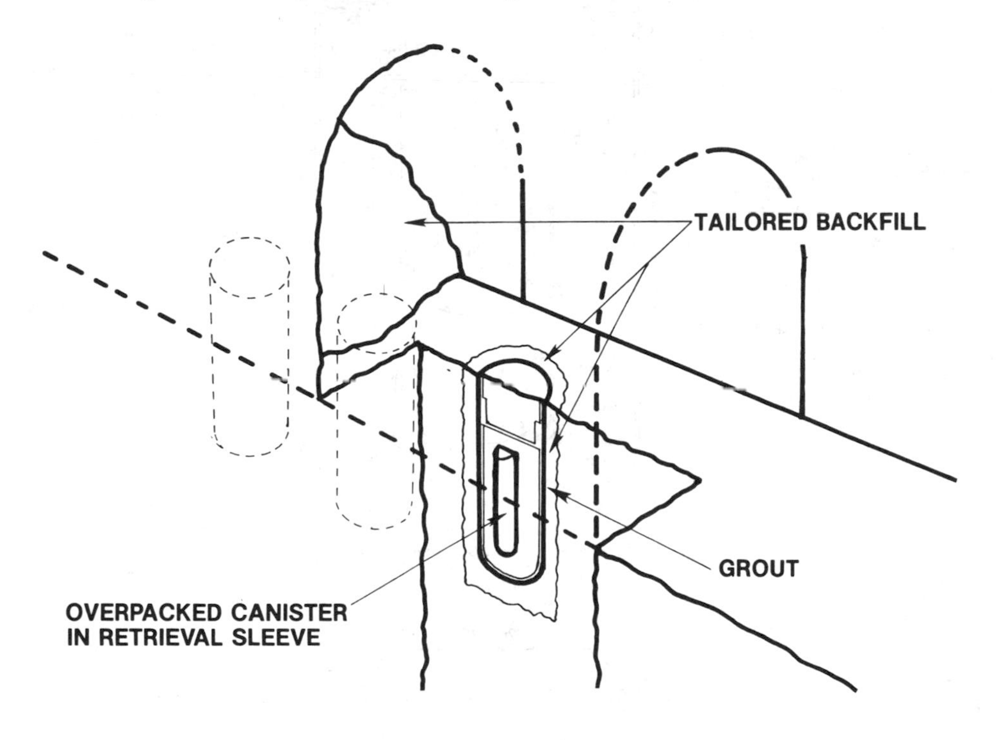

Figure 5 STORAGE ROOM

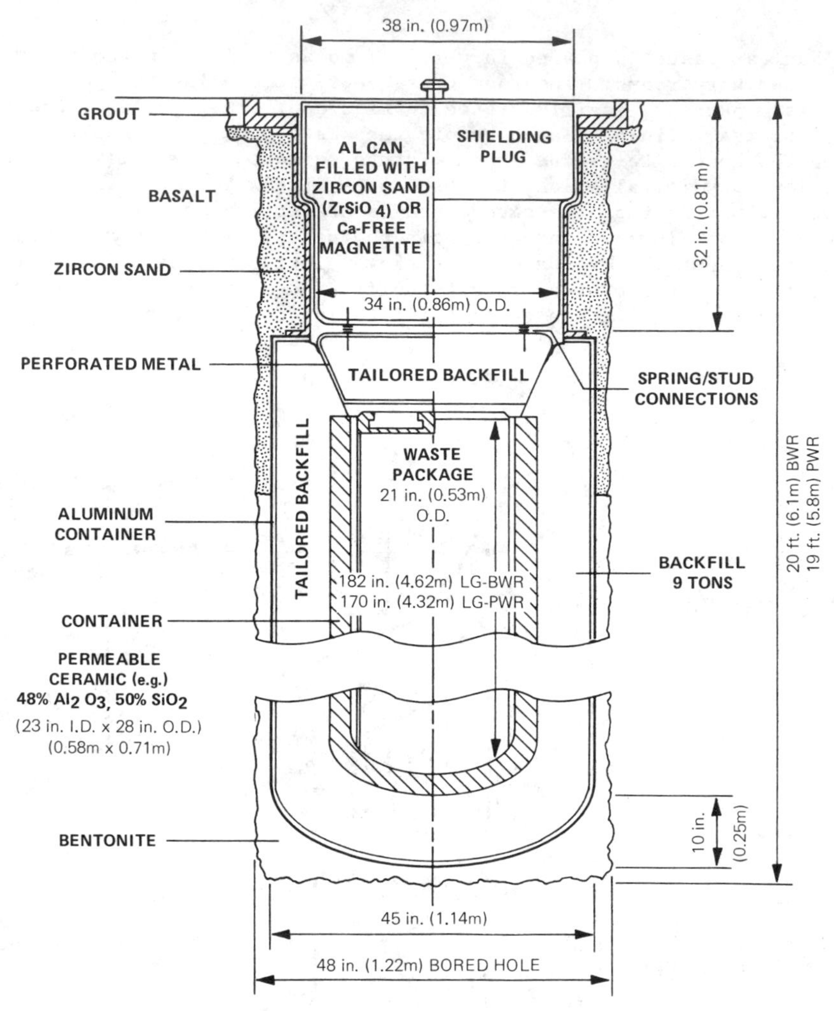

Figure 6 NWRB STORAGE POSITION

The complex waste package placement arrangement is intended to provide redundant engineered barriers against radionuclide release. In view of the uncertainty that any one barrier will be infallible, multiple barriers are planned, using different natural and man-made materials in various configurations. The ultimate barrier is the impervious repository rock itself.

Other components of the engineered barrier system include elaborate plugging of access tunnels and shafts, and backfilling of storage rooms with a compacted bentonite-crushed rock mixture.

Present plans require waste packages to be retrievable for a period of time long enough to demonstrate the safety of the repository and its components. NWRB plans to keep storage rooms open but sealed for this period, while monitoring the behavior of the waste packages, the rock, and any water that may seep in. The behavior of the room backfill will be tested in an experimental panel for as long a time as may be required, but storage rooms will not be backfilled until after the retrievable period.

PROPERTIES OF HANFORD BASALT

To predict long-term behavior of the basalt host rock, it is necessary to perform computerized modeling as well as waste package scale and room scale tests. Many laboratory tests have been performed to provide data for modeling. These tests were made on standard size cores and define properties of intact rock or individual joints. To determine properties of the fractured rock mass, applicable to modeling at a scale larger than individual joint blocks, additional, larger scale tests are required. Such tests are now being carried out in a near-surface test facility.

The laboratory tests have defined both thermal and mechanical properties of the basalt. The tests performed to date are summarized in Schmidt et al. (1980). One significant finding, probably common to many natural rocks, is that the thermal properties may be determined with much less scatter and uncertainty than mechanical data, such as strength and modulus. As a result, the thermal response of the rock to the heat from the nuclear waste can be determined more reliably from heat transfer analyses than can the resulting elasto-plastic response by mechanical analyses.

Mechanical properties of the intact basalt are highly dependent on the density of the basalt. The vesicular, lighter rock in or near a flow top is significantly weaker and has a lower modulus than the denser rock in the central parts of the flow. The relationship between unconfined compressive strength, σ_c, and density, ρ can be written

$$\sigma_c = 0.060\rho^6 \text{ (ksi)} = 0.41\rho^6 \text{ (MPa)} \quad (1)$$

for the host basalt (see Figure 7). In this equation, the density is in g/cc. For a typical entablature basalt, with a density of 2.78 g/cc, the unconfined compressive strength would be about 28 ksi (191 MPa). A similar equation is found for Young's modulus, E (See Figure 8):

$$E = 21.4\rho^6 \text{ (ksi)} = 148\rho^6 \text{ (MPa)} \quad (2)$$

The typical modulus would be about 9,900 psi (68.1 MPa). Based on equations (1) and (2), the modulus to strength ratio is equal to 357, independent of density. The ratio of unconfined compressive strength to tensile strength was found to be 13, on the average.

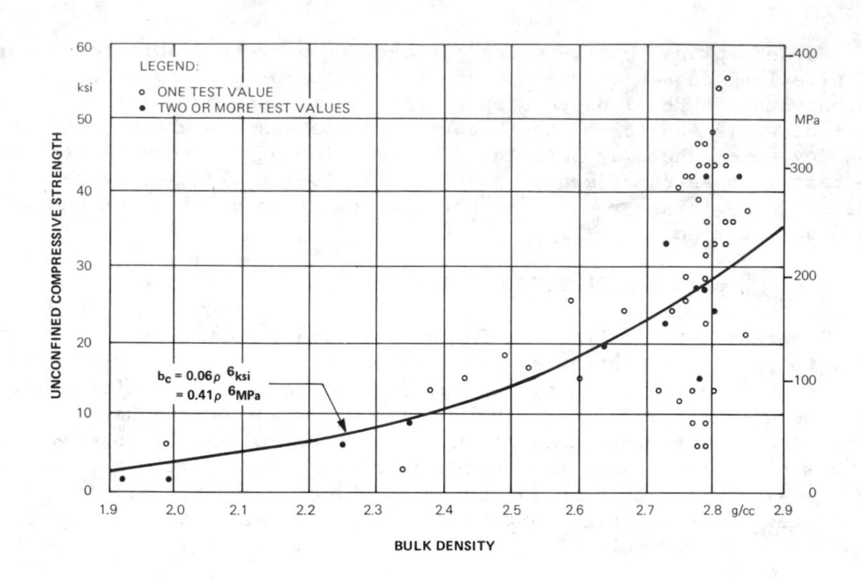

Figure 7 BASALT UNCONFINED COMPRESSIVE STRENGTH AS FUNCTION OF DENSITY

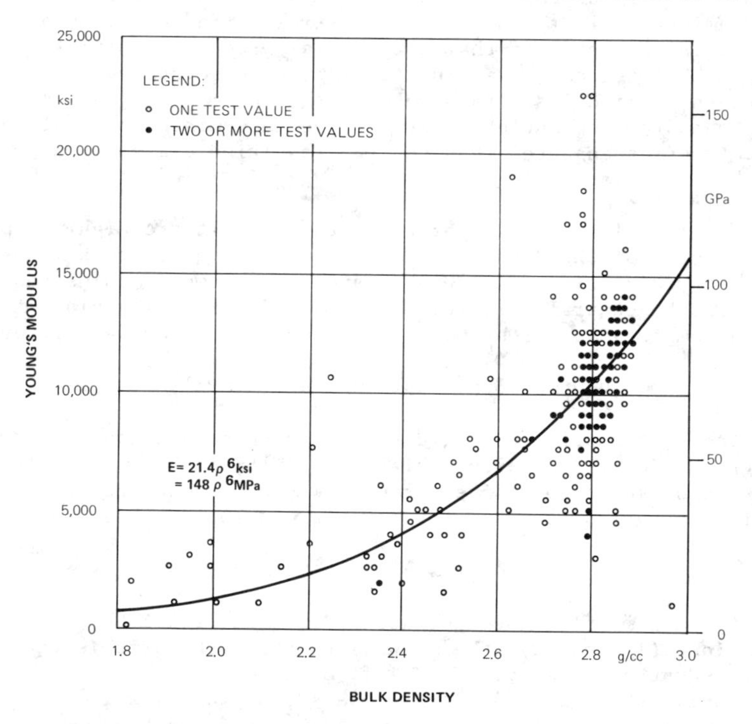

Figure 8 BASALT YOUNG'S MODULUS AS FUNCTION OF DENSITY

Triaxial tests resulted in an angle of internal friction of about 45°. Based on this friction angle, the strength of the intact basalt may be written

$$\sigma_1 = 31.6 + 5.9\sigma_3 \text{ (ksi)} = 218 + 5.9\sigma_3 \text{ (MPa)} \tag{3}$$

where σ_3 is the confining pressure. The cohesion intercept is slightly higher than given by equation (1) because equation (3) was derived from a separate, dedicated triaxial test series.

In all of the strength tests, the variation in the test data is very large; the standard deviations are of the order of 40 to 60 percent of the mean values. It may be suspected that the strength data shown do not represent the real intact strength but that latent flaws greatly affect the strength. Test series on younger and more shallow basalts (from the near-surface test facility) showed smaller variations. Thus, one may suspect that age and depth, in addition to lithologic differences, have an effect on the prevalence of latent flaws and, therefore, on the measured strength variations and mean values. The older rock has been subjected to tectonic stresses and events not experienced by the younger rock; hence, it is likely to show more obvious and latent flaws. The stress relief caused by sampling is very substantial on a core extracted from 3,700-foot (1,130 m) depth, where the vertical overburden stress is of the order of 4,500 psi (31 MPa). Many cores from this depth displayed poker-chip disking, normally ascribed to failure as a result of stress relief. Samples with large locked-in stresses and latent disking are likely to behave in an erratic fashion in a compression test apparatus, and the measured tensile strength may be even more affected.

These apparent weaknesses are mostly the result of sampling and testing. Under the existing, large confining pressures in-situ, these latent flaws may have little effect.

Young's modulus is essentially unaffected by triaxial confining pressure, but both strength and modulus of intact samples decrease with increasing temperature. Figure 9 shows the measured relationship between temperature and unconfined compressive strength as well as modulus.

To determine the stress build-up due to a temperature increase under confined conditions, the thermal expansion coefficient, α, must be known. In most instances (if the rock behaves elastically) the stress build-up at any given point is proportional to the product $E\alpha$. The thermal expansion coefficient for a rock is a complex coefficient. At low stress levels, thermal expansion is not completely reversible; therefore, a single coefficient does not entirely describe thermal expansion. This is attributed to thermally induced micro-cracking in the rock, both between and within individual crystals. At high confining pressures, micro-cracking will be limited, the thermal expansion will be essentially reversible, and the coefficient will be smaller (Wong and Brace, 1979). Tests have not been made at this time to

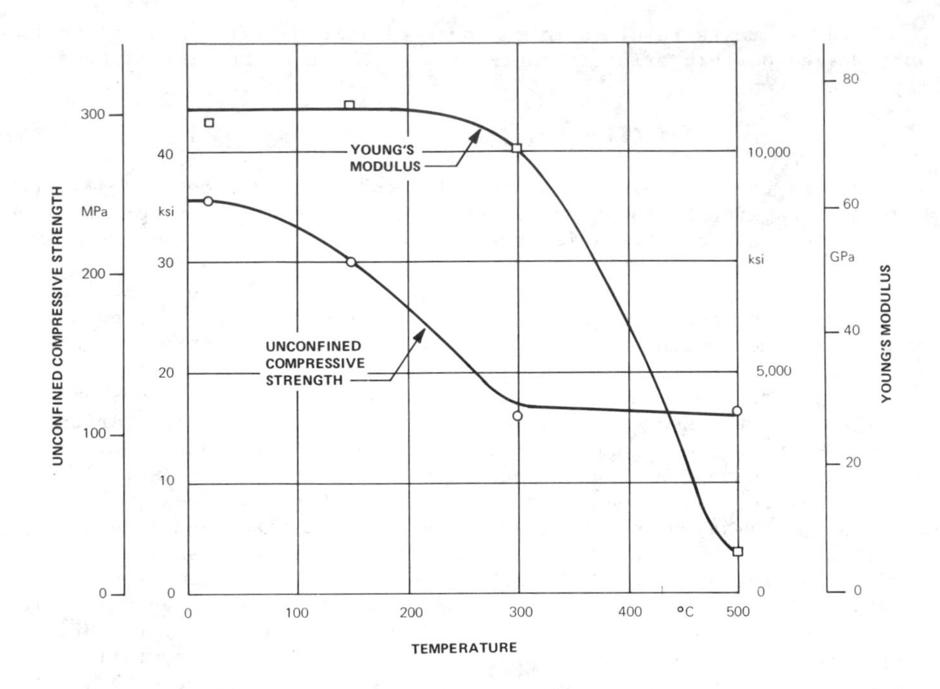

Figure 9 STRENGTH AND MODULUS AS FUNCTION OF TEMPERATURE

highlight this phenomenon. However, measured expansion coefficients are relatively close to those determined theoretically based on constituents of the basalt. The average measured thermal expansion coefficient for the host basalt is 7.5 x 10^{-6}/°C, increasing slightly with temperature.

The value of refining the expansion coefficient to a better number for analyses is limited, since the other half of the product $E\alpha$, Young's modulus E, is poorly known. Depending on the number and characteristics of the joints in the rock mass, and the confining pressure, Young's modulus for the rock mass may be one-half or one-tenth that of intact specimens. Furthermore, even if large scale tests will refine the value of Young's modulus for the rock mass, it is likely to be a parameter that will vary appreciably with location, even in a seemingly uniform rock mass. Hence, upper and lower bounds must be estimated for each type of analysis, and a refinement of a few percent of the expansion coefficient is inconsequential.

Values of thermal conductivity and specific heat have also been determined. Thermal diffusivity has been measured directly and also calculated from conductivity, specific heat and density. These thermal parameters appear to be affected by detailed laboratory procedures, even to the extent that trends (increasing or decreasing with rising temperature) are uncertain. Nonetheless, values are close enough to establish reliable parameters for analyses in the conceptual stage. The values currently used for analyses (independent of temperature) are:

- Thermal conductivity: 1.16 W/m°C
- Specific heat: 0.20 cal/g°C
- Density: 2.78 g/cc
- Thermal diffusivity: 0.0065 cm^2/sec

REPOSITORY ANALYSES

Thermomechanical analyses are required for the following purposes:

- to ascertain safety and rock support requirements for excavation
- to make sure temperatures do not exceed prescribed limits
- to evaluate requirements for, and effects of, ventilation cooling
- to predict stresses and strains around openings that may alter permeabilities, and to assess collapse risks
- to assess the risk that tensile stresses at a distance may open paths for water ingress or egress
- to assess the risk of rock bursts or induced seismicity that may alter permeabilities
- to determine probable or potential paths for escape of radionuclides and probable radionuclide travel times, considering also absorption and adsorption.

Thermal Analyses

Thermal rock properties in specimen sizes are known or may be determined quite accurately (±10 to 20 percent); they are only moderately affected by rock flaws or jointing. As long as the water content of the rock is small and the rock has a low permeability, heat transfer calculations are relatively simple and reliable, and temperatures can be predicted with confidence. As long as rooms are open, air convection in the rooms will tend to equalize temperatures immediately around the rooms and evaporating water will remove heat. These details are more difficult to evaluate but are likely to render rooms safer; they may, therefore, be ignored for conceptual design analyses.

Rock Stress Safety Factors

Openings in rock do not behave like structural members, for which a failure load can be determined. For a rock opening, the load comes from the rock itself, which also is the principal supporting member. No failure load can be defined, and a safety factor similar to that of an ordinary structure cannot be calculated. Instead of safety factors, one must deal with other expressions of satisfactory or unsatisfactory performance, defined to suit circumstances and use requirements.

For rooms in which workers are present, safety requires a sufficiently low probability of one or several modes of failure, such as rock falls, wall slabbing or rock bursts. During the period of retrievability, during which rooms are sealed and not routinely accessible, the performance is satisfactory if no major collapses occur, and if instability can be checked and repaired safely upon re-entry of the rooms. In the long term, safety against radionuclide migration requires that no continuous paths of high permeability are created that might quickly carry groundwater with radionuclides to the biosphere, or that such permeable paths are checked by a barrier at some point.

It appears from this discussion that room safety assessments must start by determining acceptable modes of performance. These may relate to purely mechanical phenomena (initial rock fall probability); thermomechanical phenomena (mechanical stability under stresses induced by higher temperatures); or changes in hydraulic characteristics induced by thermomechanical phenomena. Hydrothermal phenomena - chemical modifications of rocks, joint infills or man-made materials - must also be considered. Borehole decrepitation, such as by thermal spalling, is not ordinarily a problem in basalt, which is essentially non-spallable (Thirumalai, 1970) but may be a problem for other rock types.

Next, analyses must be performed, which specifically address the phenomenon under investigation, or experience must be studied or gained, to determine the probability of unsatisfactory performance. Most such analyses performed today are deterministic in nature; based on realistic input, the analyses produce predictions of performance that are either satisfactory or unsatisfactory. It is likely that probabilistic analyses will be developed, based on probabilistic data input, that will produce an estimate of the likelihood of satisfactory performance, or an estimate of the proportion of the room length for which unsatisfactory performance may be expected. It must then be judged if the predicted probability is acceptable.

Such types of analyses are difficult to make today, because a number of parameters are as yet poorly defined and rock mass behavior in all its complexity is poorly understood. The strength of intact rock and its variability may be tested adequately in the laboratory, but that of the jointed rock mass is much less tangible. Progress is being made to characterize rock mass strength on an empirical basis (e.g. Hoek and Brown, 1980), but little is known about rock mass strength in probabilistic formulation. Stresses induced by temperature increases are proportional to Young's modulus; yet, Young's modulus for rock masses is known only with an accuracy of a factor three at best, and no probabilistic formulation is available.

For the moment, then, one must make do with relatively simple but imperfect deterministic analyses. For scoping of conceptual designs, simplified hand calculations are adequate; more detailed designs require the use of computer models.

For the NWRB conceptual design, much of the analysis approach follows principles described by Hardy and Hocking (1980). With this approach, a rock stress safety factor is estimated for a given point by calculating the stresses at that point and estimating the strength, considering the confining stress, at the same point. The rock stress safety factor is simply this strength divided by the stress. A triaxial strength formulation is used, and a point located away from the opening a distance of one-sixth the roof span is considered. The rock strength is reduced as a function of representative volume or roof span. These principles are shown on Figure 10. As noted before, the rock stress safety factor is not a safety factor in the conventional sense; it is a relative measure of stress level.

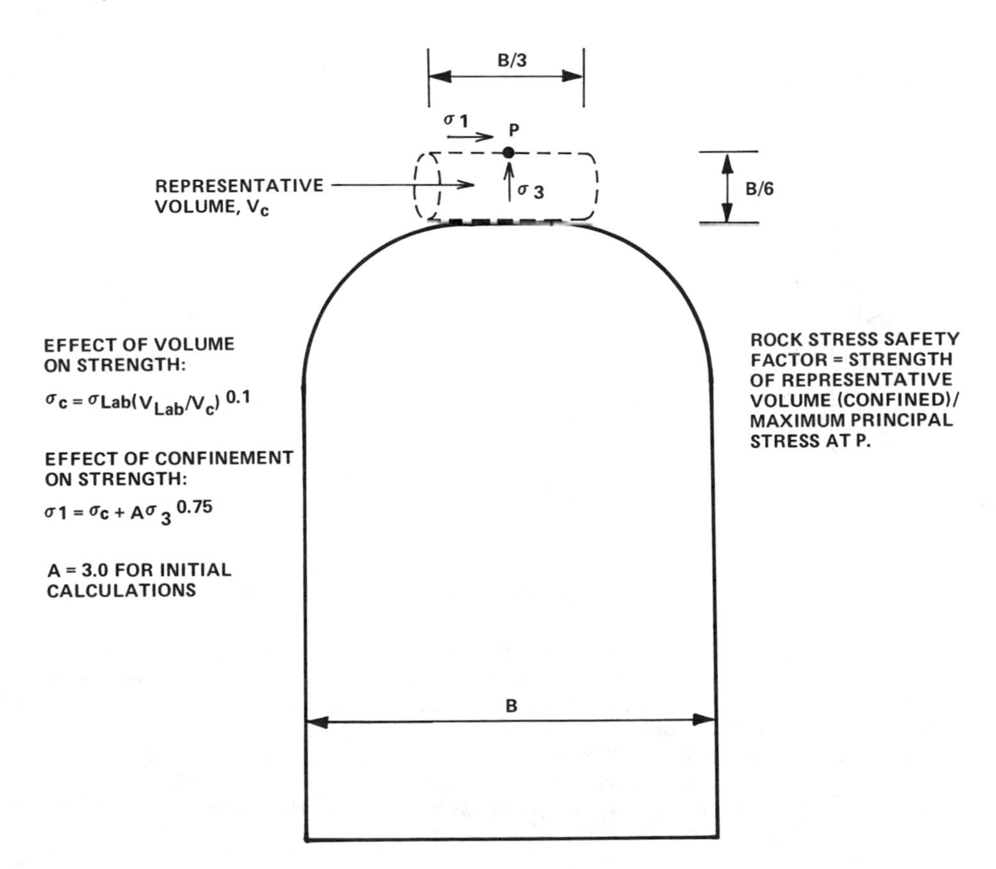

Figure 10 ROCK STRESS SAFETY FACTOR

Results of Analyses

Twenty-five years after placement of 10-year old waste (1.75kW heat generation per waste package, 53 kW/acre [131 kW/hectare]), the temperature distribution around a room would be about as shown in Figure 11.

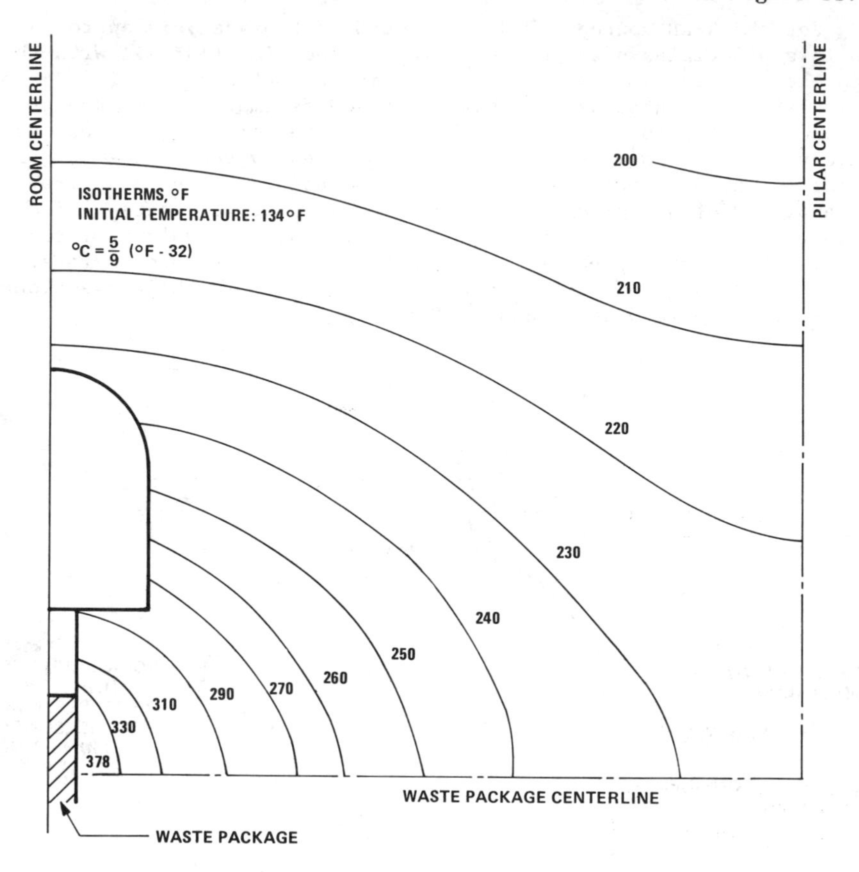

Figure 11 TEMPERATURE AFTER 25 YEARS

The temperature increase results in increased horizontal stresses since the rock is confined in a horizontal direction. By integration of the temperatures and application of the proper stress concentration factors, stresses around the room are calculated, and the rock stress safety factor estimated. The decrease in rock stress safety factor with time is shown in Figure 12. The time variation of rock stress safety factor for an equivalent circular room is also shown.

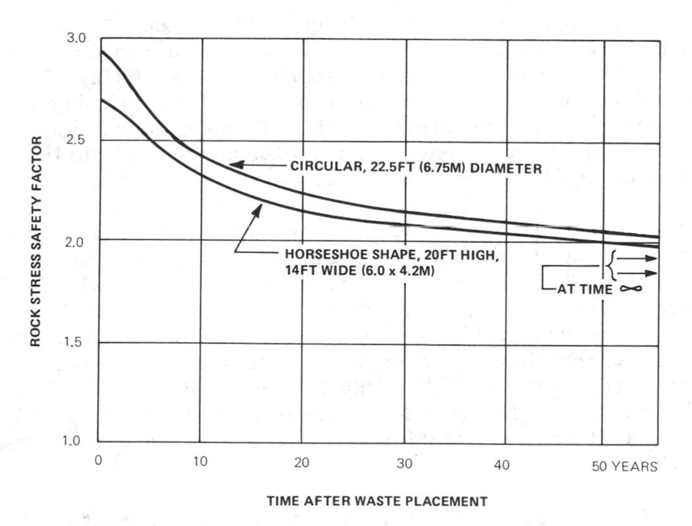

Figure 12 DECREASE IN ROCK STRESS SAFETY FACTOR WITH TIME

The rock stress safety factor is initially about 2.7 but decreases to about 2 after 50 years. Beyond this time, the decrease is small. The equivalent circular room is larger and the representative strength, therefore, smaller. However, the stress concentration is lower because of a more favorable shape; hence, the safety of a circular room is just slightly better.

The rock stress safety factors are used primarily for comparison purposes; they may be used to compare different room sizes, shapes and spacings and to determine the relative effects of temperature increases. A safety factor of two appears acceptable but does not guarantee that some type of unsatisfactory behavior would not occur locally. More detailed analyses will show if unsatisfactory performance (if any) is likely to occur in an acceptably small proportion of the room lengths.

Some additional findings of these and similar analyses are discussed below:

Rock Support: The effect of rock support on the theoretical rock stress safety factor for rooms at great depth is small. Maximum stress concentrations around the room periphery reach beyond 10 ksi (70 MPa). Should room safety not be acceptable, even a modest improvement in rock stress safety factor would require supporting loads of the order of several ksi. This would easily exceed the capacity of practical support materials. Hence, rooms should ideally be designed so that the rock stress safety factor is adequate even without considering rock support.

Minor Modes of Failure: The conclusion reached above does not mean that no supports should be applied. Regardless of theoretical rock stress safety factors, joints will frequently be located in unfavorable locations and directions, leading to potential minor modes of failure, such as roof falls, unacceptable loosening, wall slabbing, etc. These minor modes of failure will be prevented by a shotcrete application or rock bolts in a regular pattern or both. These supports would be designed according to experience gained elsewhere, and during development of the repository.

After excavation of a room section and application of shotcrete, an initial safety factor better than unity is assured everywhere. A subsequent installation of rock bolts, designed essentially to duplicate the supporting effect of the shotcrete, will add desired conservatism to the design and preserve safety also during the retrievability period, during which roof stresses will increase. The order of application of shotcrete or rock bolts may be reversed without changing the effect of redundancy. Though these supports would be designed in essentially empirical fashion, modeling tools are available to assess the redundancy effect.

Effects of Temperature and Initial Stresses: Under the initial stress conditions at 3,700' (1,130 m) depth, the safety of the rooms would decrease by about one-third with increasing temperature. This decrease is nearly proportional to the overall heat load supplied by the waste packages. To maintain satisfactory safety, therefore, there is an upper limit to the areal heat load that may be applied. In the case of the NWRB, the initial heat load is about 53 kW/acre (131 kW/hectare) (waste packages spaced 12 feet (3.7 m) apart in rooms spaced 120 feet (36.6 m) apart). Doubling the heat load would reduce the long-term safety by two-thirds, which does not appear acceptable.

If the initial stresses were significantly lower (for example, if the repository where at a shallower depth), the initial safety would be greater, and a greater reduction in safety with time could be accepted. Hence, waste packages could be placed closer together in a shallower repository. A shallower repository would, therefore, be much less expensive.

The conceptual design has been worked out under the assumption of a virgin hydrostatic stress state. Should additional explorations in an exploratory shaft test facility disclose significantly higher in-situ horizontal stresses, the density of waste placement might have to be reduced.

Effects of Stratification: The repository would be located within a basalt flow, 200 to 300 feet (60-90 m) thick. As earlier discussed, the strength of the rock, and its Young's modulus, are lower by nearly an order of magnitude near the flow top and in the interflow region. This significantly reduces the capability of the rock to transfer shear strains from one basalt flow to the next flow above or below. Hence, horizontal compressive stresses tend to stay within the host basalt flow and not be redistributed into adjacent flows. This would increase the horizontal thermal stresses within the flow beyond what they would be in a homogeneous mass. On the other hand, the likelihood of creating tensile cracks some distance above the repository (deleterious to long-term sealing) is diminished.

Maintenance During Retrievability Period: The repository rooms can provide adequate safety throughout the retrievability period without additional support. Any backfill material is likely to have a strength and modulus an order of magnitude lower than that of the surrounding rock mass. Hence, the support from the backfill is likely to be only nominal. In retrieval, the removal of backfill would be difficult and hazardous. The backfill would be quite hot (its temperature would be greater than 100°C) and therefore would require substantial ventilation and cooling efforts. Latent rock falls could be discovered and fixed if the rooms remain open; if they are backfilled, the removal of the backfill could expose workers to such hazardous rock falls without warning.

For these reasons it appears that rooms should not be backfilled (though they may be sealed) until after the retrievability period, or until such time when the probability that retrieval will be required is very small. The long-term performance of a backfilled room can be demonstrated in a dedicated experimental panel; backfilling of all rooms immediately after waste placement is not required for this purpose.

MONITORING

Two different philosophies may be applied to the subject of monitoring repository behavior after waste placement:

- Monitor to ascertain satisfactory performance of every point or cross section of every room, and every waste package
- Monitor to obtain confidence that predictions of safety are acceptably accurate.

The first philosophy places no reliance on our ability to predict behavior or to assess the gross effects of locally unacceptable performance; it ignores concepts of probability. Monitoring to satisfy this philosophy for a repository containing some 100 miles (161 km) of rooms and 35,000 waste packages for tens of years would be extraordinarily expensive and essentially infeasible.

Using a probabilistic approach, and considering that locally unsatisfactory performance may be quite acceptable for the repository as a whole, the second approach is favored. Thus, the proposed monitoring program employs a full complement of monitoring devices in a dedicated experimental panel and in a limited portion of the production panels. For the remainder of the panels, monitoring would be employed only to provide adequate statistical testing of panel behavior.

The monitoring program is still under development; it will include monitoring of microseisms, temperatures, room convergence, rock strains and displacements by extensometers, and rock stress gages. Water inflow into rooms will be monitored by measuring liquid as well as vaporized outflow from rooms. Small volumes of air pulled through repository rooms will be monitored for radionuclide contents, as will be the drainage water, if any.

Though not every point of the repository would be monitored directly, global monitoring systems, based on acoustic emissions, would detect adverse rock movements at any location. Radionuclide leaks would be detected by monitoring of air and water from each room or panel. Further investigation of suspected areas would then lead to discovery and remedial action.

ROCK DISTURBANCE DUE TO CONSTRUCTION

The mechanisms of rock disturbance around a room excavated in rock are complex and poorly understood. For another type of project, this is perhaps of minor consequence; construction experience would provide the means for designing supports for adequate safety. For a nuclear waste repository, the potential for increased permeability in a disturbed zone has significant effects on the design of schemes for eventual plugging, because such a permeable zone might create a water flow bypass around any plug placed within the opening.

Fractures created, extended or opened by blasting may reach a distance of several feet, depending on rock conditions and blasting methods. This distance would be only moderately affected by the size of the opening. If necessary, special and innovative excavation methods may be used to minimize this type of disturbance.

Irrespective of excavation methods, the creation of a rock opening causes stress changes and rock strains that may lead to minute motions along existing or new joints. Laboratory experiments have shown that microcracking in an intact compressive test sample greatly increases when the shear stress exceeds about 50 percent of failure stress. A similar phenomenon may be expected for a jointed rock mass. Hence, concern for this type of rock disturbance may require the imposition of maximum stress levels around openings, or a rock stress safety factor. The required minimum rock stress safety factor cannot be stated with confidence at this time because not enough is known of the effects of such disturbances on rock permeability. Very likely, in-situ measurements in the host horizon would be required to resolve this problem.

Finally, increasing stresses due to thermal loading could cause additional rock damage as the rock stress safety factor decreases. This would happen primarily in the emplacement rooms but only to a minor degree in accessways and shafts. Since the most important plugs would be placed in the accessways and shafts, this damage is of lesser concern than the initial construction damage.

Once these phenomena are better understood after in-situ testing, proper rock stress safety factors may be established. These would be different for initial conditions and later thermal conditions. They would also vary with location within the repository.

CONCLUSIONS

Basalt strata at Hanford appear to present a suitable geologic medium for nuclear waste disposal; they are strong and impermeable and appear to be remote from moving groundwater and usable aquifers.

Acceptable rock stress safety factors may be determined by disturbance and permeability criteria rather than rock stability; such factors and criteria must be verified by in-situ experiments.

Monitoring of repository performance after waste placement should be performed to obtain the necessary confidence on a statistical basis; not every point and waste package need be monitored.

In basalt, it is not desirable to backfill rooms until such time as the likelihood of required retrieval has become very small.

Stratification of the basalt rock would tend to concentrate thermal stresses within a single basalt flow. It would appear that adequate safety may be attained for a repository in the candidate repository horizon at about 3,700 feet (1,130 m).

Much additional work needs to be done, analytical as well as experimental, before the long-term safety of the repository is ultimately ascertained. This may include the development of analytical tools to assess rock behavior on a statistical basis.

REFERENCES

Hardy, M., and Hocking, G., 1980, "Rock Mechanics Design Criteria for Repository Design in Hard Rock", presented at ASCE Convention, Portland, Oregon, April

Hoek, E., and Brown, E. T., 1980, "Empirical Strength Criterion for Rock Masses," Journal of the Geotechnical Engineering Division, ASCE, Vol. 106, No. GT9, pp. 1013-1035.

Schmidt, B. et al., 1980, "Thermal and Mechanical Properties of Hanford Basalts - Compilation and Analyses," Report prepared for Department of Energy under direction of Rockwell Hanford Operations, Report No. RHO-BWI-C-90.

Thirumalai, K., 1970, "Rock Fragmentation by Creating a Thermal Inclusion with Dielectric Heating", U.S. Bureau of Mines, Report of Investigations No. 7424.

Wong, T.-F. and Brace, W. F., 1979 "Thermal Expansion of Rocks: Some Measurements at High Pressure", Tectonophysics, Elsevier Vol. 57, pp. 95-117.

Chapter 77

SEALING OF SHAFTS, TUNNELS, AND BOREHOLES FOR WASTE REPOSITORIES

by R. D. Ellison,[1] D. E. Stephenson,[2] and D. K. Shukla[2]

[1]Executive Vice President
D'Appolonia Consulting Engineers, Inc.
Pittsburgh, Pennsylvania

[2]Manager, Albuquerque Operations
Staff Consultant, Supervisor of Special Projects
D'Appolonia Consulting Engineers, Inc.
Albuquerque, New Mexico

ABSTRACT

Seals for man-made penetrations into or nearby nuclear waste repositories require several unique capabilities not common to seals for conventional underground activities. Design criteria include long functional use, extremely low permeabilities of the seal zone (including adjacent disturbed rock), and the potential for retarding radionuclide travel. This paper summarizes comprehensive seal programs being conducted by D'Appolonia for the Office of Nuclear Waste Isolation (ONWI) at Battelle, Columbus. The program schedule requires the first detailed conceptual design for a bedded salt site to be completed in 1982. Conceptual designs for other host media will follow as site exploration data becomes available.

The design program is supported by a variety of office, laboratory, and field activities being conducted by ONWI subcontractors. An example is provided to illustrate the variety of efforts directed toward determining the extent of disturbance adjacent to penetrations as a result of in-situ and excavation methods. Also, the current "working design" for the shaft and tunnel seal system at the candidate Los Medanos thick salt site in southeastern New Mexico is presented.

INTRODUCTION

The isolation of nuclear waste in deep, mined repositories will require the sealing of all penetrations into or nearby the facility. Types of penetrations shown in Figure 1 include exploratory boreholes, shafts, entry drifts (tunnels), and backfilling of the waste disposal chambers. The design of seals is an integral part of the Department of Energy (DOE), National Waste Terminal Storage (NWTS) program for the permanent isolation of commercial and defense waste. The design program is being conducted by D'Appolonia for the Office of Nuclear Waste Isolation (ONWI), which is part of the Project Management Division of Battelle Memorial Institute.

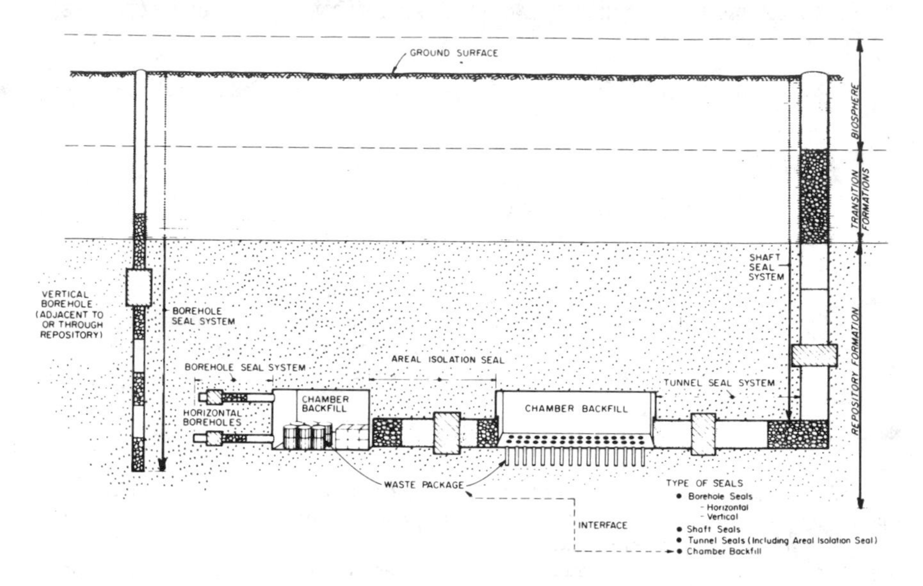

FIGURE 1: PENETRATION SEALING APPLICATIONS

The program began in 1978 with reviews of (1) work by previous investigators, and (2) sealing techniques used for petroleum production and storage, mining, civil construction, deep well disposal, and military operations (ONWI, 1978; ONWI, 1979). Conclusions were that significant materials and installation experience does exist, but the bulk of this knowledge for conventional seals is only of partial value for repository sealing. Major differences center around functions, quality and, most importantly, longevity requirements for repository seals.

Development of acceptable seal designs within overall repository licensing and construction schedules required establishment of a seal design program following two parallel but interdependent paths. One is to conduct generic studies aimed toward identifying basic sealing requirements and relating them to overall repository system needs. The second path is associated with studies at specific sites, such the Los Medanos site in southeastern New Mexico, as locations for potential candidate sites are identified.

Design program coordination is accomplished by assigning all support activities into office, laboratory, or field functions as illustrated in Figure 2. A major requirement of the design program is to determine the types, schedules, and resource requirements required for each support activity in order to satisfy overall technical and programmatic requirements.

Table 1 shows the schedule for developing conceptual designs for various geologic media. The sequence is based primarily on the rate at which exploration data are expected to be available, and does not reflect the relative importance of candidate geologies. Conceptual design is defined to mean the detailed design and specification of practical sealing systems that have high potential of being licensed. Any requirements that are not totally satisfied, and programs to resolve those remaining issues, must be identified.

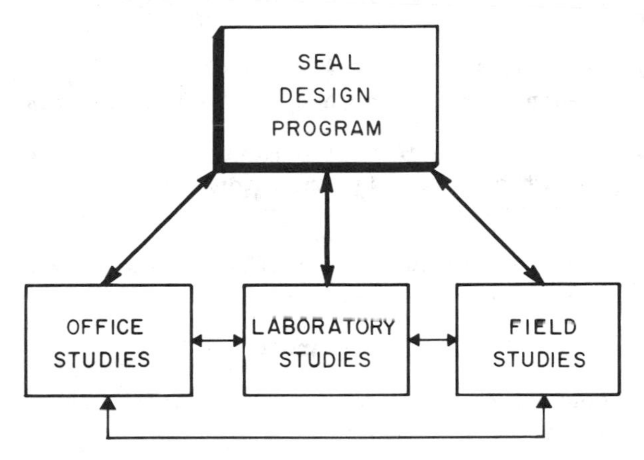

FIGURE 2: SUPPORT ELEMENTS FOR DESIGN PROGRAM

TABLE 1

SCHEDULE FOR CONCEPTUAL DESIGNS

MEDIA	CONCEPTUAL SEAL DESIGNS
BEDDED SALT (LOS MEDANOS)	8/82
DOME SALT	9/83
BASALT (BWIP)	3/84
GRANITE	9/84
BEDDED SALT	4/85
TUFF	6/85

This paper summarizes the status of the generic repository design activities and introduces the working design for shafts and access tunnels at a thick-bedded salt repository such as the Los Medanos site.

DESIGN GOALS AND CRITERIA

The basic approaches that direct the design program were developed in 1979 and published in the report designated as ONWI-55 (ONWI, 1980). Those approaches have been expanded to include all of the concepts in this paper.

The primary goals are to (1) develop safe seal designs that can be constructed at reasonable costs, and (2) obtain licensing for seals within the overall NWTS program. Resulting technical requirements are to:

- Characterize penetration, environmental, and loading conditions that will be experienced.
- Develop suitable seal materials and geometries considering specific functions, installation procedures, and cost.
- Develop techniques to verify the adequacy of designs.

The primary functions of seals are to:

- Control the magnitude of radionuclide release along any penetration.
- Control the amounts of water that may enter the repository along any pentration.

These functions may include the control of fluids and nuclides between portions of the repository.

ONWI-55 examined alternative goals or criteria that could be used to eventually quantify seal requirements. The recommended radionuclide release criterion is:

> The radioactive migration rate through the seal zone (R_{out}) should always be less by a specified factor of safety (F.S.) than an acceptable level ($R_{acceptable}$) which is determined by the consequence of such a release; hence:

$$R_{out} < \frac{R_{acceptable}}{F.S.} \qquad (1)$$

The water inflow function can be satisfied by the additional criterion of:

> The potential water inflow rate through the seal zone (Q_{in}) should always be less by a specified factor of safety (F.S.) than an acceptable level ($Q_{acceptable}$) which will not have any unacceptable impact on the repository function; hence:

$$Q_{in} < \frac{Q_{acceptable}}{F.S.} \quad (2)$$

The factor of safeties are established on a case-by-case basis considering institutional standards, material uncertainties, geologic event uncertainties, etc. The natural decay of the stored radioactive materials permit the criteria and factor of safety to be changed with time.

The seal zone consists of the three potential pathways shown in Figure 3: the seal itself; the interface (or bonding zone) between the seal and host formation; and a disturbed zone that may exist in the host rock.

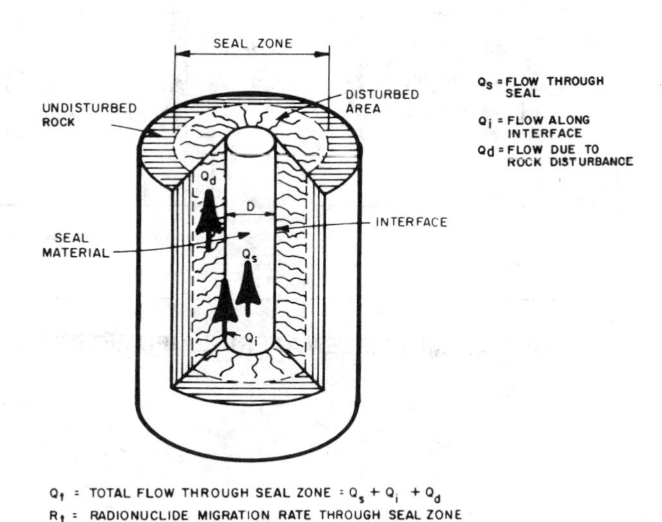

FIGURE 3: SEAL ZONE COMPONENTS

ONWI-55 also introduced the multiple material/geometry concept illustrated in Figure 4. This concept minimizes many concerns that arise from reliance on single materials that must perform for long periods under a variety of conditions. The multiple material/geometry concept provides (1) high redundancy, which greatly reduces failure potential due to any uncertainties, (2) a variety of materials resistant to different environmental conditions, (3) means to improve interface and disturbed zones, and (4) the opportunity to control both the quantity and chemical flow characteristics by sequencing selected geometries and materials.

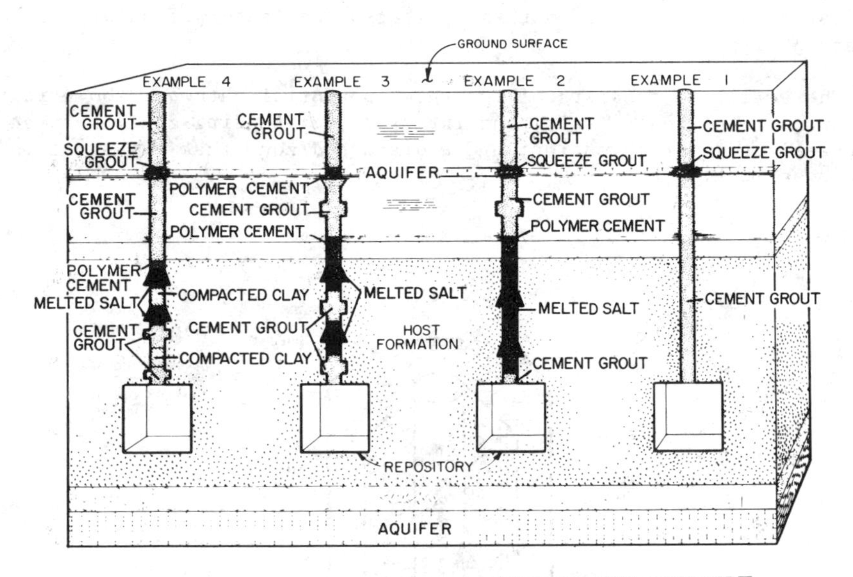

FIGURE 4: MULTIPLE MATERIAL/GEOMETRY CONCEPT

DESIGN SUPPORT ACTIVITIES

Tables 2, 3, and 4 summarize the ranges of activities being undertaken in the office, laboratory and field support functions. The final two sections of this paper introduce examples of current activities.

TABLE 2

OFFICE ACTIVITIES IN SUPPORT OF SEAL DESIGN PROGRAM

- ESTABLISHMENT OF REQUIREMENTS FOR BOREHOLES, SHAFTS, TUNNELS, AND BACKFILL
- EVALUATION OF MATERIAL AND GEOMETRIC COMBINATIONS
- PARAMETRIC AND SENSITIVITY ANALYSES
- ESTABLISHMENT OF PRIORITIES FOR LABORATORY AND FIELD PROGRAMS
- DETERMINATION OF INSTRUMENTATION REQUIREMENTS
- CONDUCTANCE OF WORKSHOPS AND COORDINATION MEETINGS IN SUPPORT OF ALL ACTIVITIES
- EVALUATION OF EFFECTIVENESS OF DESIGNS AND SPECIFICATIONS

TABLE 3

LABORATORY ACTIVITIES IN SUPPORT OF SEAL DESIGN PROGRAM

MATERIALS DEVELOPMENT

- DETERMINATION OF SEAL-RELATED THERMOMECHANICAL, GEO-HYDROLOGICAL, AND CHEMICAL ROCK PROPERTIES
- DEVELOPMENT OF CANDIDATE SEAL MATERIAL PROPERTIES
- DETERMINATION OF RADIONUCLIDE RETARDATION MECHANISMS AND MAGNITUDES FOR ROCK AND SEAL MATERIALS
- EVALUATION OF MATERIAL VARIATION IMPACTS
- DETERMINATION OF LONG TERM STABILITY OF SEAL SYSTEMS UNDER SIMULATED AND/OR ACCELERATED ENVIRONMENTS
- EVALUATION OF SEALS RECOVERED FROM FIELD PROGRAMS
- EVALUATION OF ANCIENT CONCRETE SAMPLES

FIELD SIMULATIONS

- DETERMINATION OF DRILLING IMPACTS ON LARGE ROCKS UNDER IN SITU PRESSURE CONDITIONS
- CONDUCTANCE OF PERMEABILITY TESTS OF FULL SIZE SEALS IN LARGE ROCK SAMPLES

PORTIONS OF INSTRUMENTATION DEVELOPMENT

TABLE 4

FIELD ACTIVITIES IN SUPPORT OF SEAL DESIGN PROGRAM

- COORDINATION WITH CANDIDATE SITE EXPLORATION AND TEST FACILITY PROGRAMS, INCLUDING:
  - LOS MEDANOS (BEDDED SALT)
  - PARADOX BASIN (BEDDED SALT)
  - SALT DOMES
  - NORTHWEST BASALT
  - NEVADA TEST SITE ACTIVITIES
  - CSM ROCK DISTURBANCE TESTS
  - OTHER PROGRAMS AS THEY ARE INITIATED
- REVIEW OF ACTIVITIES AT INTERNATIONAL PROGRAMS INCLUDING:
  - STRIPA IN SWEDEN
  - ASSE SALT MINE IN WEST GERMANY
  - THE CANADIAN GRANITE PROGRAM
- EVALUATION OF "GENERIC" CONDITIONS AT EXISTING SHAFTS AND TUNNELS
- DEVELOPMENT OF FIELD PROCEDURES FOR DETERMINING SPECIAL CONDITIONS, SUCH AS:
  - LOW PERMEABILITY OF ROCKS
  - PERMEABILITY OF ANY DISTURBED ZONE
  - EFFECTIVENESS OF GEOPHYSICAL METHODS FOR DETERMINING THE EXTENT OF DISTURBANCE
- FUTURE CONDUCTANCE OF FIELD TESTS TO:
  - EVALUATE INSTALLATION PROCEDURES
  - MONITOR TEST SEAL BEHAVIOR
  - RECOVER PREVIOUSLY PLACED SEAL MATERIALS
  - DEVELOP INSTRUMENTATION

Costs and schedules usually increase as work progresses from analyses, to lab studies, to field investigations. At the same time, however, certain factors (such as the extent of disturbance, chemistry of the interface, and suitability of an installation technique) can only be determined in the lab or field. Analytical office studies must be used to plan and supplement the limited numbers of tests by performing parametric analyses of a wider range of conditions. Accordingly, all support activities must be integrated to develop quantitative parameters and verification results for numerous combinations of: geologic and hydrogeologic conditions; penetration characteristics; seal materials and configurations; loading and environmental conditions; and installation techniques.

A very important continuous design function is the determination of "optimum" scope and schedule of office, lab, and field activities. This is accomplished using matrix evaluation techniques to:

- Determine the appropriate combinations of activities.

- Prioritize the activities to best suit program schedules, technical issues, and available resources.

- Establish schedules so that improved information is available when needed.

This design function requires frequent reevaluation of all activities so that modifications can be made to suit new information as it becomes available.

EXAMPLE CURRENT ACTIVITIES TO INVESTIGATE THE DISTURBED ZONE

A very important characteristic of some penetrations will be any disturbed zone in the rock that could be a preferred flow path. Actual conditions will be site specific depending on factors such as rock type, in-situ stresses, penetration size and shape, and construction methods. This issue is used in this section as an example of how office, lab, and field support activities can be integrated to determine required design information.

An initial office activity has been determination of the impacts of a disturbed zone and interface conditions on flow characteristics at a seal. These analyses permit variations of seal material, interface and rock properties, and seal dimensions to be efficiently evaluated so that the cost-effectiveness of various seal configurations can be made. One of the preliminary results of the flow analyses reported by Chabannes, et al., 1980 is shown in Figure 5. These types of analyses are now being expanded to also predict radionuclide retardation for a variety of materials, shapes, and conditions.

Similar office analyses will be used throughout the entire program to: determine the types of seal systems that yield desired results; design lab and field experiments; evaluate actual results of lab and field tests; determine the sensitivity of various design alternatives; and to demonstrate anticipated performance of the resulting conceptual, preliminary, and final seal designs.

Current laboratory investigations of the disturbed zone fall into two categories: determination of drilling impacts on large samples under simulated in-situ conditions; and "microscopic" evaluation of physical and chemical conditions surrounding cores recovered which contain previously placed seals. These activities are initially concentrating on salt site conditions, but will be expanded to other candidate rock types as samples become available.

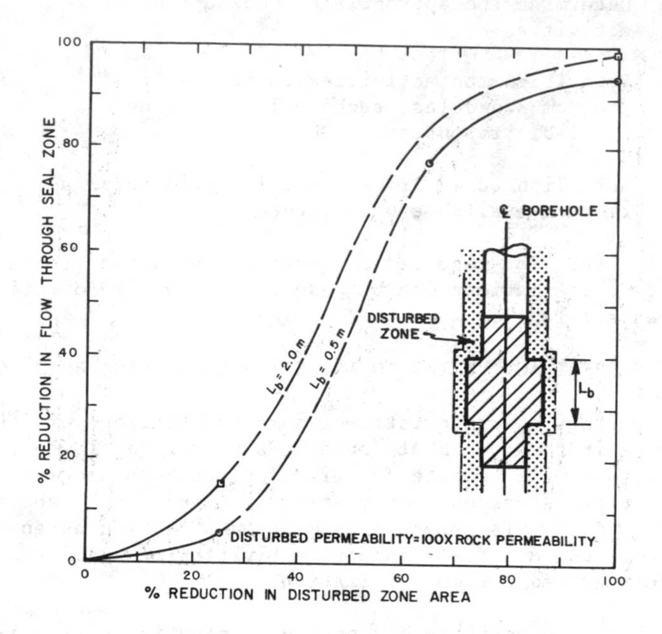

FIGURE 5: EXAMPLE—INFLUENCE OF SEAL CUTOFF ON FLOW THROUGH SEAL ZONE.

The simulated in-situ tests (Pratt, 1980) are being conducted at the Drilling Research Laboratory in Salt Lake City. This facility permits 39.4 cm (15.5 in) by 91.4 cm (36 in) samples to be tested at confining pressures corresponding to depths of 1,200 m (4,000 ft). Various drilling bits are being used to evaluate the disturbance conditions resulting around 20 cm (7-7/8 in) boreholes.

Disturbance is evaluated by injecting dye into the disturbed zone and subsequent sidewall core and thin section analyses of the test area. Borehole leakage tests will be conducted for short plugs placed in selected drilled holes to simulate field test conditions similar to those discussed below for the Los Medanos site.

Field activities in support of seal design have had two major components: the evaluation of sealing related field experiments conducted by Sandia National Laboratory (SNL) at the Los Medanos site; and the evaluation of site exploration activities at other locations and major field tests being conducted for other repository related purposes.

The most notable sealing experiment at the Los Medanos site has been conductance of the deep Bell Canyon test seal program (Christenson, 1980 and Peterson, 1980). That test consisted of setting of 1.52 m (5 ft) and 6.08 m (20 ft) cement plugs in a borehole at a depth of 1,368 m (4,490 ft). In that test, the plugs were tested by using pressure of about 12.4 MPa (1,800 psi) from a deeper aquifer. This program has provided valuable information regarding seal and instrument installations at depth, borehole preparation and testing procedures, and how flows at short seals can be used to evaluate material, interface, and disturbed zone permeabilities.

An example field test activity is the evaluation of tests being conducted by the Colorado School of Mines (CSM) to evaluate the disturbance effects of construction techniques on the sidewalls of hard rock tunnels (Hustrulid, 1980). A similar evaluation activity includes monitoring of the results from major experiments in granite being conducted in Stripa, Sweden. These types of evaluations will lead to specific sealing related programs at selected existing sites during this fiscal year.

WORKING DESIGN FOR LOS MEDANOS SHAFT, TUNNEL, AND BOREHOLE SEALS

A major design function this year is the development of working designs for the various types of candidate sites. Primary purposes are to (1) identify areas where current generic information is not adequate, (2) identify specific areas where performance confirmation is required, and (3) stimulate thoughts and comments among the technical community.

The first working design under ONWI is for the Los Medanos thick salt candidate site. This site has been selected for development of the first conceptual design because it has been explored in the greatest detail. A conceptual arrangement of shafts and tunnels leading to a repository at this site is shown in Figure 6.

The extensive investigations conducted by SNL for the DOE (Powers, et al., 1978) at this candidate site have been directed toward the Waste Isolation Pilot Plant (WIPP), being planned as a defense repository with no high level waste. However, the Carter Administration determined that this area should also be considered as one of the candidate sites being considered for the NWTS program. On that basis, the WIPP generated information is being used for designing seals that could be appropriate for a high level waste repository.

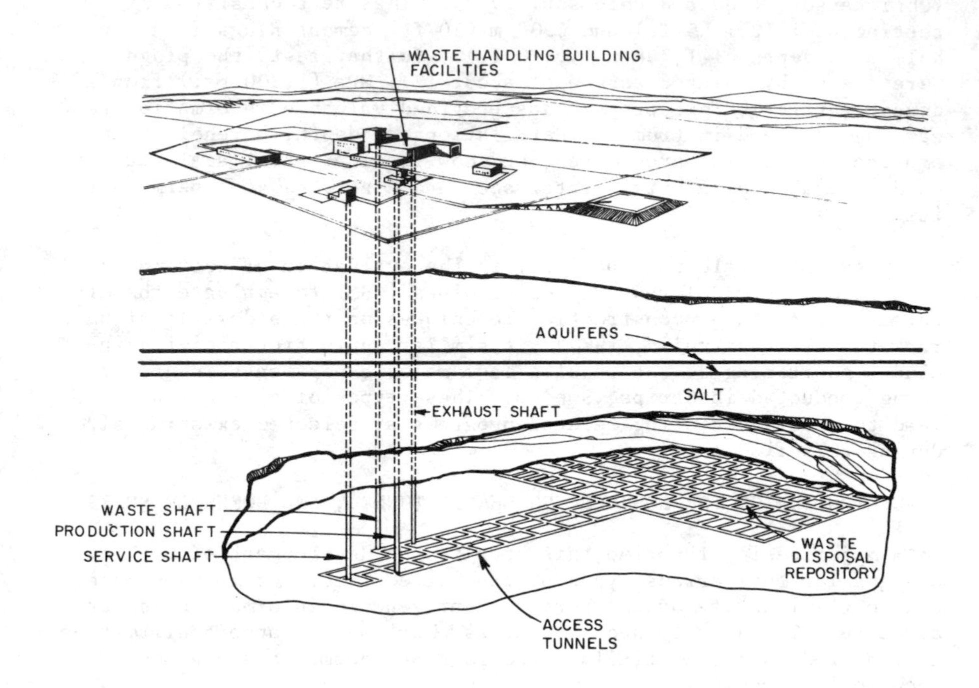

FIGURE 6: HYPOTHETICAL LOS MEDANOS REPOSITORY LAYOUT

Figure 7 shows the generalized geology at the Los Medanos site. An important feature is that the salt formation is very thick at this site so that there is 492 m (1,500 ft) through which shaft sealing can be accomplished. Impurities in the salt consist of thin anhydrite layers and very thin clay seams. These materials have different thermomechanical permeabilities and chemical properties from the salt, and must be considered in determining details of the seal. The shafts will have steel liners through the overburden materials and into the top of the salt. No linings are planned for the salt portion of the shafts.

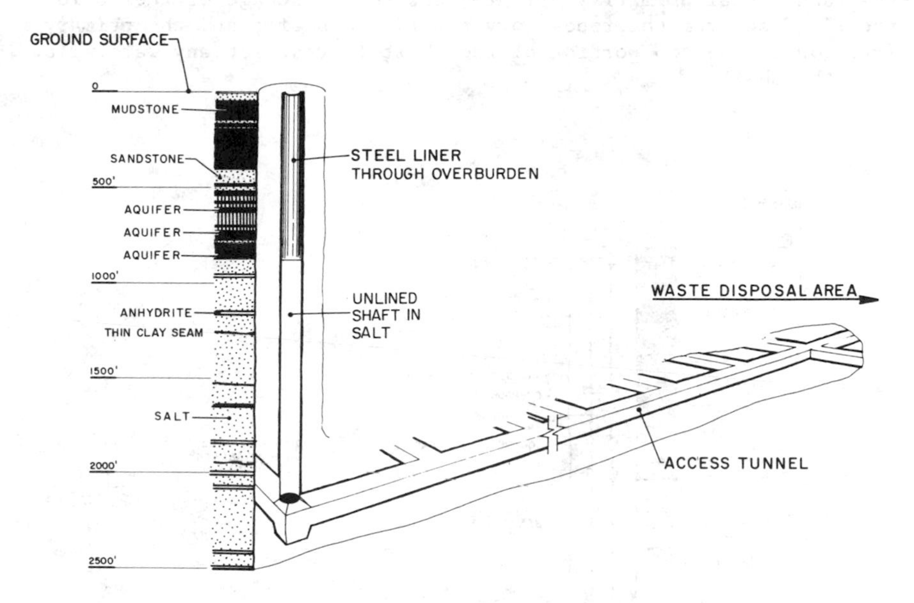

FIGURE 7: GENERALIZED GEOLOGY LOS MEDANOS SITE

The existence of aquifers near the top of the salt is of primo importance. The key "aquifer" is that which may be located at the interface between the salt and the overlying rock. Available data indicate that there may be water flow at this location but that its quantity is very low. Also, quantities of flow in the two dolomite aquifers above that zone are also relatively low.

Basic design philosophies are that (1) all potential water sources will be stopped from entering into the seal zone so that solutioning of salt along the seal does not occur, and (2) that any potential nuclides released should be reduced below acceptable levels at the lower portion of the seal so that they do not ever touch the first aquifer. The function of the seal within the overburden rock itself is of lesser importance.

An additional basic philosophy is that all materials should be readily available, easy to construct, and should possess well-understood properties. If more exotic or sophisticated materials are required to satisfy subsequent design analyses, they should be limited to only areas where their existence provides needed redundancy or properties to resist particular conditions.

The working design for this entire tunnel-shaft seal system is shown in Figure 8. This entire seal is designed to function as a system by: making the primary function of the right-hand side of the tunnel seal primarily oriented toward a blockage of the radionuclide flow from the repository toward the shaft; and the primary function of the top portion of the shaft to restrict any water flow into the shaft.

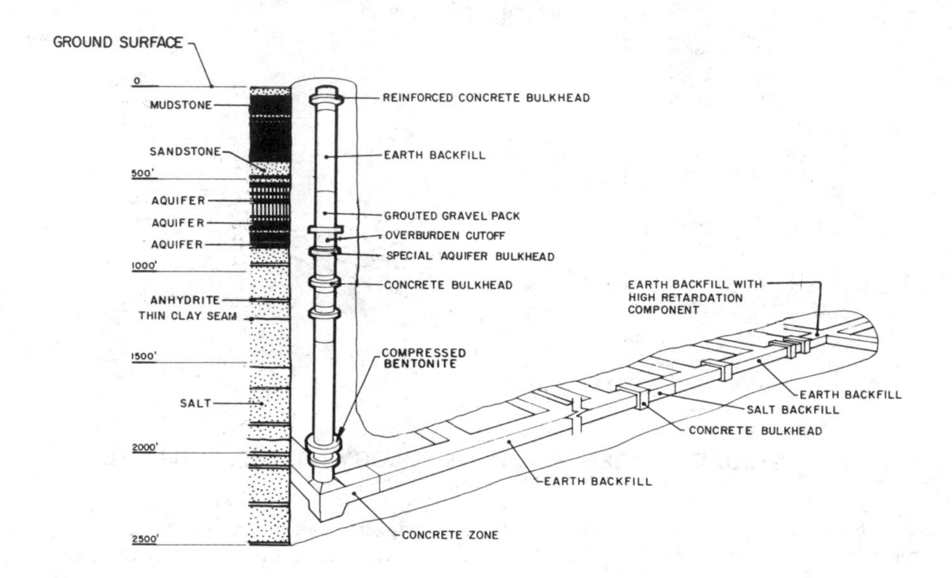

FIGURE 8: TUNNEL-SHAFT SEAL SYSTEM

Four high density concrete bulkheads are planned in each access tunnel with the configuration illustrated in Detail A in Figure 9. The bulkhead locations are planned to separate different types of tunnel backfill material and to provide redundancy. Each bulkhead has cutoff collars planned to extend into the floor, roof, and sidewalls as required to cut off preferential flow paths through any disturbed zone. The length and shape of the bulkhead ends are designed to control stress concentration effects, particularly near the center where the primary cutoff must occur. Detail A illustrates anticipation that the bulkheads will have to be poured in sections to control hydration temperatures and resulting rock disturbance and interface disruptions. In addition, there are provisions to grout through the bulkhead so that the interface conditions can be improved after curing of the concrete has occurred. The grouting techniques will require special detailed designs to assure that the grout system itself does not cause potential discontinuities in the bulkhead.

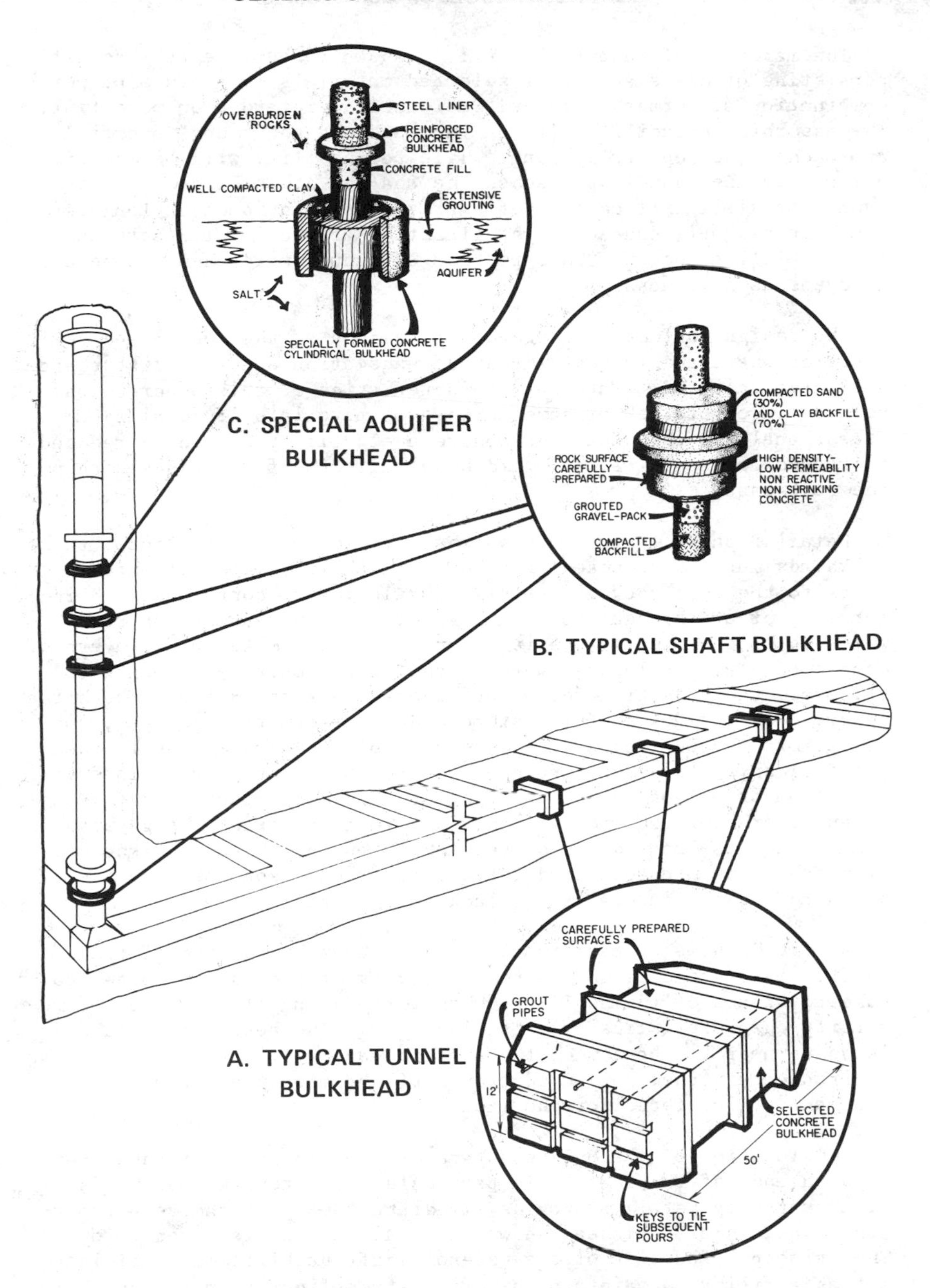

FIGURE 9: BULKHEAD DETAILS

The majority of tunnel backfill is shown to be an earth backfill consisting of clays and other selected materials to yield a proper combination of permeability and radionuclide retardation potential. The absorbing capability will be increased as the tunnel backfill approaches the repository zone; while permeability will be more important as the tunnel approaches the shaft. At least one section of tunnel backfill will consist of salt in anticipation that long-term creep stress will cause recrystallization of the in-situ salt and the backfill to occur. This portion of tunnel will then become a homogeneous salt mass.

The design includes a large concrete zone at the tunnel and shaft junction where the largest amount of excavation and salt disturbance will have occurred. Material characteristics of this concrete may require incorporation of some earth-type materials if detailed stress analyses show that the concrete elasticity should be reduced to reduce any undesirable "rigid body" effects of the block within the salt mass.

Detail B shows three shaft bulkheads. The major portion of these bulkheads must be composed of a low permeability material which bonds to the host rock, is stable, and leaves no connected void internally or at the seal/rock interface. A high density concrete which is slightly expansive is planned for this material. Layers of compacted clay are located between the three concrete segments to (1) avoid the potential for a continuous crack formation through the concrete system due to temperature and/or deformation changes, and (2) permit the bulkhead to be more flexible to deformation in the event of any outside disturbance. Sodium bentonite may be used for a portion or all of the clay component depending upon its resistance to environmental (chemical) conditions that may exist. A grouted gravel pack is located immediately above and below each bulkhead to illustrate the probable need for a transitional zone between the bulkhead and the general shaft backfill material.

Figure 8 shows an additional bulkhead near the bottom of the shaft, constructed of compressed or highly compacted bentonite, to take advantage of the swelling (when wetted) and its very low permeability characteristics of this clay type. The bentonite bulkhead is shown near the bottom of the shaft because it is anticipated that environmental (chemical) conditions will be more predictable and constant at the repository horizon.

The location of the bulkheads are planned to provide redundancy at both ends of the shaft. In particular, the top two bulkheads illustrated by Detail B provide immediate backup to the very important "water seal" bulkhead shown in Detail C and discussed below. The principal function of the general shaft backfill material is to act as a filler to maintain the original configuration of the shaft between bulkheads. The composition of this earth backfill will be selected to also provide permeability and retardation characteristics that complement the overall seal system.

Detail C shows the most important sealing element for a salt repository; that element that eliminates potential for water inflow along the seal that could cause salt solutioning. The working design considers that the aquifer will be extensively grouted at the time of sealing. This grout may be in addition to previous grout used for shaft construction. It is anticipated that a grouting system will be developed that can be relied upon for at least several decades. However, it is not anticipated that grout materials for low permeability aquifers can be relied upon for tens of thousands of years.

A key element in Detail C is enlargement of the shaft at the aquifer and the construction of a specially formed concrete cylinder designed to cut off completely horizontal flow of the aquifer in the vicinity of the shaft. This cylinder will be backfilled with a well compacted clay with very low permeability. Again, the use of bentonite in this clay system will depend on the anticipated range of environmental conditions that may be experienced. The construction method at this enlargement will have to be sequenced or will require special temporary support systems to minimize adjacent rock disturbance.

Seal components above the aquifer seal are primarily to restrict large rock movements into the shaft and the excessive flow of water from overlying aquifers. As previously noted, however, this portion of the system is not considered to be critical to repository performance.

A final characteristic of the working design is that it can be constructed in logical segments beginning at the repository area and working towards the shaft and ground surface. This will be important if it is determined that portions of the seal must be observed or monitored before completing the total sealing system. This feature could also be important if an initial seal must be placed before the issue of potential retrievability is resolved for that particular repository.

This working design for the Los Medanos site will be used as the "gage" for directing and evaluating all office, lab and/or field activities associated with a salt repository. Modifications will be made, as required, to achieve a highly defendable and practical conceptual design by August 1982.

REFERENCES

Chabannes, C. R., D. E. Stephenson, and R. D. Ellison, 1980, "A Preliminary Evaluation of Various Plugging Configurations," in "Borehole and Shaft Plugging," Nuclear Energy Agency, Organization for Economic Co-Operation and Development, Paris, France.

Christenson, C. L., 1980, "Results from the Bell Canyon Borehole Plugging Tests," in "Proceedings of the 1980 National Waste Terminal Storage Program Information Meeting," ONWI-212, Office of Nuclear Waste Isolation, Columbus, Ohio.

Hustrulid, W., et al., 1980, "Experimental Studies at the Colorado School of Mine Hard Rock Test Site," in "Proceedings of the 1980 National Waste Terminal Storage Program Information Meeting," ONWI-212, Office of Nuclear Waste Isolation, Columbus, Ohio.

Office of Nuclear Waste Isolation (ONWI), 1978, "Development of Plan and Approach for Borehole Plugging Field Testing," ONWI-3, prepared by D'Appolonia Consulting Engineers, Inc., for Battelle Memorial Institute, Project Management Division, Columbus, Ohio.

Office of Nuclear Waste Isolation (ONWI), 1979, "The Status of Borehole Plugging and Shaft Sealing for Geologic Isolation of Radioactive Waste," ONWI-15, prepared by D'Appolonia Consulting Engineers, Inc., for Battelle Memorial Institute, Project Management Division, Columbus, Ohio.

Office of Nuclear Waste Isolation (ONWI), 1980, "Repository Sealing Design Approach - 1979," ONWI-55, prepared by D'Appolonia Consulting Engineers, Inc., for Battelle Memorial Institute, Project Management Division, Columbus, Ohio.

Peterson, E. W., 1980, "Analysis of Borehole Plug Performance," in "Proceedings of the 1980 National Waste Terminal Storage Program Information Meeting," ONWI-212, Office of Nuclear Waste Isolation, Columbus, Ohio.

Powers, D. W., et al., 1978, "Geological Characterization Report, Waste Isolation Pilot Plant (WIPP) Site, Southeastern New Mexico," SAN 78-1596, 2 Vols., Sandia National Laboratory, Albuquerque, New Mexico.

Pratt, H. R., et al., 1980, "Borehole Simulation Program," in "Proceedings of the 1980 National Waste Terminal Storage Program Information Meeting," ONWI-212, Office of Nuclear Waste Isolation, Columbus, Ohio.

Chapter 78

TECHNICAL CONSERVATISM IN DESIGN OF NUCLEAR WASTE REPOSITORY IN BEDDED SALT

by James E. Monsees, Michael R. Wigley
and Wayne A. Carbiener

Battelle Memorial Institute
Office of Nuclear Waste Isolation
Columbus, Ohio

ABSTRACT

This paper illustrates an approach to quantitatively document the degree of technical conservatism to be incorporated into the design of a waste isolation system in bedded salt. It is anticipated that for an actual repository site the key performance constraints and/or design bases identified in this paper will be reviewed, and modified or supplemented as required. Ultimate acceptance of a repository will be dependent upon scientific peer input and scrutiny of the demonstrated conservatism inherent in each specific repository site and design.

INTRODUCTION

The Department of Energy's (DOE) National Waste Terminal Storage (NWTS) Program has as its principal objective the safe disposal of commercially generated nuclear wastes. The NWTS Program is focusing on excavated geologic disposal for the first generation disposal option in accordance with strategies recommended by the Interagency Review Group on Nuclear Waste Management (IRG, 1979) and implemented by President Carter in his Message to Congress on February 12, 1980 (Carter, 1980). DOE recognizes that long-term disposal in an excavated geologic repository will contain inherent uncertainties. These uncertainties arise in every phase of the program from geologic characterization; to design; to performance analysis; to construction; to operation. To mitigate these uncertainties and thereby increase the confidence that the geologic waste isolation system will perform in an acceptable manner, technical conservatism must be prudently applied in the conduct of the entire program. The methods used in each phase of the program must be clearly stated and the technical basis well documented so that scientific peer input and scrutiny can be readily accommodated. Acceptance by the regulatory bodies, the technical community, and the general public will be dependent upon the demonstrated conservatism inherent in each specific repository site and design.

This paper introduces a strategy for quantitatively describing the degree of technical conservatism incorporated into a sample design. The design chosen for this paper consists of a waste disposal system located in a generic bedded salt stratigraphy.

Because this paper draws upon information from a number of reports in the open literature, details of the isolation system may vary slightly from one calculation to another. It is important to remember that the purpose of this paper is to illustrate the approach. Consequently, these variations are not considered critical to the discussion. It should also be emphasized that the NWTS program is a dynamic one and that new data, methods of analyses, and site characterization information are constantly evolving. As this evolution continues, it will surely be necessary to revisit and modify the approach illustrated herein.

Finally, readers are cautioned to remember that this paper is based on an assumed (generic) site. For each candidate site, a set of calculations based on actual site properties and conditions will be performed following criteria being established in the NWTS program (ONWI, 1980). Criterion 3.1.1, System Performance Limits - Safety, for example, requires that: "The mined geologic disposal system shall meet all applicable standards and shall contain and isolate radioactive wastes to the extent necessary to assure that releases of radionuclides to the biosphere do not result in an unacceptably high incremental increase in doses to individuals and to the general population".

Technical Objectives and Implementation

From its review of the U.S. waste management program, the IRG identified three technical objectives that it felt the program must achieve (IRG, 1979):

(1) "The selected technical option must meet all of the relevant radiological protection criteria as well as any other applicable regulatory requirements; although zero release of radionuclides cannot be assured, any potential releases should be within preestablished standards and, beyond that, be reduced to the lowest level practicable."

(2) "The technology selected for waste disposal, as well as the reasons for its selection, must be well understood, clearly articulated, and widely accepted."

(3) "The existence of residual technical uncertainties must be recognized and provided for in the program structure."

The IRG amplified on the second and third objectives by suggesting the manner in which they should be implemented. For example, they stated (IRG, 1979):

- "The approach to permanent disposal of nuclear waste should proceed on a stepwise basis in a technically conservative manner."

- "Regardless of how minimal hypothesized adverse effects might be, the IRG finds that the Federal government should maintain a technically conservative approach in pursuing the development of mined repositories for high-level and TRU waste disposal."

Conservative Approach

The implementation of the DOE policy on technical conservatism takes two forms: (1) conservatism in the conduct of the program and (2) conservatism in the performance of the disposal system. The first form of conservatism is achieved by a stepwise approach to repository development and operation; a systems (multibarrier) approach to containment and isolation; the requirement for retrievability; and the extensive use of peer reviews in the conduct of the program. The latter form, emphasized in this presentation, is achieved by the proper selection and application of conservatism to design and operational limits.

To establish confidence, the steps followed in implementing the design approach must be derived from a sound technical basis and result in a design and related assessments that will clearly document the conservative margins and their bases. The method used to achieve this consists of several interrelated steps that are carried out sequentially. Design and analysis iterations are then performed to assure and demonstrate that the performance goals for normal system operation are met. These steps are discussed in the paragraphs below and shown in Figure 1.

Identify Performance Constraint Limits. The first step consists of identifying a set of performance constraints for crucial factors or parameters of the repository system that are expected to strongly affect its isolation capability. Based on sensitivity analyses and tests at several scales, limits are established such that exceeding those limits are defined as "failure" or loss of intended function, based on current technical knowledge. The limit will be established at the conservative end of the deleterious behavior. Consequently, staying within or below each of the constraints results in a system expected to isolate wastes satisfactorily.

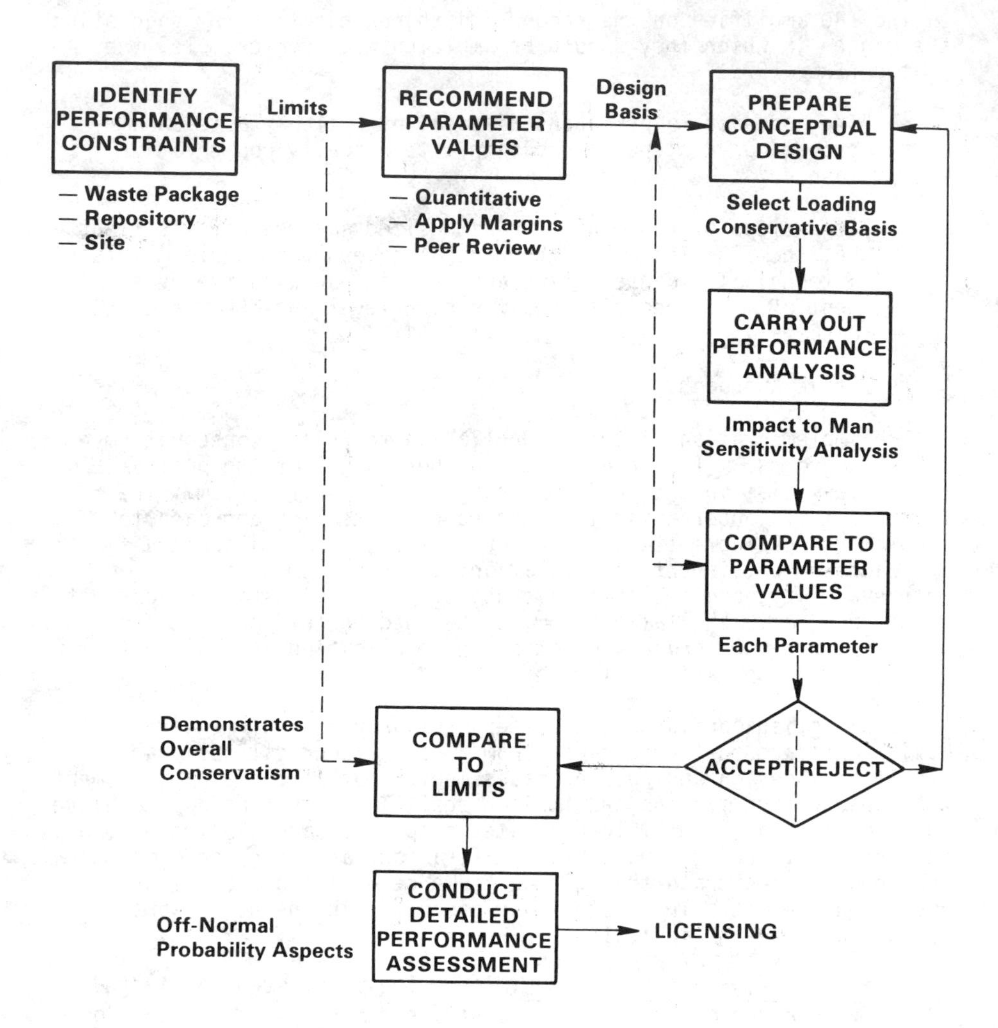

FIGURE 1. IMPLEMENTATION METHOD

Establish Design Values. There is some uncertainty associated with each constraint. Accordingly, on each limit a certain confidence level exists that is expected to increase with future testing. To be conservative, a design value will be established that is incrementally different from the limit to compensate not only for the uncertainty in the limit value, but for uncertainties in the performance analyses as well. These values are determined judgmentally, based on current knowledge, experience, the degree of conservatism desired, and the fundamental importance of the parameter as established through sensitivity analyses. It is anticipated that for an actual repository site, peer review will be used extensively in determining the appropriate values. For this example, the design bases were established simply to demonstrate the approach. However, they are representative of current program thinking. This set of parameter (design) values then becomes the design basis to provide an overall margin of conservatism.

Prepare Conceptual Design. A conceptual repository system design is then formulated using the conservative parameter values as the design basis. At this point the design for a specific geologic setting or site is flexible enough to accomodate various thermal loadings (i.e., spacings can be varied), a different mix of emplaced waste, or additional aging of the waste, etc. Proposed specifications are selected for the analysis based on reference analyses conducted earlier as a part of the NWTS Program.

Carry Out Performance Analysis. Performance assessments of the projected design are conducted for the very near field, near field, and far field. The expected repository environments, that is, the impacts of the waste emplacement, are determined. Parameter variations in the form of sensitivity analyses are included in this step to assess the impact of an individual parameter on the performance. These analyses are carried to the determination of the impact upon man and his environment.

Compare Results to Design Values. The results of the analyses are compared to the parameter values or design basis previously established, recognizing that conservatism has been applied in selecting the design basis. If the analyses show that no parameter value has been exceeded, then adjustments in specifications can be made to approach the design value. Using sensitivity analyses as the guideline, these analyses may be repeated until a single design basis is reached for a single point in time. Alternatively, the design can be accepted as is with a greater amount of conservatism. If the analyses show that a value has been exceeded, then design adjustments are made, and the analyses are repeated until all design values are met and the design is accepted.

Compare Results to Performance Constraints. It is expected that different individual parameters will be controlling at different points in time over the repository lifetime, but only a single parameter will control at a given point in time. Other parameters will be below the selected design basis for all points in time. The overall level of conservatism for the system is shown by comparison of the set of expected values to the performance constraints or failure limits identified in the initial step, on the premise that this set constitutes a technically acceptable repository system. The composite of these increments demonstrates the conservatism of the system design.

Conduct Detailed Performance Assessments. The final design is analyzed on a detailed basis to investigate the consequences of a suite of off-normal scenarios to complete safety and licensing assessments of the repository.

WASTE ISOLATION SYSTEM DESCRIPTION

The waste isolation system considered in this case consists of a generic bedded salt site as given in Figure 2, a repository located at a nominal depth of 610 m (2,000 ft), and a waste package consisting of spent fuel incorporated into a carbon steel canister (Claiborne, Rickertson, and Graham, 1980; Callahan, 1979). Each canister will have a thermal power as defined by Figure 3. The emplacement hole will be lined with Schedule 40 carbon steel pipe. No other components of the advance waste package presently being considered are included in this analysis.

The repository consists of a room-and-pillar configuration, composed of very long rooms with a nominal width of 5.5 m (18 ft) and a nominal height of 6.4 m (21 ft). The adjacent pillar thickness is, nominally, 21.3 m (70 ft). This gives a pillar height to pillar width ratio of 3:10. The repository is symmetrical around its centerline and has a total nominal length, as measured down the main haulage way, of 3,048 m (10,000 ft) (Claiborne, Rickertson, and Graham, 1980; Callahan, 1979).

The boundaries of the site consist of the earth's surface, a depth of 2,134 m (7,000 ft), and a horizontal extent of approximately two repository radii from the centerline. Figure 4 shows the model geometry and the boundary conditions used for the thermomechanical analysis (Callahan, 1979). A similar model was used for the thermal analysis (Claiborne, Rickertson, and Graham, 1980).

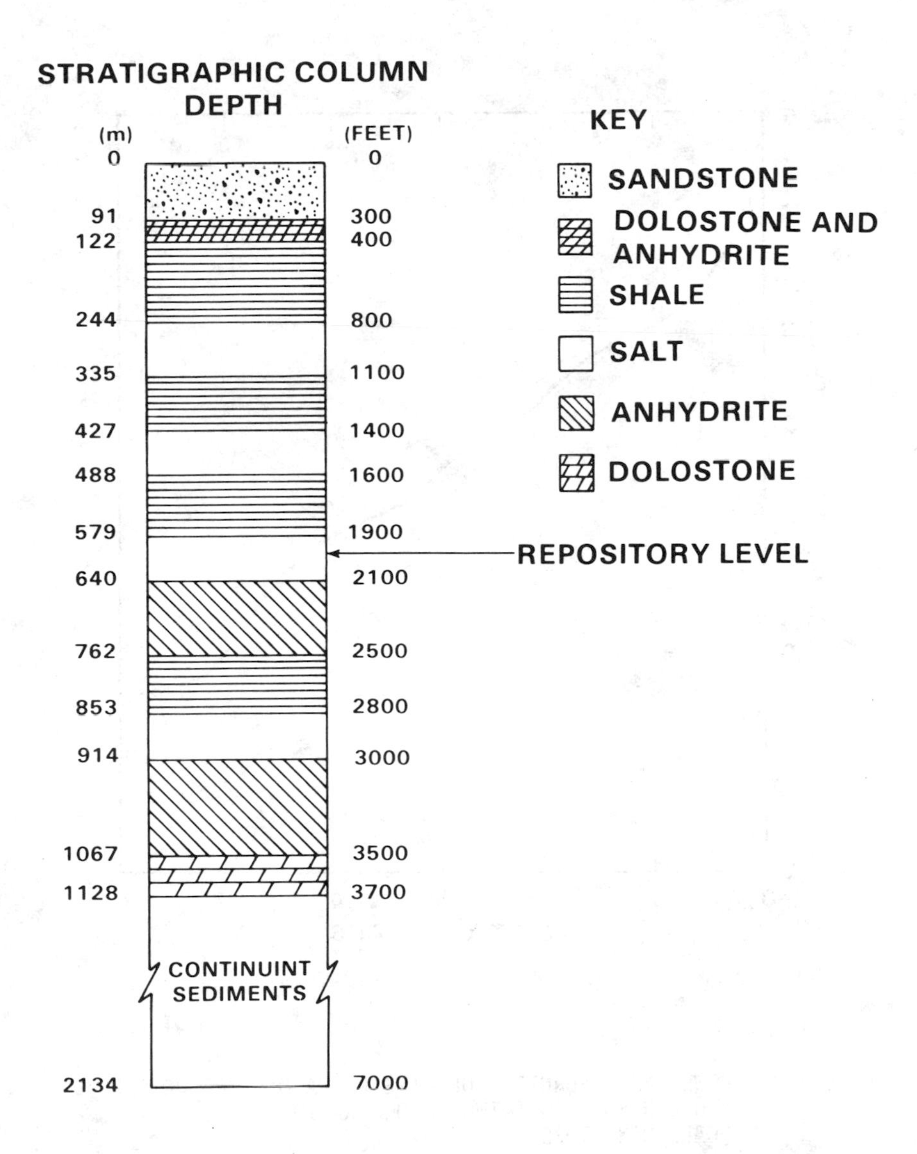

FIGURE 2. GENERIC BEDDED SALT STRATIGRAPHIC COLUMN (CALLAHAN, 1979)

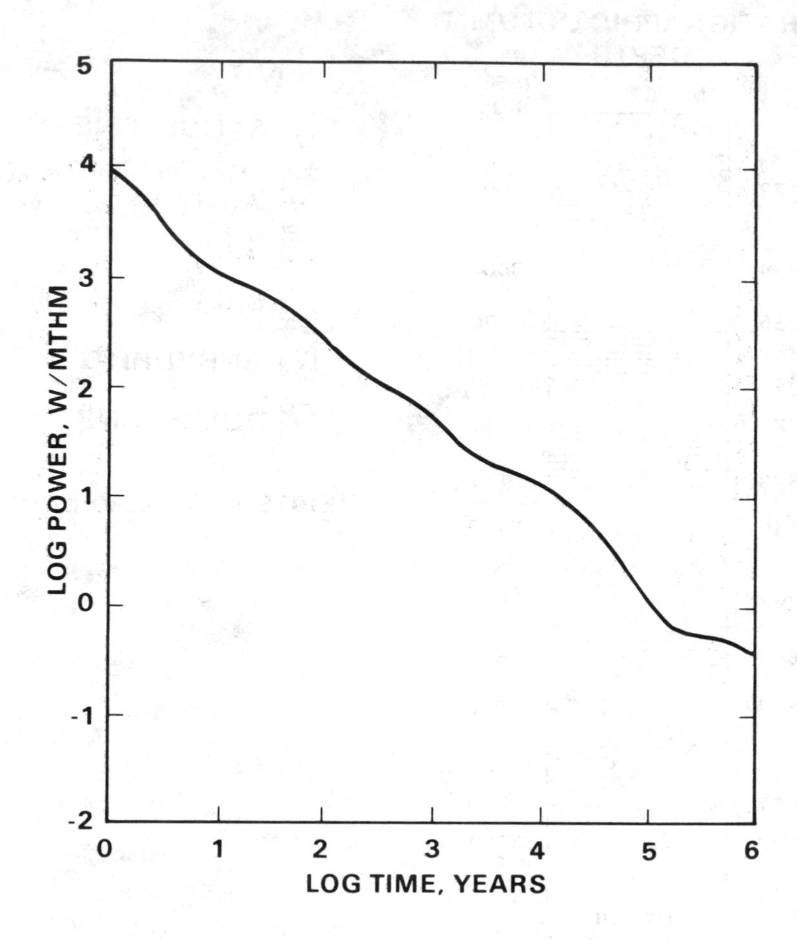

FIGURE 3. POWER AS A FUNCTION OF TIME FOR A MIXTURE OF PWR AND BWR SURF IN A TWO TO ONE RATIO (CALLAHAN, 1979)

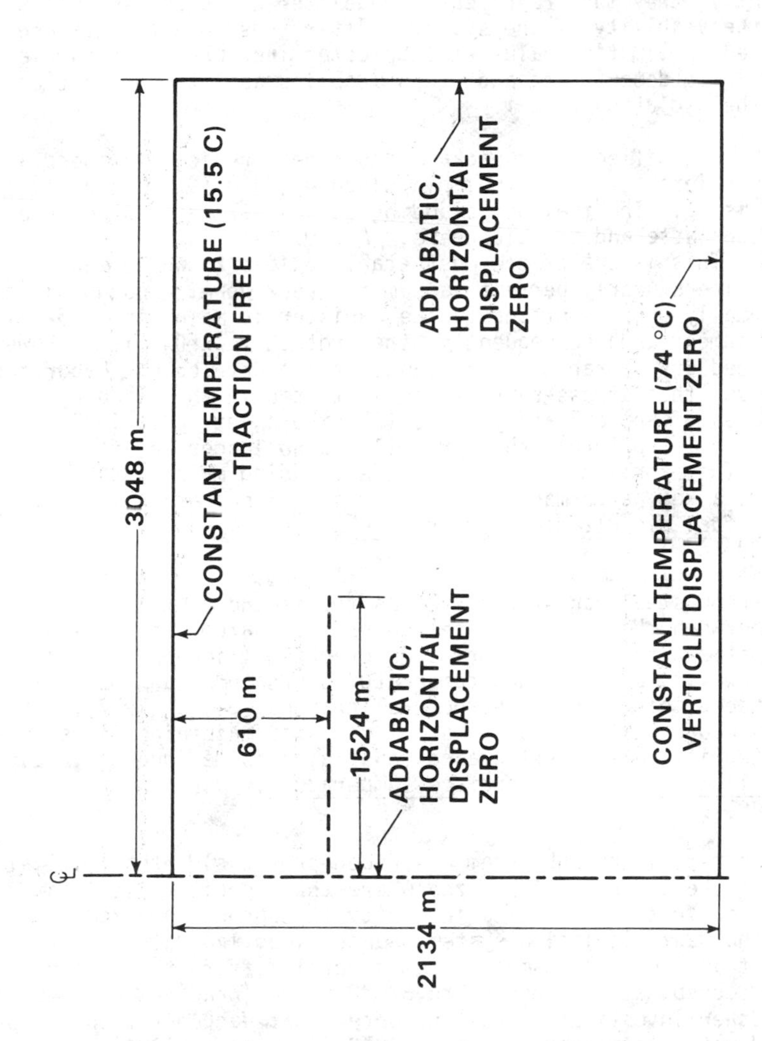

FIGURE 4. THERMOMECHANICAL BEDDED SALT MODEL GEOMETRY AND BOUNDARY CONDITIONS (CALLAHAN, 1969)

IDENTIFY PERFORMANCE CONSTRAINTS AND ESTABLISH LIMITS

The key performance constraints must be selected so as to maintain the integrity of each of the barriers throughout its expected life. Consequently, they must represent the deleterious processes which control the viability of the system. After those constraints are established, a limiting value will be determined where the barrier could begin to deteriorate and thus lose its ability to function as part of the isolation system.

For the simplified waste package described previously, there are two key barriers: (1) the fuel pin cladding, and (2) the carbon steel canister. The fuel pin cladding serves as the first barrier between the waste and the biosphere. A ZrO_2 film is present on the cladding. This is one of the most stable oxides known to man and would require a nearly perfect vacuum to break down. Enough oxygen would normally be present inside the canister to maintain an oxidizing environment and, consequently, the protective ZrO_2 film. However, for extended dry storage, Hanford Engineering Development Laboratory (HEDL) found that stress-rupture was initiated in the cladding at temperatures of approximately 396°C (Blackburn, et. al., 1978). Once the cladding is ruptured, the ZrO_2 film is no longer an effective barrier. Therefore, to ensure that the cladding maintains its integrity, a key performance constraint is defined as: (1) maximum allowable fuel pin cladding temperature.
Limit: 390°C

The carbon steel canister serves as the second containment barrier between the waste and the biosphere. Carbon steel is extremely resistant to stress corrosion cracking (Simonen and Slate, 1979). However, at sustained temperatures greater than 400°C, it may be susceptible to other structural changes (Jenks, 1977). Therefore, to ensure that the carbon steel canister maintains its structural integrity, a key performance constraint is defined as: (2) maximum allowable canister surface temperature.
Limit: 400°C

For the repository subsystem described previously, the critical barrier is the bedded salt horizon where the repository is located. This horizon must maintain its integrity throughout the expected life of the waste isolation system. Unconfined laboratory tests indicate that rock salt samples from several different locations began to decrepitate in the 260 to 320°C range (Bradshaw and McClain, 1971). Other investigators have reported that decrepitation is not initiated until temperatures reach 400°C (Gevantman, 1980). To ensure that the integrity of the salt is maintained, a key performance constraint is defined as: (3) maximum allowable salt temperature.
Limit: 250°C

The underground repository structure must remain open throughout the operational phase to ensure the safety of personnel and to retain the option to retrieve the waste. Consequently, to ensure that the opening is maintained, a key performance constraint is defined as:(4) minimum allowable room height prior to decommissioning.
Limit: 5.44 m (17.8 ft)

For this generic bedded salt site, the critical barrier is the stratigraphy itself. The stratigraphy must provide a barrier between the repository and the biosphere. A significant increase in temperature at the surface of the earth could have deleterious effects on biota, biota cycles, surface waste supplies, etc. The normal seasonal variation for most parts of the contiguous U.S. is in the range of 10 to 30°C. To ensure that adverse environmental consequences do not occur, a key performance constraint is defined as: (5) maximum allowable temperature rise at the surface of the earth.
Limit: 10°C

The generic bedded salt stratigraphy must also provide the thermal/mechanical/hydrological barrier between the waste and the biosphere. A possible release scenario involves water entering the repository, leaching the waste, and then transporting the radionuclides away from the site and into the biosphere. For this particular stratigraphy, the aquifer bed (sandstone) is at the top of the stratigraphic column. Two aquitard beds (the shale beds) reside between the aquifer and the repository horizon (Figure 2). These stratigraphic units act as barriers between the aquifer and the waste. Should these aquitards become pervasively fractured as a result of thermally-induced stresses, conduits for the flow of water into the repository would be created. Both tensile and/or shear cracks could be hypothesized as a mechanism for fracturing the aquitard beds. Since the aquitard beds are located relatively close to the surface of the earth, it is probable that some discontinuities already exist in the formations. These discontinuities could propagate as a result of the thermal stress. Therefore, to ensure that the thermal/mechanical/hydrological integrity of the site is maintained, a key performance constraint is defined as: (6) maximum tension allowable in the aquitard beds.
Limit: 0.069 MPa (10 psi) tensile stress (tensile strength of the discontinuities).

The waste isolation system as a whole must provide a thermal/mechanical/hydrological/chemical barrier to the release of the waste to the biosphere. This must comply with Criterion 3.1.1 (ONWI, 1980), as previously described. Consequently, to ensure that the integrity of the entire system is maintained, a key performance constraint is defined as: (7) maximum allowable individual whole body dose.
Limit: 500 mrem/year

Rationale - The Nuclear Regulatory Commission (NRC) has established radiation standards which apply to all licensees. These standards are given in 10 CFR 20 (NRC, 1980). The NRC allows, under normal operating conditions, an occupational whole body dose in restricted areas of 5,000 mrem/year. For unrestricted areas, it is specified that no individual will receive a whole body dose greater than 500 mrem/year. An analogy with the standard for unrestricted areas is made as an upper bound for this analysis. The standard on system performance is currently being developed by EPA and will be reflected in NRC regulations for nuclear waste repositories. In addition, the ALARA (AS Low As Reasonably Achievable) concept will be applied. For interim use, 500 mrem/year maximum individual whole body dose will be applied as the limit.

Establish Design Values

Having established the limits for each key performance constraint, the next step in quantitatively documenting the degree of technical conservatism incorporated in the design of this illustrative waste isolation system is to establish a technically defensible quantitative design basis for each key performance constraint. Each design basis will reflect the degree of uncertainty associated with the behavior of the material, the predictive techniques available to analyze this behavior, and the consequences should the behavior deviate from the expected. The margin between the limit and the design basis quantitatively documents the minimum degree of technical conservatism available for this generic bedded salt waste isolation system. This represents a minimum because the designer will iterate on the design until the design basis is reached for one of the key parameters at one point in time. Consequently, all other parameters remain below their design bases for all times.

(1) Maximum Allowable Fuel Pin Cladding Temperature
Design Basis: 300°C

Rationale: This temperature provides a 90°C margin below initiation of stress rupture in the fuel pin cladding. If this temperature did exist at the time of emplacement, additional conservatism would be gained as the waste decayed with time.

(2) Maximum Allowable Canister Surface Temperature
Design Basis: 350°C

Rational: A large data base is available on the behavior of carbon steel in a variety of environments. Consequently, the uncertainties associated with its behavior are established and a 50°C margin is adopted.

(3) Maximum Allowable Salt Temperature
Design Basis: 150°C

Rationale: The behavior of geologic materials in situ is not understood as well as engineered material, thus there is a higher degree of uncertainty associated with its behavior. Since brine migration, chemical reaction rates, and creep are also controlled by either the absolute temperature or the thermal gradient, reducing the temperature in the salt will increase the confidence in repository performance. A design basis of 150°C is selected to provide a 100°C margin to compensate for these uncertainties.

(4) Minimum Allowable Room Height Prior to Decommissioning
Design Basis: 5.76 m (18.9 ft)

Rationale: This design basis will ensure safe entrance into the disposal room of men and equipment in the event retrieval is required, based on the anticipated size of the equipment.

(5) Maximum Allowable Temperature Rise at the Surface of the Earth
Design Basis: 1°C

Rationale: Since there is considerable uncertainty associated with the effects that an increase in surface temperature might have on the environment, a design basis which is comparable to the daily temperature variations is selected.

(6) Maximum Allowable Tensile Stress in Aquitard Beds
Design Basis: Zero tensile stress

Rationale: The behavior of rocks in natural (large scale) settings is much more uncertain than the behavior of engineered materials. Discontinuities within the geologic material will also lead to uncertainties in how the material will perform under load. To compensate for such uncertainties in design and analyses, no tensile stresses will be permitted in beds to be considered aquitards.

(7) Maximum Allowable Individual Whole Body Dose
Design Basis: 150 mrem/year

Rationale: The background radiation levels in the United States vary from 250 mrem/year in Colorado to 100 mrem/year in Louisiana (Klement, et. al., 1972). Since very few, if any, citizens in the United Stated base their decision on where to live solely on the background radiation at a given location, 150 mrem/year is established as the design basis. As stated earlier, this standard is currently under evaluation by EPA. The limit of 150 mrem/year is consistent with the Confidence Rulemaking document (DOE, 1980).

Design Analyses

The key performance constraints, their associated limits and design bases, and the results of the design analyses are summzrized in Table 1. As discussed earlier, these analyses were extracted from a number of different reports. Consequently, the reference waste isolation system varies slightly from analysis to analysis. However, since the approach is the primary concern of this paper, such differences are not considered significant.

(1) Maximum Allowable Fuel Pin Cladding Temperature

Reference: Claiborne, Richertson, and Graham, 1980.

Results: For a thermal loading of 14.8 w/m^2 (60 kw/acre) and immediate backfilling of the emplacement hole and disposal room, the maximum temperature peaks at 140°C after approximately 10 years after emplacement. This offers an additional margin of 160°C compared to the design limit and a total margin of 250°C compared to the failure limit.

(2) Maximum Allowable Canister Surface Temperature

Reference: Claiborne, Richertson, and Graham, 1980.

Results: For the same conditions as (1) above, the canister surface temperature peaks at 115°C after approximately 25 years. This offers an additional margin of 235°C compared to the design basis and a total margin of 285°C compared to the limit.

(3) Maximum Allowable Salt Temperature

Reference: Claiborne, Richertson, and Graham, 1980.

Results: For the same conditions as (1) above, the temperature peaks at 100°C at approximately 60 years. Thus, an additional margin of 50°C compared to the design basis and a total margin of 150°C compared to the limit are offered.

(4) Minimum Allowable Room Height Prior to Decommissioning

Reference: Wagner, 1980.

TABLE 1. SUMMARY OF DEGREE OF TECHNICAL CONSERVATISM INCORPORATED INTO THE DESIGN FOR A THERMAL LOADING OF 14.8 w/m^2 (60 kw/acre)

Key Performance Constraint	Limit	Design Basis	Maximum Calculated Values Over Analysis Period for 14.8 w/m^2 (60 kw/acre)	Total Margin
WASTE PACKAGE				
1) Maximum Allowable Fuel Pin Cladding Temperature	390°C	300°C	140°C at 10 years	250°C
2) Maximum Allowable Canister Surface Temperature	400°C	350°C	115°C at 25 years	285°C
REPOSITORY				
3) Maximum Allowable Salt Temperature	250°C	150°C	100°C at 60 years	150°C
4) Minimum Allowable Room Height Prior to Decommissioning	5.44 m (17.84 ft.)	5.76 m (18.89 ft.)	5.97 m at 25 years (max. analyzed) (19.55 ft.)	.53 m (1.74 ft.)
SITE				
5) Maximum Allowable Temperature Rise at the Surface of Earth	10°C	1°C	0.10°C	9.9°C
6) Maximum Allowable Tensile Stress in Aquitard Beds	0.069 MPa (10 psi) Tensile Stress	Zero Tensile Stress	Tension limited to top 122 m (400 ft.), i.e. no aquitard breached within first 200 years	488 m (1600 ft.) competent rock between aquifer i.e. both aquitards
SYSTEM				
7) Maximum Allowable Individual Whole Body Dose	500 mrem/year	150 mrem/year	30 mrem/year at 600,000 years	470 mrem/year

Results: For thermal loading of 7.41 w/m^2 (30 kw/acre), 8.89 w/m^2 (36 kw/acre), and 11.12 w/m^2 (45 kw/acre) closures of approximately 0.29 m (0.94 ft), 0.32 (1.04 ft), and 0.36 m (1-18 ft), respectively were found. Extrapolation of this data indicates that a closure of approximately 0.43 m (1.42 ft) could be expected for 14.8 w/m^2 (60 kw/acre). This indicates a closure less than the design basis, but the actual calculation should be made for a true design case.

(5) Maximum Allowable Temperature Rise at the Surface of the Earth

References: Claiborne, Richertson, and Graham, 1980; Russell, 1979.

Results: For thermal loadings of 9.88 w/m^2 (40 kw/acre), 14.8 w/m^2 (60 kw/acre), and 25 w/m^2 (100 kw/acre), the temperature rise at the earth's surface was less than 0.10°C over the first 1000 years. Thus, a margin of 0.9°C compared to the design basis exists.

(6) Maximum Allowable Tensile Stress in Aquitard Beds

Reference: Callahan, 1979.

Results: Using a thermoelastic analysis out to 6000 years, only the upper dolostone bed of 31 m (100 ft) thickness is shown to experience tension from a loading of 14.8 w/m^2 (60 kw/acre). This leaves both shale aquitards intact.

(7) Maximum Allowable Individual Whole Body Dose

Reference: Cloninger, Cole, and Washburn, 1980.

Results: Analyses of a bedded salt case generally repretative of, but not the same as the reference case, shows that the maximum whole body dose to the maximum individual occurs approximately 600,000 years after emplacement. The seventy-year dose at this time is 2.2 rem, or 30 mrem/year to the maximum individual (primarily of 226 Ra). This offers an additional margin of 120 mrem/year compared to the design basis and a total margin of 470 mrem/year compared to the limit.

CONCLUSIONS

The approach described in this paper enables the designer to quantitatively document the degree of technical conservatism incorporated into the design of a waste isolation system in a generic bedded salt repository. Table 1 summarizes the key performance constraints, the limits, the design bases, the maximum calculated values over the various analysis periods, and the total margin. This table indicates that none of the design bases were violated over the time frames of concern. It also shows, in every case, that the total margin is considerable. Consequently, for this generic bedded salt stratigraphy, the waste isolation system previously described with an areal thermal loading of 14.8 w/m^2 (60 kw/acre) would be considered technically conservative design. Because none of the design bases were reached during the analysis periods, the thermal loading for this case could be increased until one of the design bases became restrictive. In this case, it is likely that the controlling performance constraint will be either the minimum allowable room height prior to decommissioning, depending on the length of time between emplacement of the waste and backfilling, or the maximum allowable tensile stress in the aquitard beds, should the thermal load be increased to the point where the thermally-induced tensile stresses become prohibitive. It is anticipated that for an actual repository site, the architect/engineer will iterate on the dependent variables until a design has been established which meets all the design bases for the appropriate times. In this way, technical conservatism can be documented for the review of the regulatory agencies, the technical community, and the general public.

REFERENCES

Blackburn, L.,., Farwick, D.G., Fields, S.R., James, L.A., and Moen, R.A., 1978, "Maximum Allowable Temperature for Storage of Spent Nuclear Reactor Fuel - An Interim Report", HEDL-TEM 78-37, May, Hanford Engineering Development Laboratory, Westinghouse Electric Corporation.

Bradshaw, R.L. and McClain, W.C., (Eds.), 1971, "Project Salt Vault: A Demonstration of the Disposal of High-Activity Solidified Wastes in Underground Salt Mines", ORNL-4555, April, Oak Ridge National Laboratory, Union Carbide Corporation, Oak Ridge, TN.

Callahan, G.D., 1979, "Inelastic Thermomechanial Analysis of a Generic Bedded Salt Repository", RSI-0087, May RE/Spec, Incorporated, Rapid City, SD, for the Office of Nuclear Waste Isolation, Battelle Memorial Institute, ONWI-125 (Draft).

Carter, J.E., 1980, "Comprehensive Radioactive Waste Management Program", February, Weekly Compilation of Presidential Documents, Vol. 16, No. 7 (Presidential Message to Congress).

Claiborne, H.C., Richertson, L.D., and Graham, R.F., 1980, "Expected Environments in High-Level Nuclear Waste and Spent Fuel Repositories in Salt", ORNL/TM-7201, August, Oak Ridge National Laboratory, Union Carbide Corporation, Oak Ridge, TN, for the Office of Nuclear Waste Isolation, Battelle Memorial Institute.

Cloninger, M.O., Cole, C.R., and Washburn, J.F., 1980, "An Analysis of the use of Engineered Barriers for Geologic Isolation of Spent Fuel in a Reference Salt Site Repository, PNL-3356 (Draft), April, Pacific Northwest Laboratory, Richland Washington, for the Office of Nuclear Waste Isolation, Battelle Memorial Institute.

Department of Energy (DOE), 1980, "Statement of the Position of the United States Department of Energy in the Matter of Proposed Rulemaking on the Storage and Disposal of Nuclear Waste" (Waste Confidence Rulemaking document), DOE/NE-0007, April, Washington, D.C.

Gevantman, L.H., (ED), 1980, Handbook of Rock Salt Properties Data, Monograph 167, U.S. Department of Commerce, National Bureau of Standards, 1980

Interagency Review Group (IRG), 1979, "Report to the President by the Interagency Review Group on Nuclear Waste Management", NTW Report TID-29442, March, Washington, D.C.

Jenks, G.H., 1977, "Maximum Acceptable Temperatures of Waste and Containers During Retrievable Geologic Storage", Y/OWI/TM-42, August, Oak Ridge National Laboratory, Union Carbide Corporation, Oak Ridge, TN, for the Office of Waste Isolation, Union Carbide Corporation - Nuclear Division.

Klement, A.W., Jr., Miller, C.R., Minx, R.P., and Shleien, B., 1972, "Estimates of Ionizing Radiation Doses in the United States: 1960-2000°, ORP/CSD 72-1, August, U.S. Environmental Protection Agency, Office of Radiation Programs, Rockville, MD.

Office of Nuclear Waste Isolation (ONWI), 1980, "NWTS Program Criteria for Geologic Disposal of Nuclear Waste - General Program Policies and Criteria", OWNI-33(1) (Draft), May, Battelle Memorial Institute, Columbus, Ohio.

Nuclear Regulatory Commission (NRC), 1980, "Part 20, Standards for Protection Against Radiation", Code of Federal Regulations, Title 10 - Energy, Chapter I, U.S. Government Printing Office, Washington, D.C.

Russell, J.E., 1979, "Areal Thermal Loading Recommendations for Nuclear Waste Repositories in Salt", Y/OWI/TM-37, June, Oak Ridge National Laboratory, Union Carbide Corporation, Oak Ridge, TN, for the Office of Waste Isolation, Union Carbide Corporation - Nuclear Division.

Simonen, F.A. and Slate, S.C., 1979, "Stress Analysis of High-Level Waste Canisters: Methods, Applications, and Design Data", PNL-3036, October, Pacific Northwest Laboratory, Battelle Memorial Institute, Richland, WA.

Wagner, R.A., 1980, "Parametric Study Involving Thermo/Viscoelastic Analyses of a Room and Pillar Configuration", RSI-0070, July RE/SPEC, Inc., Rapid City, SD, for the Office of Nuclear Waste Isolation, Battelle Memorial Institute, ONWI-115.

Chapter 79

THERMOMECHANICAL BEHAVIOR OF BACKFILLED DISPOSAL ROOMS FOR WASTE RETRIEVAL CONSIDERATIONS IN A SALT DOME REPOSITORY

by Joe L. Ratigan, Ralph A. Wagner, and Paul F. Gnirk

RE/SPEC Inc.
P. O. Box 725
Rapid City, SD 57709

ABSTRACT

This thermomechanical analysis used the finite element method to investigate the behavior of crushed salt backfill in a waste disposal room situated in a salt dome repository. The first of two objectives was to determine the transient temperature rise and degree of thermomechanical consolidation that occur in the backfill as a function of drillhole depths. The second objective involved the evaluation of closure due to salt creep of unlined emplacement drillholes and the determination of pressure on steel sleeve liners in the drillholes should liners become necessary for canister retrieval. The retrievability period was considered to extend for 25 years after waste emplacement. The canisters were assumed to contain ten-year old high level waste with a thermal output of 4.3 kW at the time of emplacement.

INTRODUCTION

The reference repository concept for dome salt involves the emplacement of canisters of radioactive reprocessing wastes in vertical drillholes in the floors of storage rooms (Mattern et al., 1979). The storage rooms are developed in the sense of a lane-and-pillar mining system at a depth of 610 m (2,000 ft.). During the development of this repository concept, a special study was undertaken by Stearns-Roger Engineering Company (1978) to determine the consequences of, and engineering design modifications necessitated by, immediate backfilling of the storage rooms with crushed salt after emplacement as regards 25-year waste canister retrievability.

RSI PUBL. NO. 81-01

An integral part of that study involved evaluations of the thermal and thermomechanical responses of the backfilled storage rooms and canister emplacement drillholes. These evaluations were performed by RE/SPEC (Ratigan and Wagner, 1978), and the methodology and results therewith are presented in this paper.

The objectives of this study were two-fold. The first was to determine the transient temperature rise and degree of thermomechanical consolidation that are induced in the crushed-salt backfill in a storage room as a function of the depth of high level waste canister emplacements in drillholes in the storage room floor. This information is necessary for an assessment of ventilation and cooling requirements during backfill excavation, and for selection of the appropriate excavation method and equipment. The second objective involved evaluations of the closure of unlined emplacement drillholes due to salt creep, and of the increase of salt pressure on steel sleeve liners in the drillholes in the event that liners are necessary for canister retrieval. This information is important for determining equipment needs for waste canister retrieval, and for ensuring that the canisters are not structurally damaged or that retrievability is not compromised by excessive drillhole closure. These objectives were addressed in the context that the time period of waste canister retrievability is 25 years after emplacement.

The requisite analyses, necessary to make these evaluations and assessments, were accomplished by means of thermal and thermoviscoelastic modeling procedures, with the use of constitutive laws of deviatoric creep for intact salt and consolidation creep for crushed salt (Ratigan and Wagner, 1978). The numerical simulations were performed with various elements of the SPECTROM finite-element code. The constitutive laws of deformational behavior for salt were derived from laboratory tests on specimens from the Avery Island dome salt mine in Southwestern Louisiana. The geometrical aspects of the disposal rooms and reprocessing waste emplacements, as well as the facility depth, were based on the reference conceptual design developed by Stearns-Roger Engineering Company (SRENCO) for a reprocessing waste repository in dome salt (Mattern et al., 1979). We wish to note that the modeling study discussed herein was only a part of a much broader preliminary investigation of waste retrievability performed by SRENCO. Furthermore, it should be emphasized that the Avery Island mine is <u>not</u> a potential site for a waste repository.

DESCRIPTION OF CONCEPTUAL REPOSITORY

The conceptual repository design for storage in dome salt of radioactive wastes from the reprocessing of nuclear power-plant fields, as described by Mattern et al. (1979), envisages a canistered waste storage area of approximately 4.85 km^2 (1,200 acres) situated at a depth of 610 m (2,000 ft.) in a salt dome. The canistered waste storage area consists of 580 rooms, developed according to a lane-and-pillar concept and grouped into panels. The height and width of a storage room are 4.88 m (16 ft.) and 6.1 m (20 ft.), and the centerline-to-centerline spacing between rooms is 36.6 m (120 ft.). A nominal decay heat density, or gross thermal loading, of 150 kW/acre (37.1 W/m^2) is considered to be a principal repository design parameter.

The high-level reprocessing waste (HLW) is assumed to be vitrified calcine, which is contained in canisters with diameters of 30.5 cm (12 in.) and lengths of 3.05 m (10 ft.). The cladding-hull (CHW) and intermediate-level wastes (ILW) are supposed to be contained in canisters with diameters of 61 cm (24 in.) and lengths of 3.05 m (10 ft.). For the purpose of this study, the emplacement configuration entails three rows of parallel drillholes in the floor of a storage room, with a single canister of HLW emplaced in alternating drillholes in the center row and CHW canisters in all remaining drillholes. The center-to-center pitch between drillholes along a row is specified as 1.93 m (6.33 ft.), and the center-to-center spacing of drillholes between two rows is 1.52 m (5 ft.). The nominal drillhole diameters are 50.8 cm (20 in.) for the HLW canisters and 86.4 cm (34 in.) for the CHW canisters. The reference repository design considers canister drillhole depths of 4.57 m (15 ft.). In this study, consideration is given also to HLW drillhole depths of 7.6, 15.2, 45.7, and 76.2 m (25, 50, 150 and 250 ft.), with the canisters emplaced in the bottom 3.05 m (10 ft.) in all instances.

For the purpose of this study, the HLW canisters assumed to be emplaced ten years after reprocessing, at which time a canister would have a power output of 4.3 kW. The decay curve for the radiogenic heat dissipation is illustrated in Fig. 1, and is representative of radioactive wastes from the reprocessing of spent fuel from pressurized-water reactors (PWR). Finally, the CHW canisters are assumed not to be heat generating.

MATERIAL CHARACTERIZATION

Intact Salt--Thermomechanical

The deformational behavior of intact domal salt can be characterized as being viscoelastic, where the transient viscous, or creep, behavior can be represented by a power law formulation. By the use of data obtained from preliminary constant-stress creep tests in the RE/SPEC laboratory, the transient creep law for Avery Island domal salt, for the purpose of this study, can be written as:

$$\varepsilon^c_{ih} = 2.58 \times 10^{-9}(t/t_o)^{0.48}(T/T_o)^{11.1}(J_2/\sigma_o^2)^{1.21}(S_{ij}/\sigma_o) \qquad (1)$$

where: ε^c_{ij} = creep strain

t = total time

T = absolute temperature

J_2 = second invariant of the deviatoric stresses

S_{ij} = deviatoric stress tensor

t_o = 1 sec.

T_o = 295.5 °K

σ_o = 1 MPa

i,j = 1,2,3

Recent, more detailed, creep tests on Avery Island dome salt have not changed substantially either the form of the creep law or the values of the material constants from those given above (Carter and Hansen, 1979).

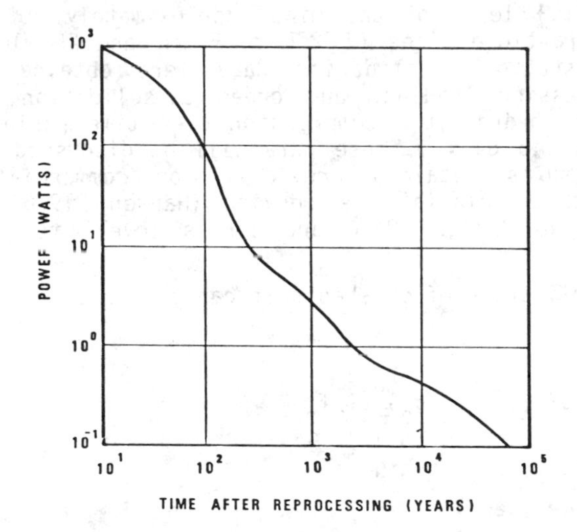

Figure 1. Pressurized Water Reactor Reprocessed High Level Waste Heat Generation (Per Metric Ton Heavy Metal).

Quasi-static compression tests on Avery Island dome salt, as well as similar tests on Jefferson Island dome salt (Stickney, 1977) and Lyons, Kansas bedded salt (Hansen, 1978), provided data for selection of a modulus of elasticity of 1.38 GPa and a Poisson's ratio of 0.4. The coefficient of thermal expansion of the intact salt was taken as 1.22×10^{-5}°C^{-1} (Bradshaw and McClain, 1971; Hansen, 1978). Based on data from the literature, the specific heat and thermal conductivity of the salt were selected as 921.1 J/kg-°C (Cheverton and Turner, 1972) and 4.76 W/m-°C (Clark, 1966; Cheverton and Turner, 1972). Finally, the density was chosen as 2.16 gm/cm^3 (Stickney, 1977; Hansen, 1978).

Intact Salt--Geotechnical

The geothermal gradient in the salt dome was taken as 27.3 °C/km (1.5°F/100 ft.), with a constant temperature of 15.6°C (60°F) at ground surface. The in situ state of stress was selected as being lithostatic, which corresponds to a vertical stress gradient of 21.2 MPa/km for a density of 2.16 gm/cm^3.

Crushed Salt--Thermomechanical

Laboratory consolidation tests were performed on cylindrical specimens (10 cm in diameter by 20 cm in length) of granulated (crushed) salt from the Avery Island mine, for temperature levels of 24 and 52°C and hydrostatic compressive stress states to 13.8 MPa (2,000 psi). The salt sample was obtained at the crusher station on the 268 m (880 ft.) level of the mine; approximately 70% of the sample exhibited particle sizes of 2.5 to 5 mm, and 25% less than 2.5 mm. Quasi-static consolidation data were obtained during hydrostatic compression loading, and creep consolidation data at constant levels of hydrostatic compression over time periods of a few hours to about 13 days. These data will be discussed in conjunction with results obtained previously on commercial grade (cattle) salt with a uniaxial test device (Hansen, 1976), for a temperature range of 21 to 204°C and stress levels to 27.6 MPa (4,000 psi).

The creep consolidation of crushed salt can be represented by the relationship:

$$e = A(t/t_o)^m \, (I_1/\sigma_o)^n (T/T_o)^p \tag{2}$$

where: e = volumetric strain

t = time (sec.)

I_1 = first stress invariant (MPa)

T = temperature (°C)

t_o = 1 sec.

σ_o = 10 MPa

T_o = 100°C

A, m, n and p are material constants, and are quantified in Table 1 for Avery Island and Commercial Grade crushed salt. For all practical purposes, creep of crushed salt is independent of temperature level, at least to about 200°C. The differences in the material constants A and n for the two salt samples are due primarily to relative variations in particle size and quantity distribution.

TABLE 1

Material Constants for Creep Consolidation of Crushed Salt

MATERIAL CONSTANTS	AVERY ISLAND CRUSHED SALT	COMMERCIAL GRADE CRUSHED SALT
A	2.225×10^{-2}	3.418×10^{2}
m	0.221	0.265
n	0.793	0.439
p	1.074	1.070

The consolidation of crushed salt due to creep at a constant hydrostatic stress is small as compared to that induced strictly by the application of stress. Fig. 2 is a plot of mean hydrostatic stress as a function of volumetric consolidation for quasi-static loading for both Avery Island and Commercial Grade crushed salt. For both salt types, the scatter in the data permitted only the plotting of a "band width" of volumetric consolidation over the range of applied stress. The time-invariant constitutive relationship can be written as:

$$I_1 = C[\exp(Be) - 1] \tag{3}$$

B and C material constants, and are given in Table 2 for both types of crushed salt. For this study, it was assumed that the values of constants for the Commercial Grade crushed salt represent a lower limit, while the values for the Avery Island crushed salt represent an upper limit with regard to volumetric consolidation.

TABLE 2

Material Constants for Quasi-Static Consolidation of Crushed Salt

MATERIAL CONSTANTS	AVERY ISLAND CRUSHED SALT (MAXIMUM)	COMMERCIAL GRADE CRUSHED SALT (AVERAGE)
B	17.9	5.27
C (MPa)	0.39	30

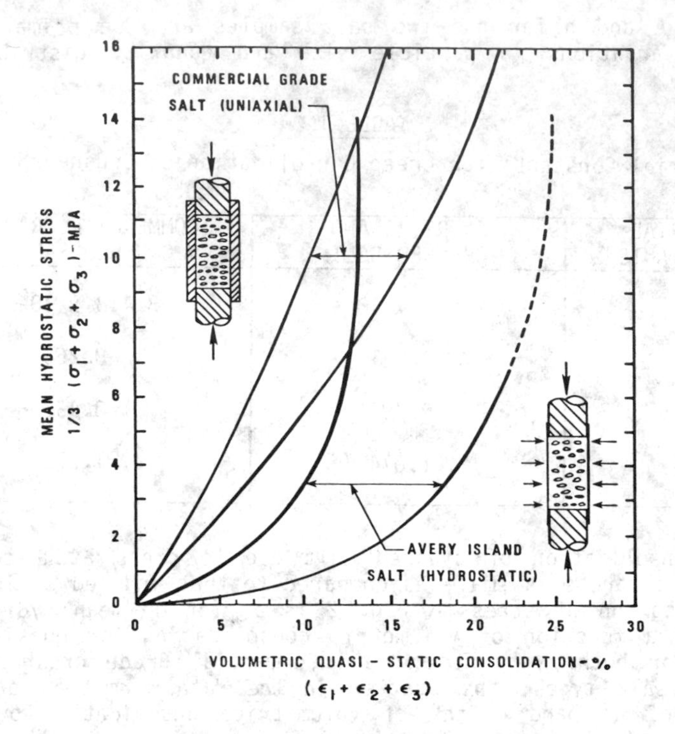

Figure 2. Volumetric Quasi-Static Consolidation of Granulated Salt as a Function of Mean Normal Stress over a Temperature Range of 22 to 204°C.

The unconfined compressive strengths of the consolidation specimens are presented in Fig. 3 as a function of total volumetric consolidation. The results indicate that the unconfined compressive strength increases nonlinearly with increasing volumetric consolidation, and is effectively independent of the temperature conditions during consolidation. In the range of 15 to 25% volumetric consolidation, the unconfined compressive strength ranges between 2.5 and 6 MPa with an average of about 4 MPa. The anamolous value of relatively high strength at a volumetric consolidation of about 29% represents a consolidation specimen, with a relatively greater amount of fines, that was subjected to a combination of both elevated temperature and relatively high hydrostatic stress over an extended time period. This specimen also exhibited a deformation modulus of about 14 GPa, as compared to an average value of approximately 1.4 GPa for the other specimens.

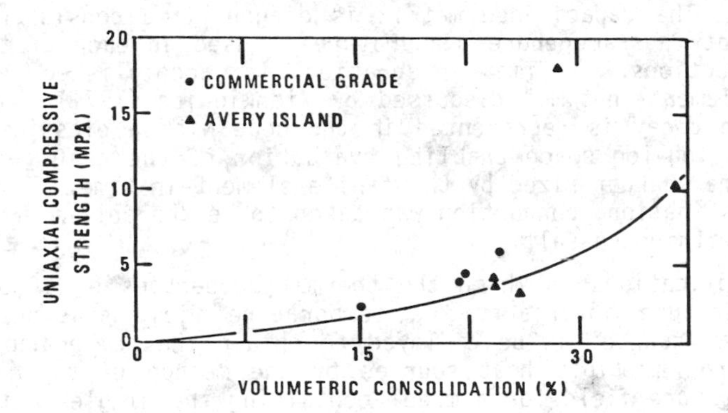

Figure 3. Unconfined Compressive Strength of Granulated Salt as a Function of Volumetric Consolidation.

In order to evaluate the propensity of granulated salt to cohere into a competent mass at elevated temperature in the absence of an applied stress field, specimens of crushed salt from Avery Island were encapsulated in metal containers and subjected to a temperature level of approximately 300°C for periods of time ranging from 1 day to 60 days. Apart from a slight confinement pressure due to differential thermal expansion between the metal container and the salt, the granulated salt was effectively free of applied stress. After 8 days of heating, the salt was observed to exhibit minimal coherence and could be easily crushed with finger pressure. For heating periods of 13 to 60 days, the salt develops regions of coherence within a specimen; however, these regions of "clods" can be crushed with relative ease by finger pressure. Based on the results of these simple experiments, it is not anticipated that purely thermal heating (in the absence of applied stress) will give rise to any appreciable consolidation of a granulated salt mass.

On the basis of limited data from the literature (Cheverton and Turner, 1972), the specific heat and thermal conductivity of the crushed salt were chosen as 921.1 J/Kg-°C and 0.47 W/m-°C, respectively. The density was taken as 1.36 gm/cc (Hansen, 1978). Finally, the coefficient of thermal expansion was assumed to be identical to that of intact salt.

MODELS

Numerical Simulation Procedures

The thermal results presented in this paper were obtained with the aid of the finite-element code SPECTROM-41. This code is capable of handling two-dimensional plane and circular-symmetric problems, and makes exclusive use of eight-noded isoparametric elements. The capacitance matrix is diagonalized consistently and three point Gauss-Legendre quandrature is used in each of the spatial directions. Time integration is accomplished via the "finite-element-in-time" discussed by Zienkiewicz (1971). The heat generation decay is represented in the code with a classical cubic spline in log-log space enabling evaluation of the heat generation at the time characterized by the finite-element-in-time. Throughout this investigation, conduction was taken to be the only mode of heat transder within the salt.

For applications in which the thermal properties of a rock mass are temperature invariant, the temperature field arising from a single heat source can be employed to obtain the temperature field arising from multiple heat sources by the method of superpostion. The temperature field for a model containing the single heat source is generated with SPECTROM-41, and the superposition of multiple heat sources in time and space is performed with the SPECTROM-42 code. By comparison of results from the three-dimensional finite-element code SPECTROM-341, the above technique has been shown to provide an excellent representation of the three-dimensional temperature field around heat-generating waste canisters (Waldman, 1979).

The thermoviscoelastic results were obtained with the finite-element code SPECTROM-21. This code uses eight-noded isoparametric elements, and is capable of treating plane stress or plane strain problems in x-y geometry. It has provisions for handling initial stress states and for simulating sequential excavation in space and time. Two-point Gauss-Legendre quadrature is employed in each spatial direction, and time increments are selected according to a predictor-corrector technique which makes use of the ratio of the norms of total strain and incremental creep strain rate (Zienkiewicz, 1971).

Room-and-Pillar Models

In order to assess the influence of the depth of emplacement of reprocessing-waste canisters below the storage room floor on temperature rise in the crushed-salt backfill and on room closure with and without backfill, it was necessary to develop two finite-element models. The model with crushed-salt backfill is illustrated in Fig. 4. The model without backfill is identical in all respects, apart from the absence of the crushed salt in the room. Each model is two-dimensional and represents half of a pillar and one-half of a room, due to the symmetry which exists about the room and pillar centerlines. In this situation, the HLW canisters along the length of the room are averaged into an equivalent heat-generating "trench". Whereas temperatures directly above the canisters will be higher than those in the backfill not directly above the canisters, this model adequately represents the average backfill temperatures along the length of the room. The depth of the trench and the heat-generating region within it was adjusted to account for a range of drillhole depths from 4.6 to 76.2 m (15 to 250 ft.). The cross-sectional dimensions of the room-and-pillar geometry are consistent with the conceptual design, and the crushed-salt backfill is assumed to extend from the floor to within 0.61 m (2 ft.) of the roof. The CHW canister drillholes were excluded from the models, as their presence will not significantly perturb the transient temperature field induced in the salt and backfill by the heat-generating waste.

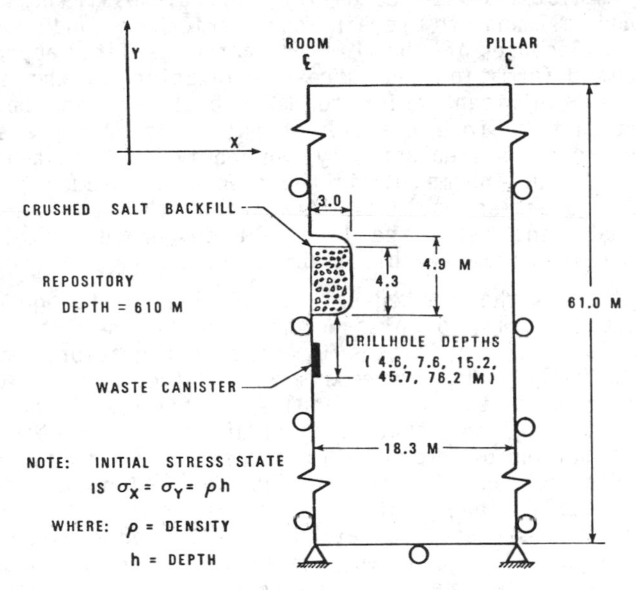

Figure 4. Room-and-Pillar Model with Crushed-Salt Backfill.

For purposes of the thermal analyses, the vertical model boundaries are taken to be perfectly insulated (adiabatic) and a transient flux is applied to the upper and lower horizontal boundaries which approximates an infinite medium in the vertical direction. The peripheral boundary of the storage room or of the air space between the backfill and roof, is assumed to be perfectly insulated. This assumption is conservative in that it tends to overestimate, but not significantly, the temperature rise in the salt between the heat source and the insulated boundary.

For purposes of the viscoelastic analyses, the horizontal displacements of the vertical boundaries and the vertical displacement of the lower boundary of the model are not permitted. The upper boundary is subjected to a force which is equal to the weight of the salt overburden. A condition of plane strain is imposed normal to the plane of the model, i.e. parallel to the length of the storage room. The vertical extent of the model is sufficient such that viscoelastic effects at the upper and lower boundaries have negligible influence on the room deformation.

In effect, the numerical procedure simulates the excavation of an infinite sequence of parallel rooms in a salt mass in which the in situ, or pre-mining, state of stress is lithostatic. Emplacement of the HLW and crushed-salt backfill is assumed to take place at the instant of room excavation, and viscoelastic response of the salt due to excavation-induced and thermally-induced loadings is supposed to follow immediately. In actuality, the disposal rooms will be excavated and allowed to remain open prior to and during HLW emplacement. Because of the low extraction ratio, approximately 17%, the room deformation and stress relaxation in the salt mass should not be significant prior to HLW emplacement and backfilling with crushed salt. Since the row of HLW canister emplacements in the storage room is replaced by an equivalent heat-generating "trench", the conducting medium in the trench is assumed to have the same thermal properties as salt. Apart from the canisters and the immediately adjacent salt, the transient temperature field is not influenced significantly by this assumption.

Consolidation of the crushed-salt backfill in a storage room will be the result primarily of pressure exerted by the intact salt on the backfill as the room closes by creep deformation, and secondarily of thermally-induced stresses within the confined backfill. It is assumed that the crushed-salt backfill will not support deviatoric stresses, and that consolidation is strictly a time-independent function of hydrostatic stress. Continuity of normal stress and displacement is required at the interface between the backfill and the periphery of the storage room. By use of the laboratory-derived stress-deformation relation for crushed salt, as defined by eqn. (3), and an iterative numerical process in SPECTROM-21 to handle the interface continuity requirements, the volumetric consolidation of the backfill was modeled as a function of time-dependent temperature rise and storage room closure.

Canister Drillhole Models

In order to assess the influence of depth of HLW canister emplacement below the storage room floor on drillhole closure and salt pressure buildup on a drillhole sleeve, it was necessary to develop three finite-element models. The first model was employed to calculate the temperature field around the emplaced waste canisters, and the other two models were used for the thermoviscoelastic analyses.

The thermal model involved a single HLW canister situated in a drillhole within an infinite medium with a region of crushed salt backfill above the canister. The vertical distance between the base of the backfilled region and the canister could be adjusted to account for a range of drillhole depths from 4.6 to 76.2 m (15 to 250 ft.). In effect, the model represented a large circular cylinder of salt, with the drillhole and cylindrical backfilled region situated along the centerline of the cylinder. The vertical and horizontal boundaries of the cylinder were perfectly insulated and situated sufficiently far from the drillhole so as to not influence the induced temperature field around the HLW canister for a period of 25 years after emplacement. The thermal properties of the waste canister are assumed to be identical to those for salt. For all practical purposes, this assumption only influences the temperature rise in the canister, which is of no interest to this study.

By the use of the above model and SPECTROM-41, the transient temperature fields in the salt were determined for the range of drillhole depths. For the geometric arrangement of HLW canisters in the conceptual repositories, the temperature fields of all single canisters were superposed in space and time with SPECTROM-42 for each drillhole depth, assuming instantaneous emplacement of all canisters.

Due to the consideration of drillhole depth, it was necessary to develop a thermoviscoelastic model for a HLW drillhole depth of 4.6 m (15 ft.), which included the adjacent CHW drillholes, and a second model for deeper drillholes, which excluded the CHW drillholes. As illustrated in Fig. 5, the first model represents a horizontal section which passes through the midpoint heights of the HLW and CHW canisters. Due to symmetry considerations, the drillholes were modeled in a quarter section, and a condition of zero displacement normal to the model boundaries (lines of symmetry) was prescribed, except where the drillholes were located. A condition of plane strain was prescribed normal to the plane of the model, i.e. parallel to the axes of the waste canisters. The second thermoviscoelastic model was identical in all respects to the first, except that the CHW canister drillholes were excluded. The drillhole diameters and spacings are consistent with those envisaged in the conceptual repository design.

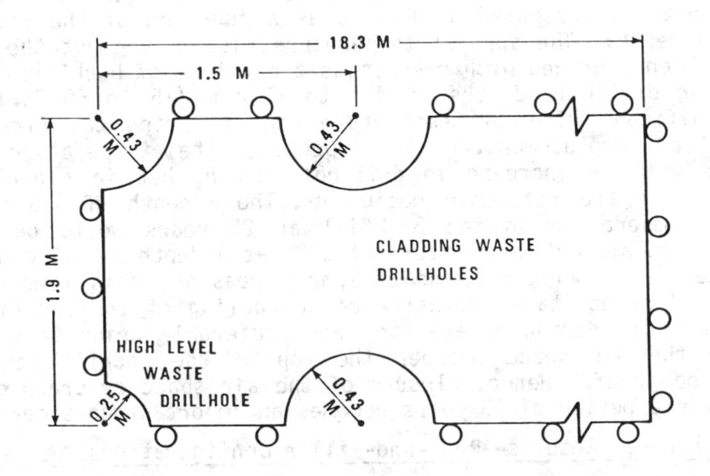

Figure 5. Canister Model for Reference Case (Drillhole Depth of 4.6 m).

In the thermoviscoelastic simulation with SPECTROM-21, the elastic solution at time zero is appropriate to a plate of unit thickness which is subjected to the prescribed set of displacement boundary conditions and an initial state of hydrostatic stress, corresponding in this case to the weight of the salt overburden, and into which holes are cut instantaneously according to a prescribed geometrical arrangement. The transient temperature perturbations in the plate due to heat generation from the HLW are taken from the results of the thermal modeling described previously. Thus, for time greater than zero, the viscoelastic response of the plate is due to a combination of the stress perturbations arising from drillhole excavation and the induced temperature field. In the absence of steel liners in the drillholes, closure of a drillhole due to creep is allowed to proceed without resistance from the canister. Since the diameters of the drillholes are greater than those of the canisters, diametrical closures of about 30 and 40% for the CHW and HLW drillholes, respectively, would be required before the salt would contact the canister. For a situation in which a 40.6 cm (16 in.) diameter steel sleeve is emplaced in a HLW drillhole prior to canister emplacement, the annulus between the drillhole wall and sleeve is backfilled with crushed salt. As the drillhole diameter decreases due to thermoviscoelastic deformation, the consolidation of the crushed salt against the "rigid" body of the steel sleeve is simulated by SPECTROM-21.

DISCUSSION OF RESULTS

Thermal Results--Backfilled Storage Rooms

The transient temperature rise in the crushed-salt backfill in a storage room is presented in Fig. 6 as a function of the time and drillhole depth. The spatial temperature rise throughout the backfill has been averaged with respect to the volume of backfill in the room. For drillhole depths of 4.6 to 15.2 m (15 to 50 ft.), the most significant rise in temperature occurs during the first ten years after emplacement. As expected, the temperature rise decreases with an increase in drillhole depth, but in a nonlinear fashion. For the reference design drillhole depth of 4.6 m, the absolute temperature in the backfill at 25 years would be about 125°C, for an ambient temperature of 32°C at a depth of 610 m in the salt dome. For personnel and equipment reasons, this temperature level would necessitate intensive blast cooling of the backfill by ventilation air during excavation, and preferably prior to excavation via the air space between the top of the backfill and the storage room roof. Hence, closure of the air space by creep deformation over a period of 25 years becomes an important consideration.

Thermomechanical Results--Room-and-Pillar Configurations

The purpose of the thermomechanical analysis of the room-and-pillar configurations is to determine the degree of consolidation and subsequent mineability of the crushed salt backfill. The volumetric room closure for the reference case (drillhole depth of 4.6 m) without backfill provides the upper limit regarding the influence of the consolidation of the crushed salt backfill. The volumetric room closure after 25 years for this case is approximately 42 percent (Fig. 7). Also shown in Fig. 7 are the resulting vector profiles of room deformation obtained with the lower and upper limits of the laboratory-derived stress-deformation (consolidation) relation (Eq. 3). The crushed salt consolidation for the two cases employing the lower and upper limits of consolidation is 11 and 22 percent, respectively. The prediction of these degrees of consolidation considered the allowable volumetric room closure required (approx. 12.5 percent) before consolidation could occur due to the air space between the backfill and roof. The comparison of these two amounts of consolidation with the laboratory-derived relation presented in Fig. 3 indicates that the unconfined compressive strength of the crushed-salt backfill should vary between 1.4 and 3.1 MPa 25 years after emplacement. Rock with these relatively low compressive strengths could be excavated with a continuous miner or a backhoe.

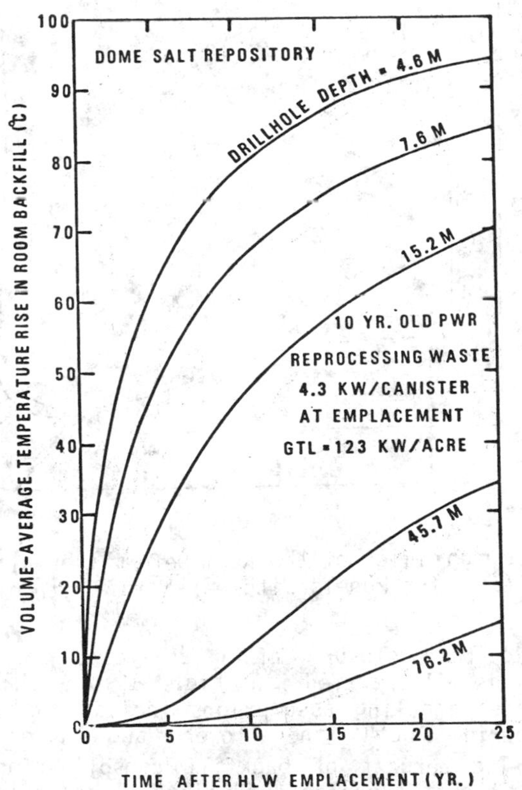

Figure 6. Volume Average Backfill Temperature Rise as a Function of Time and Drillhole Depth.

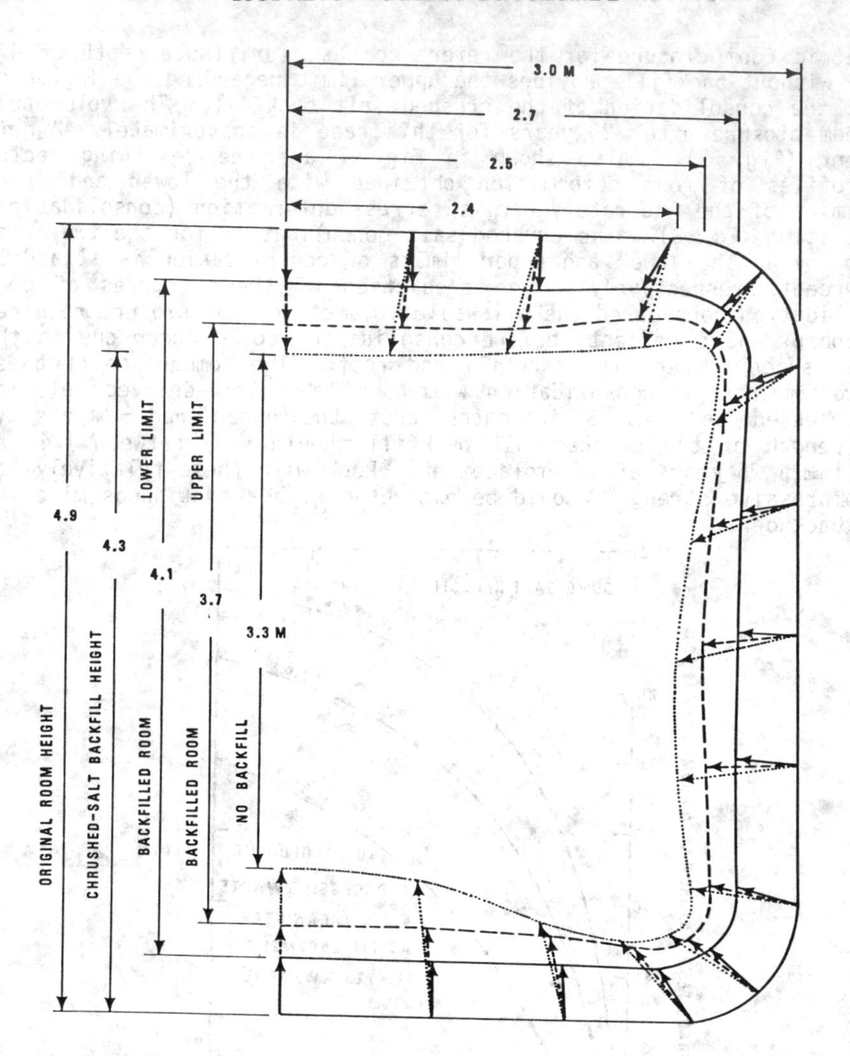

Figure 7. Vector Profiles of the Room Deformation After 25 Years for Models with Drillhole Depth of 4.6 m.

The volumetric room closure after 25 years for the deeper drillhole cases is illustrated in Fig. 8 for three modeling assumptions. These modeling assumptions include no backfill, and backfill considering both the lower and upper limit of consolidation. The percent of backfill consolidation for these cases considering backfill can be determined by deducting 12.5 percent from the volumetric room clsoure. The consolidation of the crushed salt backfill for the 15.2 m drillhole model should vary between 4 and 8 percent. The two deeper drillhole models (45.7 and 76.2 m) will not experience any backfill consolidation since the volumetric room closure is not anticipated to exceed 12.5 percent. Basically, the degree of backfill consolidation is the greatest for the reference case (drillhole depth of 4.6 m) and decreases non-linearly with increasing drillhole depth.

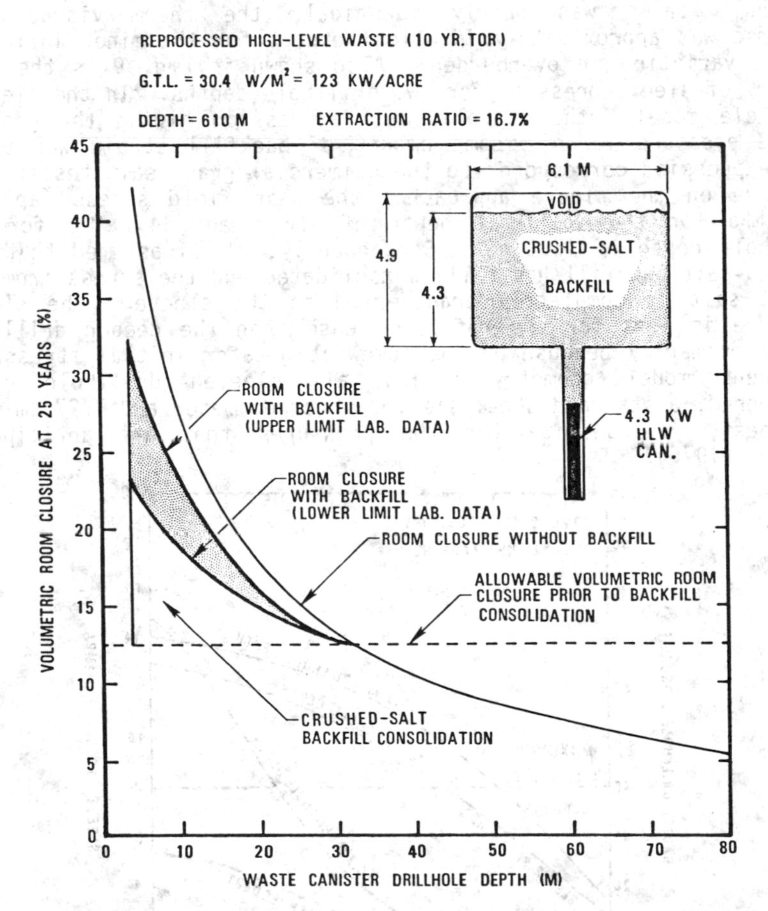

Figure 8. Volumetric Room Closure at 25 Years as a Function of Drillhole Depth for a Disposal Room With and Without Crushed-Salt Backfill.

Thermomechanical Results--Canister Drillhole

The amount of radial drillhole closure for the models without sleeves is much greater for the deeper drillhole depths than for the reference case (drillhole depth of 4.6 m) as shown in Fig. 9. The variation in radial drillhole closure can be largely attributed to the two model configurations considered. As previously stated, both CHW and HLW drillholes were included in the reference case whereas, only HLW drillholes were modeled in the deeper drillhole depths (7.6, 15.2, 45.7 and 76.2 m). Since the modeling for the deeper drillhole cases was nearly identical, the thermo/viscoelastic response was approximately identical except for the minor influence of the variation in overburden. Also shown in Fig. 9 is the time history of sleeve pressure for two drillhole depths. In the sleeved drillhole models, the consolidation expression giving the greater sleeve pressure for the same amount of backfill strain was used. This expression corresponds to the commercial grade salt tests. The pressure on the sleeve approaches the near field stress (approx. 13.0 MPa for the drillhole depth of 4.6 m and 14.1 MPa for the drillhole depth of 15.2 m). Consequently, it is assumed that the crushed-salt backfill has fully consolidated and the stress from the intact salt is completely transferred to the sleeve. The sleeve pressure is less for the reference case than the deeper drillhole depths primarily because of the somewhat greater initial stress and different model geometry. For all sleeved drillhole cases considered, a standard steel sleeve, 40 cm diameter and 1.27 cm wall thickness, is adequate for the pressures that are anticipated (Hansen, 1976).

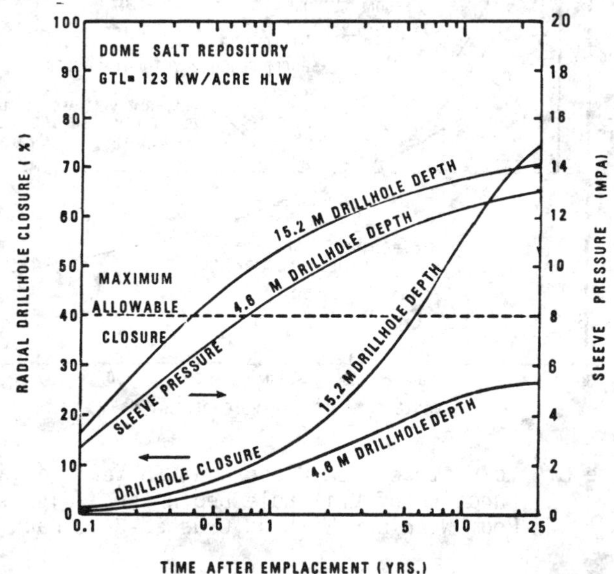

Figure 9. Drillhole Closure and Sleeve Pressure as a Function of Time for 4.6 and 15.2 m Drillhole Depths.

CONCLUSIONS

Some interesting trade-offs as regards techniques and costs for retrieval have been revealed. For the reference design case (drillhole depth of 4.6 m), the drillhole closure is relatively small and the strength of the crushed-salt is such that a continuous miner or a backhoe could be used for excavation of the rooms; however, the temperature of the backfill necessitates cooling prior to mining. For greater drillhole depths, the backfill temperature and consolidation strength decreases, but the drilling costs increase and the drillhole closure is accentuated which requires the use of sleeved drillholes.

An increase in drillhole depth beyond 4.6 m results in significant drillhole closure. Consequently, a sleeve would be necessary for the protection of the waste canister from structural damage. The pressure induced on a protective sleeve will not be great enough to induce yield of the sleeve for any of the drillhole depths after 25 years, neglecting corrosion effects.

ACKNOWLEDGMENTS

The authors wish to recognize the people who contributed to the analysis presented herein. Firstly, we would like to acknowledge the Stearns-Roger Engineering Company (SRENCO) for whom this work was performed (Subcontract No. 7002-C19150). Their consent to allow RE/SPEC Inc. to conduct this study and present the findings to the technical community is most appreciated. The testing program was administered by Mr. Francis D. Hansen and Mr. Kirby D. Mellegard. Dr. Arlo F. Fossum and Mr. Gary D. Callahan provided guidance regarding the modeling of the crushed-salt. Ms. Julie S. Annicchiarico and Ms. Judy C. Hey are responsible for the typing and professional appearance of this paper.

LIST OF REFERENCES

Bradshaw, R. L. and McClain, W. C.: "Project Salt Vault: A Demonstration of the Disposal of High-Activity Solidified Wastes in Underground Salt Mines", Oak Ridge National Laboratory Report ORNL-4555, April, 1971.

Carter, N. L. and Hansen, F. D.: "Mechanical Behavior of Avery Island Halite: A Preliminary Analysis", RE/SPEC Inc., Rapid City, SD, RSI-0097, Prepared for Office of Nuclear Waste Isolation, ONWI/SUB-79/E512-02300/17, January, 1980.

Cheverton, R. D. and Turner, W. D.: "Thermal Analysis of the National Radioactive Waste Repository: Progress Through March 1972", Oak Ridge National Laboratory Report ORNL-4789, September, 1972.

Clark, S. P., Jr. (Editor): Handbook of Physical Constants, The Geological Society of America, Inc., 1966.

Hansen, F. D.: "Experimental Consolidation of Granulated Rock Salt with Application to Sleeve Buckling", RE/SPEC Inc., Rapid City, SD, RSI-0044, Prepared for the Oak Ridge National Laboratory, ORNL-SUB-4269-21, June, 1976.

Hansen, F. D.: "Quasi-Static Strength and Creep Deformational Characteristics of Bedded Salt From the Carey Mine Near Lyons, Kansas", RE/SPEC Inc., Rapid City, SD, RSI-0067, Prepared for Office of Waste Isolation, Y/OWI/SUB-78/22303/13, June, 1978.

Mattern, J. C., Pervich, M. P., Weigand, F. L., and Wrenshall, R. B.: "Description of an NWTS Repository for Reprocessing Waste in Domed Salt", Proc. NWTS Program Information Meeting, U.S. Dept. Energy-Richland Operations Office and ONWI-Battelle, 1979.

Ratigan, J. L. and Wagner, R. A.: "Thermomechanical Analysis of Crushed-Salt Backfilled Disposal Rooms in a Conceptual Radioactive Waste Repository in Dome Salt", RE/SPEC Inc., Rapid City, SD, RSI-0068, Prepared for Stearns-Roger Engineering Company, September, 1978.

Stickney, R. G.: "Case History Rock Mechanics Examination of the Jefferson Island Salt Mine: III. Evaluation of Laboratory Specimen Dimensions on the Uniaxial Strength and Deformation Characteristics of Dome Salt", RE/SPEC Inc., Rapid City, SD, RSI-0059, Prepared for Office of Waste Isolation, Y/OWI/SUB-77/22303/7, September, 1977.

Waldman, H.: "Evaluation of the Thermomechanical Behavior About a Waste Container/Sleeve in Salt", RE/SPEC Inc., Rapid City, SD, RSI-0102, Prepared for Office of Nuclear Waste Isolation, ONWI/SUB-79/E512-02300/21, (Draft), 1981.

Zienkiewicz, O. C.: The Finite Element Method in Engineering Science, McGraw-Hill, 1971.

Chapter 80

OPTIMIZATION OF PYRITE IN MINE WASTE BACKFILL

by Ruston A. Ford and Barry J. Hansen

Chief Mining Engineer - Exxon Minerals Company
Rhinelander, Wisconsin

Manager of Technical Services - Exxon Minerals Company
Rhinelander, Wisconsin

ABSTRACT

Production of mine backfill from the tailings produced in a proposed Crandon concentrator is described. A process has been developed capable of producing suitable fill for the mining method selected for the Crandon orebody. It maximizes the placement of pyrite underground as fill and segregates tailings into pyrite and nonsulfide fractions. To determine the suitability and engineering characteristics of the backfill product for use underground, laboratory and physical stope simulation model testing was conducted. The results of the testing and the application of those results to the design of the backfill system ultimately affecting mine geometry and subsequent mine production will be presented.

INTRODUCTION

Exploration efforts conducted by Exxon in northern Wisconsin returned an aerial electromagnetic geophysical anomaly near Crandon in Forest County in 1974. This anomaly was verified through interpretation of ground survey data and a surface diamond drilling program was begun in mid-1975. From 1975 through to mid-1978, 200 drill holes were completed outlining the physical limits of the deposit and determining the quality of the zinc-copper mineralization. An extensive program of predevelopment and mine planning activities has been conducted since that time.

The deposit is located in the Northern Highlands region of northeastern Wisconsin, approximately 483 kilometers northeast of Madison, the state capital. Crandon, the county seat of Forest County is located eight (8) kilometers due north of the proposed project site.

GEOLOGY

The orebody is about 1 520 meters long, dips approximately 80 degrees north, and averages about 38 meters wide and 720 meters beneath the surface. Current estimates of the probable tonnage and grade of the deposit are 75 million metric tons that average 5.0 percent zinc, 1.1 percent copper, and 0.4 percent lead.

The deposit contains equal amounts of two major ore types. The first ore type, designated as "stringer ore", consists of copper mineralization containing minor amounts of zinc in a silicified volcanic rock matrix. Overlapping the stringer ore and extending to the east, is the other ore type designated as "massive ore". This zinc-copper-lead ore consists mostly of sphalerite with chalcopyrite and minor amounts of galena within a matrix consisting mainly of pyrite.

MINING METHOD

It is proposed that the mining method will be sublevel blasthole open stoping utilizing mill tailings as the backfill material. This method involves the simultaneous development and operation of several vertical stope blocks of ore between mine levels (Figure 1). The stope block size as dictated by rock mechanics studies will be 45 meters wide measured along strike, and will extend from hanging wall to footwall with a vertical height of 120 meters.

To facilitate the mining method, main levels and/or drawpoint levels will be established at 120 meter intervals. Sublevels will be located at regular vertical intervals above the main levels. The number of sublevels employed between the main levels will depend on the shape of the orebody, its width, and the stoping sequence or mining plan. Generally, one drilling sublevel will be established between each of the main levels. A 15 to 17 percent internal access ramp will interconnect all levels.

All level, sublevel, and ramp development will be accomplished using electric hydraulic drill jumbos. Three point eight cubic meter (3.8 m^3) and six point one cubic meter (6.1 m^3) LHD units will be used for mucking along with 13.6 metric ton and 23.6 metric ton trucks.

Drilling from the main levels and sublevels will consist of vertical 150 millimeter downholes drilled to pre-engineered depths in a 4 x 4 meter pattern. The drilling will be accomplished using high pressure air, down-the-hole drill rigs drilling from pre-excavated stope drill drifts arranged in an appropriate pattern. Vertical crater retreat blasting techniques will be used

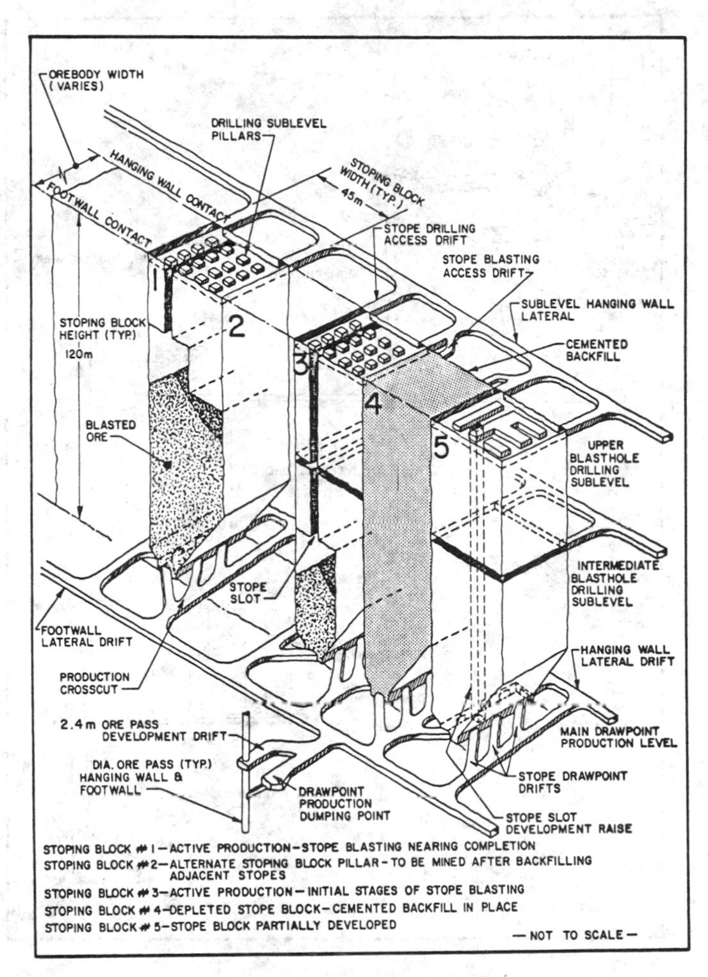

Figure 1 -- Conceptual Stope Dimensions and Sequence of Ore Extraction Proposed for the Crandon Mine

to excavate the slot followed by bench blasting of vertical rings into the slot thus created.

Refer to Figure 2. The blasted ore will be drawn from the stopes using six point one cubic meter (6.1 m^3) LHD units to 2.4 meter diameter ore passes located both in the hanging wall and footwall, providing a maximum haul distance per stope of 183 meters. The strategic location of these ore passes in both the hanging wall and the footwall further provides for the effective separation of the two ore types. An electric rail haulage system will be utilized to collect ore from the ore passes on the 710

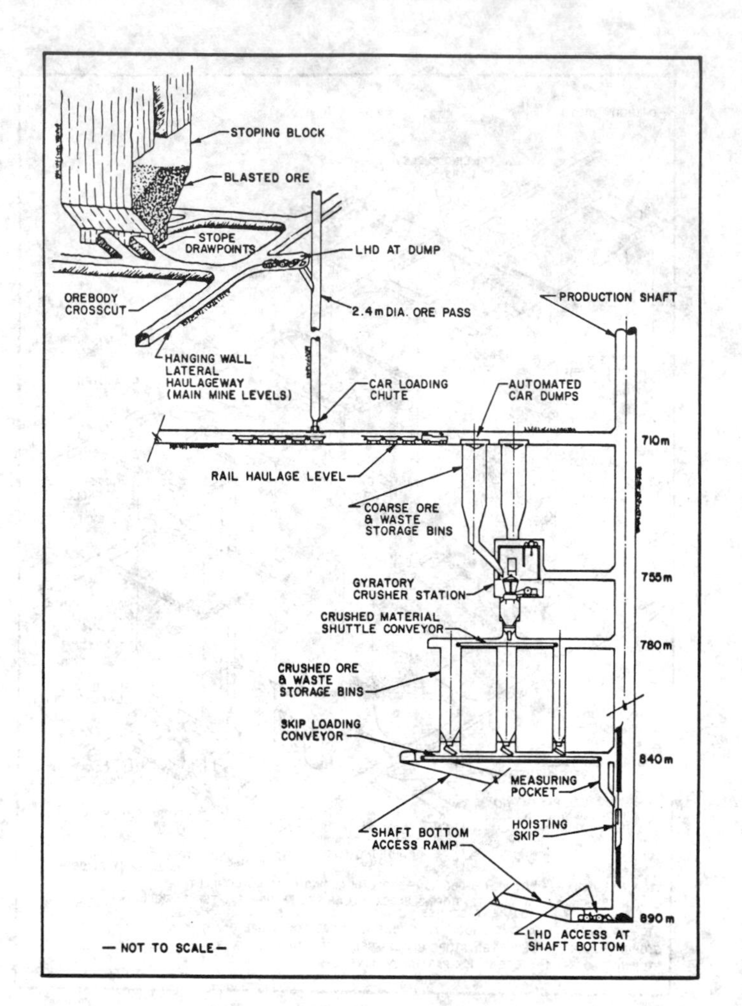

Figure 2 -- Underground Ore Handling Schematic Designed for the Proposed Crandon Mine

meter level ahead of an underground gyratory crusher. The crusher will reduce run of mine ore and waste to minus 150 millimeters for hoisting. Adequate storage for both ore types and waste will be provided by bins located above and below the crusher.

The production shaft (Figure 3) measuring 7.3 meters in diameter will provide primary access into the mine. This shaft will be a concrete lined structure sunk to a depth of 884 meters. The production hoist will be a tower-mounted friction hoist with two skips in balance. The main service hoist will also be a tower-mounted friction hoist with a counter weighted double-deck

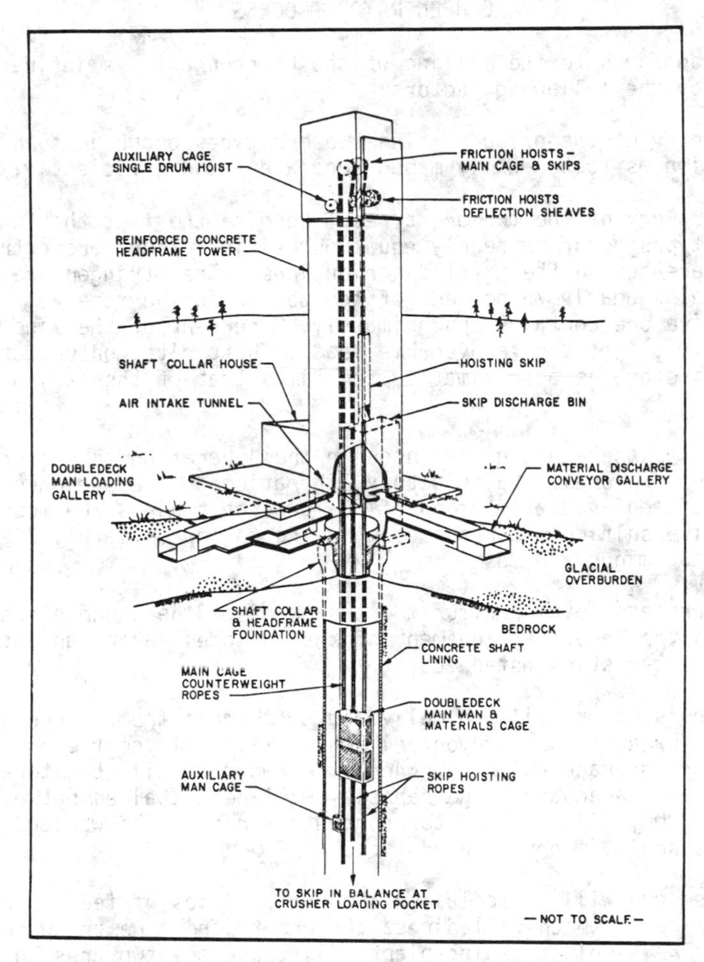

Figure 3 -- Production Shaft Headframe Collar and Shaft Conveyance Schematic Designed for the Proposed Crandon Mine

cage for transport of both men and materials. In addition, an auxiliary single drum man and materials hoist will be installed.

Ore will be mined underground and hoisted to surface at a daily rate of approximately 12 700 metric tons, five days a week. The mill will have a capacity of 9 100 metric tons per day and will maintain a 24-hour, seven day week schedule.

CONCENTRATOR PROCESS

The approach to the milling of the Crandon ores is influenced mainly by the following factors:

- Geometry of the orebody. The two ore types occur in such a fashion as to be easily mined separately and efficiently.

- Mineralogy of the two ore types. Despite the fact that the two ore types occur in nearly equal quantities, there are extreme differences in the metal distributions. The stringer ore contains nearly 75 percent of the copper in the reserve. The massive ore contains approximately 90 percent of the zinc and nearly all of the recoverable lead. The pyrite content of the massive ore is approximately ten times that of the stringer ore.

- Finally, there are differences in the liberation characteristics of the two ores. Satisfactory liberation of the stringer ore can be achieved at a grind of 70-75 percent minus 200 mesh. The massive sulfide ore requires grinding to approximately 80-85 percent minus 200 mesh.

The process developed for the treatment of the Crandon ores is based on the separate treatment of the two ores taking advantage of the characteristics noted above.

The hoisted ore will be delivered by feeders from an ore bin in the headframe, to a conveyor belt which will deliver the ore to the coarse ore storage building, where the two ores will be stored separately. Adequate surge capacity will be installed between the mine and the mill to carry the concentrator over the weekend when the mine shaft is not in operation.

Coarse ore will be reclaimed through a series of feeders onto conveyor belts which will direct the ore to the fine crushing plant. The single crushing plant will crush the two ores in a batch fashion (Figure 4) utilizing secondary cone crushers and shorthead cones operating in closed circuit with vibrating screens. The crushed screened ore, minus 13 millimeter will be conveyed to one of two sets of fine ore bins. Massive and stringer ore will be crushed and stored separately and will be processed in separate circuits.

The ores will be ground in rod mill-ball mill circuits. The ball mills will operate in closed circuit with cyclone classifiers. Two identical grinding circuits will be utilized. Figure 5 illustrates a schematic flowsheet of the concentrator.

After grinding and conditioning with reagents, a bulk copper-lead concentrate will be produced from the massive ore. The

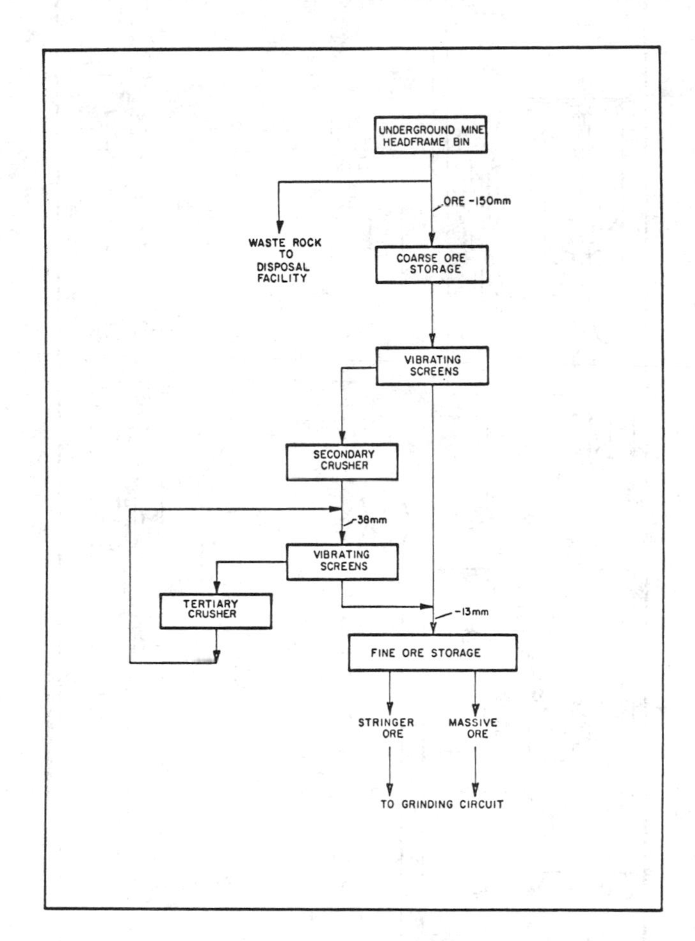

Figure 4 -- Schematic Flowsheet of the Crushing and Ore Storage System for the Proposed Crandon Concentrator

copper-lead rougher concentrate will be pumped to a regrind circuit containing a ball mill and cyclone classifiers. Following regrinding of the concentrate, copper minerals will be separated from the lead by means of flotation. Copper concentrate will then be pumped to the combined copper cleaning circuit for the stringer ore. The copper tailing will then be pumped to a lead circuit to produce a lead concentrate.

After regrinding and conditioning with reagents, the stringer ore will be treated by flotation for the production of a copper concentrate and tailing containing recoverable zinc. The copper

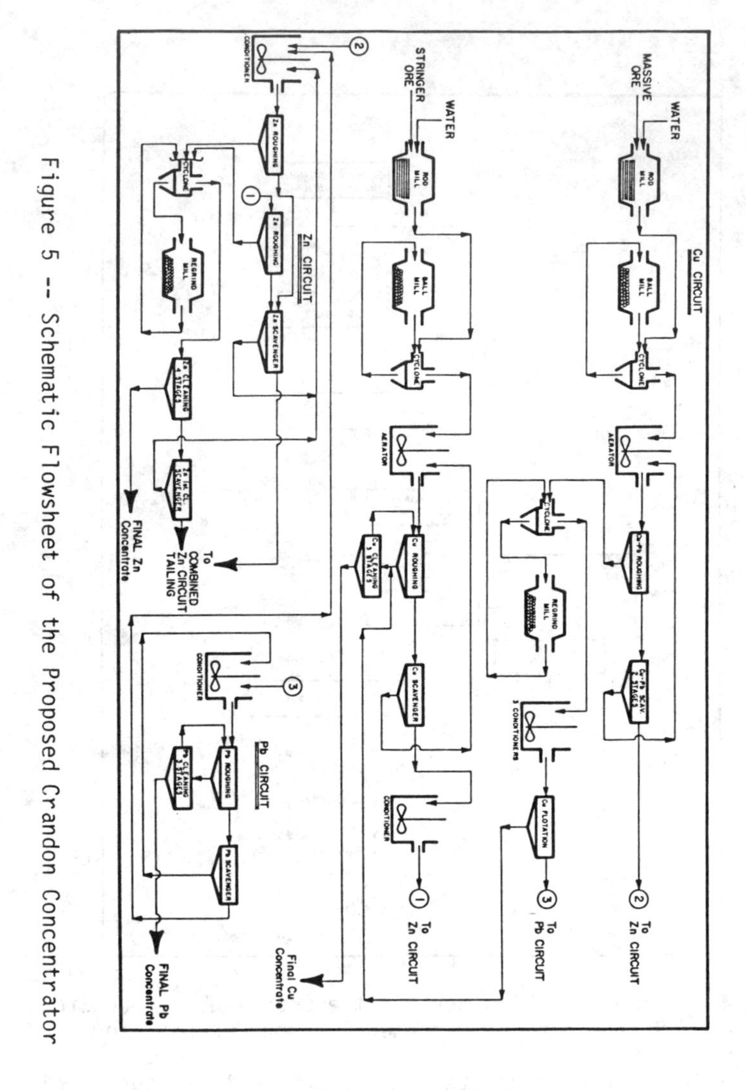

Figure 5 -- Schematic Flowsheet of the Proposed Crandon Concentrator

flotation circuit will be similar to the massive copper-lead circuit containing roughing and scavenging steps.

The copper rougher concentrate, together with a copper concentrate produced in the copper-lead separation circuit from the massive ore, will be cleaned in a separate step. This cleaning will result in the production of a final copper concentrate.

The tailings from the copper-lead flotation of the massive ore and the tailings from copper flotation of the stringer ore will be combined and directed to zinc flotation. Zinc rougher and scavenger concentrates will be produced. The zinc scavenger concentrate will return to the head of the circuit for reprocessing and the zinc rougher concentrate will be reground prior to cleaning. Following regrinding, the concentrate will be cleaned at least three times to produce the final zinc concentrate. The zinc scavenger tailing will then pass on to the backfill preparation circuit.

The mine backfill preparation circuit consists of the recovery of pyrite concentrates and the production of nonsulfide sand products (Figure 6). The final zinc flotation tailings will be separated into a pyrite concentrate and a pyrite tailings by means of flotation. The pyrite flotation concentrate will be classified in two stages of cycloning to remove the minus 30 micron particles and to produce a sand product. The pyrite sand product will be pumped to the backfill preparation circuit, where it will be combined with the sand product from the pyrite flotation tailing. The fine pyrite cyclone overflow will be pumped to the tailings disposal area.

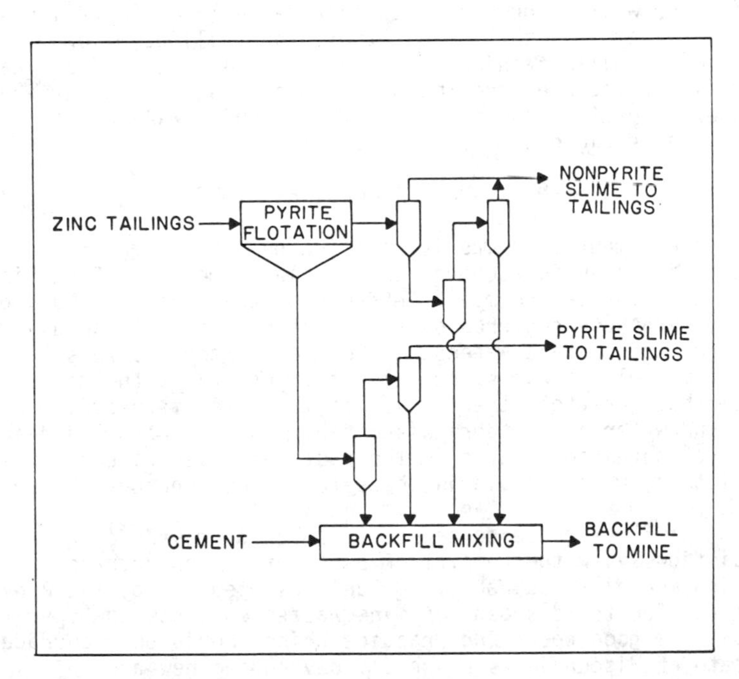

Figure 6 -- Schematic Diagram of the Proposed Crandon Mine Backfill Preparation Circuit

The pyrite flotation tailings will be classified in two stages of cycloning in a similar fashion to the pyrite concentrates, to produce a nonpyrite sand and a product containing the minus 30 micron nonsulfide material. The nonpyrite sand then will be pumped to the backfill preparation plant, where it will be combined with the pyrite sand and cement to produce mine backfill. The mine backfill will then be pumped to the mine for deposition underground in the mined out stopes. When there are no available stopes to receive backfill, the sand product will be pumped to the waste disposal area for temporary storage. As needed, the sands will be reclaimed from the waste disposal area and returned to the mine for deposition underground.

The nonpyrite tailing will be the largest volume of material produced by the concentrator. It consists of a stream containing approximately minus 30 micron nonsulfide fines. The slurry will leave the concentrator containing approximately ten percent solids and will be pumped through a pipeline to a nonsulfide storage area. The slurry will be impounded behind dams, the solids allowed to settle, and the clear water decanted and sent to the reclaim water pond.

The pyrite fines, which are also approximately minus 30 microns in diameter, will be pumped to a separate cell in the tailings disposal system. At that point, they, too, will be allowed to settle in a similar fashion to the nonsulfide fines. The clear water will be decanted and the solids stored in the pond area. Separate disposal of the pyrite in this fashion will permit its recovery, if desired in the future.

ENVIRONMENTAL CONSIDERATIONS

The development of a massive sulfide deposit in an area such as northern Wisconsin is accompanied by a large measure of public concern over the environmental effects of the project. Many of these concerns are centered on the preservation of the quality of the ground and surface waters in the area. Many citizens, as well as governmental officials, perceive that pyrite is the major problem that threatens the quality of the lakes, streams, ponds, and ground water in northern Wisconsin. The uncontrolled disposal of pyrite containing wastes in the past has given rise to examples of pollution, which result in these fears and concerns.

As a result of these concerns, a number of governmental jurisdictions view the removal of pyrite from concentrator tailings as environmentally desirable. Guidelines prepared by the Province of Ontario for the disposal of mine wastes suggests that pyrite removal is a good operating practice which should be encouraged. The State of Wisconsin is currently developing new and comprehensive regulations for the disposal of mining wastes. The preliminary drafts of these regulations also encourage the removal of pyrite, the backfilling of mining excavation with pyritic tailings, the segregation of waste types, and the marketing of mining wastes.

Recognizing these concerns and faced with the need for underground mine backfill, Exxon embarked upon a program to develop procedures which would enable the production of a fill containing a maximum amount of pyrite. These procedures would result in disposal of a minimum amount of pyrite on the surface and the production of a nonsulfide, non-acid generating tailing.

TESTING PROGRAM

In developing the backfill production flowsheet, Exxon relied on laboratory testing, computer simulation of classification circuits, literature, plant visits, and discussion with plant operators.

The flotation and recovery of pyrite was investigated at Lakefield Research using bench scale techniques on diamond drill core from exploration drilling. It was concluded that the acid generation potential for the concentrator tailings could be drastically reduced by pyrite flotation. However, due to the low alkaline content of the tailings, a high level of pyrite recovery was necessary. To produce a completely non-acid generating tailing, the sulfur content had to be reduced to approximately one percent or lower. At the time of this writing, pilot plant tests are underway to confirm the ability to consistently produce low sulfur tailings.

In order to develop predictions of the quantity of fill, the size distribution of the fill, and to design the details of the cyclone classification circuit, a series of computer simulations were performed for Exxon Minerals Company by Krebs Engineers, Menlo Park, California. This computer modeling was considered to be vital in the assessment of the production of mine fill because it was recognized that the ideal conditions experienced in the laboratory desliming tests would give rise to unreasonably high recoveries of mine backfill which would not be attainable in practice. The computer modeling of the final configuration shown in Figure 5 gave rise to the following predictions of plant performance. Based on a concentrator production rate of 9 100 metric tons a day of ore, it was expected that 4 710 metric tons of mine backfill be produced. This represents 41.8 percent of the ore recovered as fill and a utilization of 75.7 percent of the pyrite concentrate. It is expected that this fill would contain approximately 7 percent minus 20 micron material, or about 2 percent minus 10 micron.

THE NEED FOR BACKFILLING

It is proposed that backfilling of mined out stopes with classified mill tailings become an integral part of mining operations planned for the Crandon deposit. The backfill material will be hydraulically transported and placed utilizing a pipeline system interconnecting the underground workings with the mill.

Hydraulically placed backfill has been used by the mining industry for many years. It contributes to the safety of the work force, providing ground support and a working platform from which to conduct operations. The backfill material is required to absorb the transfer of inherent and induced stress supporting the stope walls during subsequent and/or adjacent excavation, thereby reducing dilution, increasing recovery, and contributing to resource conservation.

More recently the utilization of mill tailings as backfill has taken on a greater significance related to environmental considerations in the reduction of surface impoundment areas of mine waste. Ideally, the minimum environmental disturbance would be achieved through the use of the total tailing produced by the mill. However, the mill processing results in the production of a fine fraction or slime which comprises a significant portion of the total tailings. This fine fraction has a detrimental effect on dewatering of backfill underground increasing the chance of segregation and decreasing the strength of the backfill material. The mill processing also results in an increase in "in-situ" porosity of the mill tailing from that of the ore by slightly less than 50 percent (42% to 48%). Therefore, it is highly possible to produce more backfill than can be utilized unless the material is densified.

Traditionally, the mining industry has used deslimed fills rather than densified fills for use underground to enhance mine area stability eliminating the potential for subsidence. Densification of backfill is in the very early stages of research development primarily concerned with electrokinetic and mechanical dewatering of small pours. Therefore, since it is the adopted design policy of the Crandon Project Team to use the most modern but proven technology, the problem resolves in the optimum selection of a classified tailing that reduces to the greatest extent possible the surface waste disposal impact while retaining the integrity of the backfill engineering characteristics.

STUDY PLAN FOR FILL INVESTIGATION

During the preliminary feasibility phase of the project design, the basic mining method and economic production rate was selected. This selection was contingent, in part, upon a backfill product being available in sufficient quantity and having adequate engineering properties for efficient use underground, maximizing the utilization of pyrite concentrate. In order to determine the required information, John D. Smith Engineering Associates Ltd. of Kingston, Ontario, Canada were retained to provide consultation services necessary to obtain and interpret data determined from appropriate testing of mine backfill material produced from mill tailings. The backfill material required for the testing was produced from metallurgical bench scale work conducted on drill core. The results of this testing are discussed within the body of this paper and are considered indicative rather than definitive due to the small amount of backfill material available from the bench scale laboratory activities.

In June through to November of 1980, a 150 millimeter diameter surface core drilling program was conducted, procuring some 30 metric tons of ore for metallurgical testing in a small pilot plant. This pilot plant program is currently in progress. In January 1981, John D. Smith Engineering Associates Ltd. were again contracted to conduct a backfill testing program on tailings material generated by this pilot plant.

The purpose of the program will be to confirm or refute the results of the previous testing program at a higher level of confidence resulting from the acquisition of more data from a larger sample of tailings produced in the pilot plant. The test material generated by a continuous process rather than a batch process, as was the case with previous testing, will, therefore, more closely resemble backfill produced from a full scale operation.

The backfill testing program will be conducted in two phases. The first phase will test a relatively large number of small specimens of material to establish statistically significant data. The second phase will test a scale model of a backfilled stope to confirm that the characteristics determined in the first phase are in fact applicable on a larger scale. The data determined from this program and other test programs currently in progress will be used to update a previous study of the surface effects of mining and will be used in the preliminary design of a backfill plant and distribution system.

Following construction of the backfill system and eventual operation of the facilities, the "in-situ" properties of the backfill material will be investigated. The system will then be adjusted or changed as required to produce an optimum product. Throughout the life of the property, constant monitoring of the system will be maintained to assure quality product production required to meet changing conditions.

TESTING PROCEDURE AND METHODOLOGY

Three major types of fill were tested, namely:

- o Undeslimed stringer and massive pyrite concentrate mixed with plus 30 micron nonpyrite sand.
- o Deslimed stringer and massive pyrite concentrate mixed with plus 30 micron nonpyrite sand.
- o Deslimed final tailing or conventional fill, i.e., zinc final tailing that has not undergone pyrite separation or flotation.

The backfill material was mixed in ratios of 35:65 stringer to massive concentrate, 47:53 stringer to massive concentrate, and 59:41 stringer to massive concentrate to simulate the blends of the two ore types that could be most expected. This was done for the undeslimed and conventional type fills. For the deslimed concentrate fill, only the orebody average 47:53 stringer to massive pyrite concentrate ratio was considered. In addition for the deslimed backfills, the size fractions investigated were nominal plus 10 micron, plus 20 micron, and plus 30 micron.

The samples were received from the metallurgical laboratory in component parts of stringer pyrite concentrate, massive pyrite concentrate, and plus 30 micron nonpyrite sand composite. In the case of the conventional fill, batches of sample were received designated as to size fraction.

Samples were prepared by weighing and mixing component pyrites and sand, then adding water to form a hydraulic mixture at 70 percent pulp density. Each batch was poured into percolation tubes (Figure 7) and a standard percolation test was carried out.

After completion of the above test the batch was remixed and poured into the compression mold arrangement (Figure 8). After a percolation trial under zero load, the loading platen was inserted in the compression mold and the assembly was placed in a loading frame. Axial pressures of 150, 300, 600, and 1000 kPa were applied to each sample in sequence and percolation trials were carried out under each pressure. This particular test evaluates the effect on percolation rate of self-weight compression simulating in-stope conditions. The upper limit of the pressure was estimated using the stope design height of 120 meters considering the limiting effect of arching. Dial gauge readings were used to measure the axial compression of the samples and careful measurement of the initial and final height of the sample allowed the porosity of the samples to be calculated from the dry density or unit weight.

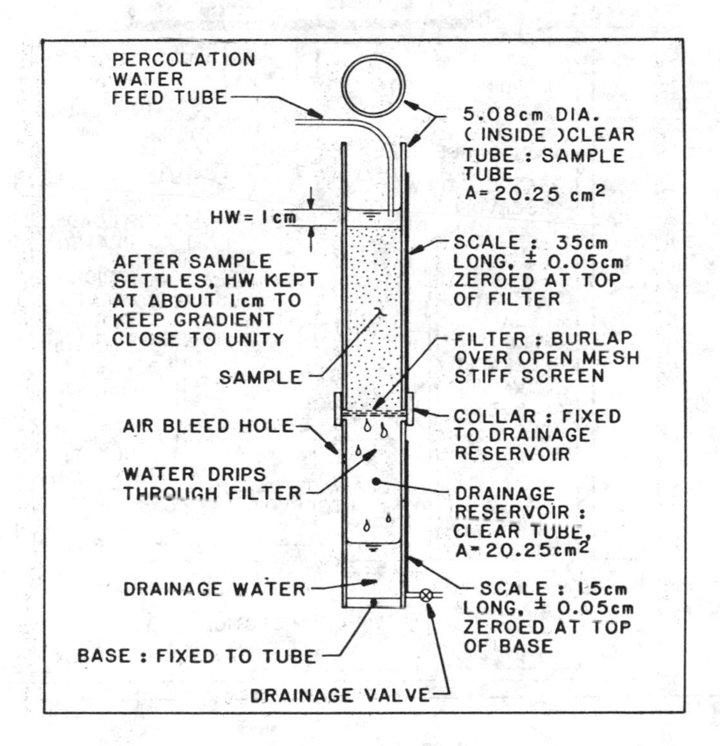

Figure 7 -- Standard Percolation Tube Arrangement

The linear filling rate and the required percolation rate were determined for a range of stope plan areas.

Following the percolation tests, the various test mixtures were combined with normal portland cement in proportions of 10:1, 15:1, 20:1, and 30:1, tailings to cement. Samples of each proportion were prepared and poured into 50 millimeter diameter molds. These samples were subjected to percolation tests and unconfined compression tests. Standard soil mechanics triaxial equipment was used to determine the unconfined strength. The porosities of the cemented samples were calculated from the unit weights of the saturated samples and an estimate made of the tailings to cement ratio required to provide a 120 meter free standing fill height.

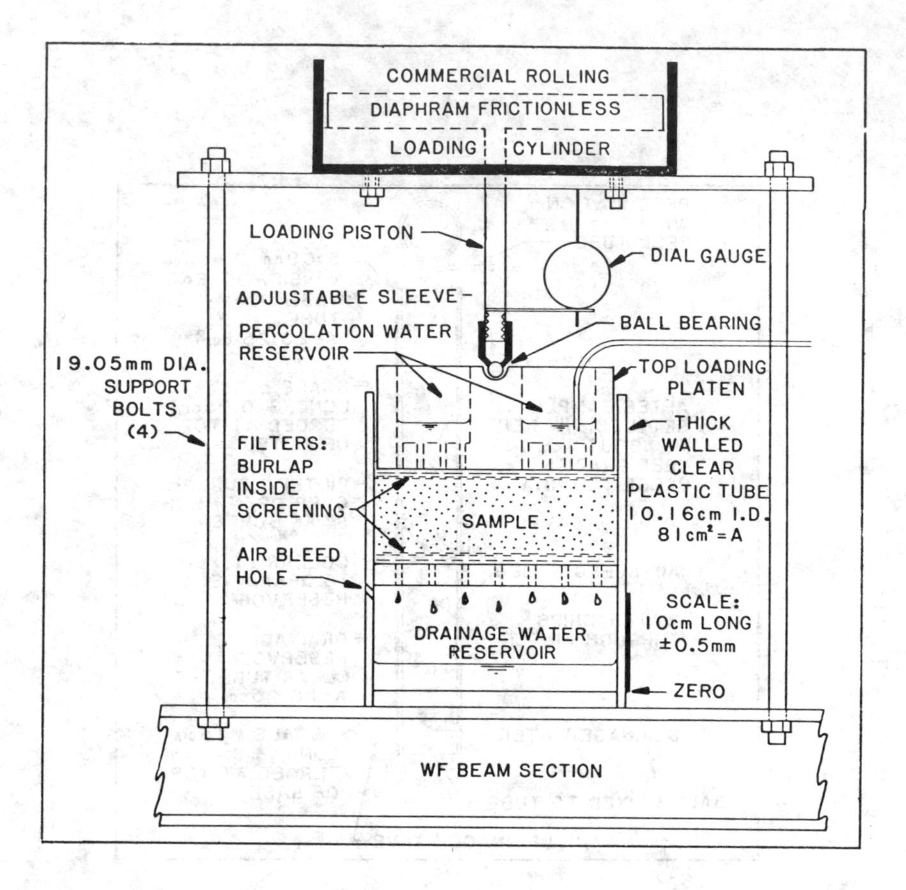

Figure 8 -- Compression-Percolation Apparatus

TEST RESULTS

The differences in the data returned from the percolation and cemented strength tests conducted on various blends of stringer and massive pyrite concentrate were not considered significant and within experimental error of the program. Therefore, for simplification purposes, only that data pertaining to backfill generated from ore blends of 47 percent stringer and 53 percent massive is presented.

Table 1 illustrates the drainage characteristics for the three major types of fill considered. It depicts the reduction in percolation rates and porosities under stress, simulating

TABLE 1

PERCOLATION CHARACTERISTICS OF BACKFILLS INVESTIGATED

TYPE OF FILL	CLASSIFICATION OF PYRITES	PERCOLATION TUBE		COMPRESSION - PERCOLATION (P)/POROSITY (n) AT STRESSES (kPa)									
				0		150		300		600		1000	
		p=cm/hr	n	p=cm/hr	n	p=cm/hr	n	p=cm/hr	n	p=cm/hr	n	p=cm/hr	n
Undeslimed M & S Concentrate	Undeslimed	3.93	.481	4.05	.492	2.18	.465	1.55	.457	1.28	.446	1.05	.439
Deslimed Massive and Stringer Concentrate	+10 μm	7.80	.499	6.61	.475	5.40	.462	4.10	.450	3.55	.438	2.64	.423
	+20 μm	9.25	.498	6.68	.462	5.85	.450	4.72	.440	4.20	.430	3.85	.419
	+30 μm	15.9	.512	14.57	.492	10.30	.475	8.73	.468	8.30	.457	6.50	.447
Deslimed Conventional	+10 μm	3.6	.496	4.60	.494	2.7	.458	2.10	.448	1.9	.435	1.3	.423
	+20 μm	10.9	.505	11.80	.506	6.3	.478	4.90	.470	3.9	.458	3.2	.447
	+30 μm	17.9	.516	14.70	.498	9.8	.475	7.30	.463	5.4	.455	3.8	.448

NOTE: +30 μm sand used as make-up in all pyrite concentrate samples.

self-weight compression and the increases in drainage rates with the utilization of larger size fractions. The table further indicates a general similarity in drainage characteristics between the deslimed massive and stringer concentrate fill and the conventional fill. However, there is distinct improvement in percolation rate, particularly at higher stress level in favor of the deslimed concentrate fill, perhaps indicating greater efficiency associated with the separate desliming process.

Table 2 illustrates the percolation requirements for various stope dimensions against the range of percolation rates available for the fill types noted. Of particular note is that the undeslimed backfill will not be free draining for even the largest stopes. The plus 20 micron and plus 10 micron fills have very similar drainage requirements and will be free draining for those stopes average in size or larger. The plus 30 micron fill can be considered free draining for all stopes having stope areas greater than 460 square meters. In actual fact, for all practical purposes, this fill can be considered free draining for all size stopes since stopes having an average area of less than 460 square meters are few in number.

Only tube percolation rate tests were conducted on the cemented backfill mixes. The reasoning behind this procedure is that the rate of cement strength gain in cemented fill generally exceeds the rate of stress increase due to filling such that self-weight consolidation does not occur to the same degree as it does in uncemented backfills. The results of percolation rate tests are illustrated in Figure 9. The data indicated that only the conventional type fill with a 20:1 tailings to cement ratio deslimed at plus 30 micron would be free draining over reasonable pour or curing times for average size stopes. All other types of cemented fill would require decant facilities in the form of drain towers even for the largest size stopes.

The results of the unconfined compressive strength tests are shown in Figure 10. These results are for 28 day curing times representing approximately 75 percent of the compressive strength that can be expected over long-term durations. It was assumed initially that the strengths developed from conventional fill would be very much the same as those returned from the deslimed pyrite concentrate fills.

Such was not the case. Indeed, the difference in strength between the conventional finer splits of plus 10 micron and plus 20 micron was even greater in favor of the deslimed pyrite concentrate fill. Suspecting chemical retardation due to sulfate attack some of the conventional fill material deslimed at plus 30 micron was mixed with type 50 sulfate resistant cement. However, the sulfate resistant cement provided only a marginal improvement in the strength of the conventional fill. Therefore, it was tenatively

TABLE 2

STOPE DRAINAGE REQUIREMENTS FOR BACKFILLS INVESTIGATED

TYPE OF FILL	CLASSIFICATION OF PYRITES	RANGE OF PERCOLATION RATES 0 kPa – 300 kPa – 1000 kPa	PERCOLATION REQUIREMENTS FOR STOPE AREAS OF:						
			135 m^2 Strike Length x HW to FW Dist. 45 m x 3 m p=cm/hr	276 m^2 Strike Length x HW to FW Dist. 45 m x 6.13 m p=cm/hr	460 m^2 Strike Length x HW to FW Dist. 45 m x 10.2 m p=cm/hr	828 m^2 Strike Length x HW to FW Dist. 45 m x 18.4 m p=cm/hr	1104 m^2 Strike Length x HW to FW Dist. 45 m x 24.5 m p=cm/hr	1710 m^2 Strike Length x HW to FW Dist. 45 m x 38 m p=cm/hr	2700 m^2 Strike Length x HW to FW Dist. 45 m x 60 m p=cm/hr
Undeslimed Massive and Stringer Concentrate	Undeslimed	4.05-1.55-1.05	58.31	28.5	17.1	9.46	7.02	4.58	2.87
Deslimed Massive and Stringer Concentrate	+10 m	6.61-4.10-2.64	41.21	20.09	12.06	6.69	5.04	3.28	2.04
	+20 m	6.68-4.72-3.85	41.82	20.45	12.26	6.82	5.11	3.31	2.09
	+30 m	14.7-7.30-3.8	28.90	14.11	8.47	4.70	3.54	2.29	1.43

NOTE: Drainage requirements for conventional fill very much similar to deslimed massive and stringer concentrate fill.

2700 m^2 represents maximum stope area available

1710 m^2 represents average stope area available

135 m^2 represents minimum stope area available (3 m = minimum mining width)

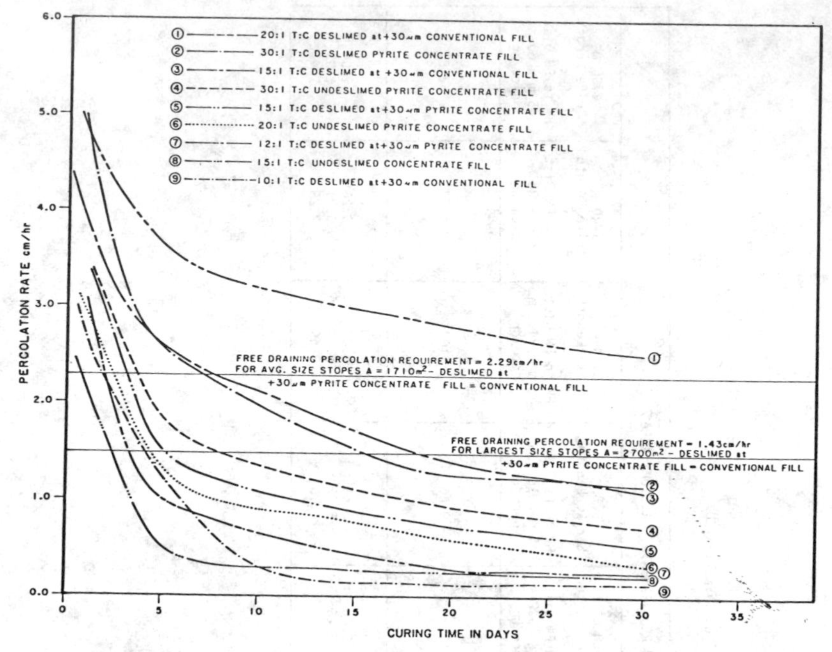

Figure 9 -- Cemented Backfill Percolation Test Data

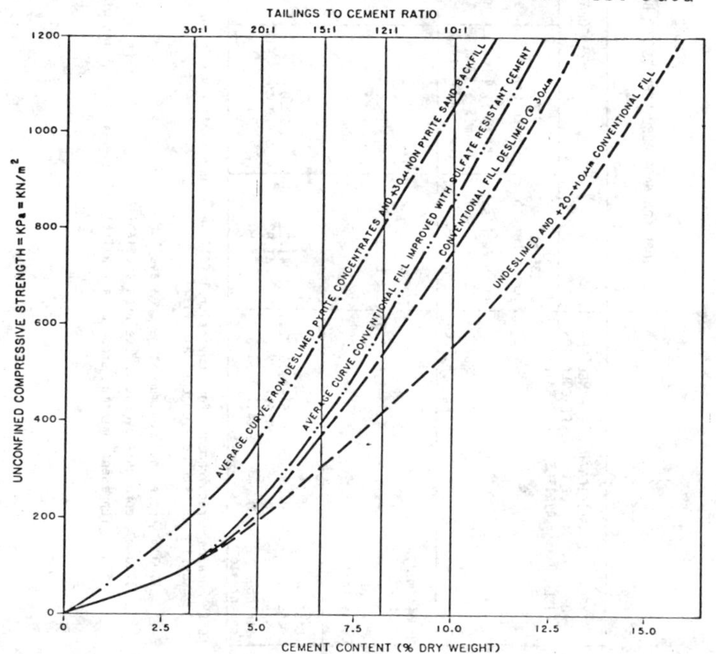

Figure 10 - Cemented Backfill Strength Test Data

concluded that the separate desliming process removed a greater percentage of the very fine pyrites that could be responsible for the cement retardation.

From the above results, the following cement percentage requirements for free standing fill heights of 120 meters were calculated over a range of hanging wall to footwall widths of 15 meters to 76 meters:

Backfill Type	Cement Requirements
Undeslimed Pyrite Concentrate	$7.5\% \leq \%\text{cement} \geq 15\%$
Deslimed Conventional	$6.0\% \leq \%\text{cement} \geq 11.25\%$
Deslimed Pyrite Concentrate	$4.75\% \leq \%\text{cement} \geq 9.75\%$

SELECTION OF DESIGN CRITERIA

It was thought appropriate at the completion of the program to select design criteria such that the parameters so selected could be input into the conceptual engineering of the surface facilities and give direction to future backfill testing programs.

Considering the undeslimed pyrite concentrate backfill, more volume will be generated for backfill than is required to fill all voids. Certainly, there is a greater utilization of pyrite in that the in-place dry density is greater for the undeslimed fill than the deslimed fill. However, this difference is not significant when compared to the plus 10 micron and plus 20 micron deslimed backfills since the in-place porosities are very much similar.

The percolation rates of the undeslimed material are very much reduced. In fact, a factor of five exists between the percolation rates required and the available percolation rate, even for the largest stopes. The addition of cement, in whatever ratio, creates an even less favorable situation. In addition, the cemented strengths of this fill were significantly lower than the other backfills tested.

It was concluded that the undeslimed backfill alternative could be eliminated since it would require the use of non-proven technology such as "dense phase flow" or mechanical dewatering techniques. If these techniques were utilized, extensive monitoring and precautions in the form of reinforced cement bulkheads would be required to guard against and withstand the possible buildup of hydrostatic heads due to resaturation and liquefication. A system designed to utilize the undeslimed backfill would be more costly, less efficient, and impart an element of risk. The utilization of this backfill in the cemented condition would also be more costly since more cement would be required to produce a free standing fill height of 120 meters.

Comparing the deslimed massive and stringer pyrite concentrate mixed with plus 30 micron nonpyrite sand and the conventional fill, the differences in the drainage characteristics tested were marginal. However, there were significant differences in cemented strengths in favor of the deslimed concentrate fill. In addition, the in-place densities of the deslimed pyrite concentrate mixed with plus 30 micron sand were greater than that of the conventional fill providing for greater underground utilization of pyrite, lessening the surface environmental impact. It is considered that the separate desliming process will cost more, but a better product will result providing a savings in underground cement and surface tailings pond costs.

Concluding that the deslimed pyrite concentrate mixed with plus 30 micron sand is superior to the conventional backfill, there remains the choice of the desliming size fraction.

In the uncemented condition, the plus 10 micron and plus 20 micron material will not have free drainage for stopes with less than 40 meter hanging wall to footwall widths. With the addition of cement in any ratio there will be no free drainage for reasonable periods of time required for stope backfill pours. Also with the addition of cement there will be a possible reduction in compressive strength due to the larger amount of fines. In addition, there will be more backfill produced than can be utilized to fill all voids. The only positive factor in favor of the plus 10 micron and plus 20 micron backfill is that the in-place dry densities are 11 percent greater.

The plus 30 micron backfill material will be free draining in the uncemented condition for a greater variance in stope dimensions and in the cemented condition at 20:1 tailings to cement ratios will be free draining for stopes of average size and larger.

It is possible that the bench scale desliming efficiencies are greater than that which may be experienced in actual practice. With this consideration in mind, it would appear prudent to choose the plus 30 micron material as the starting point for design, reserving the flexibility to produce and utilize a finer fraction where and when applicable. This consideration would be especially important in the design of a backfill recycle system. This proposed system possibly requiring regrinding and the use of long transport pipelines from the impoundment areas back to the backfill plant would give rise to a greater production of fines.

CONCLUSIONS

A mine backfill preparation circuit has been developed capable of producing sufficient quantities of fill having suitable engineering properties required for underground use at the Crandon Project. The implementation of this process predicts the production of a massive and stringer pyrite concentrate mixed with nonpyrite sand deslimed at plus 30 micron. The system will be designed such that plus 20 micron and plus 10 micron pyrite concentrate can be obtained when applicable, optimizing underground utilization. The residual tailing from the process requiring surface impoundment will, therefore, contain a significantly reduced quantity of pryite, materially reducing the potential for acid generation, heavy metal leaching, and other environmental problems. An added advantage of this process is the segregation of the fine pyrite concentrate which can be directed into a separate surface storage area.

ACKNOWLEDGMENTS

The writers wish to acknowledge those who assisted in the preparation of this paper and to thank Exxon Minerals Company for the opportunity to present it at the 1981 Rapid Excavation and Tunneling Conference.

19

New Developments in Underground Methods

Chairmen: C.R. Peterson
J. Henneke

Chapter 81

DEVELOPMENT OF AN EXTRUDED TUNNEL LINING SYSTEM

by Douglas W. Ounanian, Joseph S. Boyce, Dr. Kenneth Maser

Project Engineer, Materials and Structures Division
Program Manager, Materials and Structures Division
Manager, Materials and Structures Division

Foster-Miller Associates, Inc.
Waltham, Massachusetts

ABSTRACT

Foster-Miller Associates, Inc. (FMA), under contract to the Department of Transportation (DOT) and the Urban Mass Transit Administration (UMTA), is currently developing an Extruded Tunnel Lining System (ETLS). The ETLS would reduce ground support costs in machine bored tunneling by eliminating the need for temporary support, and by slipforming the final concrete lining directly behind the Tunnel Boring Machine (TBM). The system can advance at variable rates, from 0.6 to 3.7 m (2 to 12 ft) per hr, by combining three systems: a very high early strength concrete, continuously produced and delivered by a concrete process system; a slipform/bulkhead system for supporting the concrete prior to strength gain and exposure; and a control system for form/bulkhead alignment and concrete process control. Large-scale tests are planned to demonstrate the system in a 3 m (10-ft) diameter steel "tunnel".

INTRODUCTION

The ETLS Concept

The ETLS is a system which continuously slipforms a cast-in-place concrete tunnel liner directly behind a TBM. Figure 1 shows an artist's perspective of the slipform system. The system operates as follows: concrete raw materials are delivered separately or partially premixed to the heading. A special, pumpable, rapid-set concrete is mixed at the heading and pumped through a placing line. The placing line delivers the concrete through a sealed bulkhead into the annulus formed by the slipform and the tunnel wall. The plastic concrete is

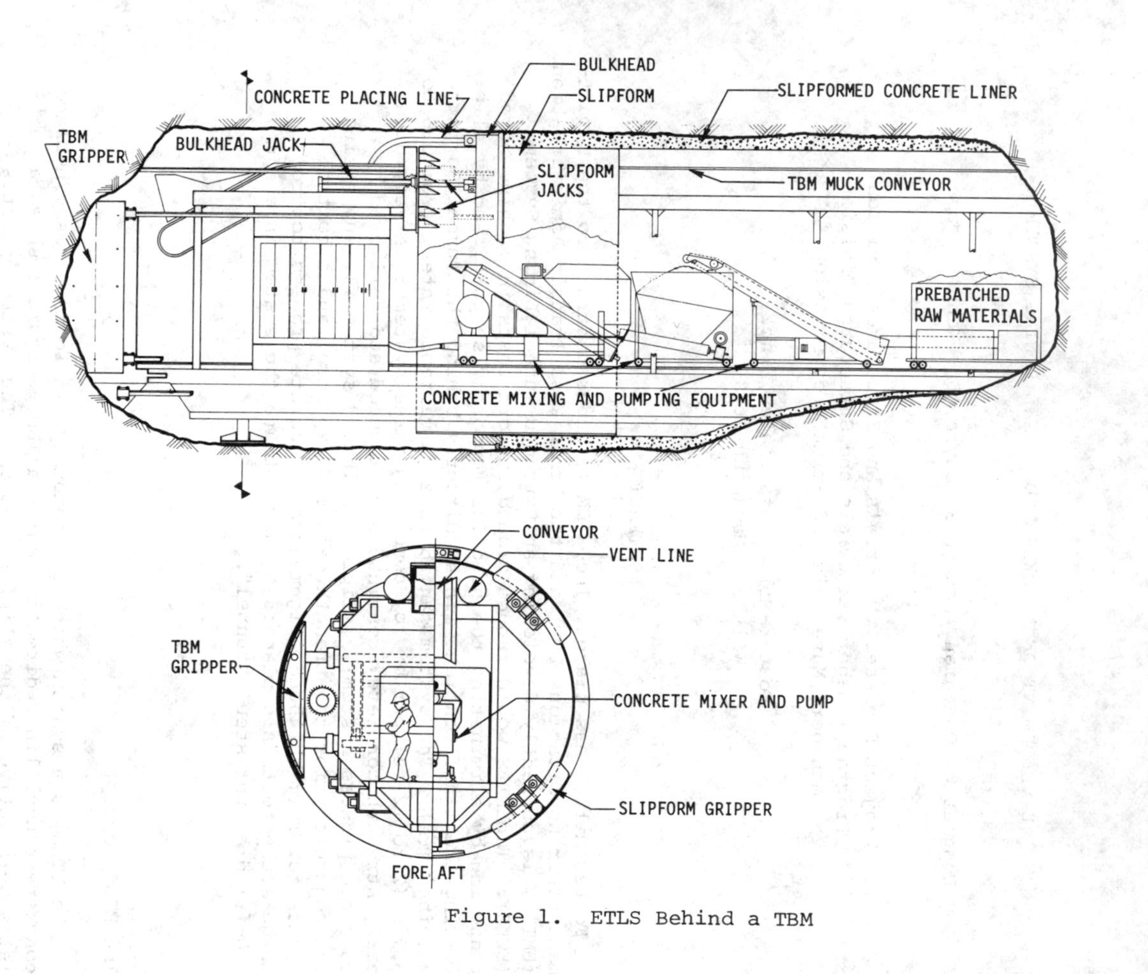

Figure 1. ETLS Behind a TBM

distributed by pressure, with the assistance of gravity, around the circumference of the form. The form is connected to the TBM through actuators that advance it at a steady rate, which averages over the TBM shoves. The concrete properties are such that, for average TBM advance rates of 0.6 to 3.8 m (2 to 12 ft) per hr, the concrete is self-supporting when it is exposed from behind the moving slipform.

Figure 2 shows a cross-section of the operational cycle (note from Figure 1 that the bulkhead is connected to the slipform through its own actuators and can move independently of the slipform). In Figure 2 a cycle begins when concrete is pumped through the bulkhead. The concrete pressure drives the bulkhead forward, and fresh concrete fills the annular space. The form remains stationary until the concrete is old enough to be self-supporting. At this point, bulkhead and slipform move together. This is the steady state slipforming operation (c), which can continue indefinitely until a shutdown, planned or unplanned, occurs. A shutdown is initiated (d), by ending the concrete delivery. The bulkhead motion then stops, but the slipform continues to move until all of the remaining concrete is exposed. If the shutdown is short-lived, concrete pumping can resume before (e), and the steady state mode can gradually be restored.

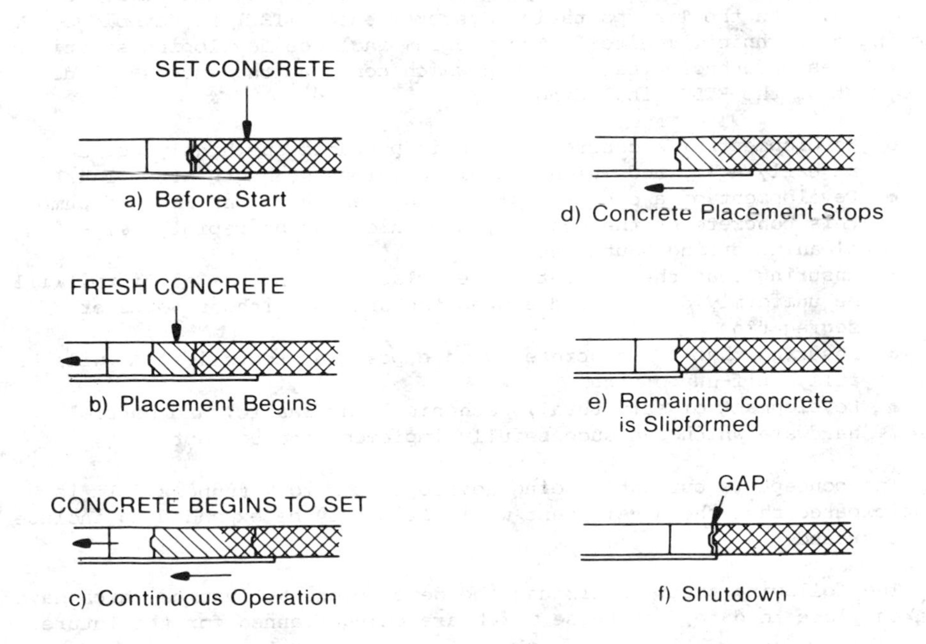

Figure 2. Slipforming Sequence

System Rationale

The motivation for developing the ETLS concept is economic. Simply stated, the system combines an ability to place the final lining directly behind the TBM with the economics of cast-in-place construction. This means:

- No primary support system
- Tunnel complete when bore is complete (time = $)
- No factory costs for precasting or unnecessary steel for handling
- No gaskets or assembly hardware (precast)
- Minimum lining thickness, as required by ground load alone
- No grouting or backpacking required, since concrete is placed under pressure.

Preliminary estimates show that tunnel costs using the ETLS can be reduced by 20% as compared to using precast concrete liners.

Technological Developments

The ETLS is a concept which is currently being developed into hardware by FMA. This development program is currently sponsored by DOT and UMTA, with the Transportation Systems Center (TSC) in Cambridge, MA acting as technical monitor. The program includes developing solutions to the basic technological problems which confront the successful deployment of the ETLS, including:

- Development of a concrete which is pumpable and highly workable at early ages, and which rapidly develops strength after 1 hr
- Development of a concrete process system which can mix and pump this concrete at the heading, and which can be rapidly self-cleaning during shutdowns
- Ensuring that the concrete, when placed behind the slipform, will be uniformly distributed around the annulus without voids or segregation
- Ensuring that the concrete, when exposed by the slipform, will be fully self-supporting
- Development of structural, mechanical, hydraulic, and control hardware which can successfully implement the concept.

The concept is currently being developed for rock tunnels. It is anticipated that the development will ultimately be expanded to include soft ground.

The following sections discuss the development activities which have taken place to date, and those which are being planned for the future.

CONCEPT DEVELOPMENT

ETLS Specifications

The specifications for the ETLS are based on background information gained from a state-of-the-art review combined with an assessment for an economically attractive system. The specifications are oriented toward urban rapid transit tunnel applications, but do not exclude other possible applications. The specifications, summarized in Table 1, are divided into the following categories:

- Tunneling conditions - Defines the ground conditions and environment in which the ETLS must function
- Tunnel Boring Machine - Defines TBM performance and design parameters which impact ETLS design requirements
- Tunnel Lining System - Defines the design and operational requirements for the ETLS components
- Liner Concrete - Defines the concrete mix and performance requirements.

Liner Design Criteria

Tunnel liners have generally been designed as a relatively rigid structure with an assumed vertical load and a horizontal load equal to some fraction of the vertical load. This approach does not fully account for the ground-liner interaction and has lead to overly conservative liner designs. This conservatism has not introduced additional costs, since the final cast-in-place liner thickness is often controlled by placement techniques and space constraints imposed by the primary support structure. The liner is often thicker than that specified by the conservative design approach. It is not uncommon to require at least a 300-mm (12-in.) liner thickness for a 6.1 m (20-ft) diameter tunnel.

The ETLS will take the place of both the primary and secondary ground support systems, eliminating the minimum thickness requirement imposed by conventional placement space constraints. Thus, it is advantageous to investigate the use of thinner liners.

Analysis techniques developed through research (Paul, et al., 1974; Brierley, 1975; Deere, et al., 1969) over the past several years, which account for ground-liner interaction, are currently finding acceptance in the tunneling industry. These techniques show it is possible to specify liner thicknesses which are significantly thinner than those specified conventionally if the liner is designed to be flexible relative to rock mass it supports. This type of analysis has been used to evaluate linings for the Washington metro stations (Brierley, 1975).

In the first phase of the present ETLS program now underway, liner thickness, strength, and reinforcement requirements were developed (Doherty, et al., 1979). It was concluded that a 150-mm (6-in.) thick,

TABLE 1. ETLS Specifications

Tunneling Conditions	
Rock type and quality	Any that can be machine bored
Depth of cover	One diameter to any depth where squeezing ground is not encountered
Water inflow	Any that can be handled in a TBM operation
Maximum external head for a water tight tunnel	30 m (100 ft) on final liner
Nominal bore diameter	4.6 to 6.4 m (15 to 21 ft)
Bore diameter variation	-300 mm in 30 m (-1 1/2 in. in 100 ft)
Bore surface roughness	13 to 25 mm (1/2 to 1 in.) maximum pitch
Rock temperature	10 to 21°C (50 to 70°F)
Ambient temperature	13 to 32°C (55 to 90°F)
Minimum tunnel radius of curvature	229 m (750 ft)
Tunnel Boring Machine	
Type	Any
Maximum advance rate	3.7 m per hr (12 fph)
Gripper slip	
Longitudinal	25 to 51 mm (1 to 2 in.)
Cimcumferential	6 to 13 mm (1/4 to 1/2 in.)
TBM deviation from alignment bullseye	76 mm (3 in.)
TBM backup for cutter replacement	1.2 m (4 ft) maximum
Shove length	0.6 to 1.8 m (2 to 6 ft)
Routine shutdown period	15 min to 2 hr
Lining System	
Lining thickness	150 to 300 mm (6 to 12 in.)
Variation in lining thickness across tunnel section	±76 mm (±3 in.)
Maximum lining rate	3.7 m per hr (12 fph)
Minimum lining rate	0.6 m per hr (2 fph)
Lining system to TBM travel	2.4 m (8 ft)
Lining Material	
Concrete workability	20 to 25 min
Tolerance on concrete set time	40 to 60 min
Final concrete strength (f'_c)	28 to 41 MPa (4000 to 6000 psi)

unreinforced liner was adequate for this application. This conclusion was derived by estimating rock loads to which the ETLS liner will be subjected along with liner behavior under these loads. The moments and thrusts resulting from different loading conditions were compared to the capacity of several plain and steel fiber reinforced liner sections.

In order to compare imposed loads to liner section capacity, a moment-thrust or interaction diagram was used. Figure 3 shows a typical moment-thrust envelope developed from experimental data (Paul and Ferrera-Boza, 1975) for 150-mm (6-in.) thick plain and fiber reinforced liner sections. The two loading paths that appear on the figure were developed for both uniform and concentrated rock loads determined from an analysis developed by others (Cording, et al., 1976). In addition to the two types of rock loadings shown, two additional design points identify thrust and moment values for rock load plus a hydrostatic head of 30 m (100 ft). In all loading conditions the failure envelope is not approached for either the plain or reinforced sections. Serviceability of the plain concrete liner is assured by the significant margin between design moment and thrust and the plain concrete cracking envelope.

The failure envelope for the fiber reinforced concrete section shows the most increase in capacity below the balance point. This would indicate that fiber reinforcement will contribute very little to the liner capacity in supporting rock that has been machine bored. In addition, experimental results (Paul and Ferrara-Boza, 1975) show that the addition of fibers neither changes the failure mode of the liner nor significantly increases its strength. In this regard, steel fiber reinforcement has not been recommended for use in ETLS liner concrete for rock tunnels.

Concrete Formulation Tests

Concrete for the tunnel liner must develop the final strength required to support the long-term loads described under the heading "Liner Design Criteria" above. In addition, the concrete must gain strength rapidly enough to support any initial loads imposed on it as it leaves the slipform. In most TBM driven tunnels the initial rock load is minimal requiring that the liner need only be self-supporting upon extrusion (Doherty, et al., 1979); however, loads imposed by other tunnel driving support equipment, such as muck cars, must be supported by the liner at early ages requiring the concrete to exhibit rapid early strength development.

The concrete material properties for the tunnel liner are summarized by the following:

- Workability - The concrete should be proportioned for pumpability and remain workable for proper consolidation
- Set Control - Concrete should set in a range of 20 to 40 min.

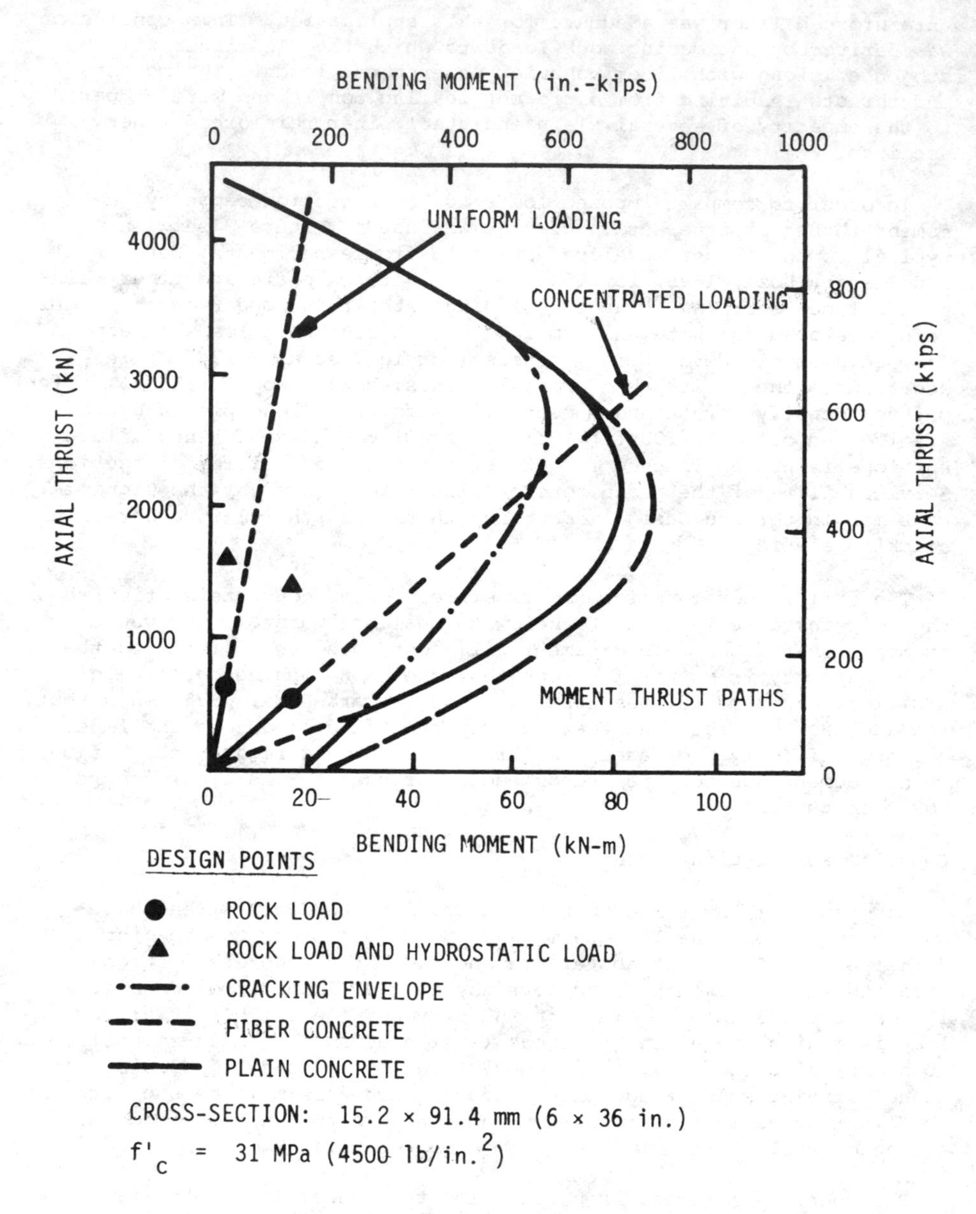

Figure 3. Evaluation of Liner Capacity

- Ultimate strength - Concrete compressive strength should be at least 35 MPa (5000 psi) at 28 days
- Durability - The constituents of the mix should be compatible and produce a durable liner resistant to water and groundwater sulfates.

Four cement candidates were chosen for testing to meet the above requirements:

- Aluminous cement
- Portland Type III cement
- Combinations of portland Type I and aluminous cements
- Very high early cement.

A laboratory testing program was conducted to evaluate these materials. Cement candidates were tested for time of setting to eliminate materials that were unable to meet the set requirement. Workability tests and preliminary strength-time tests were conducted on the most promising candidates. Extensive mix design trials and long-term strength and durability tests were performed on the final mix candidate.

Very high early cement (VHEC) was chosen for the final mix design. VHEC concrete met all of the behavioral requirements. The final mix design appears in Table 2. Strength-time testing results appear in Table 3, and the development of compressive strength with time is shown in Figure 4.

TABLE 2. Final Mix Design*

	Mix Materials, kg per cu m (lb per cu yd)						
Water-Cement Ratio	Water	Cement	Fly Ash	Sand**	Gravel**	Citric Acid	Lomar D Liquid
0.40	460 (273)	1030 (611)	160 (94)	2175 (1290)	2655 (1575)	2.5 (1.5)	23.8 (14.1)

Notes: *Properties of fresh concrete: Air content, percent - 4.6; Slump - 180 mm (7 in.); Unit weight - 2285 kg per cu m (142.5 lb per cu ft)

**Saturated, Surface Dry.

TABLE 3. Compression and Flexural Strength of the VHEC Concrete

	Strength, MPa (psi)								
	1-1/2 Hr	2 Hr	3 Hr	4 Hr	1 Day	3 Days	7 Days	28 Days	90 Days
Compression*	0.9 (125)	8.9 (1295)	19 (2694)	22 (3242)	27 (3867)	30 (4298)	33 (4828)	36 (5271)	43 (6255)
Flexural**	0.5 (74)	1.7 (251)	2.6 (377)	3.1 (444)	3.5 (508)	4.0 (577)	4.4 (644)	6.1 (890)	5.8 (839)

*150 mm diam × 300 mm long (6 × 12 in.) cylinders.
**150 × 150 × 530 mm (6 × 6 × 21 in.) beam.

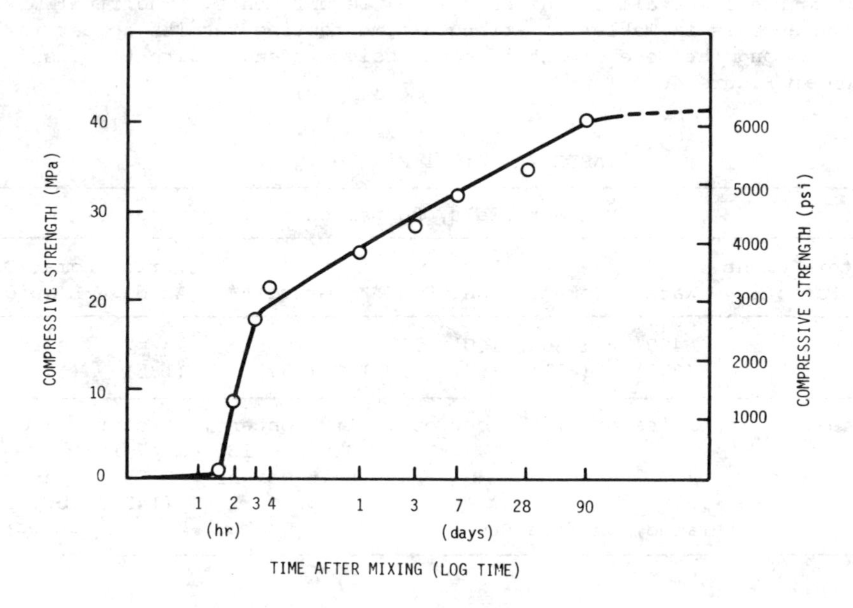

Figure 4. Strength Versus Time of VHEC Concrete

Distribution Tests

A series of tests were conducted to study the manner in which concrete would be distributed within the slipform behind an advancing bulkhead. Since only a limited amount of information was available regarding concrete placement within a closed form, a number of distribution tests were conducted. The effects of concrete mix workability, bulkhead vibration, pumping pressure, and bulkhead advance rate on distribution were studied.

A distribution rig was designed to simulate placement of concrete in a closed form behind a moving bulkhead. The rig measured 3 m (10 ft) long by 1.2 m (4 ft) wide and 150 mm (6 in.) thick. The bulkhead surface was outfitted with pressure transducers and form vibrators. Concrete was pumped into the rig through a concrete inlet port at the top of the test rig bulkhead.

At the start of each test, the bulkhead was positioned 150 mm (6 in.) away from the end of the form. Once the initial cavity was filled the bulkhead was advanced, that is, pushed away from the end plate by the concrete being pumped into the form.

A total of three distribution tests were conducted. No difficulty was encountered filling the form and maintaining it completely filled as the bulkhead advanced. Both portland Type I and VHEC concretes were used in the tests. Tests were conducted at advance rates of 0.9 to 2.7 m per hr (3 to 9 ft per hr). Form pressure was varied from 70 to 175 kPa (10 to 25 psi) by applying back pressure through the bulkhead. Bulkhead vibrators were operated for brief periods; however, the results indicated vibration was not necessary. After the slab was removed from the distribution rig, core samples were taken which verified proper consolidation.

Slipforming Tests

A series of slipforming tests was conducted to investigate the following areas in which no data was known to exist. The objectives of the tests are described by the following:

- Test the independent slipform and bulkhead concept for horizontal slipforming
- Demonstrate self-support of rapid setting concrete after it leaves the slipform
- Study the effect of form pressure on concrete compaction and finished liner quality
- Provide data on form drag.

A total of seven independent slipforming tests were conducted in both simulated invert and crown configurations.

The slipforming test rig used for the testing is shown in Figure 5. The test bed has a trapezoidal cross-section nominally 1.4 m (4.5 ft)

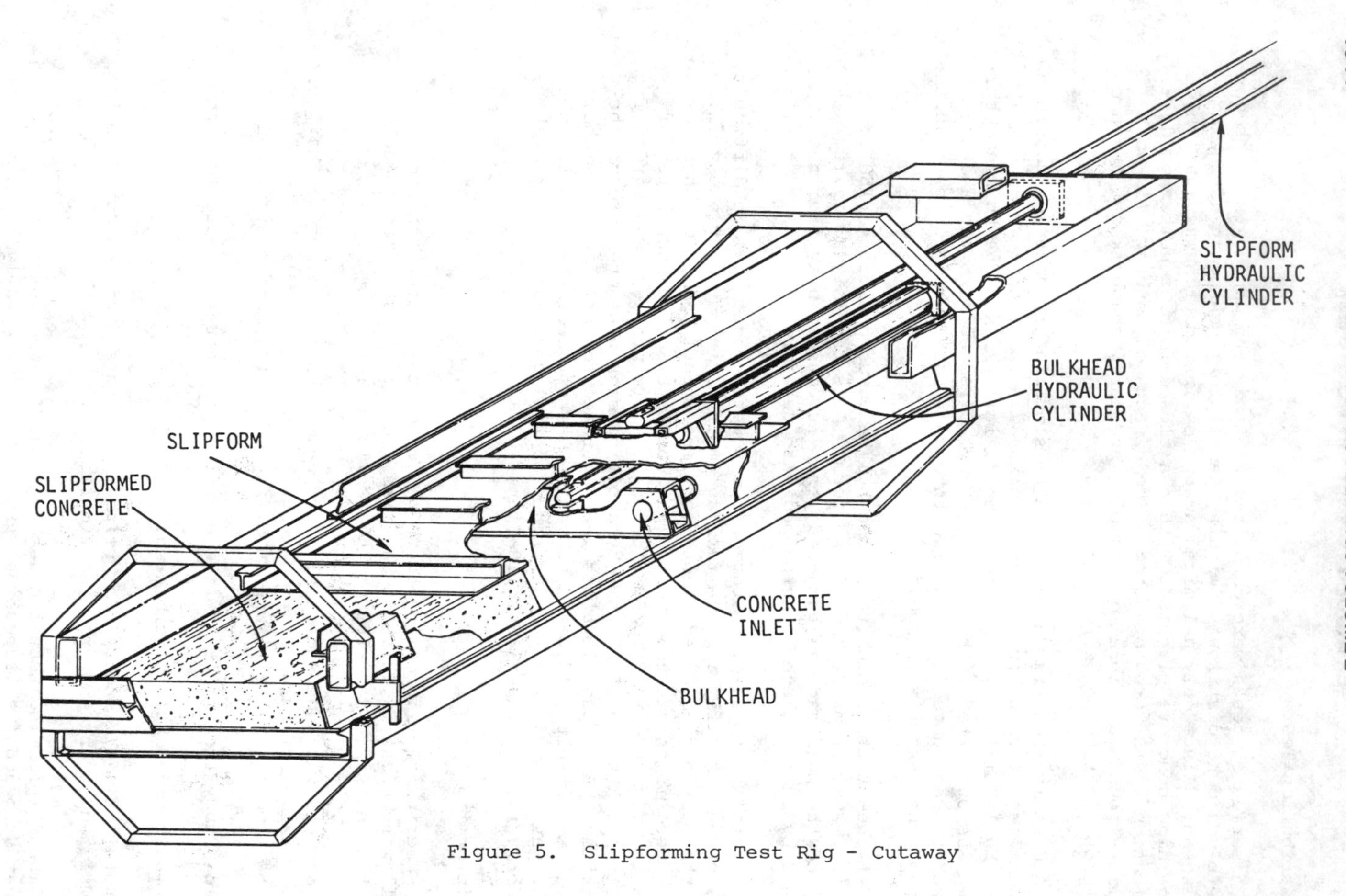

Figure 5. Slipforming Test Rig - Cutaway

wide and 200 mm (8 in.) thick which represents a 24° arc of a 6.1 m (20 ft) tunnel liner. The test rig can cast up to a 3.7 m (12 ft) long segment. The entire test rig can be rotated to simulate five circumferential sections of a cast tunnel liner.

The slipform is simulated by a steel plate with 0.9 m (3-ft) straight section and 1.2 m (4-ft) tapered section. The taper can be varied from 0 to 43 mm per meter (0 to 0.5 in. per ft). The pressure on the slipform is reacted by overhead tracks which are coated with a material having a low coefficient of sliding friction so as not to significantly effect the measurements of form to concrete friction. The slipform is moved parallel to the bed of the test rig by a hydraulic cylinder. The rate of flow of hydraulic fluid to the cylinder is regulated so that the desired form advance speed can be maintained.

The bulkhead is contoured to match the slab cross section. The bulkhead is connected to the slipform by a hydraulic cylinder which enables it to move independently of the slipform.

The bulkhead and slipform advance rate are variable between 0.3 and 3 m per hr (1 and 10 ft per hr).

Of the total of seven slipform tests, three were conducted in the invert configuration and four were conducted in the crown configuration. The first test was conducted with portland Type I concrete; the remaining were conducted with the final VHEC mix design (Table 2).

The tests demonstrated the feasibility of slipforming a well-consolidated section of rapid setting concrete. Specifically, the results of the slipforming tests are summarized by the following:

- Rapid setting VHEC concrete can support itself in the crown configuration approximately 1 hr after mixing (see Figure 6).
- Form pressure of about 70 to 105 kPa (10 to 15 psi) is required for proper consolidation and liner quality.
- Form taper may allow sloughing of the crown section and should not be used.
- The slipformed surface of the concrete is smooth without irregularities or voids.
- Heat of hydration of older-setting concrete, tends to accelerate the younger concrete.
- Estimates of form drag indicate that a force of about 710 to 890N (80 to 100 tons) will be necessary to advance a 6.1 m (20-ft) diam system.

Figure 6. VHEC Concrete Slab 1 hr After Slipforming

PROTOTYPE EQUIPMENT DEVELOPMENT AND TESTING

Laboratory Test Facility

To demonstrate the ETLS concept conclusively, a series of tests have been planned using a 1/2-scale, 3 m (10-ft) diam ETLS. The tests will be conducted indoors, in a special test facility set up to serve as a mock tunnel. The goal of the 1/2-scale tests will be solely to demonstrate the technique as a means of placing a continuous liner. The mock tunnel is an idealized environment in which the ETLS will not be subjected to rock loads, water intrusion, slough zones, and TBM vibration.

The test facility shown in Figure 7 is a sectioned, reinforced steel cylinder 3 m (10-ft) in diameter and 6.7 m (22-ft) in length. The inside of the cylinder is smooth to allow the slipforming concept to be tested independent of the sealing difficulties which would be encountered in an actual tunnel. The test tunnel has removable top covers so that the placed liners may be readily inspected and demolished.

Also part of the test facility is a simulated TBM, which is simply a steel frame structure on which the hydraulic jacks for advancing the ETLS will be mounted. Jack loads will be reacted back into the test tunnel by a skid made up of 300 mm (12-in.) wide flange beams. The jack mounting frame will be attached to the skid in such a way as to permit it to be repositioned during slipforming to simulate a TBM shove.

Figure 7. Foster-Miller ETLS Test Facility

One-Half Scale Extruded Tunnel Liner System

The equipment which comprises the 1/2-scale ETLS consists primarily of the slipform, bulkhead, and associated hardware; and the concrete mixing and placing equipment. Additionally, there is a variety of instrumentation which will be used to monitor the laboratory tests, most of which would not be present on a full size machine.

The slipforming hardware consists of the following:

- A 3 m (10-ft) diam, 3.6 m (12-ft) long, 3 mm (1/8 in.) taper slipform; made in four equal sectors from 25 mm (1 in.) thick cold rolled plate, with two hinged joints and two bolted joints, flanged on the leading end to receive the bulkhead jacks, positioned laterally by a system of eight pillow blocks on the leading end, and weighing about 7260 kg (16,000 lb)
- A bulkhead of one piece construction with low friction plastic and inflatable rubber seals inside and outside, two 76 mm (3 in.) concrete placing ports at 180° apart which can be placed either top and bottom or side to side, and eight pneumatic vibrators
- Four 150 mm (6 in.) bore, 76 mm (3 in.) rod, 3.6 m (12 ft) stroke hydraulic cylinders, mounted on the simulated TBM, for slipform actuation
- Four 100 mm (4 in.) bore, 64 mm (2-1/2 in.) rod, 3.6 m (12 ft) stroke hydraulic cylinders, mounted on the slipform, for bulkhead actuation
- A hydraulic power supply for synchronizing each group of four cylinders, synchronization being accomplished by slaving two cylinders in each group to a lead pressure control cylinder, using position servos; with the fourth cylinder connected in parallel to the lead.

The concrete mixing and placing equipment consists of: proportioning lift auger mixer; peristaltic concrete pump; a 76 mm (3 in.) port slide valve; tethered go-devil with recovery winch; and microprocessor controlled admixture and water pumps.

The concrete mixing scheme revolves around the delivery of aggregates in "prebatch" form. The prebatch consists of sand, 10 mm (3/8 in.) stone, 19 mm (3/4 in.) stone, flyash and a portion of the mix water combined to form a mixture which has sufficient cohesiveness to allow it to be moved and metered using conventional techniques. The use of prebatch offers tremendous simplification in the design of the in-tunnel mixing equipment in that only cement, admixtures, and the remaining mix water need be added at the heading.

Tests done to date with this material have shown that the 10 mm (3/8 in.) stone is retained readily in the prebatch, however, 19 mm (3/4 in.) bank-run material has shown a tendency to segregate during handling. It is hoped these problems can be solved through further testing and careful design of the moving and metering equipment.

The ability to deal expeditiously with shutdowns and concrete line blockages is also important to the success of the ETLS. When using VHEC it is desirable to keep placing lines as short as practicable for maximum workability at entry to the form, and also to initiate an immediate purge of all lines and equipment immediately following a shutdown. To this end, a placing system which includes a 76 mm (3 in.) port slide valve and a tethered go-devil has been designed (see Figure 8) and tested successfully.

Sealing Between the Bulkhead and the Tunnel Wall

Development work is in progress on a seal to prevent paste from escaping between the bulkhead and tunnel wall. The seal will be required to maintain effective sealing while passing over a slough or area of gripper damage which is 76 mm (3 in.) deep by 0.6 m (2 ft) wide by 0.9 m (3 ft) high. Larger sloughs would have to be patched ahead of the ETLS using conventional techniques. Desired seal life expectancy is from 150 m (500 ft) to 600 m (2000 ft) depending on rock conditions. Brush seals, with the brushes embedded in a rubber matrix, are the most promising designs evaluated to date. Seal specimens will be tested under slipforming conditions against an artificially roughened surface which simulates the tunnel wall.

Figure 8. ETLS Slide Valve and Go-Devil

Laboratory Testing

Over a period of about six months, beginning in March of 1981, a total of four to six 6.5 m (22 ft) lengths of liner will be slipformed at the 1/2 scale test facility. Primary objectives of testing are to:

- Demonstrate distribution/consolidation of the concrete inside the form and evaluate the effects of placing pressure, port number and location, vibration, and workability
- Demonstrate the ability of the placed liner to support itself on leaving the form
- Evaluate advance rate limitations imposed by workability and set time
- Evaluate form drag and the effects of form length, placing pressure, and form alignment
- Evaluate the performance of a sealing system to operate between the bulkhead and the tunnel wall
- Evaluate the characteristics of the finished liner, including dimensional stability, cracking, surface finish, long-term strength, and uniformity of thickness
- Evaluate effectiveness of the concrete purging system in dealing with shutdowns and line blockages
- Demonstrate that an acceptable and consistent concrete mix can be obtained for this application using volumetric mixing equipment to deliver prebatch, cement, water, and admixtures
- Evaluate effects of a TBM regrip cycle on liner quality.

Results of the 1/2 scale prototype testing will, of course, determine whether or not the development of the ETLS will be continued. It is expected, however, that the testing will demonstrate the feasibility of the ETLS as a means of placing cast in place liners directly behind a TBM, and that it will also provide a sufficient data base to enable work to begin on the design of a full scale machine.

REFERENCES

Brierley, G.S., 1975, "The Performance During Construction for a Large Shallow, Underground Opening in Rock," Ph.D. Thesis, University of Illinois at Urbana-Champaign, IL.

Cording, E.J., Mathews, A.A., and Peck, R.B., 1976, "Design Criteria for Permanent Structural Linings for Station Excavations in Rock," Washington Metropolitan Area Transit Authority, report for DeLeuw, Cather & Company, July 1976.

Deere, D.V., Peck, R.B., Monsees, J.E. and Schmidt, B., 1969, "Design of Tunnel Liners and Support Systems," report for the U.S. Department of Transportation, OHSGT, Contract 3-0152 (order no. PB-183-799 from NTIS).

Doherty, B.J., Ounanian, D.W., and Maser, K.R., 1979, "Extruded Tunnel Lining System, Phase I - Conceptual Design and Feasibility Testing," report for the U.S. Department of Transportation, Contract DOT-TSC-UMTA-1516.

Paul, S.L., and Ferra-Boza, R.A., 1975, "Concrete Tunnel Liners: Structural Testing of Cast-In-Place Liners," report for the Department of Transportation, Contract DOT FR 30022.

Paul, S.L., Kesler, C.E., Gaylord, E.H., Mohraz, B., Hendron, A.J., and Peck, R.B., 1974, "Research to Improve Tunnel Support Systems," report for the U.S. Department of Transportation, FRA, Contract DOT FR 30022 (Order No. PB-235-762 from NTIS).

ACKNOWLEDGEMENT

Foster-Miller Associates, Inc. would like to acknowledge the cooperation and support of the following people in their roles as technical monitor and sponsor, respectively: Mr. Gerald Saulnier of the U.S. Department of Transportation's Transportation System Center, and Mr. Gil Butler of the Urban Mass Transit Administration.

Chapter 82

GROOVE DEEPENING WITH DISC CUTTERS

Dominic F. Howarth

Lecturer, Department of Mining & Metallurgical Engineering, University of Queensland, Australia (formerly with the Department of Mining Engineering, University of New South Wales, Australia)

ABSTRACT

Groove deepening (deepening of a groove in rock by successive passes of a rock cutting tool) is a potential operational feature associated with tunnel boring machines. Little research has been undertaken in this area which is of direct practical relevance to the design and application of tunnel boring machines.

Laboratory experiments using single, double and triple disc arrays have revealed an important fundamental cycle of events associated with disc cutters when progressively deepening a groove. Furthermore, in contrast to pick cutters, groove deepening by discs is shown to be an efficient operation. This can be directly attributed to the increased interaction between disc cutters due to the increase in magnitude of lateral forces generated as a groove is deepened.

INTRODUCTION

There are many factors that affect the performance of a tunnel boring machine. One such factor that has received little attention but is of significant importance is that of groove deepening. The mechanism of groove deepening is best described by Roxborough (1977) - "in practice, the spacing between adjacent cutting tools in array is sometimes too great for the depth of cut taken during each revolution of the cutter head to allow the rock rib between adjacent tools to breakthrough". If this occurs the groove is progressively deepened by successive passes of the tool until breakthrough occurs. Breakthrough will occur when the optimum spacing to penetration ratio is reached for that particular tool.

Groove deepening is therefore a potential operational variable that should be taken into account at the design stage of a tunnel boring machine. The consequences of groove deepening are manifold and warrant detailed consideration.

Groove deepening occurs in tunnel boring operations as a result of disc cutters operating under conditions other than those defined by optimum S/P (spacing / penetration) ratios, for example

a) adjacent tool in an array badly worn or broken causing an effective increase in tool spacing,
b) thrust of machine poor or insufficient causing a reduction in penetration,
c) hard band of rock causing a reduction in penetration.

The concept of an optimum spacing to penetration ratio for single pass rock cutting experiments is well established (Roxborough and Phillips, 1975; Rad and Olson, 1974). Comprehensive studies of groove deepening have not been undertaken, however, small scale studies of this phenomenon have been undertaken by Rad and McGarry (1970) and Hewitt (1975).

This paper describes laboratory experiments undertaken with disc cutters in one rock type and attempts to investigate the mechanisms and fundamental behaviour of this type of cutter in a groove deepening situation.

ROCK CUTTING RIG AND INSTRUMENTATION

The cutting rig used in these experiments was an extensively modified planing machine shown in Figure 1. This machine is capable of accepting large blocks of rock, has variable cutting speed and is robust enough to sustain static and dynamic thrust forces (vertical) up to 100 kN.

In this system the cutting tool remains stationary while the rock sample is passed beneath it. The table is driven by a 7.5 kW induction motor which in turn is controlled by an AC variable frequency inverter which allows the speed of the table to be continuously varied from 50-300 $mm.s^{-1}$. Rock samples of approximately 450mm x 450mm x 350mm are mounted on the table and clamped firmly prior to cutting. Details of a specially fabricated rotating rock mounting plate designed specifically for the groove deepening experiments have been detailed by Howarth (1980).

A tensioned framework, also shown in Figure 1 was provided to give a degree of lateral constraint. The rig also has the facility to dress rock samples prior to cutting.

Instrumentation included a triaxial dynamometer, shown in Figure 1, (O'Dogherty and Whittaker, 1965) capable of resolving the force acting

Figure 1. Rock Cutting Rig

on the disc into three othogonal components. Signals are sent from the dynamometer via dynamic strain amplifiers to a microprocessor based data acquisition and mini computer facility described in detail by Howarth (1978). Data is stored in digital form on flexible magnetic discs for future analysis.

TEST MATERIAL

The experimental programme was conducted in Gosford Summersby Sandstone and has the measured properties detailed in Table 1.

TABLE 1

Properties of Gosford Summersby Sandstone

Grain Size	0.2-0.8
Quartz content%	63±5
Unconfined compressive strength MPa	42.3±2.56(A)*
Unconfined tensile strength MPa	2.84±0.36(B)*
Unconfined shear strength MPa	14.5±1.62(C)*
Static Young's Modulus GPa	9.62±2.47(D)*
Schmidt rebound number	47.4±6.43(E)*
Dry mass density kg/m^3	2200±61

* Mean value of property in two directions, one at right angles to the other

A. 20 samples, cylinders 54.2mm dia. x 108.3mm long
B. 10 samples, discs 40.6mm dia. x 19.8mm long
C. 10 samples, cylinders 40.7mm dia. x 78.5mm long
D. Tangent modulus, 10 samples dimensions as A
E. 125 values

THE EXPERIMENTAL PROGRAMME

The double and triple disc arrays referred to in this paper are actually simulated disc arrays. Each test was conducted using one disc. In the former case two sequential parallel cuts were taken and in the latter three sequential parallel cuts were taken. The tests are considered to simulate array cutting with reasonable accuracy. These tests do not take into account dynamic array effects. For example the interaction between discs while cutting. The two different cutting situations are shown diagrammatically in Figure 2.

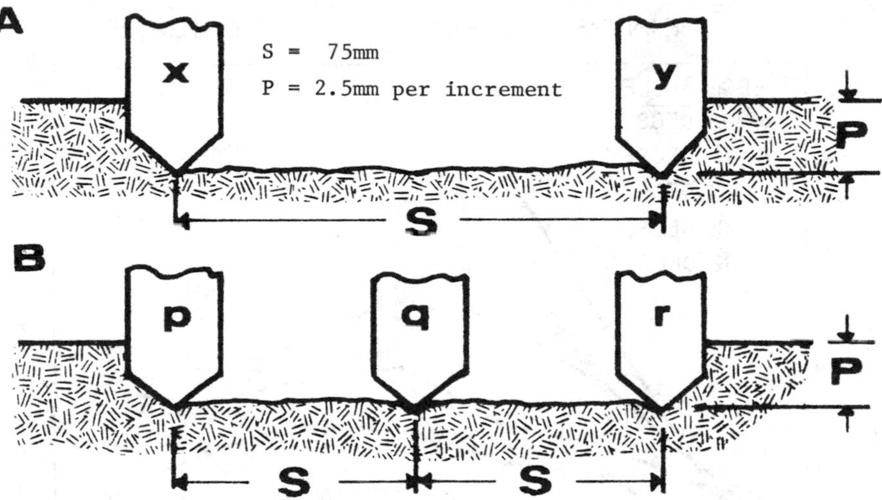

Figure 2. Double and triple disc array cutting configurations

The experiments discussed in this paper are detailed in Table 2.

TABLE 2

Experimental Programme

Experiment No.	No. of discs in array	No. of increments of cutting	Disc diameter mm	Disc edge angle deg.
A	2	8	150	30,45,60,75,90
B	2	16	200	75
C	3	16	200	75

In all cases the parallel cuts, spaced 75mm between groove centres were deepened in 2.5mm (fixed penetration) increments. The cutting speed was held constant at 150 mm/s in all cases. Each experiment was repeated four times to average out the effects of rock heterogeneity.

The graphical results presented represent force, yield, etc. *per cutter*, plotted against depth increment.[1]

EXPERIMENTAL RESULTS

Experiment A

The effect of deepening a groove on disc forces is shown in Figure 3. Thrust forces increase with increasing increment number to a maximum that occurs at either the 4th or 5th increment of cutting. This corresponds to an S/P ratio of 6 - 7.5. Thereafter the forces decrease. Increasing disc edge angle simply increases the level of force.

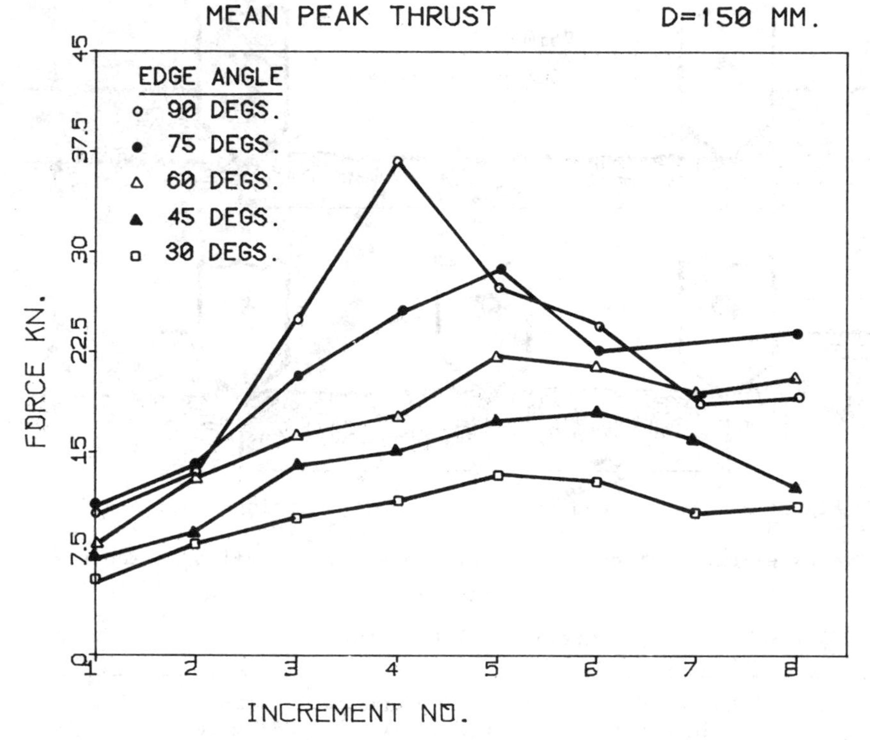

Figure 3. Effect of cumulative penetration on disc forces

---

[1] Definitions of the rock cutting parameters and notation can be found in the Appendix.

Yield increases with increasing depth reaching a maximum at the 6th increment of cutting, or at an S/P ratio of 5. This is the optimum S/P ratio where maximum breakthrough occurs. At this ratio lateral forces are sufficient to shear the ridge between adjacent grooves. This is shown in Figure 4.

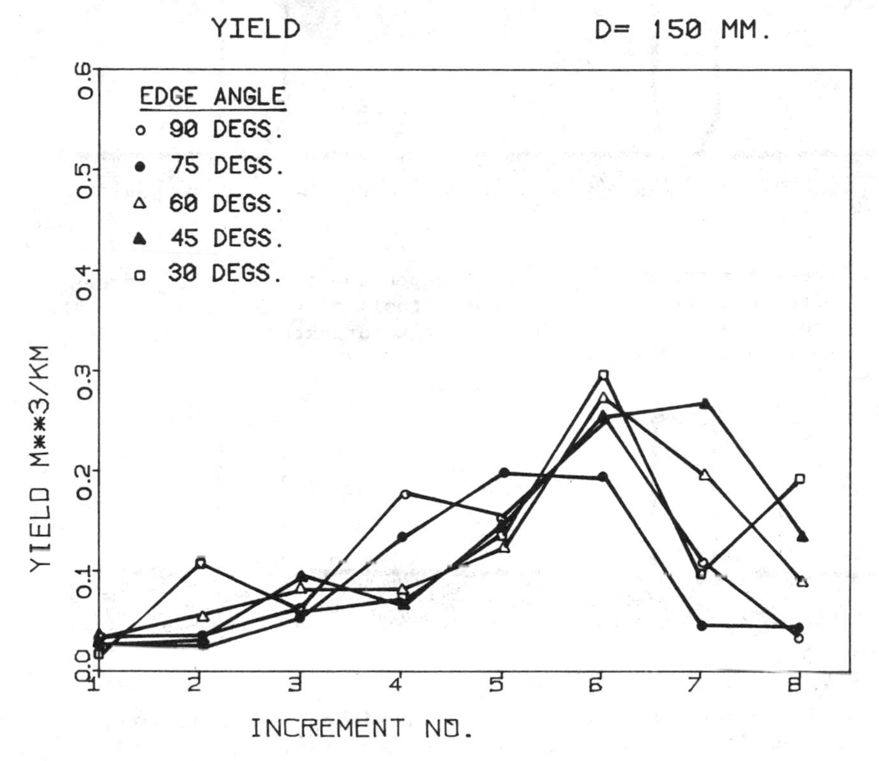

Figure 4. Effect of cumulative penetration (increment number) on rock yield

Coarseness index (directly proportional to excavated particle dimensions) was observed to be a maximum at the 6th increment of cutting. This observation is commensurate with the observation that yield is also a maximum at the same increment of cutting. This relationship between yield and coarseness index was found to be coincident throughout the entire series of groove deepening experiments.

A sequence, or cycle of events is apparent and can be summarised thus:

1. the first cut is on a fresh rock surface; the forces required to cut the rock are small and no breakthrough occurs

2. Successive passes of the tool deepen the groove, disc forces increase as contact area between tool and rock increases. The disc forces reach a maximum prior to breakthrough. At this stage no breakthrough occurs.

3. With the next pass of the tool, the ridge between adjacent grooves is sheared through (shaded area in diagram below)

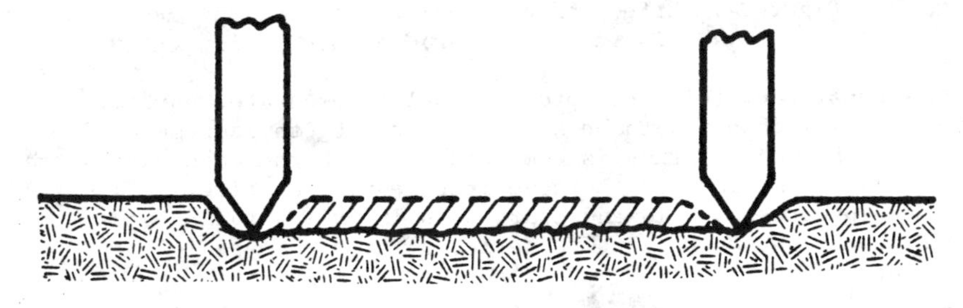

This sheared zone (shown above) would account for the increase in rock yield and the maximisation of particle size discussed previously. This is clearly demonstrated in Figure 5. Following breakthrough the disc is effectively cutting on a new surface and hence the cycle will be repeated.

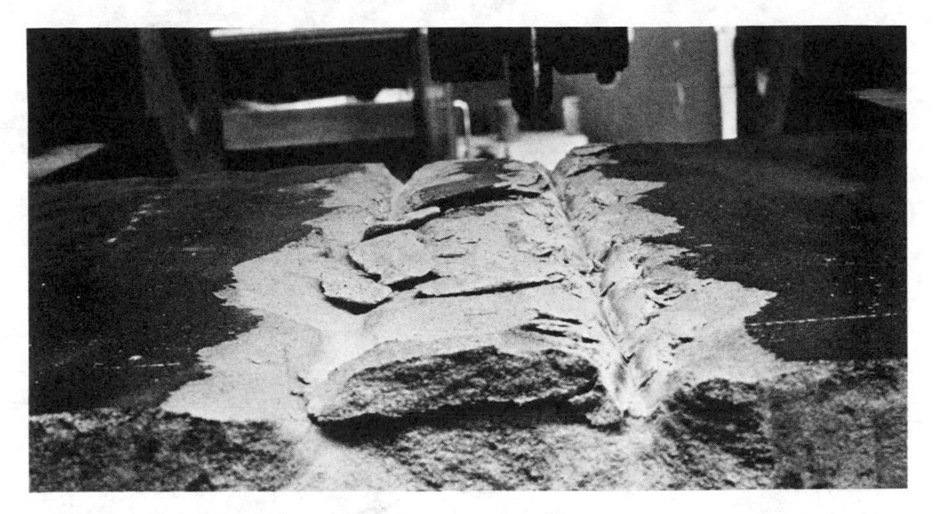

Figure 5. Breakthrough between two adjacent grooves occurring at the 6th increment of cutting

In a field groove deepening situation tunnelling machines usually operate at relatively constant thrust. It is useful therefore to examine how a constant thrust condition would effect the various disc cutting performance criteria. As an example, the effect of a constant thrust condition on penetration is presented.

The effect of a constant thrust condition on penetration is illustrated in Figure 6. This graph is an *estimate* of the effect of increasing increment number on penetration that would occur if thrust were kept constant. This curve was derived by assuming that the thrust at increment 1 was the maximum (and constant) thrust available. Since on increment 2 the thrust required to excavate the 2.5 mm increment is higher than on increment 1 it is possible to estimate the reduction in penetration as follows.

For example, on the first and second increments of cutting the thrust force required to excavate a 2.5 mm groove was found to be 12 kN and 18 kN respectively. Now, since in an unrelieved cutting situation thrust and penetration are approximately linearly related and equal increments of penetration require an approximate corresponding increase in thrust, if thrust is held constant at 12 kN we can estimate the reduction in penetration on the second increment of cutting, i.e.

$$\text{penetration on 2nd increment} = \frac{12}{18} \times 2.5 \text{ mm}$$

$$= 1.67 \text{ mm}$$

The estimated penetration per increment was calculated using the procedure outlined above. Penetration as shown in Figure 6 decreases

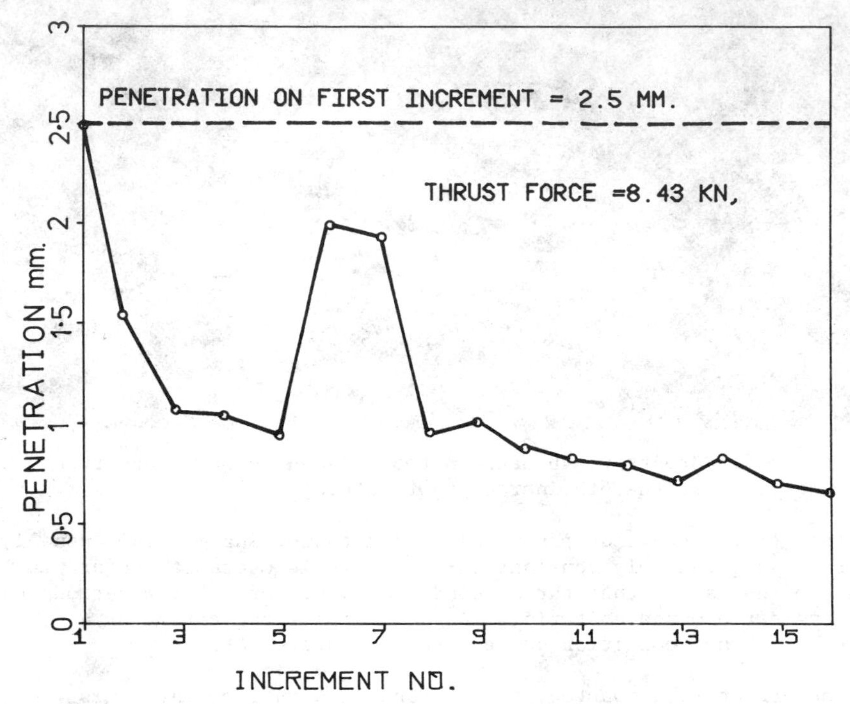

Figure 6. Effect of a constant thrust condition on penetration with increasing increment number. When breakthrough occurs penetration correspondingly increases. This graph shows that the mean effective penetration in a constant-thrust groove deepening situation is drastically reduced when compared to the penetration possible on the first or initial cut.

Rad and McGarry (1970) who undertook groove deepening experiments using a constant thrust rock cutting device, demonstrated that under these experimental conditions grooves were deepened by decreasing increments of penetration.

Experiment B

The tests reported in the previous section indicated cyclic behaviour of the major rock cutting parameters in a groove deepening situation. These tests involved incremental deepening of a groove, the initial cut being on a dressed (flat) rock surface. Since this situation rarely occurs in practice it was considered necessary to examine the groove deepening cycle on pre-excavated surfaces.

The objectives of this experiment were threefold,

1. to investigate groove deepening on pre-roughened surfaces,

2. to establish whether or not groove deepening cycles were evident subsequent to the initial cycle,

3. if a second cycle was evident; was its behaviour similar to the first cycle?

The results of these tests are presented graphically in Figures 7 and 8. Two curves are presented in each graph and represent identical experiments. When combined, however, important effects were effectively 'smoothed' out. For clarity of presentation and interpretation, therefore, curves A and B are presented separately.

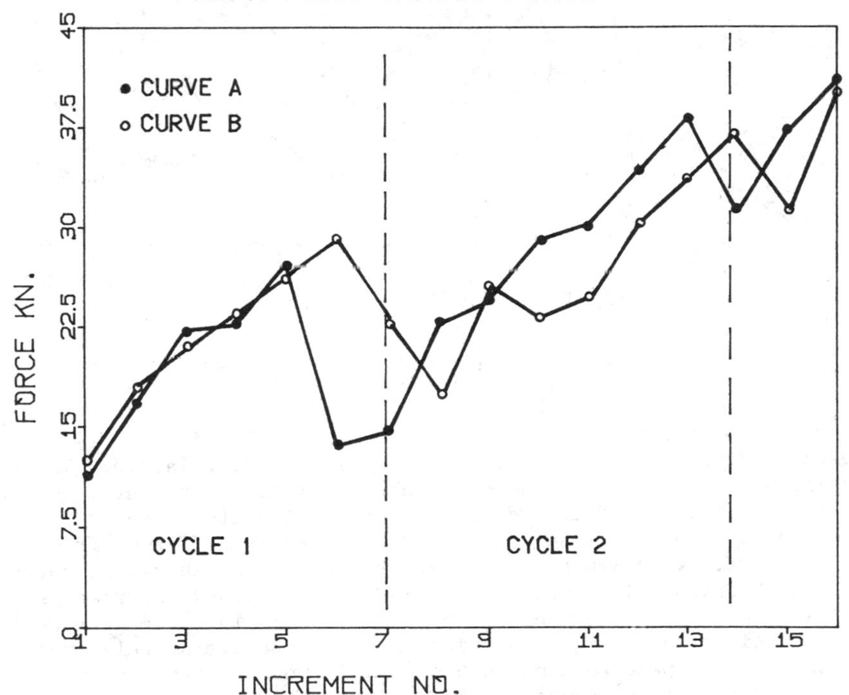

Figure 7. Effect of cumulative penetration on disc forces (16 passes in the same groove)

A second cycle of groove deepening is evident as shown in Figure 7. This second cycle, however, is somewhat 'smoothed' out. Curves of increasing depth increment against yield, presented in Figure 8, corroborate this behaviour.

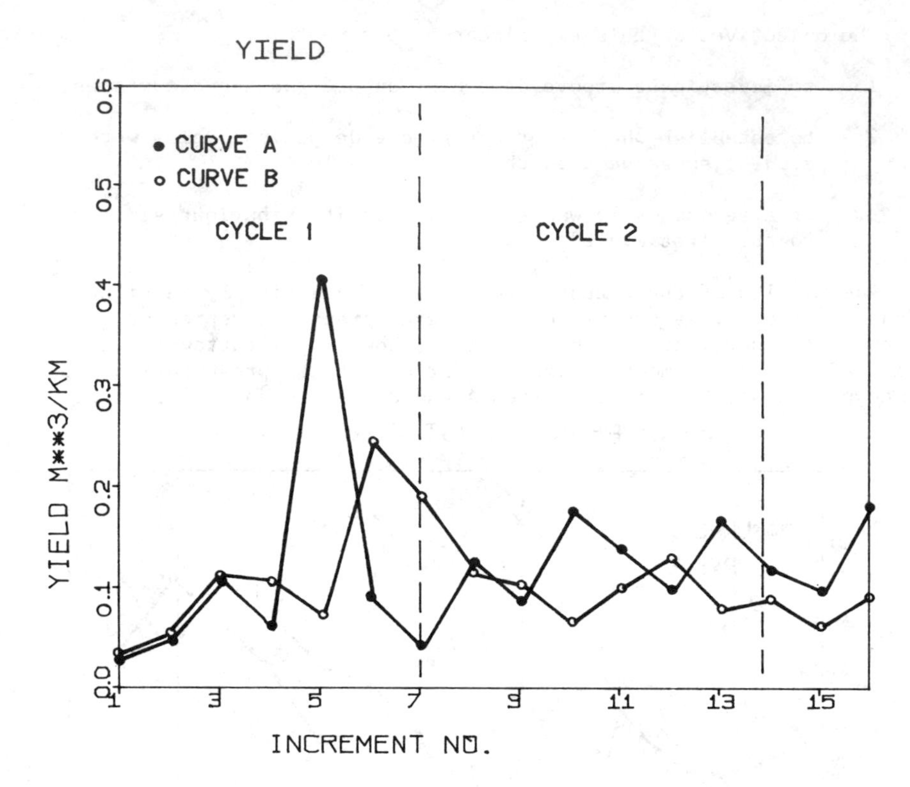

Figure 8. Effect of cumulative penetration on rock yield (16 passes in the same groove)

During experimentation it was observed that following the first breakthrough of the rock rib between adjacent cuts, relatively large quantities of rock were produced on subsequent alternate cuts. This is clearly evident in Figure 8. It appears, therefore, that breakout of rock on pre-roughened surfaces is fundamentally different from that when cutting commences from flat surfaces. It should be noted that this behaviour is probably peculiar to laboratory experiments involving cutting at constant depth increments. In a field groove deepening situation where excavating machines operate at relatively constant thrust, penetration and hence yield would attenuate until the optimum S/P ratio was reached. In this situation we could expect that, following the initial cut, yield would reduce progressively, then attain a maximum (at the first optimum S/P ratio) and then again reduce progressively until the next maximum (at the second optimum S/P ratio), ad infinitum. This behaviour is frequently demonstrated in the field (Phillips (1980), personal communication).

Experiment C

The two experiments discussed (A and B) have illustrated the fundamental behaviour of disc cutters in a groove deepening situation. A third experiment was considered necessary for two reasons.

1. it was suspected that the prominent shoulder excavated by two parallel grooves (Figure 2A) could possibly give rise to a misrepresentation of a practical groove deepening situation. In the field situation cutter arrays do not operate in isolation, as is the case with experiments A and B. Therefore, it was anticipated that by observing and comparing curves obtained from cutters in a situation described in Figure 2A with a central cutter Q shown in Figure 2B, which is relieved on both sides, that this problem could be resolved.

2. to provide a comparison between twin and triple disc arrays.

The results of this experiment are shown in Figures 9 and 10.

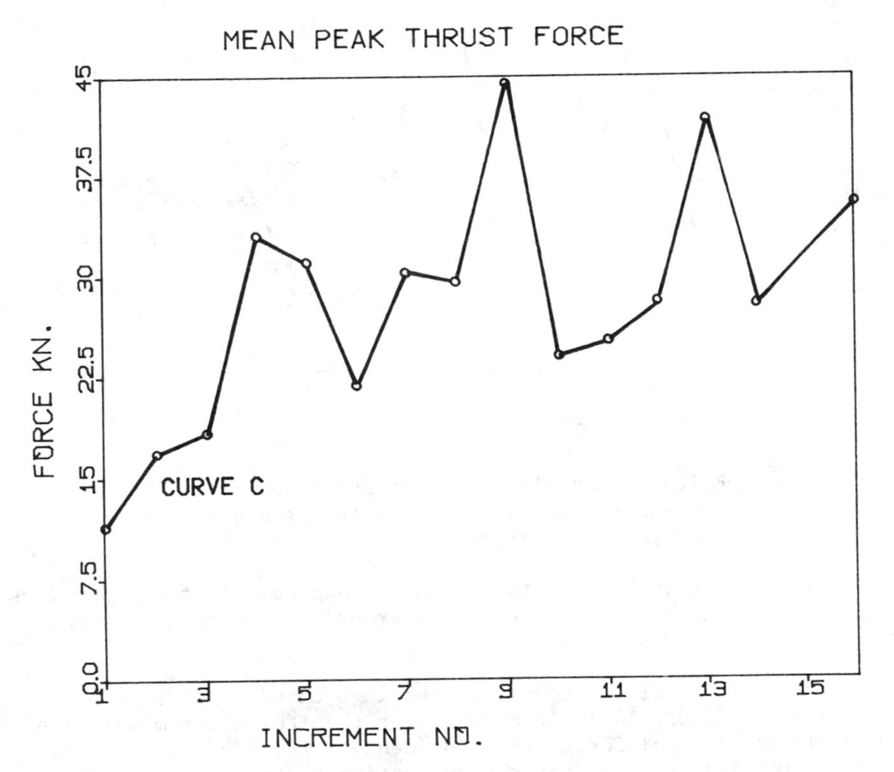

Figure 9. Effect of cumulative penetration on disc forces associated with the central cutter in a triple disc array

The curves presented refer to cutting parameters associated with cutter Q, shown in Figure 2B. The behaviour of disc forces associated with cutter Q (the central cutter) are similar in both trend and magnitude to the curves presented for the 'unrelieved' groove deepening situation (cutter X or Y shown in Figure 2A). It should be noted that rock yield is similar in trend, but the magnitude of peak yield values are somewhat exaggerated. This is due to the increased quantity of rock available for excavation in the case of the central cutter.

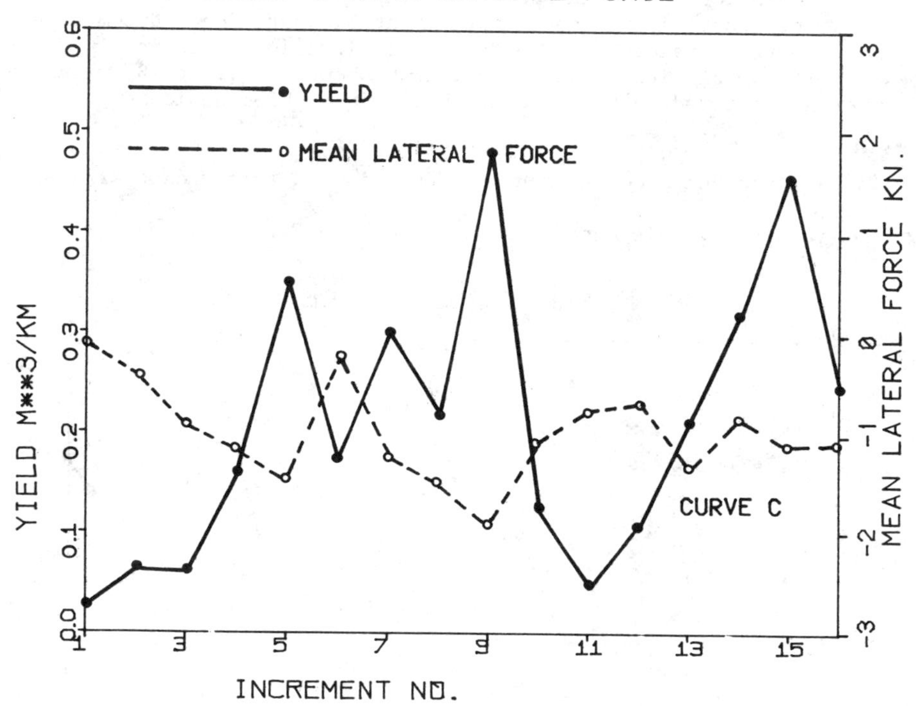

Figure 10. Effect of cumulative penetration on rock yield and lateral forces associated with the central cutter in a triple disc array.

On the basis of these results it can be concluded that the previous experiments (A and B) model a practical groove deepening situation with reasonable accuracy.

The role of lateral (sideways) forces in rock excavation is illustrated in Figure 10. It can be seen that the maximum values of rock yield and lateral force are coincident. This result provides strong supporting evidence for the suggestion that groove deepening by disc, in contrast to drag picks, is a far more efficient process in terms of rock yield and hence energy expended. This is a direct result of the increased interaction between adjacent disc cutters in array which in turn is due to the sloping sides (flanks) of the disc cutter profile.

A comparison between twin and triple disc array forces is shown in Figure 11.

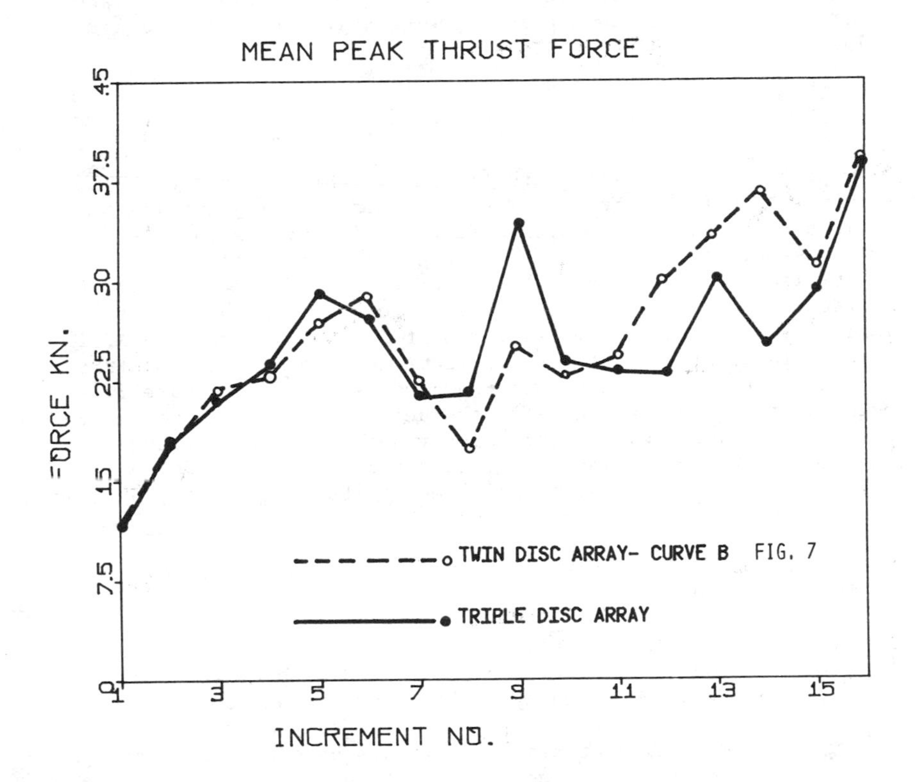

Figure 11. Comparison of double and triple disc arrays

The data for these curves represent mean values of parameters per disc. That is, referring to Figure 2A, $(F_{T.X} + F_{T.Y})/2$ is the mean value of F_T per disc in a double disc array. Referring to Figure 2B similarly, $(F_{T.P} + F_{T.Q} + F_{T.R})/3$ is the mean value of F_T for disc in a triple disc array.

The objectives of these tests were to compare cutting parameters in double and triple disc array cutting configurations and to ascertain whether or not either array offered any advantages in terms of cutting efficiency or reduced disc forces.

It can be seen from the graph presented that little difference exists between either array on the basis of disc forces. Howarth (1980) provides similar supporting data which are based on other disc performance criteria, namely yield and specific energy.

The curves for double and triple disc arrays agree well in both trend and magnitude. It can be concluded, therefore, that the cutting efficiency per disc is the same for both double and triple disc arrays. The results are in agreement with those of Ryall et. al. (1977).

CONCLUSIONS

In a practical tunnelling situation it is thrust and not penetration that is kept approximately constant during cutting operations. An example is presented that illustrates the inefficiencies associated with groove deepening in a field situation. Consider disc cutters operating in concert at constant thrust: if on the first cut the thrust is insufficient to excavate the groove optimally, unrelieved grooves will result. On the second pass, if the groove is to be excavated to the same depth of cut as the first groove, a greater thrust force is required as shown in Figure 3. However, since thrust is constant, the depth of cut must decrease. Therefore, rock yield will progressively decrease as a direct consequence of the decreased penetration and hence specific energy will increase. This situation will repeat itself until the optimum S/P is reached and breakthrough occurs.

The major conclusions relevant to the experimental work can be summarised as follows:

1. Groove deepening experiments with disc cutters indicate a sequence or cycle of events associated with a progressively deepened groove. The cycle of events, manifested in curves of disc performance criteria, are directly attributable to the gradual deepening of the groove and subsequent breakthrough of the rib of rock between adjacent cuts.

2. Following the first breakthrough a second 'cycle' of events associated with groove deepening was evident. However, groove deepening cycles subsequent to the initial cycle were not as pronounced in their local variation. They are in effect 'smoothed' out. It is suggested that this is a result of cutting on pre-cut rather than smooth (dressed) surfaces.

3. Caution should be observed before applying results obtained in laboratory groove deepening experiments to field situations. The reason for this being that these laboratory tests were under constant depth of cut conditions and machines in the field usually operate under conditions of constant thrust.

4. If excavating machines in the field operate at S/P ratios greater than optimum then cutting efficiency will fall dramatically.

5. In contrast to picks, groove deepening with disc cutters is a far more efficient process.

6. A comparison of simulated double and triple disc arrays showed that the differences between the two arrays, *per disc*, were insignificant in terms of the principal parameters of disc performance.

From an overall assessment of the laboratory results and considerations involved in field groove deepening, it is suggested that in terms of cutting efficiency disc cutters in concert operate at, or close to, optimum S/P ratios to minimise the energy requirement.

ACKNOWLEDGEMENTS

The research described in this paper forms part of an investigation into fundamental aspects of the mechanical excavation of hard rock using free rolling cutters currently being undertaken in the School of Mining Engineering, University of New South Wales.

The equipment used in this work was provided by a grant from the Australian Research Grants Committee.

REFERENCES

Barker, J.S., 1964. "A laboratory investigation of rock cutting using large picks," *Int. J. Rock Mech. & Min. Sci.*, Vol. 1, pp.519-534.

Hewitt, K.S., 1975. "Aspects of the design and application of cutting systems for rock excavation," *Ph.D. Thesis*, Univ. Newcastle upon Tyne, U.K.

Howarth, D.F., 1978. "Tunnelling machine research at the University of New South Wales," *Symp. on Rock Breaking - Equipment and Techniques*, Aust. Inst. of Min. & Metall. Melbourne, pp.43-49.

Howarth, D.F., 1980. "Fundamental studies on some special aspects of rock cutting system design," *Ph.D. Thesis*, University of New South Wales.

O'Dogherty, M.J. and Whittaker, D., 1965. "An examination of the characteristics of a solid plate dynamometer designed for triaxial force measurements," M.R.E. (N.C.B., U.K.) Tech. Mem. No. 197.

Phillips, H.R., 1980. Private communication.

Rad, P.F. and McGarry, F.J., 1970. "Thermally assisted cutting of granite," *12th Symp. Rock Mechanics.*, Univ. Missouri, Rolla, pp.721-757.

Rad, P.F. and Olson, R.C., 1974. Tunnelling machine research - "Interaction between disk-cutting grooves in rocks," *U.S.B.M.* R.I. 7881.

Roxborough, F.F. and Phillips, H.R., 1975. "Rock excavation by disc cutter," *Int. J. Rock Mech. & Min. Sci. and Geomech. abstr.*, Vol. 12, pp.361-366.

Roxborough, F.F., 1977. "A report to the Chamber of Mines of South Africa Research Organization on coal face mechanization," School of Min. Eng., U.N.S.W., Internal report.

Ryall, J. et.al. 1977. "The selection and application of rotary rock cutting tools," Second progress report to the C.I.R.I.A. working party, Project No. RP260, Univ. Newcastle upon Tyne, U.K.

APPENDIX

Notation

D	disc diameter	mm
P	penetration	mm
S	spacing	mm
Q	rock yield	m^3/km
F_T	mean peak thrust force	kN
$\overline{F}_L$	mean lateral force	kN

Definition of rock cutting parameters

Mean thrust force $\overline{F}_T$ - the average force required to be applied normal to the rock surface to effect and maintain a prescribed depth of penetration.

Mean peak thrust force F_T - the average of the peak forces acting on the cutting tool as defined above. This is relevant to the mechanical strength of the tool and bearing design.

Mean lateral force $\overline{F}_L$ - the average lateral or sideways force imposed on the cutting tool. This force, albeit small, manifests itself in relieved cutting experiments.

Yield Q - the volume of rock excavated per unit distance cut and is measured in units of cubic metres per kilometre. This parameter can be regarded as an indication of cutting "effectiveness".

Coarseness index C.I. - this is a non-dimensional number being the sum of the cumulative mass percentages recorded in the screen analyses and is a measure of the size of debris from an excavated cut (Barker 1964). Its range depends on the number of size fractions taken, but its value is arbitrary and must be related to the size of screens used. Ths screen sizes must therefore be selected to suit the product.

Specific energy - the work done per unit volume of rock excavated.

Chapter 83

Activated Roller Cutters as a Means of Rock Breakage

Initial Test Results and Future Applications

by

Dipl.-Ing. Wilhelm Knickmeyer
- Bergbau-Forschung GmbH, Essen -

Dipl.-Ing. Lothar Baumann
- Bergbau-Forschung GmbH, Essen -

In mechanized roadheading predominantly two methods of rock breakage are applied at present: the cutting method by means of picks and the cutting/crushing method by means of roller cutters. Both systems meanwhile reached a high degree of technical development and consequently show very few possibilities of further improvement. While application of hard-metal picks is limited by rock hardness, the roller cutters require a high specific thrust and, accordingly, heavy carrier systems. Roller-cutter equipped tunneling machines are therefore only cost-effective in hard-coal mining if the high investments for transport and assembly are justified by a corresponding length of road to be headed. The limit for acceptable cost-effectiveness is at present a minimum heading length of approximately 3 km.

In order to improve the specific cutting performance of roller cutters by activation, Bergbau-Forschung carried out a research project sponsored by the Commission of the European Communities and the provincial government of

Nordrhein-Westfalen.

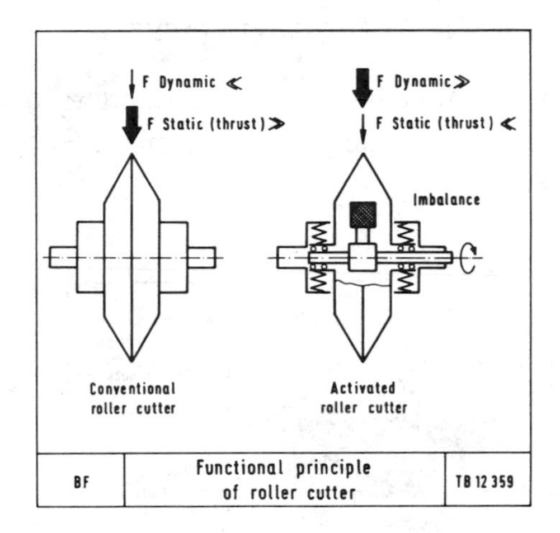

Fig. 1

The conventional roller cutters (Fig. 1 left side) require considerable static thrust for overcoming the compressive strength of the rock masses.

By installation of an imbalance generator system for activation of the roller cutters the static thrust required is smaller since the rock masses are disintegrated by impact impulses of the activation system.

Systems suitable for generation of mechanical vibrations are in commercial use with crushing equipment, concrete- and soil-compaction systems, and as drives for vibratory screens and conveyors.

These systems may be roughly divided into:

- mechanical systems
- hydraulic systems
- pneumatic systems
- electro-magnetic systems.

The common feature of these systems is the generation of vibrations by imbalance generators. Here a large variety of designs exists.

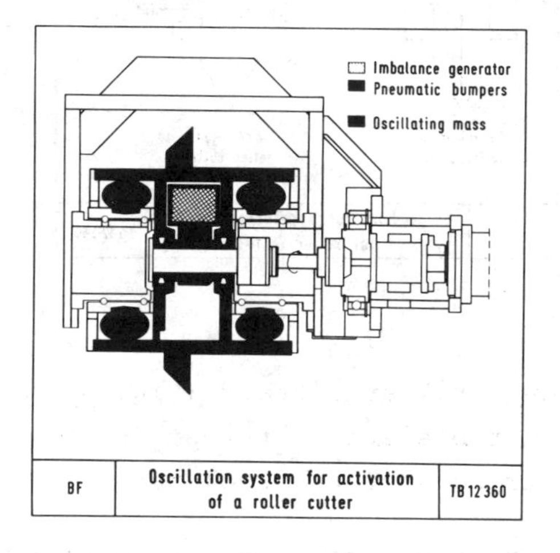

Fig. 2

For the initial activation tests a rotational system for imbalance generation was chosen. This was a familiar spring load/mass system with an imbalance generator driven by an outside hydrostatic drive.

The first test runs showed that the dynamic behaviour of the generator system was very difficult to control thus necessitating design modifications of said system. After modification dynamic behaviour and working parameters of the activated roller cutter could be controlled in idle run.

The following tests were limited in a first phase to the determination of the amplitude, the frequency, the resonance range, and the torque as a function of rotational speed. Investigations were carried out on a roller cutter of 720 mm diameter and 45° wedge angle. The cutting edge is rounded off by a radius of 3 mm. The roller cutter was made of hardened chromium steel alloy.

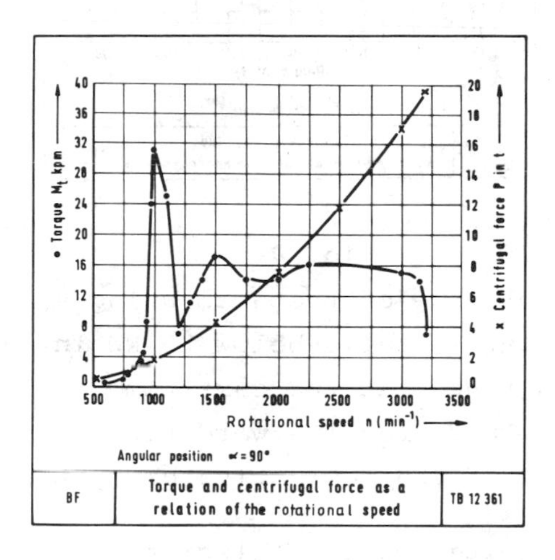

Fig. 3

Fig. 3 shows the torque and the centrifugal force as a function of rotational imbalance speed. When passing the resonance range of approximately 1000 min^{-1} (natural frequency), a torque decrease is recorded which reaches a minimum at maximum centrifugal force of 200 kN.

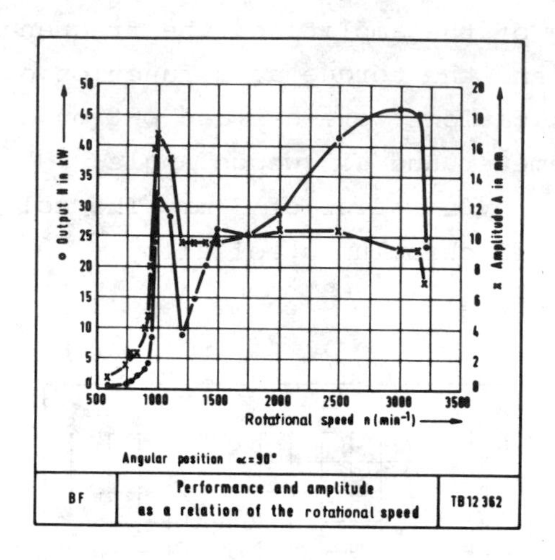

Fig. 4

The drive performance of the activating system behaves as expected, i.e. it falls below 25 kW in the hypercritical speed range. At the same time amplitudes of 7 mm were recorded. These results were taken as a basis for the development of the new activator systems.

In cooperation with Messrs. Salzgitter Maschinen AG and Messrs. Koehring GmbH Bomag Division three roller cutters with different activator designs were built. Two of the activators were designed as rotary systems and one as a linear system.

Fig. 5

Fig. 5 shows the design of a roller cutter with integrated linear activator. In this system a piston is moved by two hydraulically coupled masses oscillating against each other in phase opposition. Frequency and oscillation amplitude can be adjusted continuously from zero to maximum value.

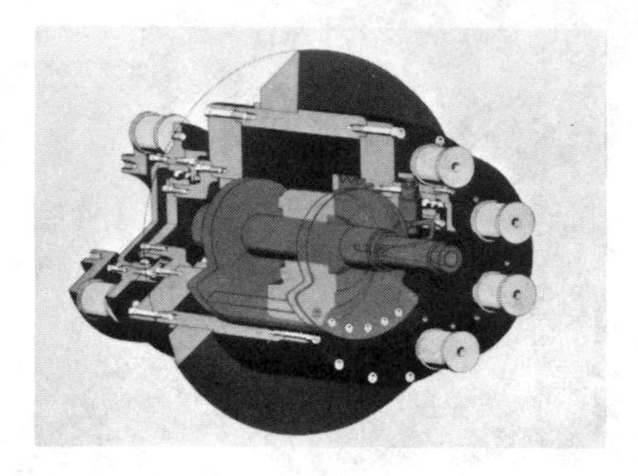

Fig. 6

The rotary activator system comprises two masses. One of them is mounted rigidly to the rotating shaft while the other one can be rotated around the shaft. The movable mass is adjusted stepwise by a cog wheel system from minimum imbalance position to maximum imbalance position and vice versa. The activator is hydraulically driven.

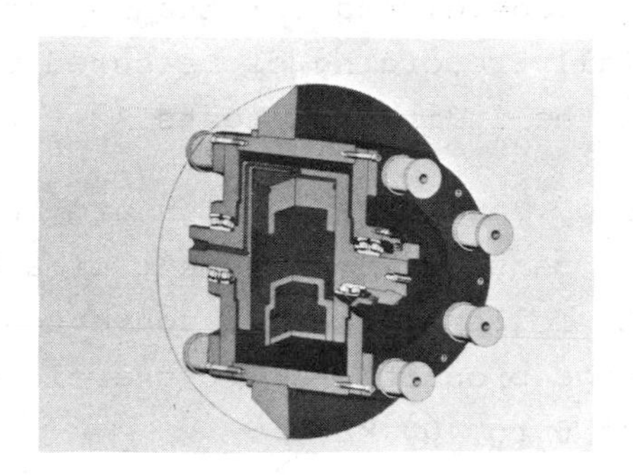

Fig. 7

The third alternative is an activator system comprising a rotating cylinder. An oil-filled cylinder housing a piston tends, when rotating, to move radially against the oil pressure. The oil pressure can be controlled continuously by a valve thus acting as control for the excentricity of the piston and consequently for the order of magnitude of the imbalance. This continuous adjustment can be made in both directions.

For testing of these three activated roller cutters the following test program was set up:

1. Functional testing of the three different activator systems
2. Determination of the main parameters of these systems, freely vibrating and under load in rock contact

3. Determination of the interdependence of working parameters and cutting performance on the test rig.

The computer program developed for the investigations comprises essentially recording of measured parameters and evaluation of the individual tests.

Amplitude, frequency, and acceleration are measured by an electro-optical sensor. The movement of a black/white mark fitted to the roller cutter is converted by remote control to a voltage proportional to travel in the frequency range of 0 to 400 kHz.

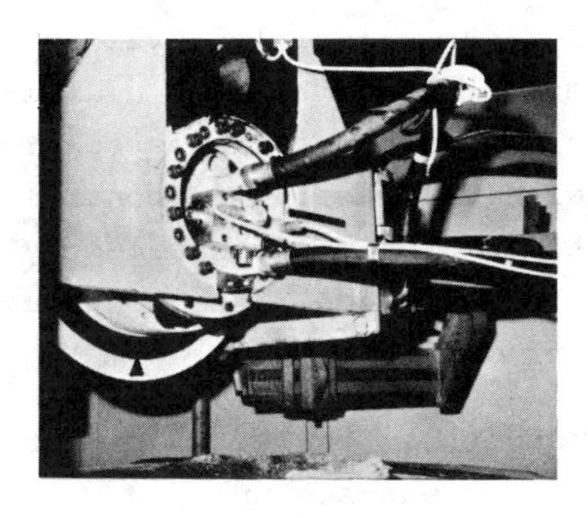

Fig. 8

After the preliminary tests it could be stated that all activated roller cutters fully met the performance specifications with respect to adjustability of amplitude and frequency.

The maximum obtainable amplitude for the different systems was determined as follows:

System	Amplitude (mm)
LE (linear activator)	8.0
KKE (rotary-piston activator)	7.5
KE (rotary activator)	8.9

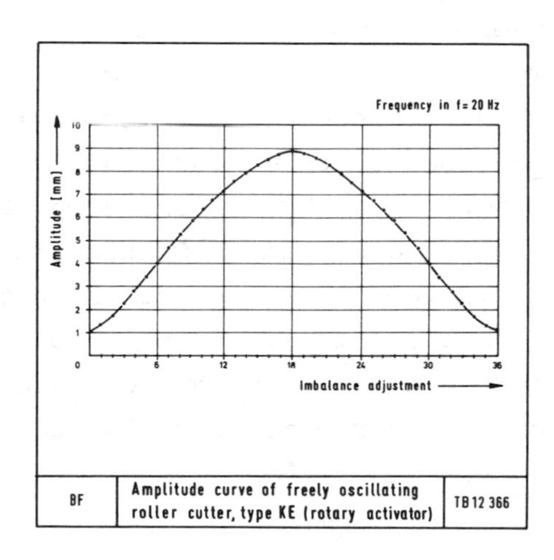

Amplitude curve of freely oscillating roller cutter, type KE (rotary activator)

Fig. 9

Subsequently further series of experimental investigations were carried out; in particular the impact forces were measured. It was found that the impact force increases with decreasing static thrust. The rotary-piston activator and the respective values may be quoted as an example:

Thrust (kN)	Frequency (Hz)	Impact (kN)
0	20	250
0	30	325
0	40	430
8	20	185
8	30	210
8	40	270

The table indicates that maximum impact forces were recorded with a static thrust equal to zero kN with respect to each of the chosen frequencies.

After completion of the impact force measurements all roller cutters were tested on natural rock (granite). Here considerable differences in cutting performance were recorded. The lowest performance was recorded for the linear activator which at the same time accounted for the highest power consumption. On the other hand, this system is definitely advantageous in that the impact is directionally stable. In any case, however, the cutting performance of all three activator systems is sufficient for good performance on the test rocks.

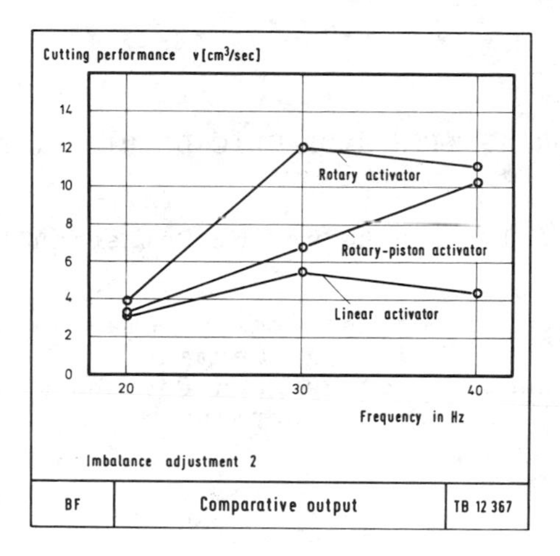

Fig. 10

The results of the investigations fully met all expectations. After completion of various mechanical improvements of the individual activator systems a large-scale test under field conditions in a sandstone quarry is intended. If these tests will yield positive results, the know-how gained will enable construction of less heavy and less clumsy tunneling systems for hard rock drivage.

Chapter 84

TUNNEL BORING WITH HYDRAULIC DEBRIS DISPOSAL

by Dr. J. Henneke and W. Setzepfandt

Director of Mannesmann Demag AG,
Duisburg, Germany
Project-Engineer of Bergbau-Forschung GmbH,
Essen, Germany

PREFACE

Debris disposal can very often be a severe problem and major restriction on tunnel boring projects, especially for small diameter tunnels and in underground mines. Hydraulic transport could provide a suitable solution. Investigations have therefore been made in connection with a full-scale project of 4.8 km length and 2,3 m diameter, to obtain the required technical and economical data for planning an optimized transport system, e.g. for a tunnel boring drivage of 6 - 7 m diameter in underground coal mines.

INTRODUCTION

The Radau-Tunnel, chosen for the investigations, has been designed for transferring flood peaks between the rivers Radau and Grosse Romke in the Harz-Mountain of Lower Saxony. A DEMAG TVM 20/23 H tunnel boring machine was used to drive the tunnel on a rising gradient of 0,53 %. The rock consisted of shale and hornblende (55 %), granite (15 %), diabase (15 %), chert (8 %) and gabbro (7 %). The project has been sponsored by the Federal Ministry of Research and Technology.

HYDRAULIC SYSTEM

The debris cut by the tunnel borer was loaded on a scraper conveyor from where it got on a telescopic conveyor and finally into a mixing tank of the hydraulic transport system (Fig. 1).

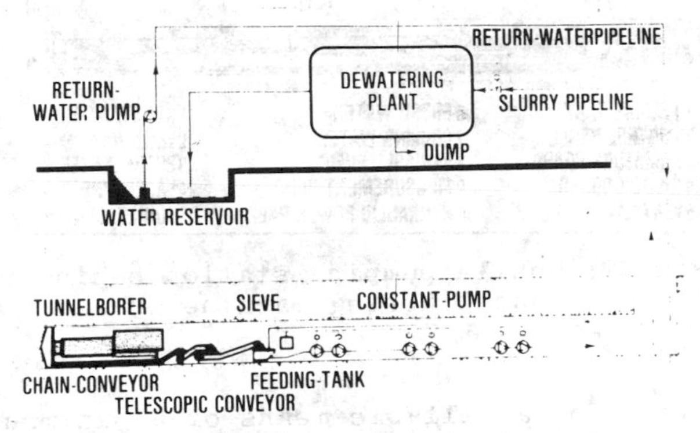

Fig. 1: Hydraulic transport system on Radau-Tunnel drivage

A screen arranged between telescopic conveyor and mixing tank prevented cuttings of more than 80 mm grain size from getting into the transport system. A pumpable suspension was produced in the mixing tank by adding recycling water with a solids content of about 60 g/l below 60 µm grain size. During the mixing procedure the debris was led directly to the input orifice of the solids pipe, via funnel-shaped arrangements in the tank. The recycling water/cuttings mix was sucked in by a hydraulically adjustable pump and then fed into the solids pipeline via a subsequent constant delivery pump (Fig. 2).

The entire system, including the first pumping station, arranged behind the heading machine moved on a track of 600 mm gauge. The steel pipes through which the slurry was transported had a diameter of NW 150 and 3 mm wall thickness. For water recirculation NW 200 PE tubings were used. Upon each drivage section of 18 m length the telescopic conveyor was retracted, pulp- and recycling water pipelines were cut behind the first pumping station and extended by 3 x 6 m each.

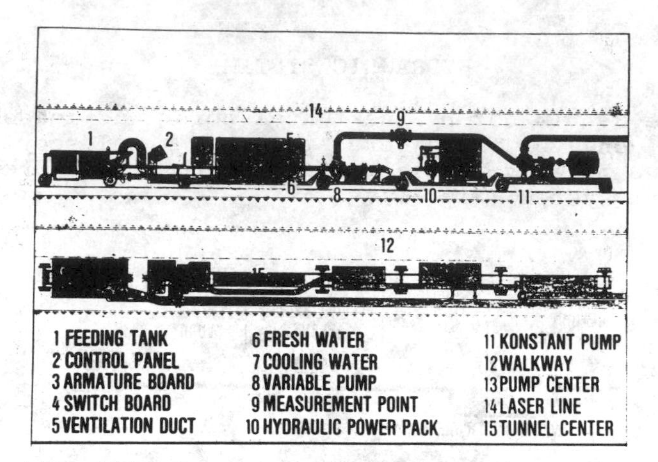

Fig. 2: Mobile pumping station behind tunnel boring machine

In default of a reliable means of adjustment the installation was manually operated. For this purpose an operator at the control desk in front of the feed tank observed the liquid level in the mixing tank and adjusted the speed of the first pump accordingly. All of the subsequent pumps were constant delivery pumps.

Upon 1800 m of drivage the first pumping station at constant speed had to be installed in a tunnel bay (Fig. 3). The station included 2 dredging pumps driven, like any suction pump, by 75 kW motors.

The transport system in its ultimate phase consisted of 2 dual pump stations covering a horizontal transport length of approximately 1.8 km per station plus 1200 m for the mobile pump set behind the feed tank (Fig. 1).

The separation of the suspension into solid and liquid matter was done in a separating plant (Fig. 4). For reasons of space this plant was located at a distance of about 100 m from the tunnel portal. The slurry loaded with cuttings was first led into a baffle tank, which had been designed for converting the kinetic energy and at the same time as a feed to the subsequent pre-screening installation of 8 mm mesh width. The waste fraction above 8mm was immediately loaded on a tipping conveyor. The fraction passing through the screen of 8 mm mesh width was fed from the pump outlet tank into a hydrocyclone

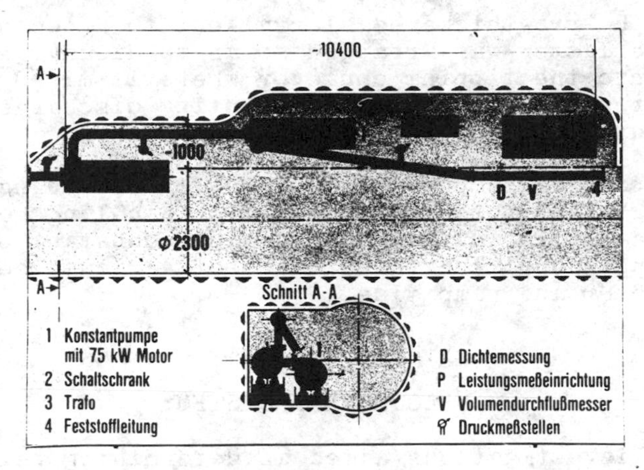

Fig. 3: Tunnel niche with constant delivery pumps station and measurement instruments

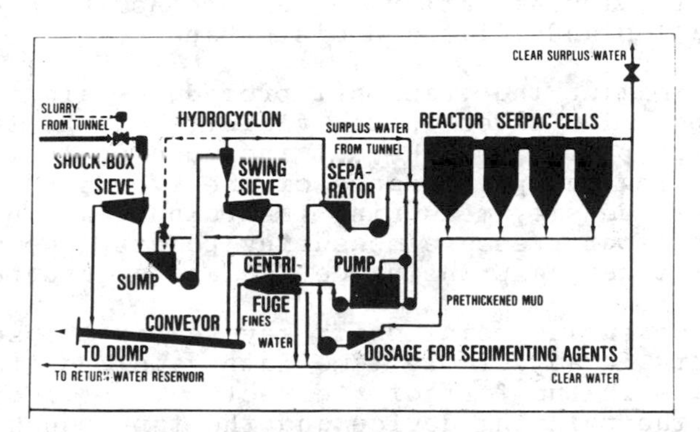

Fig. 4: Dewatering plant on Radau-Tunnel drivage

whose underflow, at an effective separating size of 0.06 mm, was transferred via a vibrating drainage installation and a chute to a tipping conveyor. Some 50 % of the cyclone overflow containing solids under 0.06 mm went to the recycling water tank whereas 50 % were fed into a dewatering plant for further treatment. In this decantation plant separation was brought about by means of flocculants into a water almost free of solids and a slurry containing some 40 % by vol. of solids. The water to be reused was fed into the recycling water tank whereas the pre-thickened slurry went to a decanting tank. The latter was arranged so as to discharge the solids onto the tipping conveyor where it mixed with the other solids. The liquid decanting discharge was also returned to the recycling water tank.

A dredging pump was used also for returning the recycling water into the tunnel. The handling volume of approximately 190 m^3/h was maintained constant over the increasing tunnel length by means of various vee-pulleys on the motor and pump side.

MEASUREMENT SYSTEM

The investigations aimed at determining reliable planning data for a hydraulic transport system in combination with a full-face tunnel boring machine of 6 to 7 m diameter, consisted in the logging of transport procedure data, investigation on wear phenomena and recording of all standstills and disturbances.

For logging the transport procedure data a measuring set had been installed in the vicinity of the first constant pump station. The set included an instrument for measuring the performance of the two 75 kW motors, a radiometric density measuring instrument, an inductive flowmeter, four pressure measuring points, one measuring point shift key, a printing device and a tape punch.

The measuring point shift key scaned the seven measuring points in adjustable time intervals and transfered the signals in the form of a direct current loop of 0 to 20 mA to the printing device and the tape punch. Scanning intervals were adjustable by increments from 0.5 s up to 1 h. By means of a program, synchronized with the aforementioned data logging, the perforated tape was subjected to a subsequent statistic evaluation. The mean values resulting from this evaluation then served as a basis for pressure loss calculations.

The solids pipeline and the solids handling pumps appeared to be the elements of the transport system which were most prone to wear. In order to improve cost-efficiency in this field it was important to find out pipeline and pump materials best suited for the specific application of hydraulic transport.

In a pipeline section, situated between the first

constant delivery pump station and the separating plant, a trial section consisting of pipes of various qualities was arranged, e.g. PVC pipes, glassfibre reinforced pipes, polyamide pipes, pipes coated with cast basalt, steel pipes out of St 37, 42 and 54, and, finally, of a Trellex transport hose.

The wall thickness of fitted PVC-, polyamide-, and steel pipes could be determined by a special ultrasonic measuring instrument. In the Radau tunnel an instrument was used which yielded an accuracy of $\pm$ 0.01 mm. When trying to select the best materials for pump coatings and impellers , one was reduced to the materials offered by the pump manufacturer which in the present case included two steel qualities, i.e. HBN 440 or Ni-Hardt 4 as well as HBV 450 VG, containing 15 % chrome and 2 to 3 % molybdenum.

Whereas the first of these steels is considered to be tough and resistant to wear, the second steel may be characterized as being brittle and highly resistant to wear. When starting the trials it was doubtful whether the highly wear-resistant material would support the impact load resulting from the maximum grain size of 80 mm, without spalling. Complementary to the aforesaid observations it was necessary to describe the nature of the transported material and its behaviour in the transport system.

For this purpose core samples of the worked rocks were obtained at regular intervals and examined as to their mechanical strength and mineralogical composition. Screen analyses of the cuttings prior to being fed into the mixing tank, were carried out and solids contents of the recycling water were determined as well.

The movement of the slurry within the pipeline could be observed with appropriate lighting through 40 mm thick plexi windows.

For determining the proportions of different causes of disturbance, accounting for the totality of standstill periods, all operational disturbances were recorded on a list which was complemented daily by the master mechanic.

RESULTS

Tunnelling Operation

When starting tunnelling operations, the first 415 mm of

the tunnel were worked using a shuttle car. Subsequently the installation of the mobile pump set was started which took about one week to do. Then the working staff had to get familiarized with the novel technique and the whole system had to be completed. Furthermore the separating plant had to be extended by an installation for water treatment and a decanting tank, as the actual yield of fines turned out to be by some orders of magnitude higher than anticipated. In addition all the pumps had to be operated with a sealing water system due to excessive wear at the threaded bushings and seals.

After 1940 m of stable shale, worked through at satisfactory performances, a disturbed zone came up which had not been anticipated and whose direction of strike was almost in parallel to the tunnel axis. The disturbed zone prevailed over a length of 300 m, delaying the work by approximately nine months. Although the rock prior to the disturbed area was of relatively high mechanical strength, the daily advance rate averaged 19 m/d at a 20 hours-a-day service. The mean compressive strength was 112 N/mm^2 and the mean tensile strength 15 N/mm^2. In this section peak advance rates of 30 m/day or 138 m/week or 408 m/month were achieved.

After having overcome the disturbed zone at 2240 m and returned to a normal working schedule, a strongly metamorphic diabase was encountered at 2660 m. Although with 132 N/mm^2 compressive strength and 18.5 N/mm^2 tensile strength the characteristics of this rock exceeded only slightly those of shale, the boreability was by some orders of magnitude worse due to lacking stratification. This did not only result in a higher wear of roller cutters but also in reduced advancing rates which during the three last months averaged 6.7 m/day only, in spite of a 24-hour-a-day service.

Hydraulic System

The measuring data were logged as described above. The subsequently decoded data were then statistically evaluated which included the determination of mean values, variance, standard deviation, range of variation, maximum and minimum values.

Additionally the number of measuring data of each trial was printed out. The relevant mean values formed the basis of the subsequent evaluation (Table 1).

I. MEASUREMENT RESULTS:			
VOLUME FLOW	T =	206.0	m/H
TEMPERATURE	T =	15.0	°C
SLURRY DENSITY	RHO =	1058.0	kg/m
POWER CONSUMPTION	PE =	146.941	kW
PRESSURE BEFORE PUMP 3	P3 =	0.696	bar
PRESSURE BEHIND PUMP 4	P4 =	9.226	bar
PRESSURE AFTER 187 m	PL =	8.191	bar
LENGTH OF PRESSURE DROP	L =	187.0	m
II. DATA EVALUATION			
PIPE CROSSECTION	AR =	0.018	m
FLOW SPEED	VM =	3.24	m/s
POWER CONSUMPTION	PS =	48.807	kW
EFFICIENCY	ET =	33.2	%
PRESSURE DROP (187 m)	PD =	1.0350	bar
REL. PRESSURE DROP	PDL =	0.5535	kpA/m
VOLUME CONCENTRATION	CV =	3.93	%
WATER DENSITY	RHOW =	998.986	kg/m
DYN. VISCOSITY	ETA =	1 140E −3	PAS
CIN. VISCOSITY	NY =	1.140E −6	m/s

Table 1: Measurement results and evaluation

The low volume concentration of 3-4 %, appearing in the evaluation, was a striking phenomenon which had to be attributed mainly to the temporarily low advance rate in the diabase.

Causes of Downtime

As shown on Tabe 2 the recording of downtime periods was made in three sections, section 1 including the starting up phase, section 2 and 3 cover the characteristic data of "normal" drivage. Whereas the different causes of downtime are specified in the form, the table classifies them in five categories for better readability.

A closer look on the percentages shows that the operational time of machinery diminishes with work progress which is probably due to general wear of all of the heading equipment. The category "tunnelling machine" remains stable at 30 % from the beginning of the job. As to the category "hydraulic transport", a clear decrease of disturbances along with work progress can be seen. This is not only a proof that the working staff has become familiar with the unusual technic, but also that the additions and improvements introduced over the time have

	26.7.77 - 13.11.77 85 OPERATING DAYS	24.8.78 - 17.11.78 60 OPERATING DAYS	1.2.79 - 1.5.79 75 OPERATING DAYS
(1) TOTAL OPERATION TIME	120.960 min	86.005 min	109.800 min
(2) TUNNELBORER OPERATION	48 %	49 %	43 %
(3) DOWNTIME	52 %	51 %	57 %
(4) TUNNELBORER	33 %	30 %	31 %
(5) HYDRAULIC TRANSPORT	28 %	23 %	13 %
(6) MECHANICEL TRANSPORT	3 %	15 %	26 %
(7) MAINTENANCE	16 %	9 %	8 %
(8) PIPE EXTENSION	7 %	10 %	8 %
(9) OTHER	13 %	13 %	9 %

Table 2: Downtime of overall tunnelling system

had a positive effect.

The percentage of disturbances of lately 13 % mainly account for the categories "solids pipeline" and "pumps".

The mechanical transport installation, transferring the waste from the cutter head towards the feeding tank, turned out to be an unexpected point of weakness. The percentage of disturbances of originally 3 % had lately reached 26 %. The weak point in this system was not so much the telescopic conveyor but rather the scraper conveyor which, when the water flow at the face was strong, over its entire length moved in a kind of mud rich in solid matter, acting like an abrasive paste on the mobile elements of the scraper conveyor

The percentage of maintenance had been reduced due to the fact that initially there was only a 20-hour-day service so that, with a 24-hour service, the 4 hours/day of maintenance work were no longer included in that figure.

Energy Consumption

Apart from the wearing of pipeline and pump elements, it is the energy consumption which has a critical influence on the cost of hydraulic transport. When plotting the monthly cost of electric current for hydraulic transport on the transport distance, the curve as per Fig. 5 is obtained for the excavation of the Radau tunnel. The diagramme makes it obvious that in this specific case

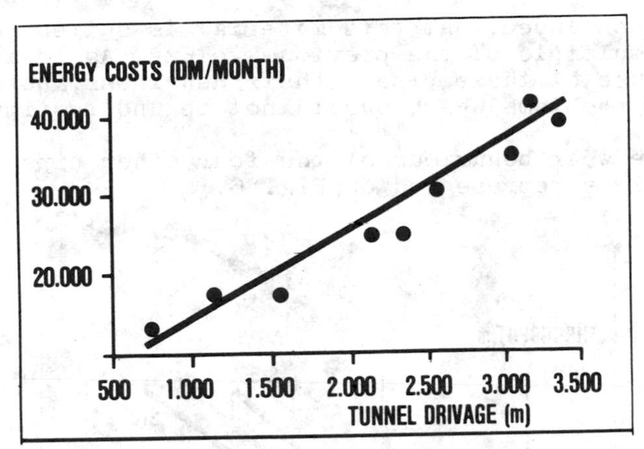

Fig. 5: Energy costs of hydraulic debris disposal on Radau-Tunnel drivage

the energy cost shows a stronger dependency on the transport distance than on the solids concentration.

Wear and Tear

As already outlined, a test section out of various pipe materials had been assembled in order to determine the pipe qualities best suited for the hydraulic transport of debris. The results, however, are of limited nature only, since the instrument for measuring the various wall thicknesses was not available for a longer period of time. It turned out within relatively short that neither PVC pipes nor glass fibre reinforced pipes are suited for the hydraulic transport of solids. The throughput of solids was of approximately 1500 m^3 which is equivalent to a tunnel length of 360 m.

The pipe section subjected to the most severe load was, as with many pipes, directly behind the flange joint. This is the reason why much attention should be given to a careful pipe installation with perfectly aligned joints in order to exclude any formation of turbulences.

Whereas with glass fibre reinforced pipes, when worn down to the minimum wall thickness, a hole due to pressure occurs at the weakest point, PVC pipes burst lengthwise.

Pipes coated with cast basalt showed negligible traces of wear after a throughput of 4500 m^3 from which may be concluded that this material is suited for handling a multiple of the previous volume. As to an underground use of these pipes, their heaviness, however, creates problems which should not be underestimated.

The wear behaviour of the four other pipe sections on trial is represented on Fig. 6.

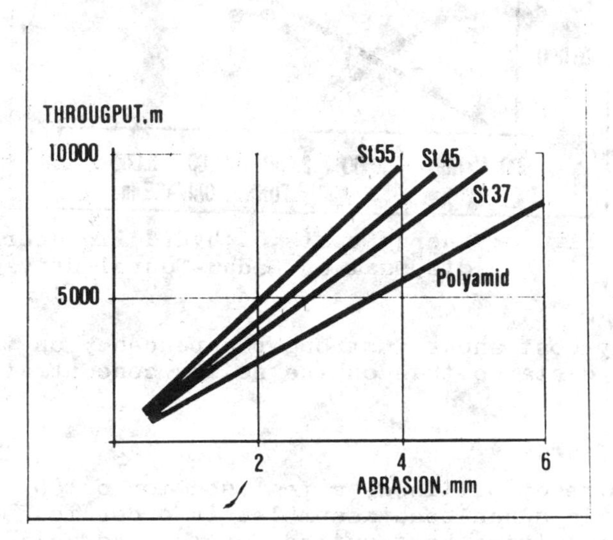

Fig. 6: Pipe wall abrasion for various pipe materials and qualities as function of throughput

The wall thickness of the polyamide pipe was 7 mm. It can be assumed to reach a service life of sharply 8000 m^3 rock throughput or 1900 m of drivage length.

As to the regular type of steel pipe St 37-2, having wall thickness between 3 and 4 mm, the measured wear can be checked by the calculable pipe consumption. Thus, for a drivage length of 1230 m, i.e. for a solids throughput of 5200 m^3, an average of 3000 m of pipe length is required, corresponding to 2.43 times the tunnel length.

Taking the ordinary quality St 37 as 100 %, one may say that with pipes of St 45 + 13 %, of St 55 + 30 %, and with polyamide pipes 25 % of debris throughput are attainable.

Since the cost of solid pipeline is crucial overall cost factor, one should at any rate make use of the possibility of measuring wall thickness and of turning the pipes around systematically. If these precautions are carefully observed, the attainable throughput can be increased by three times.

Nearly no abrasion occurred in the water recycling pipeline of polyethylene NW 200. When working through the diabase zone the recycling water had a mean solids content of 12 to 15 g/l of fines with grain sizes below 60 µm.

With the conditions in the Radau tunnel, and with a transport speed of 3.5 m/s, the solids distribution in the slurry became inhomogeneous in so far as the solids concentration increased towards the pipe bottom, forming a heterogeneous suspension.

It could be observed through the plexi-window sections that with said speed no solids deposited on the pipe bottom so that a case of rolling/bouncing movement was obtained. Due to gravity the bigger grain sizes rolled on the pipe bottom whereas with decreasing grain sizes the movements gradually developed into bounces and, ultimately, into a floating movement of the small particles.

Pumps

Originally all the pumps had been equipped with impellers of HBV 450 VG and with casings of the softer HBV 440 material which, however, showed signs of heavy wear within short. Therefore the highly abrasion resistant, but at the same time brittle HBV 450 VG material was adopted as the best solution also for pump casings.

Table 3 lists the pump components having caused the highest proportion of disturbances.

The high percentage of disturbances by defects at threaded bushings and shaft protection sleeves has to be attributed to the fact that in the initial phase of hydraulic transport the solids-handling pumps were operated without sealing water. Thus, due to the alterating bending stresses on the pump shaft, very small particles penetrated into the seals between shaft and impeller hub. When all other means of reducing the wear of these pump components had failed, a sealing water system was installed. The initial troubles in supplying water, at a pressure of approx. 12 to 15 bar, to the seals of the solids handling pumps were overcome soon. The majority, i.e. 40 % of disturbances was due to wear at casings, impellers, flanges, and bends. Relevant damages had almost exclusively the

THREADED BUSHINGS. CASING SEALINGS. AND SHAFT PROTECTION SLEEVES	26 %
EXCHANGING OF CASINGS AND PUMPS	17 %
FLANGE AND WEAR PLATES	9 %
BENDS IN THE SURROUNDINGS OF PUMPS	14 %
SEALING WATER SYSTEM	12 %
COUPLINGS AND SHAFTS	8 %
HYDRAULIC DRIVE	3 %
EL. DISTURBANCES OR OTHER	11 %
TOTAL	100 %

Table 3: Downtime of solids-handling pumps

shape of erosions in areas exposed to specifically high flow loads. Provided that in the future highly abrasion resistant materials are used from the beginning, the results in this sector will certainly improve.

On a drivage length of 3000 m, the total expenditure for the purchase of five solids-handling pumps plus hydraulics and including all parts, amounted to DM 277000 or DM 22/m^3 solids throughput.

ECONOMICS OF HYDRAULIC TRANSPORT

Based on the experience with the hydraulic transport system in the Radau tunnel, Table 4 represents the expenditure incurred for "hydraulic transport and separation", given the present state of the art.

Under the heading "investments" is included the expenditure for the first equipment of pumps and drivages, water recycling pipeline, separation plant, electric installations, and other. Cost depreciation of the project is 100 % so that the ultimate cost, calculated on the involved rock volume of 20200 m^3, is relatively high.

The solids pipeline which is highly prone to abrasion as well as cost of spare parts and pump repairs are separately listed. On 3000 m of tunnel length a wear factor of

	DM/m
(1) INVESTMENTS	67.6
(2) SLURRY PIPELINE	17.3
(3) PUMPS	13.0
(4) ENERGY	25.9
(5) MATERIAL	4.5
(6) PERSONNEL	71.4
(1) - (6) TOTAL	199.7

Table 4: Effective costs of hydraulic debris disposal on Radau-Runnel drivage

2.43 for the solids pipeline was found. Thus for a total tunnel length of 4800 m the resulting pipe length is 11660 m. The cost of the pipe quality St 37 used for the Radau tunnel is DM 30/m including joints.

The indicated energy cost is a calculated average on 3000 m of tunnel length; the figure is expected to slightly increase with continued drivage.

The amount spent on consumables is mainly due to flocculants required for separation.

As to the recording of labour, 5 manshifts per day were calculated, whereof 2 men account for operating the control desk and one man per day for maintenance and repair. Labour cost for the Radau tunnel amounted to DM 45/h. 9 m of daily drivage performance was taken as a basis for a 24 hours job site occupancy.

FURTHER DEVELOPMENTS

Any efforts of improving hydraulic transport in combination with a full-face tunnel boring machine are mainly aimed at a safe limitation of the preferably low maximum grain size as well as at an optimum utilization of the installation by ensuring a uniform solids feed.

Although the pumps can handle grain sizes up to 80 mm diameter, their mechanical load increases along with the grain size of the pulp.

Still more important is the fact that the required transport speed and, thus, the energy consumption of the pumps is a function of the maximum size fraction and its settling speed.

It could be clearly observed through the plexi window section that due to varying transport speeds the coarse size fraction acts as a kind of die restriction of the following faster small size fraction. These phenomena are doubtlessly responsible for pipe cloggings. Important prerequisite of an optimum solids concentration would therefore be a safe limitation of the upper grain size which for the Radau tunnel job should not be above 25 mm. Screen analyses of the cuttings showed that 12 to 15 % of the feed material, however, were above 25 mm, not to forget that this proportion was probably considerably higher when cutting through disturbed zones. It would be useful therefore if a crusher with subsequent screening installation can be installed between telescopic conveyor and feed tank.

When designing the Radau tunnel transport installation, a maximum solids volume concentration of approximately 12 % was assumed. As can be seen from Table 1, giving examples of plant utilization, the average concentration obtained, however, lay between 3 and 4 % only, as the scheduled drivage speed had not been attained. Since the amount of energy cost is mainly a function of transport distance and operational time of the transport system, which means that these factors would hardly decrease with lower solids concentration, it should be possible to reduce energy cost by as much as 75 %, provided an optimum plant utilization.

Intercalation of a bunker having a capacity between 8 and 10 m^3 could help to solve the problem. This would not only allow a uniform feed of solids but, furthermore, the design of the hydraulic transport system would not need to comply with the maximum speed of one length of drivage, instead of which it would be fully sufficient if the system were synchronised to the average bunker throughput rhythm of 15 to 25 minutes.

Another important item is the adjustability of the transport system.

It may be supposed that with feable density variations of the transport pulp the consistency of the pumped mix will be adjusted automatically. The extent of automatic adjustment, however, is not sufficient in case of a non homogeneous solids feed and longer transport distances.

In order to cope with such a situation, the adjustable pump should be maintained at the speed required for the addition of solids as long as there are solids in the line. If the solids flux stops abruptly, consequently more recycling water should be pumped into the tank. Within the Radau system the recycling water pump had not been integrated into the regulating circuit.

When using hydraulic transport in combination with tunnelling, there is another problem in so far as pressure conditions between the mobile pump set and the constant delivery pumps are always changing.

This specific situation requires a control device which integrates any and all transport elements and, additionally, the whole range of changing conditions.

POSSIBLE COST SAVINGS

Finally it has to be examined where and to which extent cost reduction against the Radau tunnel project will be possible. Similar to the simplified representation of expenditure used previously, the cost-saving effect of possible improvements has been determined (Table 5).

	DM/m³
(1) INVESTMENTS	76.3
(2) SLURRY PIPELINE	11.9
(3) PUMPS	6.5
(4) ENERGY	6.5
(5) MATERIAL	4.5
(1) - (5) TOTAL	105.7

Table 5: Optimized costs of hydarulic debris disposal on Radau-Tunnel drivage

The extraordinarily high expenditures on energy for the Radau tunnel are mainly a consequence of the low volume concentration of solids between 3 and 4 %. Any relevant improvements, however, require not only a control installation including the whole transport system but, moreover, a safe limitation of maximum grain sizes as well as a bunker facility. All this would mean an increase of investment capital to some 76.3 DM/m^3 (by 8.7 DM/m^3) whereas energy cost would drop by 19.4 DM provided an optimum utilization of the plant. As regards the solids pipeline, there is a chance of saving 1.9 DM/m^3 on condition that the polyamide pipes on which the calculation is based, be checked for wear, installed carefully and turned as required.

By the experience gained it should be possible to reduce by 50 % the cost of spare parts and pump repairs whereas no saving is possible with regard to operational cost. Labour cost has not been included in the table since it depends critically on the average drivage performance. A cost saving of approximately 10 % may be possible.

The still relatively high costs are mainly influenced by the investments because of the short length of tunnel for depreciation. Most parts, included in the investments, have, however, a far longer lifetime. The overall costs for hydraulic transport can therefore be further reduced to perhaps such a degree that they can compete with conventional transport methods, allowing, however, higher advance rates for tunnel boring of small diameter and long tunnels.

LARGE SCALE SYSTEM

The companies participating in the Radau project have carried out studies showing the orders of magnitude of cost to be expected for a large scale hydraulic transport system in connection with mechanical tunnel drivage (Table 6).

Following design data served as a calculation base: road diameter of 6,0 m, road length of 5000 m, average drivage performance/day of 15 m.

From these figures a cost charge of ca. 33 DM/m^3 of rock, i.e. ca. 950 DM/m of tunnel drivage for the removal of drillings can be derived. These costs are comparable with conventional methods for debris disposal, i.e. mine car or conveyor belt system. Hydraulic debris disposal can therefore be considered as technically and economically feasible means of transport technique for tunnel boring projects in underground coal mines.

	DM/m
(1) INVESTMENTS (incl. pipeline)	14.0
(2) ENERGY	5.0
(3) MATERIAL	5.0
(4) MAINTENANCE & REPAIRS	1.5
(5) EXCAVATIONS & FOUNDATIONS etc.	2.0
(6) TRANSPORT EQUIPMENT	0.5
(7) PERSONNEL	5.0
(1) - (7) TOTAL	33.0

Table 6: Calculated costs of hydraulic debris disposal from large scale tunnel boring with 6 m diameter

SUMMARY

Debris disposal is a major disturbing factor for tunnel boring under coal mining conditions. Experience has shown that the capacity of tunnel boring machines could not be fully utilized hitherto without creating bottlenecks in the subsequent road transport system. The Radau tunnelling project in the Harz region made use of a hydraulic transport system for the removal of cuttings.

Based on this pilot installation the fundamentals of the system and the mechanical concept of hydraulic waste removal in combination with a full-face tunnel boring machine of 6 m diameter have been elaborated.

Aside from measurements on the transport flow, abrasion tests were carried out and causes of breakdowns recorded. A final study on the economics included a comparison of expenditure incurred in the Radau project against the cost-saving effect of eventual improvements. Furthermore a cost estimate of a hydraulic transport installation in combination with a full-face tunnel boring machine of 6 m diameter has been performed.

20

Ground Control in Mining

Chairman: D. Pentz

Golder Associates, Inc., Kirkland, WA

Chapter 85

A NEW DEVICE OF A HYDRAULIC DRILL FOR ANCHORS

Yasuo Takeuchi and Yuji Tsuneno

Tobishima Corp. (General Contractor)
Tokyo, Japan

Yoshikazu Mikami

Furukawa Co., Ltd.
Tokyo, Japan

ABSTRACT

A new device was successfully developed in order to overcome the difficulty of drilling longer holes for anchors in soft soil bedrocks or swelling bedrocks, which is one of the major impediments to rapid excavation by NATM (New Austrian Tunnelling Method). With higher rotation (1200 - 1800 r.p.m.) and lower percussion energy (4 - 6 kg.m), the new drill has following advantages:

(1) Applicability covers soils and medium hard rocks with the same drifter.
(2) Longer hole (more than 9m) is achievable only with air flushing even in cohesive soils or rocks.
(3) Better borehole stability is obtainable even in earth or in fissured rocks.

I. NATM IN JAPAN

1. Introduction of NATM to Japan

It is only 5 to 6 years since tunnel engineers in Japan first came to know about NATM. Until about 1975, literature and information on NATM, which had already been widely used in Europe, was gradually finding its way to Japan. During the past several years, however, a great amount of information, on the theory and practice of NATM has rapidly flooded into Japan and has had a great influence on Japanese tunnelling technology at a time when tunnelling engineers in Japan are encountering numerous technical problems.

Today, almost all Japanese engineers realise that NATM, --- compared to conventional methods which have long been in use in Japan, --- is an extremely rational and useful tunnelling method based on a new application of rock mechanics.

During the period 1955 - 60, the steel rib support system was introduced to Japan from the USA. This was considered a revolutionary method and has made a great contribution to rock tunnelling in Japan. Use of the steel rib support had many advantages; to secure more work space in the tunnel, to improve safety, and efficiency of performance, to reduce the number of skilled labourers, etc. This method was also found economically satisfactory aside from the problem of the endurance of tunnel. Nevertheless, this method of support was considered almost the only one available at the time.

Today many engineers believe that NATM tunnels where the method is used give better endurance. This unique method, when it is further studied and improved, is now perceived as the dominant method in the future not only for rock tunnelling but also urban tunnelling. NATM is considered to have brought about another revolution in tunnel construction even greater than the aforementioned steel rib support method.

2. To what degree is NATM practiced in Japan?

About five years have passed since NATM was introduced to Japan and the method is already so popular that many engineers believe that it will certainly become the most widely used method of rock tunnelling. In fact, the number of tunnelling sites using NATM has been increasing greatly.

Apart from actual construction work, various organizations mentioned below have seriously taken up the subject of NATM and played a role as a driving force:

1) The Japan Society of Civil Engineers (JSCE) and the Japan Tunneling Association (JTA) (who have been actively engaged in research and study.)
2) Japanese National Railways (JNR), Japan Railway Construction Public Corporation (JRCPC), Ministry of Construction (who have played a pioneering role)
3) Japan Highway Public Corporation (who, in the past one-two years, has employed NATM on its projects.)

What is noteworthy is the fact that local autonomous authorities have shown keen interest in NATM and are using this method extensively for construction of roads, subways and sewerage projects. In the electric power industry, the method is being actively adopted not only for water tunnels, but for the excavation of large scale underground caverns for underground power houses.

At an early stage when NATM was being introduced to Japan, the method attracted our interest in relation to tunnelling in swelling rock or unsolidified ground. The tendency in the past 2 to 3 years is for the application of NATM to attain almost the level in Europe, and it has been extended to medium and hard rock for the waterways of hydro power plants. More recently, NATM has been applied not only to mountain rock tunnels but also to urban subway tunnels, tunnels for water supply and drainage, and for electric cables in lieu of the shield driving method, in order to prevent ground subsidence above the tunnel, although the application in urban areas is still limited. In line with the tendency mentioned above, Japanese National Railways and Japan Railway Construction Public Corporation have started the preparation of standard designs for various bedrock classifications for NATM, and JSCE through its research activities has been making efforts to formulate a standard specification for this method.

3. Problems associated with NATM

The execution of NATM is still at an early stage, although there are not a few precedents in Japan. Tunnelling engineers have come to notice in the course of designing and executing NATM that there are many problems which need to be examined in relation to the particular circumstances and environments in Japan, in order to promote this Method.

In regard to execution, the major areas for study are technical developments with respect to excavation, shotcrete and measurement as well as worker's proficiency in applying the new method, and the development of machines related to NATM by contractors and machinery manufacturers. In this connection, Tobishima Corporation, as a contractor, together with Furukawa Company, a machinery maker, have joined together to develop a rock bolt jumbo in order to improve the efficiency of the rock bolting work.

I would like to explain how rock bolts have been used in Japan, before I describe the rock bolt jumbo in detail, the theme of this paper. Rock bolting was gradually introduced in tunnelling work in Japan during the years 1960 to 1965. During this period, some testing of rock bolting was carried out in certain mines and mountain rock tunnelling. However, since steel support had been in wide use, rock bolting was not used on a large scale.

Since it was recognized, however, as an economical support in hard rock tunnelling, rock bolts gradually came into use in the latter half of the nineteen sixties, e.g. mainly for the hard rock tunnels of the Sanyo New Trunk Line, the Tomei Highway and various underground power houses. But, in these cases, the advantage of rock bolting as compared with steel rib supports was not fully apparent. Therefore rock bolting did not prevail widely.

As mentioned above, NATM had been gaining popularity since around 1975. As it can be used in soft rock tunnels, rock bolts, especially fully grouted rock bolts, came to attract attention, because of their superior supporting capability. NATM was applied experimentally at the JNR Joetsu New Trunk Line, Nakayama Tunnelling Project where much difficulty was encountered due to swelling rock conditions at the site. In this trial, NATM proved effective in restraining the expansivity of the rock. Soon after, in pioneering spirit, NATM was adopted in a decomposed granite soil at the site of JNR Tohoku New Trunk Line, Daiichi Hiraishi Tunnelling Project and some other projects. Owing to the successful execution of NATM for these projects, this new method became the centre of engineers' attention. (In the years 1978, 1979 successively, the Japan Society of Civil Engineers Prize for technology, the highest prize for civil engineering technology in Japan, was awarded to projects where NATM had been used.) It has been definitely demonstrated that rock bolts have as much efficacy as supporting means and a wide range of application. With spread of NATM, various kinds of rock bolts have come on the market and their range of application is extending from hard rock to brittle and plastic rock. Consequently both the length of the hole and the rock bolts must be made longer. In addition, the use of special machines is required to promote drilling efficiency (and it is also required that the booms of machine are designed efficiently to cope with the drilling capability and systematic rock bolting).

Fig. 1 Rock bolts in the Seikan Tunnel

II. THE REASONS FOR DEVELOPMENT OF A ROCK BOLTING JUMBO

There is no denying the fact that the speed of the execution of NATM in Japan --- is almost one half to one third of that of European countries --- and this has been an obstacle to its development as an up-to-date construction method.

Rock bolting, which is one of the major work processes in the execution of NATM, usually consists of the repetition of a cyclic operation, namely --- drilling, bolt insertion and bolt fastening.

It is necessary to achieve a maximum of efficiency with a minimum of workers and to keep progress ahead of the tunnel excavation work.

According to the interim construction report for the Nabedate Tunnelling Project, (a site which is notorious for its swelling mudstone) rock bolting work takes as much as a half of the whole excavation working time. At the tunnelling technology symposium promoted by Japan Tunnelling Association, held in November, 1980 --- "Rock bolting work for NATM" ---, panels earnestly discussed the following subjects.

* As the drilling work takes most of the cycle time in the rock bolting, a long-hole drilling machine should be developed which can be applied to every type of ground from hard to soft rock, including swelling rock conditions.

* Above all, a more effective method for drilling in swelling rock should be devised.

* Some opinions were expressed that a suitable drilling machine would be more likely hydraulically than pneumatically powered drills. Hydraulic drills exceed pneumatic drills in speed of penetration and in the capacity to drill long holes. Further they have an advantage with respect to better working conditions, that is to say, they do not generate so much noise. But we must not overlook the fact that hydraulic drills require more maintenance than pneumatic drills.

* Hydraulic drills are not necessarily limited to hard rock, --- they have the possibility of wide-spread application. The worse the ground condition, the more the section for excavation is sub-divided, --- for this reason a reduction in machine size should be sought in the development of suitable drill.

* High speed and high torque hydraulic, and percussive drills should be devised, because the use of water for drilling a hole in swelling rock caused much trouble. The shape of the rods and bits, as well as the machine itself, holds the key for greater efficiency, so they should be designed in accordance with the respective ground conditions at various sites.

As may be seen from the above, there was a lively discussion and the necessity for the early development of an ideal drill was fully emphasized.

III. PROCESS OF DEVELOPMENT

Tobishima Corporation is placed among the ten best Japanese general contractors. Above all, tunnelling work is one of its strong points, and Tobishima Corporation enjoys the well-established reputation of "Tobishima for Tunnelling".

When it comes to NATM projects Tobishima realized a pioneering achievement when it completed the Daiichi Hiraishi Tunnel for JNR Tohoku New Trunk Line. While carrying out this project, the staff realized that prompt execution depended upon the superior operating efficiency of long drills particularly in soft layers and that this was essential in order that NATM takes root and spreads in Japan.

For this reason Tobishima Corporation has been developing a drill, for NATM in collaboration with The Furukawa Company, Ltd. This combination has been responsible for the design and manufacture of many new kinds of tunnelling machines.

Their new machine was put into experimental use at The Narita Airport Tunnel Project in a saturated sandy silt, and for the construction of headrace and spillway tunnels, for the Arima dam project mainly in chert and clayey slate. The results of these tests were given at a public presentation in August, 1979.

We firmly believe that the Tobishima-Furukawa machine will improve the speed of tunnelling and become a milestone in the development of NATM in Japan.

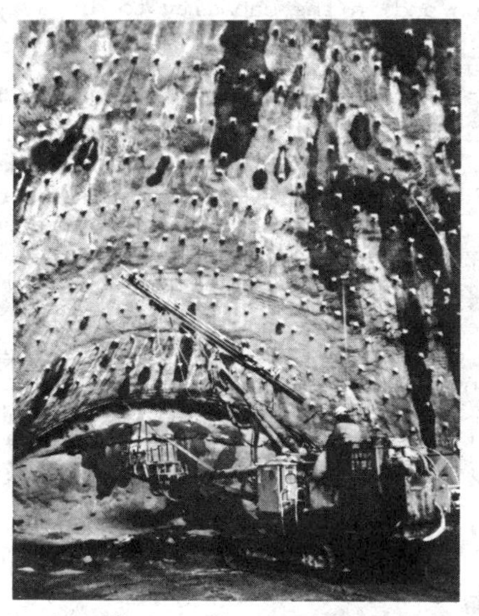

Fig. 2. Rock bolt jumbo in spillway inclined tunnel of Arima dam project

VI. MECHANISM AND CHARACTERISTICS

Until 1979 when the Tobishima-Furukawa machine was made public, no machine had been devised for the use exclusively for drilling long holes in soft or swelling rock. A foreign-made machine was used experimentally only at one mine site. In fact, certain problems would occur if we applied the machine, as it is, to common tunnelling.

The following types of drills have been used for rock bolting in common rock tunnelling:

1) The most common leg-drills or leg-hammers which were devised mainly for drilling blast hole in medium or hard rock and occasionally stopers for upward drilling.
2) Crawlers and big machines such as grantry-mounted-jumbos.
3) Pneumatic rotary-drills which were mainly used for drilling in soft rock and sandy rock.

These conventional machines, however, tended to limit the range of possible drilling angles. In particular, the long boreholes in clayey ground containing gravel stratum were almost impossible to drill with such machines and, even when successful, there was considerable loss of time and other problems especially in the case of upward or downward holes required for rock bolting works. In the soft and swelling rock frequently encountered in Japan, the rapid drilling of holes 2 - 9m in length and 40 - 50mm in diameter without using water, with subsequent bolting, is sometimes required to be done adjacent to the face immediately after excavation. For these reasons, the new machine had to comply with these conditions and at the same time achieve a shorter work cycle and improved quality of workmanship. The special rock bolt jumbo which we have recently developed can comply with most of these requirements. It has the following characteristics:

1) It can cope with almost all types of bedrock inclusive of soils.
2) The problem of the debris which adheres to the rod when a cohesive soil is drilled by rotary-drill has been solved by a system of high rotation speed and low percussive power of the rod hence enabling the drilling of pebble and gravel formations. Drilling hard rock can also be readily accomplished, if only the high powered hydraulic drill with greater percussive power instead.
3) The fan-cut and face-cut are possible with only one boom and also the radial drilling system makes for easy upward, downward and horizontal drilling. The machine is also small enough to be handled within the limited work space in the tunnel. It has been designed so as to be operable together with mucking loaders in the top heading excavation (with sectional dimensions of $17m^2$) of a single track-type tunnel of Japanese National Railways.
4) The simultaneous use of the drill rod which we developed concurrently with the rock bolt jumbo also helps to make efficient drilling possible in more complex geological conditions.

a) In cohesive geological conditions, the wet debris is easily discharged with the help of speeded air-flushing effect created by the adoption of a larger air supply hole at the center of the rod and the reduced discharge sectional area obtained by diminishing the gap in diameters of drill hole and rod. The debris which has adhered to the rod surface is shaken off by the centrifugal force caused by the increased speed of rod rotation, and the percussion of the rod itself. These improved conditions resulted in relatively smooth hole surfaces and achieved a long drill-hole length by air-flushing without use of water. The trials performed on the tunnel at Narita Airport proved that it is possible to drill a 9m long hole at a speed three times as fast as with the conventional drill. In hard rock drilling, it also indicated approximately twice the efficiency in speed in comparison with a D95 Drifter which is considered one of the most common pneumatic models of heavy-drill in use in Japan.

b) The automatically controlled drill with measured feed, power and number of percussion ensures highly efficient drilling without causing the jamming of the bit in soft rock conditions with friable rock, pebbles and gravel stratum where conventional drills are almost incapable of coping.

5) The hydraulic percussion system is adopted in order to increase the percussion power on the bit. This is particularly required when drilling gravel formations and rock. The efficiency of energy consumption has thus improved approximately three-fold compared to that of the pneumatic drill.

6) Large holes up to about 125mm in diameter can be drilled.

Because of the above features, rock bolting for NATM has been speeded up two-fold and realized savings in bolting cost, the shortened work period and the enhanced quality of workmanship and has led to a reduction in manpower.

The drifter mounted on the machine has a high drilling capacity capable of handling from soft soils to medium and hard rock up to 98 MN/m^2 (1000 kgf/cm^2). Its specifications are detailed in the attached sheet (see Tables 1 and 2). The rpm and torque are 1,800 and 98 - 245 N·m(10 - 25 kgf·m) respectively and the frequency of percussion 1,000 - 1,500 blows/m. This is 6 times the rpm but ¼ times the percussive power of a conventional hydraulic rock drill while 1.8 times the rpm and 5 - 6 times the torque of a conventional pneumatic rotary drill (see Table 2).

V. OBJECTIVES OF FURTHER DEVELOPMENT

Encouraged by the successful achievement of high quality drilling of undisturbed boreholes of 9m in length in swelling rock and cohesive ground which was once believed almost impossible to deal with, we have embarked upon the further development of the following two objectives; one, to modify the present unifunctional machine into a multi-functional drill to meet the various work requirements, and the other is to speed up its operational efficiency.

With these two objectives in mind, we now intend;

a) To develop a light weight extension guide shell in order to cope with the variety of sectional dimensions of tunnel by a single machine.
b) To develop a rod changer of small size.
c) To automate the process of injecting the grouting materials for rock bolts into the boreholes.
d) To improve the drills so as to meet a wider range of ground conditions and ensure high speed drilling.
e) To modify the drill gear to standardized units so as to be easily adapted to the various models of basic machines.
f) To develop an automatic control system for positioning the drills.

Some of the above objectives are already in the stage of development especially for hard rock tunnelling in Japan. However, those intended to deal with swelling rock, and cohesive geological conditions of friable or soft character remain unsolved, and we intend to make continuous efforts to reach a solution.

TABLE 1. Rock bolt jumbo Technical Specifications

(1) Dimension and weight including base machine

Length	7,800 mm
Width	1,990 mm
Height	2,030 mm
Total weight	11,000 kg

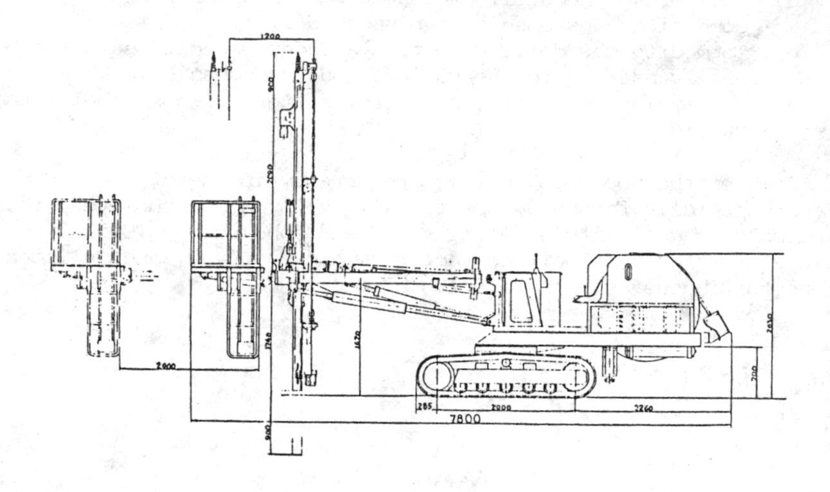

Fig. 3. Rock bolt jumbo

(2) Hydraulic auger drill (with percussion device for soft rocks)

Type		ZC 3725-2
Rotation speed		1200 - 1800 rpm
Torque		98 - 245 N·m (10 - 25 kgf·m)
Number of percussion		1000 - 1500 blows/min
Percussion energy		39 - 59 J/blow
Working oil pressure		
Percussion	maximum	17.5 MPa (175 bar)
	normally	8 - 10 MPa (80 - 100 bar)
Rotation	Maximum	14 MPa (140 bar)
	normally	10 - 12 MPa (100 - 120 bar)
Feed	forward	10 MPa (100 bar)
	backward	14 Mpa (140 bar)
Rod		shank rod or spiral rod (ø32 mm)
Bit		rotary bit (ø34 - 38 mm)
Flushing water system		water swivel or blow

(3) Guide shell

Type	ZC 3725
Length	3,000 mm
Centralizer	Sub-centralizer and end hydraulic centralizer

(4) Boom

Type ZC 3725
Length maximum 4,220 mm
minimum 3,000 mm
Working oil pressure 17.5 MPa (175 bar)
Rotary angle (left/right) $150^{o}/150^{o}$ (total 300°)
Lift angle (up/down) $50^{o}/30^{o}$
Swing angle (left/right) $45^{o}/45^{o}$
Slide Length 1,200 mm
Guide tilt angle (up/down) $105^{o}/50^{o}$ (total 155°)

(5) Charging platform

Type ZC 3725
with synchronized cylinder system
Working oil pressure 17.5 MPa (175 bar)
Boom lift angle (up/down) $50^{o}/30^{o}$
Boom swing angle (left-right) $45^{o}/45^{o}$
Guide tilt angle (up/down) $50^{o}/40^{o}$
with rock bolts rack and control valve

(6) Automatic control and safety system

a) Anti-jamming: To avert rod jamming by monitoring the torque, if the bit encounters difficult rock or fault.

b) Monitoring of water: The feed automatically stops, if water pressure drops less than 0.3 MPa (3 bar) or water flow drops in case of choking in the bit.

c) Monitoring of hydraulic oil: The motor óf the hydraulic pack automatically stops if the oil level in the reservoir drops by some leakage or the oil temperature increases more than $70^{o}C$.

d) Monitoring of electrical accidents: The motor of the hydraulic pack automatically stops in case of electrical leakage, overload, one phase or reverse phase.

TABLE 2. Comparison of Specifications with Other Drills (by Furukawa Co., Ltd.)

drill type	drill for rock bolt jumbo			face drill		auger drill	
	ZC 3725-1	ZC 3725-2	ZC 3725-3	HD-100	D95	AA-1	AAL-5
power	hydraulic	hydraulic	hydraulic	hydraulic	pneumatic	pneumatic	pneumatic
applicable rock condition	hard	medium, soft to soil	soft to soil	hard	medium to hard	soft to soil	soft to soil
weight (kg)	100	100	100	150	90	8.8	12
rotation speed (rpm)	0 - 360	1200 - 1800	1200 - 1800	0 - 360	230	900 - 1000	1000 - 1100
torque (N·m)	294	98 - 245	98 - 245	268	490	20 - 39	20 - 44
percussion energy (J/blow)	127 - 176	39 - 59	—	196	118	—	—
rod	shank rod H 25	shank rod ø 32	shank rod ø 32	shank rod ø 32	inserted taper type	shank rod ø 38	shank rod ø 38
bit	insert bit ø 34 - 38	rotary bit ø 34 - 38	rotary bit ø 34 - 38	insert bit	inserted taper bit	auger bit ø 42	auger bit ø 42
flushing water system	inner water swivel	outer water swivel	outer water swivel	inner water swivel	water tube	outer water swivel	outer water swivel

Chapter 86

AN INVESTIGATION OF STAND-UP TIME OF TUNNELS IN SQUEEZING GROUND

Larry R. Myer[1], Tor L. Brekke[1] Corey T. Dare[2], Robin B. Dill[3], and Gregg E. Korbin[1]

[1]University of California, Berkeley, California
[2]Converse, Davis, Ward and Dixson, San Francisco, California
[3] Haley and Aldrick, Inc., Cambridge, Massachusetts

ABSTRACT

A study was conducted to develop a fundamental understanding of the relationship between the size of an advancing tunnel face, the rate of excavation, and stand-up time in squeezing ground. Stand-up time is defined as the time elapsed after excavation that an unsupported tunnel face will remain stable. Squeezing ground is argillaceous rock or soil that exhibits pronounced time dependence of deformation and strength properties in-situ. A case history study documented the nature, causes, and solutions of several cases of stand-up time problems observed in the field. Then, in the laboratory, a series of physical model tests were performed in which model tunnel size, face advance rate, material properties, and pressure (representing overburden pressure) were varied. Stand-up time was found to increase as advance rate was increased or tunnel size decreased. In addition, an influence of advance rate on the definition of stability ratios was established.

INTRODUCTION

This paper summarizes the results from a laboratory investigation of the relationship between the size of an advancing tunnel face, rate of excavation, and stand-up time in squeezing ground. Stand-up time is defined as the time elapsed after excavation that an unsupported tunnel face will remain stable. Instability should be thought of as not only complete collapse but also the conditions in which the magnitude or rate of ground movement has increased to the point of inhibiting tunnel progress e.g. when a shield is locked in position by squeezing ground. Squeezing ground is a cohesive soil and/or rock that exhibits pronounced time dependence of deformation and strength properties. Clays, fault gauges, decomposed serpentine, highly stressed and sheared weak shales, mudstones, and claystones are examples of such materials.

Stand-up time of a tunnel depends upon the interaction of specific properties of the ground and the physical characteristics of the excavation. Historically, however, there has been little attempt to either define the pertinent properties and characteristics or explain their interaction. Terzaghi (1946) observed that the stand-up time of a tunnel depended to a large extent on the distance from the face to the first support, i.e. the reach. From a number of observations in Europe, Lauffer (1958) observed that for any given ground condition the stand-up time decreased drastically with increasing length of the active span as defined in Figure 1. Lauffer's findings are illustrated in Figure 2. As there must be a resonable relation between the active span and the height of the tunnel face, Lauffer, by inference, found a pronounced reduction of stand-up time with increasing tunnel size. Although his work has been somewhat updated and modified by Underwood (1968) and Bieniawski (1974), Lauffer's results have essentially remained the only semi-quantitative assessment of stand-up time.

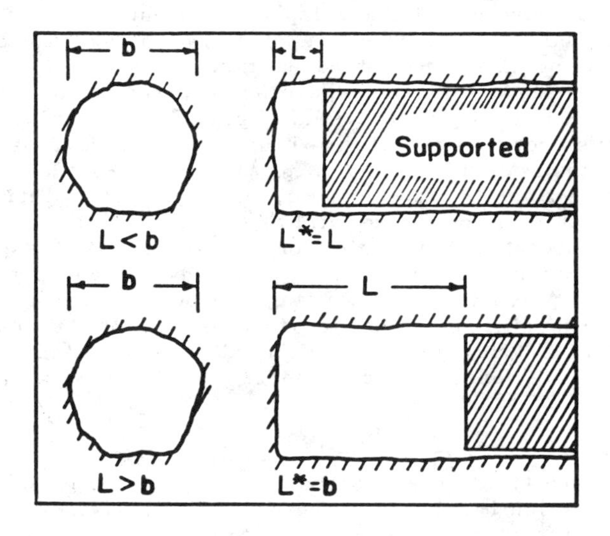

Fig. 1. Definition of "Active Span", L^* (after Lauffer, 1958).

A case history study was performed to document the nature, cause, and solution of stand-up time problems observed in the field. Numerous factors were identified as influencing stand-up time. Of these, four were selected for further investigaiton: (1) Advance rate of the face; (2) In-situ stress conditions; (3) Tunnel size, and (4) Material properties of the ground. The most pertinent material properties appeared to be the time dependent, or creep properties, and material strength.

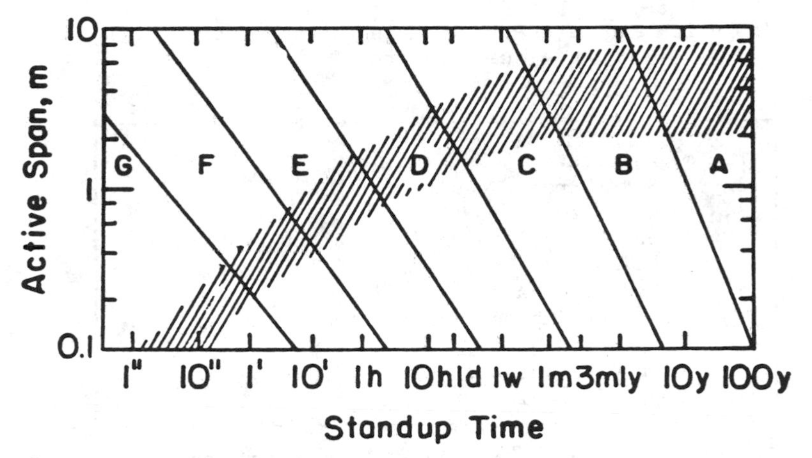

Fig. 2. Active span versus stand-up time. A - Best Rock Mass, G - Worst Rock Mass. Shaded area indicates the practical range (after Lauffer, 1958).

A physical model was selected as the means to investigate the factors mentioned above. A set of model scaling laws were derived and, based on these, a modeling material and model equipment were developed. Squeezing ground was represented by a mixture of sand and wax. Equipment to continuously excavate a model tunnel while simultaneously lining it was also developed. Model tests were then performed in which tunnel size, advance rate, overall boundary stresses and material properties were varied. The effects of these parameters on stand-up time were studied by recording the movements of the material around the tunnel both during and after excavation.

LITERATURE REVIEW AND CASE HISTORY STUDY

As indicated by case histories, some of the most important factors influencing stand-up time are listed in Table 1. This study also demonstrated that actual stand-up time problems are caused by combinations of these factors making it impossible to single out any one factor as the most important. Nevertheless, the first four factors reappeared persistently enough to warrant further consideration.

Strength of the ground

A reasonable representation of material strength relative to tunnel stability is the ratio of strength to depth of cover. Such a ratio was first suggested by Broms and Bennermark (1967) for vertical openings such as a hole in a sheet pile retaining wall and, by analogy, for a tunnel face. In a laboratory model they determined that stable conditions were maintained for

$$(P_z - P_a)/S_u < 6.3 - 7.5,$$

Table 1. Parameters influencing stand-up time in a squeezing ground

1. Advance Rate
2. In-Situ Stress Conditions
3. Tunnel Size
4. Strength and Deformation Characteristics of the Excavated Ground (material properties)
5. Method of Excavation
6. Method of Support/Reinforcement/Lining
7. Unsupported Span
8. Groundwater Conditions
9. Shape of Opening

where P_z = total overburden pressure, P_a = air pressure greater than atmospheric, and S_u = undrained shear strength. A similar study by Attewell and Boden (1971) found the minimum ratio for stability to be 4.5. From a compilation of case histories, Peck (1969) suggested that a stability ratio of 5 be used. As an example, the Tyholt Tunnel in Norway (Hartmark, 1964; Broms and Bennermack, 1967) was excavated in soft clay with no stability problems except when values of $(P_z - P_a)/S_u$ were greater than 6.

While the stability ratio using depth of center and strength as parameters is helpful in normally consolidated materials, it can be misleading in other geologic settings. For example, high horizontal stresses are often encountered. In addition, narrow zones of weak materials such as clay gouge may not exhibit squeezing because of arching or a size effect. The stability ratio is also not sufficient in itself to determine if a stand-up time problem will arise because it does not take into account factors such as size and advance rate. For example, stability problems were experienced during full face excavation of some of the Antwerp, Belgium, gas storage chambers (deBeer and Buttiens, 1966) in clay with a P_z/S_u ratio of 4.1 (Peck 1969). Excavation was successfully continued by preceding the main face with a smaller pilot bore which was then enlarged to full size.

Time Dependence of Deformation and Strength Properties of the Ground

This study was restricted to ground types which exhibit time dependent or creep behavior, i.e., under uniaxial load a laboratory sample will continue to deform even though the load remains constant. If the ratio of applied load to strength is sufficiently large, samples will often deform at a constant rate for a period of time followed by accelerated deformation to failure (Figure 3).

Behavior analogous to that observed in laboratory samples was noted in the case histories. Time dependent material properties

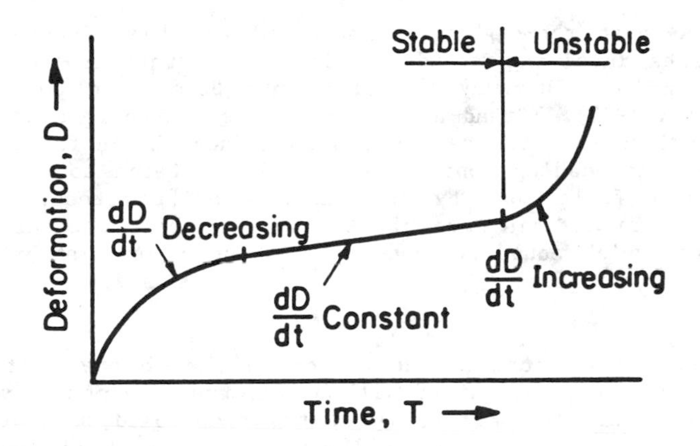

Fig. 3. Typical deformation-time history of a laboratory sample of a material which exhibits creep

were evidenced by continued movement of walls and face into the tunnel after excavation had stopped. Instability was preceded by accelerating deformations. Reporting on a highway tunnel constructed in the Alps, Rabcewicz (1975) noted that the major difficulty was one of large deformations, which if not checked, led to collapse or large fallouts. During remining of a collapsed zone in the Carly V. Porter Tunnel in the Tehachapi Mountains of California (Arnold et al., 1972), the ground squeezed into the tunnel at rates which varied from a few centimeters per day to about a half meter per day. Subsequently, the squeeze accelerated, and in one 48 hour period the ground advanced 4.5 m to 6 m into the tunnel, sweeping away the breastboards at the face. Brekke and Howard (1972) reported an incident in the Henderson Mine Haulage Tunnel, Colorado, in which a bulkhead had been erected due to squeeze in a fault zone. The squeezing ground pushed the bulkhead into the tunnel at a rate of a few centimeters per hour and then accelerated to move run over the bulkhead, filling the tunnel.

Excavation Size

In several cases where instability threatened or occurred, adequate stand-up time was obtained through reduction in the size of the face being advanced in any one heading. The troubled area of the Carly V. Porter Tunnel mentioned above was finally advanced using the multiple drift method. Prior to using this method, a top heading and wallplate drift were attempted, but abondoned due to instability. The 4.6 m by 5.2 m Henderson Haulage Tunnel was pushed through the fault zone using the top heading and bench method. During full face excavation of the Wilson tunnel in silty clay in Hawaii (Peck 1969), ravelling became a problem. By advancing the face by a multiple drift method the stand-up time was increased to the extent that overbreak and ravelling were eliminated.

One of the most thoroughly investigated and best documented tunnel projects involving stand-up time considerations was the Dwight D. Eisenhower Highway Tunnel, North Bore, in Colorado (Hopper, et al. 1972). Stand-up time problems at the face of the top heading driven from the east and a full face shield frozen in place in the west heading contributed to the decision to advance through a major fault zone by the multiple drift method. The finished tunnel dimensions were about 14.6 m by 15 m whereas the size of drifts which could be advanced without major instability were about 2 1/2 m by 3 m.

Advance Rate.

A few cases were found which supported the theory that an adequate advance rate, maintained without interruption could avert stand-up time problems. For example, the decomposed serpentine encountered in the Bay Area Rapid Trasit Fairmount Hill Tunnel (Myer et al., 1977) had a stand-up time of one to six hours. The cutter head of the mole persistently clogged in this material, slowing excavation progress. As the stand-up time was exceeded, additional material washed and collapsed into the tunnel heading. At one point, the overbreak resulted in a 3 m by 3 1/2 m cavity in the roof and a 2 m cavity in the wall.

Underwood (1965) reported on the construction of the Oahe Dam tunnels in Pierre shale. Using a mole, the advance rate in one tunnel was about 21 m per day until a fault was intersected. Progress decreased drastically to 28 m in 30 days with an average overbreak of 6 m. In another instance, 4 1/2 m of unsupported ground was left over the weekend. By Monday, the face had collapsed. The author points out that the major excavation problem was the lack of appreciation of the short stand-up time of the material. Initially, when a fault was encountered and fallout blocked the cutter head of the mole, the practice was to withdraw the machine and "take another run at it" This took too much time and large cave-ins ahead of the machine resulted. When this practice was reversed and the machine was not backed off in bad ground, progress improved.

PHYSICAL MODEL STUDY

Model Laws for the Stand-up Time Model

In any physical model study it is necessary to relate the forces and geometric quantities of the model to analogous quantities of the prototype. The modeling process was greatly simplified by assuming the model tunnel represented an opening "at depth", i.e., greater than three or four diameters below the surface. Thus the scales (numerical relation between model and prototype quantities) of stress and length could be selected independently. The "at depth" assumption allowed the weight of the model material to be ignored. This was reasonable because the stresses due to the weight of the model material were much less than those due to the model loading mechanism.

The scale of stresses was selected as 1 and the scale of length as 1/40. Thus, all stresses in the model were assumed equal to those in a prototype while all dimensions of the model were 1/40 of those in a prototype tunnel.

Scaling of material properties requires information on the constitutive behavior of the prototype material. This information for squeezing ground is, unfortunately, not well defined. Because the time dependent deformation response of the ground appeared to be of major importance, the theory of rheologic behavior of clayey soils was applied to squeezing ground. Some justification of this choice was provided by Semple (1973) who showed that certain fault gouges (a typical example of squeezing ground) could be treated analytically as a clayey soil.

Creep behavior (one dimensional) up to failure of many clayey soils has been satisfactorily described by an equation developed by Singh and Mitchell (1969):

$$\dot{\varepsilon} = Ae^{\overline{\alpha D}}(t_1/t)^m \qquad (1)$$

where A = strain rate at time t_1 and $\overline{D}$ 0 (projected value)
$\overline{\alpha}$ = Slope of linear position of plot of log $\dot{\varepsilon}$ vs log $\overline{D}$ at constant time
$\overline{D}$ = Normalized stress level, deviator stress divided by stress at failure.
t = time
m = minus slope of plot of log $\dot{\varepsilon}$ vs log t

This equation was assumed to describe the rheologic behavior of squeezing ground. As will be discussed, it was possible to develop a model material which closely resembled a natural clayey soil as characterized by the above equation. Assuming the model material was essentially "real" also allowed a time scale of 1.

Model Material Selection

The model material had to meet several criteria: (1) similar in constitutive properties to squeezing ground; (2) reproduceable properties, and (3) workable during model construction to allow embedding of instrumentation.

Based on work by Korbin (1975) a sand-wax mixture seemed most capable of meeting these criteria. Selection of an appropriate sand-wax mixture proceedced in two stages: (1) initial selection from results of unconfined compression tests, and (2) final selection and characterization from results of unconfined creep tests. During the first stage, various waxes and various ratios of wax to sand were tested. In stage two, the parameters in equation (1) were identified to determine if the sand-wax mixture was "reaslistic". By this process two sand-wax mixtures were selected: (1) a mixtue by weight of 0.6 percent CD 150/160 wax, 0.4 percent Shaping wax, 49.5 percent Monterey #0 sand and 49.5 percent

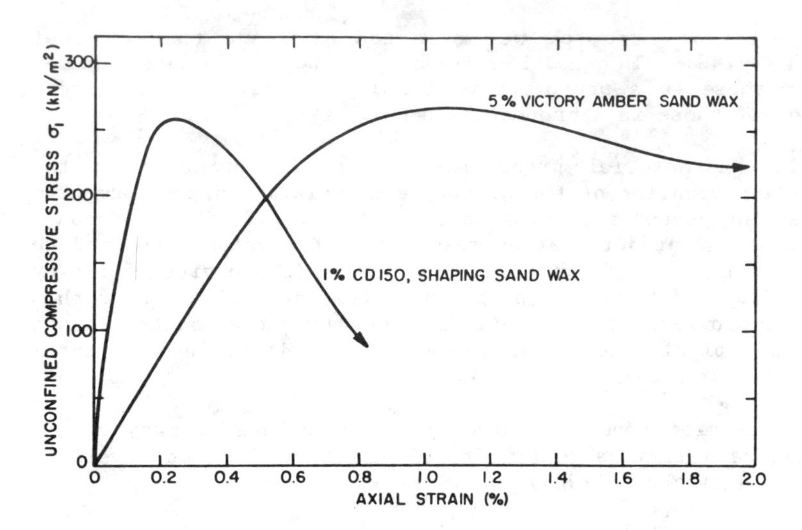

Fig. 4. Unconfined compressive stress vs axial strain for 1 percent CD150, Shaping wax and 5 percent Victory Amber sand-wax.

Monterey #20 sand; and (2) a mixture by weight of 5 percent Victory Amber wax and 95 percent Monterey #0 sand. The second model material was developed specifically because of its greater ductility and larger deformation under creep loading. The ductility of the 5 percent Victory Amber mixture is illustrated in the stress-strain curves of Figure 4.

In Table 2 values of m, $\overline{\alpha}$ and A of the two sand wax mixtures are compared with values of these parameters for natural clayey soils. Based on these values, both sand wax mixtures fall within the range of other real materials, justifying the scaling of material properties by a one to one ratio.

Model Test Equipment

The model test chamber was a .6 m diameter, 1.22 m long vessel designed by Korbin (1975) for earlier model tests. A cross section of the chamber is shown in Figure 5. A neopreme membrane fit tightly inside the vessel. Air pressure applied between the membrane and the cylinder simulated overburden pressure.

Deformations in the model were measured by twentyfour electromagnetic sensors positioned in two radially oriented lines and one axially oriented line as shown in Figure 5. These sensors were accurately placed in the chamber while it was being filled with the hot sand-wax mixture. The sensors were 3.2 mm thick and ranged in size from 12.7 mm to 25.4 mm in diameter.

Table 2. Comparison of creep parameters for model and real materials

Material	Reference	m	-	A
Undisturbed Seattle Clay	Mitchell (1976)	0.5	-	---
Undisturbed London Clay	Bishop (1966)	0.97	1.4	1.4×10^{-5} %/min
Undisturbed Bay Mud	Singh and Mitchell (1968)	0.8	6.0	3.4×10^{-3} %/min
Undisturbed Straight Creek Gouge	Semple (1973)	0.95	3.0	1×10^{-4} %/min
.6% CD150 .4% Shap Sand and Wax	Myer *et al.*, (1979)	0.6	4.3	6.4×10^{-4} %/min
5% Victory Amber Sand and Wax	Dare *et al.*, (1979)	0.47	3.1	2.4×10^{-3} %/min

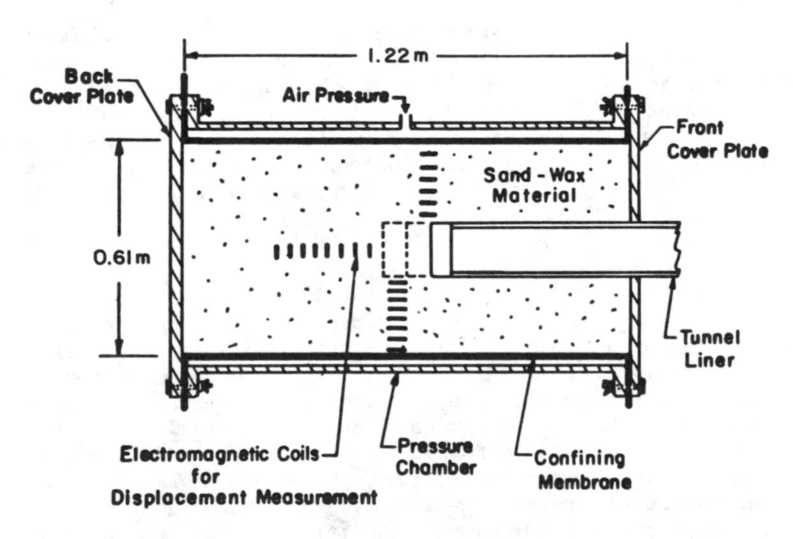

Fig. 5. Cross section of model test chamber. Dotted lines represent rounds yet to be excavated.

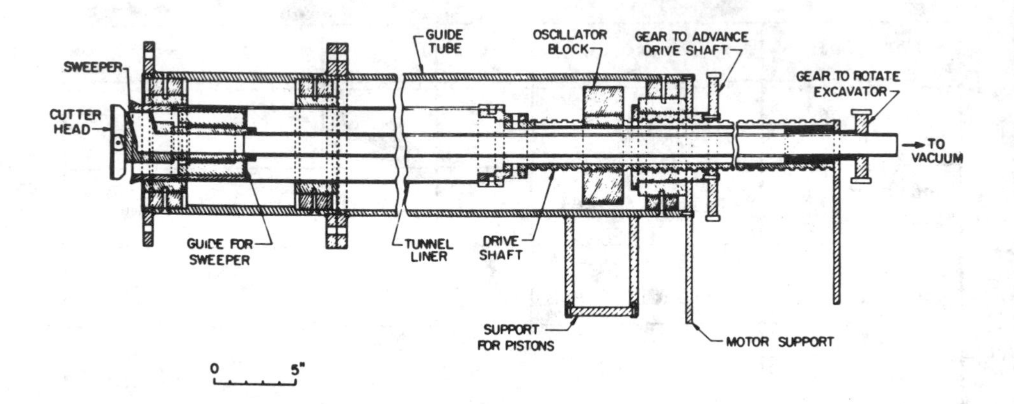

Fig. 6. Cross section of model tunnel excavator.

Stand-up time problems occur during tunnel construction. Consequently, it was necessary to build an apparatus capable of reproducing a reasonable construction sequence in the model. Figure 6 is a cross section of the excavator which was bolted onto the front of the pressure vessel. Material was excavated by the rotating cutter head and removed by suction. The liner was advanced simultaneously with the cutter at a constant distance of one tunnel radius behind the advancing tunnel face. Tunnels were excavated for a distance of about half the length of the chamber before excavation was stopped. To model the unobstructed deformation of ground behind the head of a shield, a 1.6 mm "bead" was added to the front of the liner. By the length scale of 1:40 this bead represented a 60 mm prototype bead. The tunnel liners were mainly steel with wall thicknesses selected such that the liner stiffness was similar to that of a prototype tunnel in squeezing ground (Myer et al, 1977).

Model Test Results

A total of seventeen model tests were performed in a program consisting of two phases. In the first phase (Myer et al, 1977), twelve tests were carried out in which the model material was held constant but tunnel size, advance rate, and test chamber pressure were varied. In the second phase (Dare et al, 1979), five additional tests were performed to further study size effect and behavior due to changes in material properties. Table 3 is a list of the various tests and pertinent parameters. Scaled quantities are also given to indicate the selection of model parameters to those in a prototype tunnel.

Table 3. Model Test and Prototype Tunnel Parameters

Model				Prototype		
Model No.	Tunnel Diameter mm	Advance Rate mm/hr	Confining Pressure kPa	Tunnel Diameter m	Advance Rate m/hr	Depth of Cover / Material Strength* P_z/q_u
I	124	8	576	5.0	0.3	2.3
II	124	8	576	5.0	0.3	2.6
III	124	8	748	5.0	0.3	3.0
IV	124	8	690	5.0	0.3	2.8
V	124	8	662	5.0	0.3	2.7
VI	124	32	662	5.0	1.3	2.7
VII	124	32	576	5.0	1.3	2.3
VIII	124	8	518	5.0	0.3	2.1
IX	124	8	576	5.0	0.3	2.3
X	64	8	576	2.6	0.3	2.3
XI	190	8	576	7.6	0.3	2.3
XII	190	8	518	7.6	0.3	2.1
XIII	124	8.4	576	5.0	0.3	2.3
XIV	64	4.2	576	2.6	0.17	2.3
XV	190	15.0	576	7.6	0.6	2.3
XVI+	124	8.4	576	5.0	0.6	2.1
XVII+	64	4.2	576	2.6	0.17	2.1

* q_u (Unconfined compressive strength) was used instead of undrained shear strength as reported in the literature because the sand-wax material had a friction angle greater than zero.

+ Five percent Victory Amber wax sand mixture used

Evaluation of test results was carried out through a comparison of accumulated strains with position and time, rather than through an actual measurement of a "stand-up time" for each model tunneling condition. This approach was necessary because no failures or collapses of model tunnels occurred for which a reasonable stand-up time could be defined. All the instances of tunnel collapse occurred before the end of excavations and were a direct result of interaction of the stress field with the model boundary (Myer et al., 1977). If excavation was completed without collapse, deformation rates gradually decreased toward zero, indicative of stable conditions. Only a 5 percent decrease in chamber pressure between models IV and V resulted in stable behavior in model V as compared to model IV in which catastrophic failure occurred when the face was 1/2 radius from the final position.

It should be noted that the model tests were performed in a homogeneous continuum, free of major discontinuites other than the model boundary. Reasons for the lack of failure after excavation stopped are speculative, but catastrophic failures in prototypes as well as models may be precipitated by the interaction of discontinuiites or inhomogeneities with the stress and displacement fields around an advancing tunnel. In addition, the model materials had relatively high residual strength at large strain as compared to many natural materials which can result in stand-up time problems. Consequently, the materials may not have weakened or strain softened to the point at which major fallouts or collapse would occur as described in several case histories.

The use of accumulated strains to characterize degree of instability was utilized for two reasons. First, instability and stand-up time problems need not be evidenced by catastrophic failure alone. Deformations which are too large or too rapid, whether or not associated with total collapse, can severely inhibit tunnelling operations. Second, collapse would be preceded by large rapidly increasing deformations, an accurate indication of impending instability, and thus, stand-up time problems.

Results of the model tests are discussed relative to the four factors identified in the case history study.

In-situ stress conditions. Under consideration were the in-situ stresses due to the overburden weight alone. As noted previously, various investigators have suggested stability ratios (P_z/S_u) ranging from 4.5 to 7.5. Several model tests were performed using the 124 mm diameter liner and an advance rate of 8 mm/hr with varying confining pressures. Representative deformations at a point ahead of the face are shown in Figure 7. Note that the ratio of confining pressure (representing P_z) to unconfined compressive strength was used because of the non-zero friction angle of the sand-wax material. A sharp increase in deformations is noted when the ratio of confining pressure to

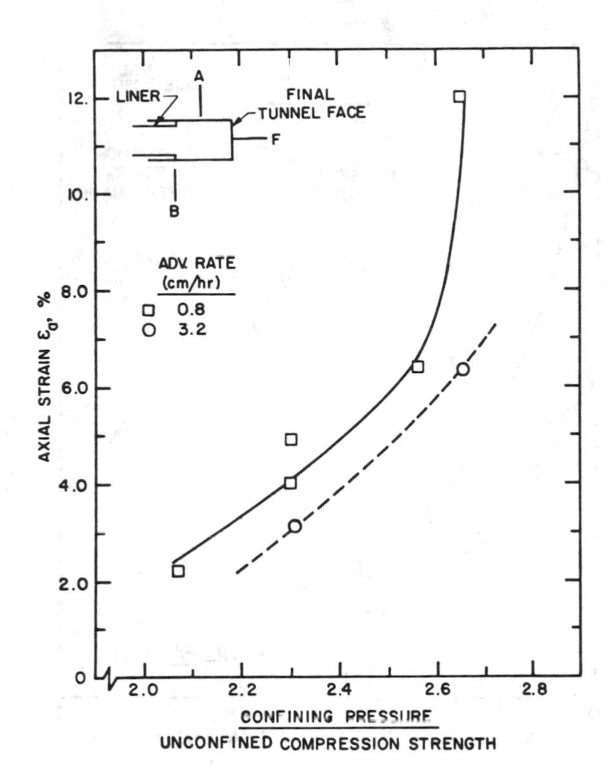

Fig. 7. Effect of confining pressure on magnitude of strains. Strains calculated at end of excavation 0.4 radii from tunnel boundary (after Myer et al., 1977).

unconfined compressive strength is about 2.6. This sharp increase is probably indicative of potential instability. All models with a ratio of confining pressure to unconfined strength greater than 2.7 failed catastrophically. Based on a friction angle of 20° for the sand-wax material, the unconfined compressive strength is approximately 2.8 times the undrained shear strength (S_u). Thus the stability ratio (P_z/S_u) for the 124 mm diameter model tunnels with an advance rate of 8 mm/hr was about 7.7. It is important to observe that this stability ratio applies only to one tunnel size and one advance rate. The lower curve in Figure 7 represents axial strains from models in which the advance rate was changed to 32 mm/hr instead of 8 mm/hr. The strains are less, particularly at the higher ratio of confining pressure to strength. Though not shown, a similar trend was seen in radial strains. Though the data is not conclusive, it is tempting to speculate that the increased advance rate would shift the curve to the right. Thus, for this size tunnel, the stabilty ratio would be higher for increased advance rates.

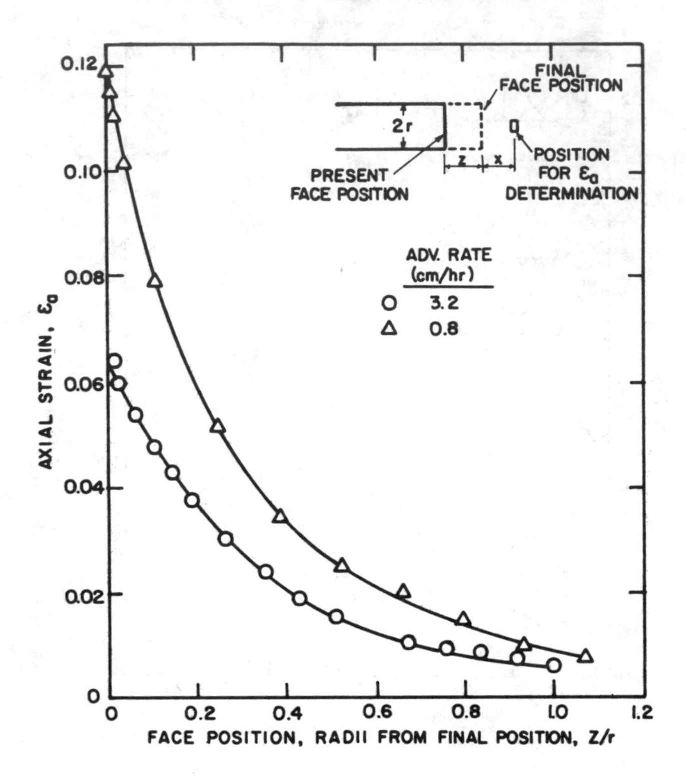

Fig. 8. Comparison of axial strain ε_a at position x/r = .4 on sensor line F for tests at different advance rate; confining pressure = 96 psi.

Advance rate. As discussed above the model tests showed that an increase in advance rate led to a decrease in tunnel deformation and improved stability. A further illustration of this behavior is provided by Figure 8 which compares axial strains from model V and VI. The notation x/r = .4 means that each data point is the calculated strain at a point .4 radii ahead of the final face position. When the tunnel face was one radius from its final position (z/r = 1) the strains in both models were nearly equal. By the time excavation was stopped, (z/r = 0) the strain in the model excavated slowly was twice that of the quickly excavated model. In terms of prototype deformations, these strains would have corresponded to face movements of 120 mm and 65 mm respectively.

Excavation size. The effect of excavation size on stand-up time was evaluated by comparing the behavior of two models which were different only in their size (models IX and X). By the end of excavation the strains at geometrically similar points in the small tunnel were 35 percent to 60 percent less (depending on location) than in the large tunnel. In terms of displacements in a prototype tunnel for a point .4 radiis ahead of the face, the displacement of the ground would have been reduced from 40 mm to 14 mm.

To investigate a true size effect, however, it was necessary to perform tests in which the tunnel size was different but in which each element of material would theoretically experience the same stress-time history. This was done through adjustment of the advance rate. If a tunnel of radius R is advanced at one half the rate of a second tunnel of radius 2R, geometrically similar points would experience the same loading and deformation history if no size effect exists.

Model tests XIII and XIV were performed according to this rationale. Model XIII was a 124 mm diameter tunnel advanced at 8.4 mm/hr while model XIV was a 64 mm tunnel advanced at 4.2 mm/hr. Figure 9 compares the axial strain along the entire sensor line F in the two models at various times during the test. The label ".8r" refers to the time when the face was .8 radii from its final position, "EOE" refers to end of excavation, and "720 min" refers to 720 minutes after excavation was completed. Significantly greater strains in the larger tunnel indicate a definite size effect. The difference in strain was small when the face was .8 radii from its final position. Between the time required to excavate from this position (0.8r) to the final position (EOE), the major difference in strain between the large and small tunnels occurred. After excavation the difference was relatively constant alghouth both tunnels exhibited continued strain due to material creep. Thus, the size effect, as evidenced by the difference in accumulated strains, was manifested mainly during the actual tunnelling operation and not after the face had become stationary.

Model tests XVI and XVII were similar to those just described except for the use of a more ductile model material. The same general behavior, i.e., a distinct size effect, was also noted. In the more ductile material the size effect became apparent earlier in the tunnelling operation and lasted longer after excavation stopped. In comparing models XIII and XVI it was noted that the volume of material affected by the presence of the excavation was greater in the more ductile material.

Time dependent material properties. Time dependent deformations observed in the models were clearly related, at least qualitatively, to the time dependent behavior seen in laboratory samples of the model materials. It was anticipated that the tendency for laboratory samples to fail under creep test loading would also have analogous behavior in the models. That is, it was anticipated that after excavation of the model tunnel was completed, failure would follow due to creep rupture of the material around the unsupported opening. As noted previously, no such

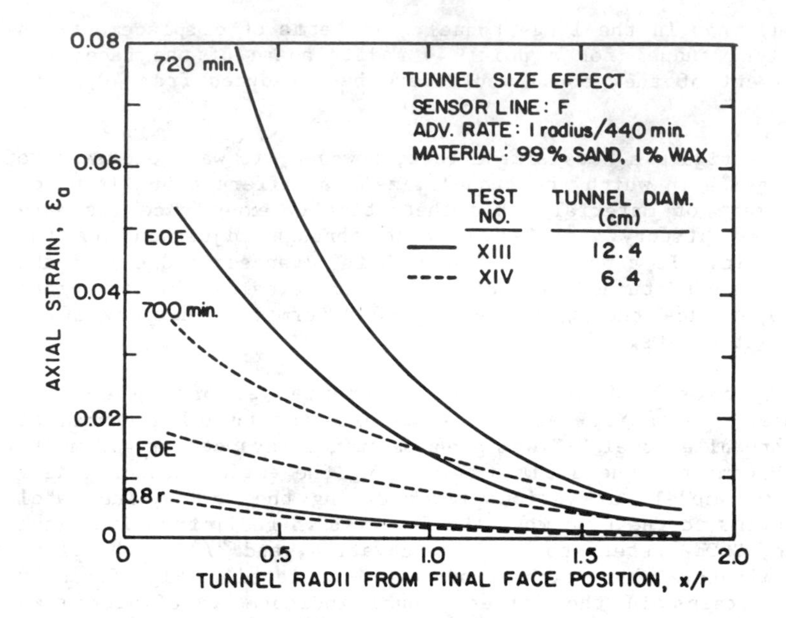

Fig. 9. Comparison of sensor line Fε_a distributions for tests XIII and XIV. Strains compared at three times during test (see Figure 8 for definition of x/r).

failure was observed, or detected in the sensor displacement data. Explanation of this behavior requires a better understanding than now exists of the constitutive behavior of rheologic materials subject to failure under creep loading.

CONCLUSIONS

A case history study of several tunnels which experienced stand-up time problems revealed four factors as pertinent to these problems: (1) ratio of depth of cover to strength of the ground; (2) time dependent material behavior; (3) tunnel advance rate, and (4) excavation size. A series of physical model tests were performed to investigate the effect of these parameters on stand-up time behavior. The results of these tests qualitatively agreed with the observations of the case history study. Though no stand-up time, per se, could be measured in the models, differences in accumulated strains were taken to infer differences in stand-up time. The importance of taking advance rate and tunnel size into account when defining a stability ratio was established. Increasing tunnel advance rate was found to decrease accumulated strains in the models, or increase stand-up time. By properly sealing the advance rate such that the material in each model underwent the same time-loading history, a size effect was established. This was measured as a significant difference in strain at geometrically similar positions in the different sized tunnel models. Use of a model material exhibiting greater ductility resulted in a larger volume of disturbed material around the excavations.

ACKNOWLEDGEMENTS

Funding for this work was provided by the U. S. Department of Transportation, Office of the Secretary, Office of University Research, under contract DOT-OS-50108. Technical monitor was Mr. Russell K. McFarland. His continued support of this work was greatly appreciated, as was the interest of Mr. G. Butler of the Urban Mass Transit Administration. The physical model tests were carried out at Richmond Field Station. Valuable assistance was provided by Mr. C. Chan, Research Engineer, Mr. B. Debeling, Machinist, and Mr. T. Pickrell, Electronics Technician. Dr. E. Kavazanjian and Mr. J. Vais, Research Assistants, aided in the material characterization work. Co-principal ivnestigators on the overall project were Professors I. Finnie, J. K. Mitchell, and R. L. Taylor.

REFERENCES

Arnold, A. B., Bisio, R. P. Heyes, D. G. and Wilson A. O., 1972, "Case Histories of three tunnel-support failures, California Aqueduct," Bull. of the Assoc. of Eng. Geol., Vol. 9, No. 3, pp. 265-299.

Attewell, P. B., and Boden, J. B., 1971, "Development of stability ratios for tunnels driven in clay," Tunnels and Tunnelling, May, pp. 195-198.

Bieniawski, Z. T., 1974, "Geomechanics classification of rock masses and its applications in tunnelling," Tunnelling in Rock, Z. T. Bieniawski, ed., S. African Inst. of Civil Eng., Pretoria, pp. 89-103.

Bishop, A. W., 1966, "The strength of soils as engineering materials," Geotechnique, Vol. 16, pp 91-128.

Brekke, T. L., and Howard, T. R., 1973, "Functional Classification of Gouge Materials from Seams and Faults in Relation to Stability Problems in Underground Openings," U. S. Bureau of Mines (ARPA) Contract No. H0220022.

Broms, B. B., and Bennermark, H., 1967, "Stability of clay at vertical openings," J. of Soil Mech. and Found. Div., ASCE, Vol. 93, No. SM1, pp. 71-94.

Dare, C. T., Dill, R. B., Brekke, T. L. and Korbin, G. E., 1979, "Stand-up Time of Tunnels in Squeezing Ground, Part III: Final Investigation", U. S. Department of Transportation, Contract No. DOT-05-50108.

deBeer, E. E., and Buttiens, E., 1966, "Construction de reservoirs pour hydrocarbures liquefies dans l'argile de Boom a Anvers. Etude des mouvements du sol provoques par cette realisation," Traveaux, Sept., pp. 1087-1093, and Oct., pp. 1167-1174.

Hartmark, H., 1964, "Geotechnical observations during construction of a tunnel through soft clay in Trondheim, Norway," Felsmechanik und Ingenieurgeologie, Vol. 2, No. 1, pp. 9-21.

Hopper, R. C., Lang, T. A., and Mathews, A. A., 1972, "Construction of Straight Creek Tunnel, Colorado," Proceedings, North Amer. Rapid Exc. and Tunneling Conf., Chicago, Vol. 1, pp. 501-538.

Korbin, G. E., 1975, A Model study of Spiling Reinforcement in Underground Openings, Ph.D. Dissertation, University of California, Berkeley.

Lauffer, H., 1958, "Gebirgsklassifizierung fur den stollenbau," Geologie und Bauwesen, Vol. 24, No. 1, pp. 46-50.

Mitchell, J. K., 1976, Fundamentals of Soil Behavior, Wiley, New York, 422 pp.

Myer, L. R., Brekke, T. L., Kavazanjian, E., Korbin, G. E. and Mitchell, J. K., 1977, "Stand-up Time of Tunnels in Squeezing Ground, Part 1: A Physical Model Study," U. S. Department of Transportation, Contract No. DOT-05-50108.

Peck, R. B., 1969, "Deep excavations and tunnelling in soft ground," Proceedings, 7th Int. Conf. on Soil Mech. and Found. Eng., Mexico City, Vol. 3, pp. 225-290.

Rabcewicz, L. V., 1975 "Tunnel under Alps uses new cost saving lining," Civil Eng., ASCE, Vol. 45, No. 10, pp. 69-74.

Semple, R. M., 1973, The Effect of Time-Dependent Properties of Altered Rock on Tunnel Support Requirements, Ph.D. Dissertation, University of Illinois, Urbana.

Singh, A. and Mitchell, J. K., 1968, "General stress-strain-time funtion for soils," J. of Soil Mech., and Found. Div., ASCE, Vol. 94, No. SM1, pp. 21-46.

Singh, A. and Mitchell, J. K., 1969, "Creep potential and creep rupture of soils," Proceedings, 7th Int. Conf. on Soil Mech., and Foundation Eng., Mexico City, Vol. 1, pp. 379-384.

Terzaghi, K., 1946, Rock Tunnelling with Steel Supports, Proctor and White, eds., Commerical Shearing and Stamping Co., Youngstown, Ohio, 292 pp.

Underwood, L. B., 1965, "Machine tunnelling on Missouri River dams," J. of the Const. Div.,, ASCE, May, No. CO1, pp. 1-27.

Underwood, L. B., 1968, "Future needs in site study," Rapid Exc., Problems anmd Progress, Proc. of Tunnel and Shaft Conf., Minn., pp. 24-31.

Chapter 87

GROUND CONTROL SYSTEM IN NEAR VERTICAL ROCK EXCAVATION

By Chandra S. Brahma, M. ASCE

Professor of Civil Engineering
California State University, Fresno, California

Consultant, Sverdrup & Parcel And Associates, Inc.
St. Louis, Missouri

INTRODUCTION

The process of predicting ground condition with exactitude and of ascertaining appropriate ground control measures is pertinent to each and every excavation. The control and support of soil and/or rock during and subsequent to excavation is essential in order to overcome or avoid excessive movement, maintain stability or preserve integrity of the excavation, handle or prevent excessive water intrusion or hydrostatic pressure build up, and produce an excavation that is safe and suitable for its intended purpose. The design of support systems has primarily been, until recently, based upon experience and empirical or semiempirical guidelines, which do not lend themselves to thorough analytical calculations giving rise to the desired degree of confidence in design of such systems and consequently, several, if not a majority of support systems, no doubt, are overdesigned. The primary objective of this paper is, therefore, to briefly outline engineering considerations leading towards the design of ground control systems for near vertical excavations extending to shallow depths in metamorphic rock formations.

Several engineering considerations including the selection of temporary support systems, technical aspects of design, and the sequence as well as details of construction, are briefly outlined. Since excavation for mining purposes or for civil engineering works frequently must pass through highly decomposed, weathered, fractured, sheared or faulted rock masses, the problem of general interest in underground engineering involving analysis of the stability or the support requirement for an excavation in an incompetent rock medium is considered. While recognizing the fact that the design of the ground control system for near vertical excavation is largely influenced by the complexities of the geologic environment present at a site, geologic considerations are discussed only insofar as these materially influence rock mass behavior patterns for which temporary supports and protective measures are generally found necessary.

GEOLOGIC CONSIDERATIONS

Lithology, rock structures, weathering, rock quality, groundwater, and engineering properties of rock are considered important from a geological standpoint. Of the rock structures, foliations, bandings, faults, shears, shear-zones, and joints may be examined with respect to possible ground behavior. The nature of the individual discontinuity shall preferably be defined in terms of attitude, frequency, location, continuity, shape, roughness, tightness, and coating and/or filling materials so that anticipated behavior of the discontinuity could appropriately be estimated during construction. In addition, information regarding strength and deformation characteristics, and swelling as well as squeezing properties of rock may be obtained in order to assess their influence on rock mass behavior.

Lithology. The lithology, along with information regarding the geologic setting and history, plays significant roles in formulating important design considerations at various stages. Metamorphic rocks, formed by recrystallization due to intense heat, deforming pressure, movement within the crust, penetration of chemically active fluids from below or any combinations thereof, display various textures and compositions of solid rock. These rocks would not only exhibit differences in mechanical properties, but would show structural anistropy in some rock types as well. Schists, for example, have foliated textures with directional differences in both strength and deformation modulus. Some rock structures can often be associated with certain rock types and geological processes. For example, foliation shear zones have frequently occurred in Mica Schist with high mica content or in rock formations containing bands of Mica Schist or Gniesses. Again, when flexural-slip and slip folding are closely associated in rock formations rich in either mica or quartz alternating in the gniessic and schistose sequence, successive lithological layers may show foliation parallel to the axial plane and to the layering.

Weathering. Underground excavations at shallow depths frequently encounter weathered rock zones along the length of such openings. Weathering often progresses downward and outward along joint planes and notably much deeper in layers rich in micas along foliation shear zones and faults. The variations in the depths of the zones of weathering are often dictated by the differences in lithology. Depending upon the degree of weathering, the reduction in the strength of the weathered rock may vary. The strength properties of slightly weathered rock may be comparable to that of intact unweathered rock while severely weathered rock may have strength properties more nearly represented by those of residual soils. Consequently, plastic flow resulting from overstressing of the ground due to excavation may be a distinct possibility in highly weathered or altered rocks requiring support for the full length of the opening. In addition, immediate measures to control deterioration of the excavated surfaces may sometimes be found necessary. Excavations in weathered rocks may require special protections against the ground ravelling and falling, and the likelihood of serious collapses and problems caused by mixed-face conditions. Soldier piles carrying heavy loads could settle if weathered rock near the tip is relatively compressible.

Rock Quality. The behavior of the rock mass controls the deformations as well as stress distributions that will occur around the opening. The rock mass properties are influenced by the discontinuities and the degree of weathering or alteration present in the rock. The rock mass quality has been used by the designers in defining the approximate bounds of the rock mass behavior or in locating the zones of poor quality rock. Among several procedures available to quantitatively describe rock quality, the RQD (rock quality designation) System based on modified core recovery is often used during the early stages of design to estimate the average quality of the rock mass. This system can be used to estimate rock loads or support requirements and the modulus of the rock mass for calculating displacements around the opening. However, the RQD System may not be sensitive enough to reflect various properties of discontinuities, such as orientation and character, which may affect both rock load and modulus. In the design of the support system, if a more precise estimate of rock load or modulus is needed, detailed information concerning various parameters affecting rock mass behavior should further be required.

Discontinuity. Discontinuities such as shears, joints, shear-zones, foliations and faults influence the behavior of the rock mass through interactions between rock blocks and discontinuities. Under adverse conditions, discontinuities probably cause some of the most difficult problems in excavation and deserve careful consideration. For instance, shear zones and fault zones, as identified by the width of zone of fracturing and presence of gouge materials or sheared surfaces or a number of joint sets forming very blocky and seamy rock, may cause fallout resulting in high loading conditions in the support system. These zones may often require a long time to stabilize, particularly where gouge materials contain an appreciable amount of clay minerals or alteration products. Several engineering properties of discontinuities including attitude, frequency, location, continuity, shape, roughness, tightness and coating and/or filling materials are considered important in assessing behaviors of rock mass and individual blocks of rock contained herein.

The attitude (strike and dip) of discontinuities with reference to the excavation wall could determine magnitude as well as location of support problems along the vertical wall of the opening. For instance, steeply dipping single-plane discontinuities such as foliations, joints and shears, when run parallel or subparallel to the excavation wall, are prone to extensive overbreak and fallout and could cause support problems, while gently dipping discontinuities irrespective of their strike, may probably form shallow wedges.

The frequency of discontinuities has a significant influence on engineering behavior in that, for an unweathered formation degraded only by fracturing, for example, a low fracture frequency could be indicative of in-situ properties approaching those of the intact specimen. Furthermore, the spacing of discontinuities such as joints and shears in a set or shear-zones and fault-zones could identify the extent of support requirements if such discontinuities are present. However, the rock at a site is likely to be hetrogeneous with respect to lithology, weathering and properties of discontinuities. Accordingly, discontinuities may preferably be identified as to their location along the length of the opening. The continuity of rock structures, such as joints, influences the formation of rock wedges. Failure of rock blocks bounded by discon tinuities which terminate in rock mass may involve the failure of intact rock unless intersecting joints form stepped failure surfaces.

The character of discontinuities which must be considered in determining the support requirements, should include the following: 1) shape in terms of plane, curved, stepped or irregular; 2) roughness in terms of rough, very rough or smooth; 3) tightness in terms of tight or open; and 4) types of gouge or coating and/or filling materials. For instance, rock blocks bounded by very rough and irregular joints develop considerable resistances against fallout while potential caving may be anticipated if joints forming wedges are plane and smooth. A tight joint ordinarily displays a higher rock modulus than that of the open joint. Talc, serpentine or chlorite when wet are very slippery and have low resistances. Weathered or alteration products in fillings may cause swelling, squeezing, or slaking conditions depending upon their mineralogical composition and properties.

Groundwater. Groundwater causes flow problems resulting in excessive dischage and stability problems due to high hydrostatic pressures and loss of strength along the discontinuities if filling materials therein absorb water. The groundwater seepage could also cause loss of ground due to piping. These difficulties are frequently associated with differences in permeability of the rock due to heterogeneities introduced by various sources including thin linings placed directly over rock surfaces, discontinuities, or changes in rock type.

Swell Characteristics. Free swell or excessive swelling pressure is generally encountered in filling materials or in weathered or altered zones. The extent of these is largely dictated by the amount, composition and properties of material. Montmorillonites, for example, because of their large negative charge and osmotic pressure, are probably capable of large volume expansion in the presence of water and are susceptible to considerable swelling if significant amounts of such minerals are present. Clay mineral and particle size determinations, Atterberg limit tests, and free swell tests are often used in ascertaining swelling index properties of rock minerals.

Uniaxial Compressive Strength. The uniaxial compressive strength and modulus of the intact rock samples are used to classify rock materials and to verify the visual determination of the degree of weathering or alteration in the rock. The compressive strength could also be used in ascertaining whether a particular ground is susceptible to plastic squeeze or fracture formation. If the uniaxial compressive strength is equal to or less than the stresses developed about the opening, the ground material in highly weathered or altered zones may exhibit squeezing behavior and associated plastic flow. The formation of fresh fractures in the intact rock due to overstressing of material may also be indicated if the insitu stresses developed around an opening are high compared to the uniaxial compressive strength of the rock.

Shear Strength. The strength along a discontinuity is generally derived from the basic shear strength and the resistance against dilation due to interlocking surface projections. An actual surface of discontinuity may not always be regular and that an irregular surface profile may show first order and second order projections. Under low normal stresses, the steeper second order projections with smaller surface irregularities may govern the initial dilation while as these projections are broken off with increasing normal stresses, the gentler irregularities of the first order with larger wavelengths may dictate further movement. In excavations where the first order projections ordinarily control the behavior, the angle of inclination of such projections varies with the character of the discontinuity. For example, plane discontinuities may have a very low angle of inclination, whereas very irregular surfaces may display a high angle of inclination.

The shear resistance along the discontinuity depends also on the roughness and character of the filling materials. A smooth slickensided joint may, for example, display a low resistance, while the resistance with very rough surfaces are much higher. The shear strength of discontinuities with fillings is largely dictated by the thickness and properties of the filling materials such as composition, grain size, moisture content and plasticity. For instance, highly plastic clayey fillings of significant thickness generally have low frictional resistances. In discontinuities with very thin filling or coating materials, the initial strength properties may be dictated by the fillings or coatings but the rock surface properties may control the final strength under increasing normal stresses as the fillings or coatings are ruptured through.

ENGINEERING AND DESIGN CONSIDERATIONS

Excavations through metamorphic terrain for civil engineering works or for mining purposes frequently involve near the surface various proportions of sands, silts, and clays above and below the groundwater table. These soils are often underlain by decomposed and/or intensely weathered to unweathered rock as shown in the typical soils profile (figure 1). Near the surface, the weathering is usually complete and reduces rock to soil where no relict rock structures can be identified. Weathering effect decreases and tends to concentrate along rock discontinuities such that the weathering profile grades with depth into a transition zone. Weathering in this zone is usually incomplete and relict rock structures can easily be recognized. In addition, the amount of fresh rock fragments in the transition zone is likely to increase with depth. Below the weathered rock may lie relatively fresh rock consisting typically of foliated gneiss, thinly foliated schist, fine to coarse grained amphibolite or the like. Due to their origin and subsequent modifications, the rock types may vary significantly over short vertical or horizontal distances. The general attitude of the rocks may often be described by foliation planes which may range from indistinct to highly developed. Depending upon the degree of weathering along discontinuities and upon the number of shears, joints, or other discontinuities present, the rock quality designation at a particular site may vary anywhere from zero to 100 percent.

Engineering and design considerations for excavation in such complex ground should include, among others, the types of wall as well as bracing system commonly incorporated in design, technical aspects of design, and construction sequence and details. While

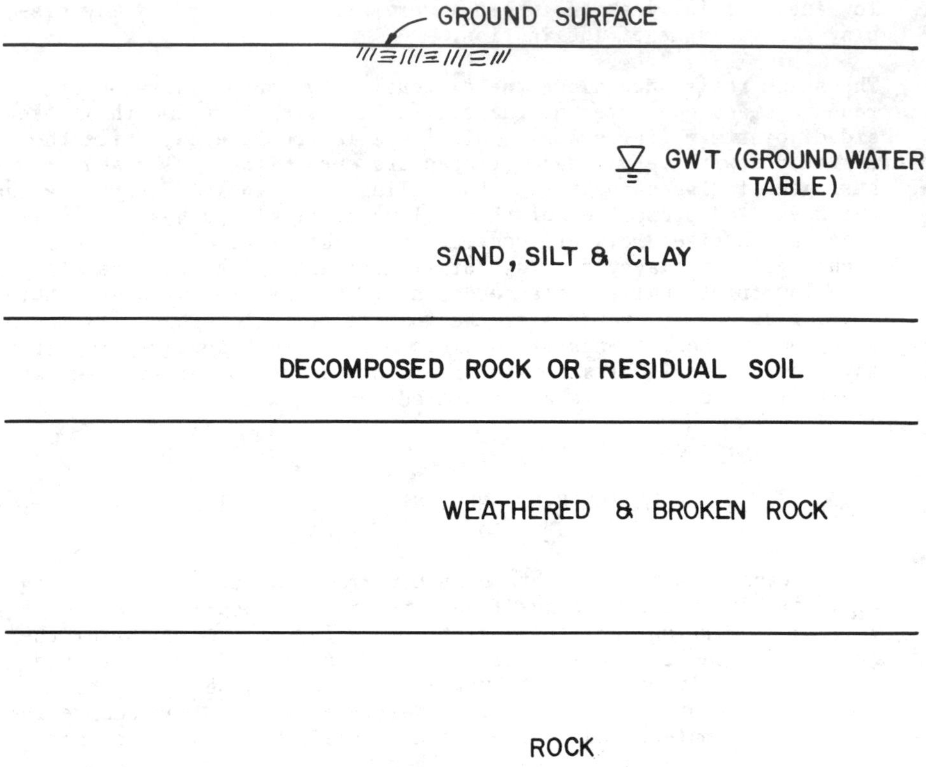

GROUND SURFACE

GWT (GROUND WATER TABLE)

SAND, SILT & CLAY

DECOMPOSED ROCK OR RESIDUAL SOIL

WEATHERED & BROKEN ROCK

ROCK

TYPICAL SOIL PROFILE

FIGURE – 1

the technical aspects of design and construction procedures with excavation in soil have extensively been discussed elsewhere (Brahma, 1978a, 1978b), such considerations are outlined hereinafter insofar as they are applicable to near-vertical excavations in rock.

Wall Type and Support Method

In soil excavations, the support is usually designed to be somewhat flexible to allow the ground to deform to the extent that peak soil strengths are mobilized and used to advantage in reducing loads on the excavation support. The movement of the soil support system may be reflected by movements of the subsurface soils and of the ground surface some distance from the excavations, depending, for example, upon the types of soils and types of actual wall or support method utilized. Rock masses, on the other hand, tend to deform along existing discontinuities and the amount of movement required to develop peak strengths of such masses are ordinarily small in comparison. The magnitude of deformation required to reach peak strength is dictated by the orientation, surface roughness, type and amount of filling material, and frequency of intersecting groups of discontinuities. If rock mass is permitted to deform beyond peak strength, then the support system must be designed for excessive loads. Thus, different types of wall and bracing systems are utilized to stabilize the soil and rock sections of the excavation.

Of the several types of walls used extensively and typically for supporting excavation in soil, soldier piles and lagging and steel sheet piles provide only temporary support during construction while the cast-in-place or precast concrete diaphragm walls often combine both the function of the temporary support of excavation and the permanent retaining system into the same structure. The selection of a particular wall system will depend upon the type of soil, its standup time and relative density or consistency, groundwater conditions and compatibility with dewatering requirements, number of bracing levels required, and the magnitude of permissible movements of nearby structures, if any. Soldier piles or diaphragm walls are frequently required to penetrate badly fractured or intensely weathered rock lying within the depth of excavation in order, not only to avoid the risk of undermining as a result of rock falling from below these members, but also to minimize ground movements should highly weathered materials located below the bottom of the member be compressible.

Internal bracings are most often used in relatively narrow cuts in soil where braces run cross lot without intermediate vertical support. Inclined bracings (rakers) are also utilized in wide excavations if suitable anchor strata or legal permission are not available for tiebacks. Rock reinforcing systems, such as tiebacks, rock bolts, spiles, and shortcrete, are primarily used in recent rock cuts. Tieback systems with deep excavation are adaptable to most wall systems and have been successfully designed for suitable grounds with minimal site contraints. The use of tiebacks offers the unobstructed work space within the excavation site and eliminates the need for intermediate supports. Combined systems have been used with success on many projects. A common example would be the use of conventional soldier piles and struts for the upper levels of bracing in soils and several lower levels of bracing with tieback in rock.

Technical Aspects of Design

The excavation of an opening causes rock to deform. While both elastic and permanent deformations are at first restricted to freshly exposed surfaces, they tend to propagate with time deep into the rock mass away from these surfaces. Subsequent to excavation, the minimum principal stress at any point on the surface of vertical walls is zero while the magnitude of the remaining principal stresses are governed by the magnitude of in-situ stresses and by the stress concentration caused by the excavation. Should the material be incapable of withstanding such stress concentrations, localized failures in the form of fractures, shearing and sliding on joints and crushing of rock blocks accompanied by permanent deformation may result. Thus, the failure of near-vertical excavations in rock may, among others, be attributed to loosening and fallout of large blocks formed by the intersection of naturally occuring or man-made discontinuites and the excavation walls. While the potential system of failure surfaces already exists in the mass constituting rock slope, the kinematics of sliding should be checked to delineate the possible directions and surfaces on which it is physically possible for sliding to take place. The design or rock reinforcement may, therefore, be dictated by the detailed pattern of discontinuities including strike and dip of critical discontinuities.

Rock Stability. In figure 2, a rock slope stability problem is shown where the strike of one of the planes of weakness is parallel to the strike of the excavation wall. Similar wedges causing plane failure could also be formed by three planes, for example, where back plane strikes parallel and dips into the face of the excavation and the remaining side planes strike perpendicular to the face of excavation with a vertical dip. A rock tetrahedron bounded by two base planes which are intersecting joint sets is shown on figure 3. Failure of the wedge may occur by sliding along the line of intersection of the two planes (figure 3a) or by sliding on either one of the two planes (figure 3b). Should the dip of the line of intersection or the plane on which failure is likely to take place be steeper then the angle of shearing resistance of the discontinuities, wedges become critical and the wall can be analyzed as if

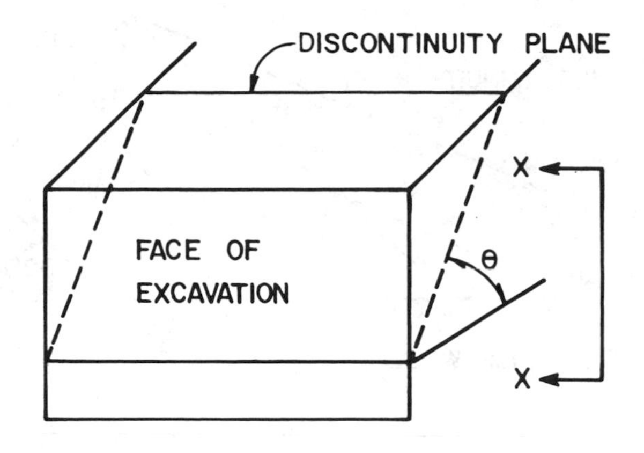

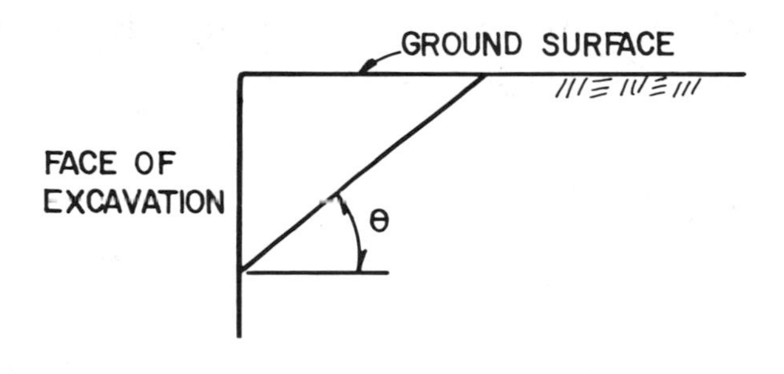

SECTION X–X

SLIDING ON PLANE STRIKING PARALLEL
TO STRIKE OF EXCAVATION FACE

FIGURE – 2

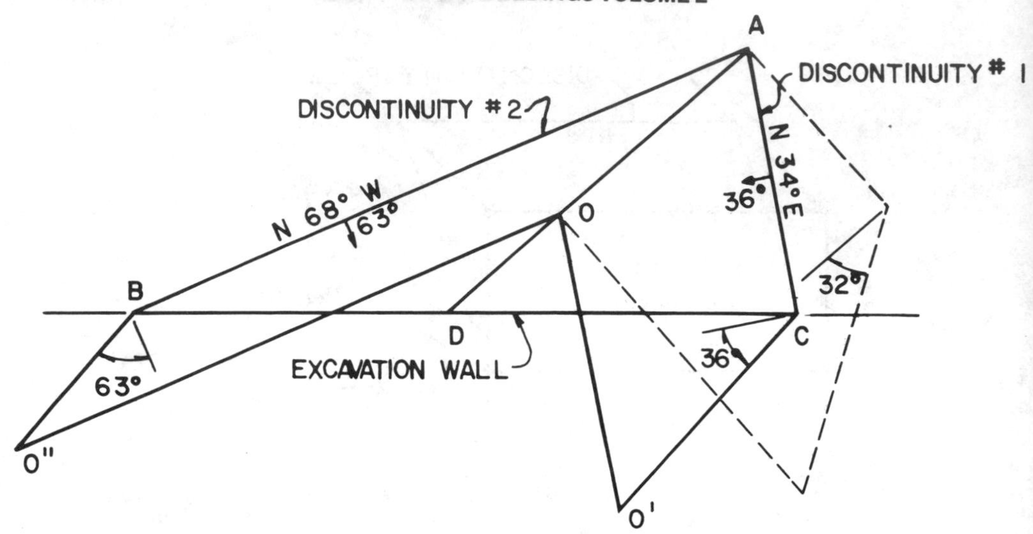

SLIDING ALONG THE LINE OF INTERSECTION
FIGURE — 3A

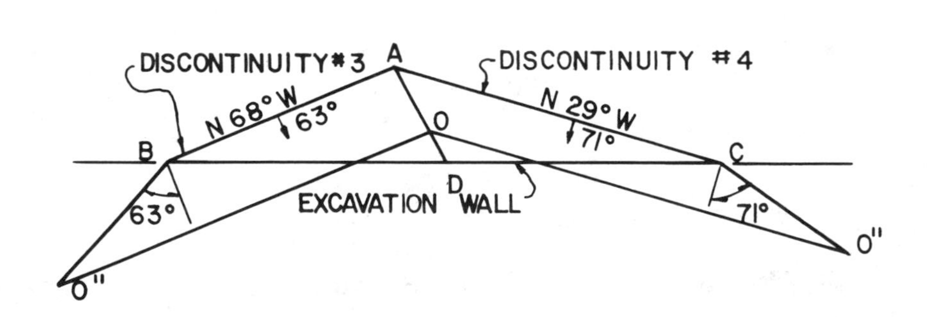

SLIDING ON ONE PLANE
FIGURE - 3B

failure were occurring on single planes or along the line of intersection; if the dip is flatter than the angle of shearing resistance, failure of wedge, in question, would not be possible. Other wedges involving many more planes can be formed along the face of a particular excavations and they should be analyzed prior to finalizing the design of temporary support systems.

Progressive ravelling may be experienced in weathered rocks, in rock areas of general low quality and locally at highly broken zones in the rock. While the angular rock fragments may in many instances interlock effectively and can help to ameliorate the ravelling action, the process, if allowed to continue, can develop to catastrophic proportions where large groups of rock wedges begin to collapse.

Highly weathered or partially decomposed rocks and gouge or filling materials, if exposed to the weather, may slake or slough in presence of water. These materials tend to deteriorate with subsequent loss of integrity under cycles of wetting and drying or freezing and thawing, causing spalling or sloughage. In addition, filling materials or materials encountered in weathered or altered zones may, as already discussed, develop free-swell or excessive swelling pressures.

The potential for rotational or toppling mode of failure in excavations in foliated rock increases with increasing discontinuity angle forming tall slender rock columns adjacent to excavation walls. While such failures are particularly important in quarries and open pit mines, complex movements of blocks involving both sliding and toppling modes may often be encountered in deep excavations.

Temporary Support. The selection of temporary support or reinforcing systems, such as soldier piles and laggings, struts, tiebacks, rock bolts, shotcrete, grouted or ungrouted rebars, and any combination thereof, must meet the fundamental requirement that the system should be installed as early as practicable in order to provide adequate protection. It is, therefore, imperative that support systems should, on the one hand, be capable of withstanding all predicated rock loads and on the other hand, be compatible with conditions existing after initial exposure. Since a higher rockload is ordinarily expected to develop as time progresses, a different system, depending upon their actual time of installation, may, therefore, be required to develop varying resistances. Consequently, a strut which is conventionally placed several hours after initial exposure may be subject to more rock loads than those developed with other systems that are installed within minutes. In addition, support systems should neither interfere with construction operations nor restrict movement in the work areas.

The deformational behavior of the rock-support interaction for systems consisting of soldier pile and lagging and struts differs significantly from those with rock bolt and shotcrete systems. In the former case, there is an actual transfer of load to the support system which offer point-wise resistance to wall deformations allowing movement of rock within the zone of loosened rock wedges. Rock improvement by means of rock bolts and shotcrete, on the otherhand, tries to overcome the deficiencies of in-situ rock mass. It develops the rock around the opening and forms composite reinforced/rock or shotcrete/rock structures which are capable of providing the necessary stability against rock loads as they develop with time. With these systems, it is often possible to restrict development of large loosened rock wedges so that the composite structure is subjected to loads from the immediate wedges along the peripheral line of excavation. Experience indicates that either the permanent stability is enhanced or the permanent loads on the final structure are reduced in excavations in which rock bolts, and shotcrete are used. These systems, therefore, not only enable the rock wedges to remain in place but also form a diaphram of material which behaves as a structural member. For example, discontinuities close to the surface frequently contain coating and/or filling materials or may be open where such materials are washed away be surface weathering. These discontinuities are likely to display low strength characteristics. Futhermore, low in-situ stresses are ordinarily encountered at shallow depths. Although confining pressures provided by rock reinforcements do not significantly increase the normal stress across the discontinuities adjacent to the opening, the increase in stress on the asperities of the discontinuities may be quite high, giving rise to a significant increase in shear strength. Consequently, a systematic bolting pattern including inclination, length, size and tension in the bolts are often designed in order to develop the continuous interaction between adjoining bolts (figure 4). Design procedures with grouted rock anchors ordinarily relate to the overall stability of the rock mass, grout/rock and tendon/grout bonds, and failure of tendon or top anchorage.

Rock bolts or prestressed rock anchors have been used most effectively is preventing rock wedges from sliding down along the line of intersection or discontinuity plane. The rock bolt tension not only reduces the driving force acting down the discontinuity surface but increases normal force and thereby frictional resistance between the wedge and the discontinuity plane. Rock bolts may also be installed to tie the tall slender rock columns together to increase the width of rock block and to restrain any movements of the key wedge in order to prevent failure due to secondary toppling.

The grouted or ungrouted rebars may be used as spiles to reduce the load on the support elements. The spile, because of its restraining effect on rock mass surrounding an opening, is highly effective not only in increasing standup time but in minimizing disturbance

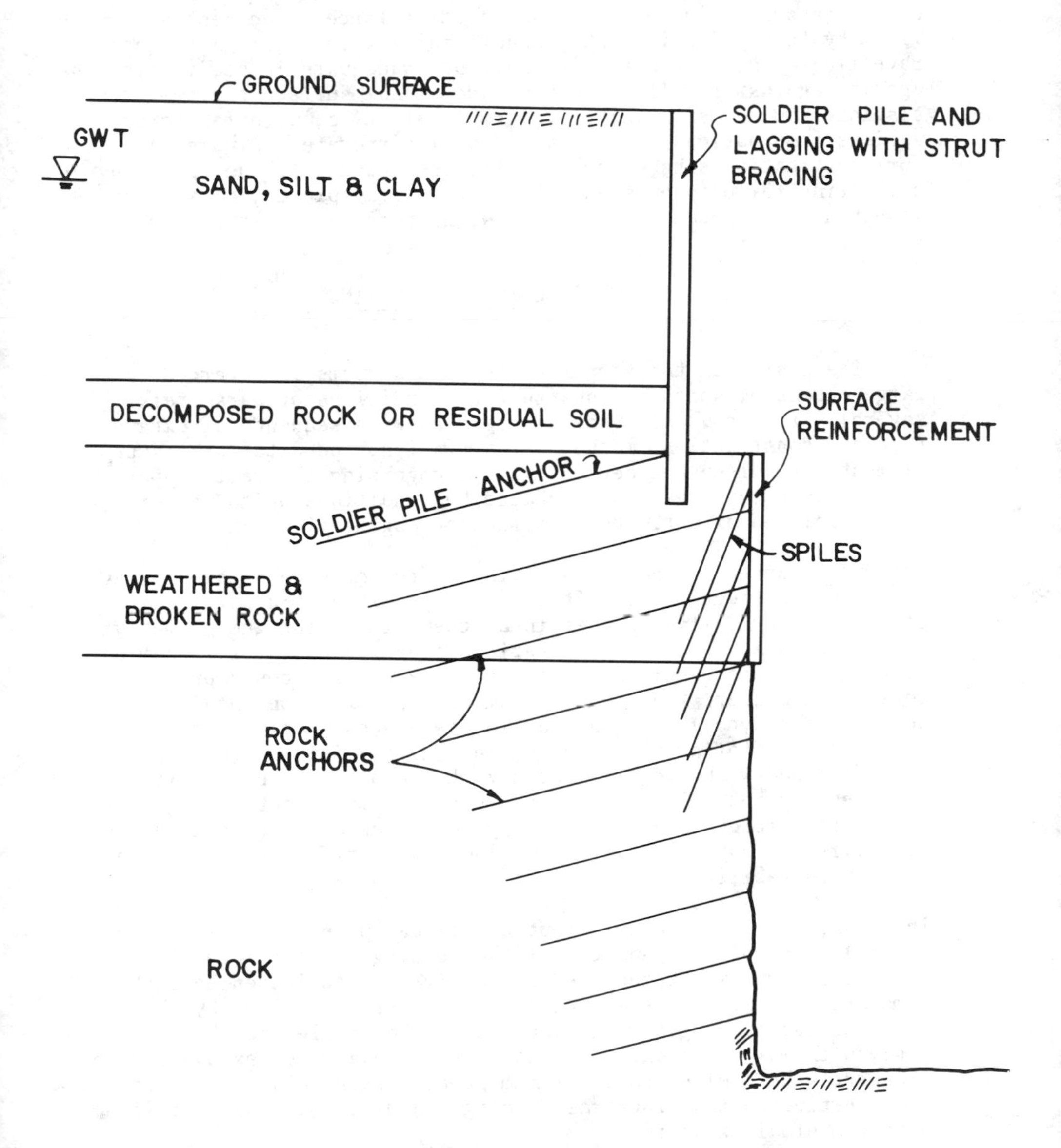

TYPICAL EXCAVATION SUPPORT SYSTEM

FIGURE — 4

causing overbreak and excessive deformation. Unlike tension rock anchors, the unstressed rebar act in a passive way to bring about a condition of equilibrium since the rock has to undergo some movement before rebars could develop any resisting force. The restraint provided by the spiles is highly beneficial in controlling progressive ravelling. Should the spiles alone be inadequate in stabilizing the opening against ravelling action, additional surface treatment consisting of wire mesh, shotcrete, rock bolt ties, wire fabric or various combinations therewith may be incorporated (figure 4). Such surface treatments have successfully been used over the years in combatting fallouts between rock bolt bearing plates, slaking and sloughing, and potential problems with shear and fault zones.

CONSTRUCTION ENGINEERING

The design of the temporary support systems is governed to a large extent by specific construction conditions or parameters. Of several parameter, only those associated with sequence of excavation and construction, method of excavation, and details of support elements are discussed herein while recognizing the fact support requirements could also be dictated by conditions which may or may not be related directly to construction engineering.

Sequence. Several schemes involving different sequences of excavation and construction may often appear feasible at a particular site. However, all sequences in a scheme including the geometry as well as size of opening at various stages need careful examination in order to assure designers that excavation could proceed in a reasonable manner. Safe and economical construction require that both support sytems and construction sequences must be compatible. For instance, for a large opening in a highly jointed (or broken) rock designed with closely spaced rock anchors and spiles, it may be necessary not only to limit the depth of lifts but also to install pre-reinforcements, if any, prior to excavating each successive lift so that such systems could provide effective restraint against instabilities.

The magnitude and type of potential fallout problems often influence the selection of the geometry of the opening. The standup time and rate of deformation associated respectively with loosening mechanisms and squeezing or swelling behaviors are controlled by the width of the opening. While benches may be carried forth simultaneously with more than one face, horizontal advance of excavation may frequently be limited to a maximum panel length consistent with its standup time so that rock reinforcing measures could be installed with a minimal exposure.

Excavation Method. The drill and blast method, whether conventional or improved, causes disturbance in the rock mass due to either migration of liberated gas along the plane of weakness or loosening of rock wedges as well as fracturing of rock. The control of rock surfaces plays a significant role in civil engineering projects as overbreakage and fracturing from excavation blasting may require placement of additional amount of concrete and blast damage may cause fallout and instability. Controlled blasting techniques including line drilling, relief hole, presplitting, cushion or smooth wall blasting, have successfully been used in order to both minimize detrimental effects of blasting on the rock surface and preserve the degree of bonding across discontinuities which the rock mass possessed prior to blasting. For instance, blasting in urban environments frequently warrants line drilling around the perimeter particularly around outside corner of the excavation. In addition, zone blasting, where a narrow berm is left adjacent to presplitting for removal during the final stage of excavation, is often resorted to in order to minimize further blast damage.

Of the several factors which affect the vibrations caused by blasting, the distance as well as charge weight per instant of time are the two most important parameters needed to determine the level of such vibrations. Other factors, such as geological conditions, characteristics of the explosive and geometry may also exert influence on blasting vibration. For instance, a soft medium is likely to transmit waves with low frequencies and large amplitude while a high frequency and low amplitude wave may be transmitted by a hard ground. Different structures have different capacities to resist vibration damage and peak particle velocities are frequently used as criteria for assessing damage potential of blasting vibration. Consequently, the limitations on peak particle velocities or vibrations in the nearby structure are often reflected in the blasting design.

Construction Procedures. While several types of anchorage, such as split wedge, expansion shell or grouted anchors, are commonly used to temporarily stabilze rock mass, the selection of the appropriate anchor system frequently merits special considerations. For instance, the use of an expansion type anchor may be warranted in good rock, while a grouted anchor may develop desired results in poor rock. In addition, should the life expectancy of the anchors exceed a limited period, the anchors may preferably be completely encapsulated in grout.

Procedures with the installation of rock anchor ordinarily involve excavating a hole for the anchor and and pressure testing the same for watertightness, installing the tendon, grouting the anchor to desired length, prestressing and testing the anchor, and making final anchorage at the rock surface. Solid bars, shanks or steel cables are generally used depending upon the length as well as desired capacity of the rock anchor. While cement, concrete, and resin grouts have satisfactorily performed under varying conditions, celcite, for example, may be used where a need for quick setting time or difficult groundwater conditions exist. Rock anchors are frequently prestressed to 125 to 150 percent and locked-off at 100 percent of the designed load. Direct tensioning by means of a center-hole hydraulic jack is often preferred when compared to tensioning by torque wrench, as the latter method is highly sensitive to various construction details.

Dewatering methods, such as wellpoints, sumps, and horizontal or inclined drain holes, may be employed to drain water or reduce hydrostatic pressure in rock mass. The selection of a technique at a site is often dictated not only by the shape, size, spacing, and location of aquifers but also by the seepage and depth to, as well as quality of the groundwater. However, these dewatering methods may be impractical for excavations where excessive inflow and hydrostatic pressure may likely be encountered. In such situations, drainage may be enhanced by grouting, cut-off wall, or the like, depending upon the rate of water flow and the location, shape, and size of voids. Should grouting be used to control groundwater, the grout barrier should be installed far away from the rock surface and preferably outside the area treated with rock reinforcements.

CONCLUSIONS

Some of the typical geologic parameters as they relate to the design of temporary support systems for near vertical excavations have been considered. Technical aspects of design including rock stability and support system and construction considerations relating to sequence, excavation method, and construction procedures are discussed. It must be recognized that while several parameters are discussed under different headings, some of these parameters are not independent but together they influence the rock mass behavior or rock-structure interaction.

ACKNOWLEDGEMENTS

The writer wishes to acknowledge assistance provided by the staff members of Sverdrup & Parcel and Associates, Incorporated in St. Louis, Missouri. Thanks are specially due to Mr. James A. Larson, Senior Project Manager, Sverdrup & Parcel And Associates, Inc., for his review and comments.

REFERENCES

Brahma, C. S., 1978, "Significance of Groundwater and Methods of Ground Control in Tunnelling", Proceedings, 29th Annual Highway Geology Symposium, Annapolis, Maryland.

Brahma, C. S., 1978, "Geotechnical Perspective on Slurry Wall System", Proceedings, 29th Annual Highway Geology Symposium, Annapolis, Maryland.

21

Instrumentation in Ground Control

Chairmen: B.C. Hamilton
J. Franklin

University of Wisconsin, Madison, WI

Chapter 88

TUNNEL INSTRUMENTATION: WHY AND HOW?

by John Dunnicliff, Delon Hampton, and Ernest Selig

Geotechnical Instrumentation Consultant,
Lexington, Massachusetts

President, Delon Hampton & Associates, Chartered
Silver Spring, Maryland

Professor of Civil Engineering, University of Massachusetts
Amherst, Massachusetts

ABSTRACT

This paper provides a summary of a two-day conference held in New Orleans in March 1980, entitled "Tunnel Instrumentation: Benefits and Implementation." The conference addressed two major questions: First, what are the benefits of using instrumentation during tunnel construction? Second, what contractual relations should be established for conducting instrumentation programs during tunnel construction? Each session consisted of brief formal presentations and extensive panel discussions with participation from attendees. Attendees included owners, designers, contractors, and instrumentation specialists. This paper presents a consensus of views expressed during the conference.

INTRODUCTION

In March, 1980, a two-day conference entitled "Tunnel Instrumentation: Benefits and Implementation" was held in New Orleans. Conference sponsors were the Federal Highway Administration (FHWA) and the Urban Mass Transportation Administration (UMTA), U.S. Department of Transportation. The conference was implemented by Delon Hampton & Associates, Chartered. The objective of the conference was to present to decision makers in the tunneling and underground construction community the reasons for a comprehensive instrumentation program, including examples of use and payoff, and to outline how such programs should be accomplished.

The conference was divided into four sessions:

1. Why instrumentation?

2. Measurement methods, planning, and contractual relations.

3. Case studies on tunnel instrumentation.

4. General discussion.

The writers of this paper served as session chairmen and panel moderators during the conference. Attendees included owners, designers, contractors, and instrumentation specialists. In an attempt to draw out all viewpoints and reach a consensus, the format of the conference emphasized panel and attendee discussions, rather than prepared presentations.

Proceedings (Hampton & Greenfield, 1980) of this conference will be published by FHWA during 1981. This paper presents a summary of the views expressed during Sessions 1 and 2.

TUNNEL INSTRUMENTATION: WHY?

The starting point for any instrumentation project is to establish a clear purpose. During conference deliberations, many reasons were illustrated for instrumenting a tunnel project. These have been grouped into the following primary categories:

- Verifying design.
- Advancing the state-of-the-art.
- Providing adequacy of new construction techniques.
- Controlling construction.
- Reducing construction cost.
- Diagnosing the cause of a problem.
- Improving construction safety.
- Documenting as-built conditions.
- Providing legal protection.
- Enhancing public relations.

Verifying Design

The tunnel designer must deal with uncertainties in soil and rock conditions, and in effects of construction methods. Thus, during construction, it is essential that the designer verify the extent to which conditions are as assumed and that the structures are performing as required. Instrumentation is a valuable tool for this purpose. If conditions are found to be unsatisfactory, changes can be made based upon field observations. This process requires rapid reduction and interpretation of the field data, and good communication between the designer, owner and contractor. The absence of these essential conditions will greatly reduce the effectiveness of the instrumentation program.

Tunnel projects are very expensive and involve high risks. Thus, instrumentation programs to learn about loads on tunnel linings and resulting stresses and deformations can result in potentially large cost savings in future construction. Observations must not only be made during construction, but also for a period of time following construction, and installed instrumentation provides valuable input to observations after construction.

An instrumentation project in Baltimore helped to assess newly designed precast tunnel liners. This led to the inclusion of precast tunnel liners in the tunnel design criteria of transit systems, e.g. those being built in Baltimore, Md. and Washington, D.C. The use of slurry walls has advanced through instrumentation studies in Boston. After problems developed in the first bore of the Eisenhower tunnel, instrumentation was used to evaluate the effectiveness of remedial work and assist in developing improved design for future construction.

In the absence of instrumentation during construction, tunnel design must necessarily be more conservative. However, those who rely on overconservatism as an argument for not needing instrumentation would do well to ask themselves, "How conservative are we? What is our real factor of safety?" Unexpected conditions or unfulfilled assumptions may result in unconservative design and unanticipated risks. Properly applied instrumentation will help to avoid these consequences.

Advancing State-of-the-Art

Understanding the nature of earth pressure on tunnel liners has increased as a result of data obtained from instrumentation on the Bay Area Rapid Transit (BART) System in San Francisco. Improvements in techniques for long-term monitoring should also result. Similar benefits have accrued from other tunnel projects, such as found on the Baltimore Rapid Transit System and the Washington Metro System. Updating of the state-of-the-art will continually occur from the accumulation of knowledge gained from such studies. This will permit better design and more effective construction on future tunnel projects, or even on continuations of the same project. An example of the latter is the design modification established on the basis of the DuPont Circle instrumentation study in Washington, D.C. which was then used in subsequent stations.

However, new designs only take partial advantage of the results of previous instrumentation studies. The reasons include limitations in the availability of past results, and reluctance to try new designs. Among the reasons which sometimes cause the designer to stick to previous design concepts are the restrictions on his fees, the lack of his involvement in construction, and potentially greater risk. However, the owner is usually in a position to correct these problems.

Proving Adequacy of New Construction Techniques

New construction techniques, like new design concepts, need verification in the field. In fact, their implementation is difficult to justify without monitoring the results to permit an adequate assessment. Instrumentation is a useful tool for this purpose.

Two significant examples of the use of instrumentation to prove new construction techniques were given during the New Orleans conference. In one case, stresses in gasketed tunnel liner plates were evaluated by the contractor, using instrumentation to prove their ability to withstand water pressure. The success of this new liner plate installation technique permitted concreting in free air, rather than under compressed air. In another case, instrumentation was used to evaluate effectiveness of compaction grouting to reduce building settlement caused by tunneling for the Baltimore subway. This gave confidence in the method, which permitted elimination of costly underpinning of many buildings in later parts of the tunnel construction.

Controlling Construction

Because of uncertainties in loads on temporary supports, uncertainties in effects of construction on ground movement and building settlement, and uncertainties in groundwater conditions, instrumentation can be a very useful aid to construction. Instrumentation, for example, can help determine the best construction technique to minimize adjacent building settlement. Instrumentation is also particularly useful in locating the nature and source of undesired ground movements.

After problems developed in the first bore of the Eisenhower tunnel, instrumentation was used to monitor rock during subsequent construction to forecast the need for remedial work. This approach was expanded during the second bore and was a factor in its completion with much less difficulty.

In a tunnel in rock, the decision on the need for a concrete liner rather than shotcrete and rock bolts was based on the rate of change of the bore diameter during excavation. The detection of these changes with adequate precision required instrumentation.

More than eight million dollars in claims was paid on one job because of construction problems. Instrumentation would have helped anticipate problems before they occurred, and helped to determine remedial action. In another case, one and one-half million dollars of added cost was required as a result of tunnel collapse. It was estimated that, in this case, $100,000 of instrumentation could have identified the problem in time to avoid collapse

Instrumentation played a very important role in Baltimore subway construction. Settlement of structures adjacent to the tunnel was monitored to determine the need for corrective action to avoid excessive movement. Other measurements on this project included loads in excavation supports, groundwater level changes, and blast-induced vibrations.

Reducing Construction Cost

Tunnels are becoming increasingly expensive to construct. Generally, the designs are overconservative, however, leaving room for cost reduction with the aid of instrumentation. The cost of instrumentation programs has been on the order of one-half to one percent of construction cost. Thus, instrumentation applications in which the cost saving is many times the cost of the instrumentation seems to be highly probable. Numerous examples of such cost savings were given during the New Orleans conference.

Construction costs can be reduced by instrumentation which discloses when underpinning of adjacent buildings is not needed, or when spacing of tunnel supports can be increased. In one case, a set of measurements of strut loads showed that the number of planned struts was more than needed. Not only was the cost of the extra strutting saved, but the tunnel construction was also expedited because of reduced interference from the struts.

For the Green River tunnel in Wyoming, the construction monitoring program, costing $43,000, enabled the contractor to reduce the quantity of steel supports by 25%. This resulted in large construction cost savings.

On the Washington Metro project, the effectiveness of chemical grouting in stabilizing the soil during tunneling operations was proven on one test section. Use of this grouting technique in adjacent sections reduced construction cost.

In a tunnel job in New York City, liner plate stress analysis was carried out by the contractor, using instrumentation, to establish requirements for shield-driven tunneling methods. This saved the contractor over one million dollars during a subsequent job. On another job, the same contractor evaluated the dissipation of jacking thrust by transfer to soil friction, using instrumentation to determine when the jacking frame at the tunnel shaft was no longer needed. Muck removal was expedited by earlier elimination of the jacking frame than otherwise would have been permitted.

Diagnosing Cause of a Problem

Near one section of a particular tunnel under construction, adjacent building disturbance was observed. Lack of instrumentation prevented proper determination of the cause of the problem and hence resulted in uncertainty about proper corrective measures. When problem areas are discovered during construction, instrumentation can help diagnose what is happening, to ensure a proper solution.

A successful example cited was on the Baltimore subway project in which extensive wall movement was observed after excavation. Instrumentation was used to determine the location of the maximum movement and establish the proper rock bolt pattern to stabilize this movement.

Improving Construction Safety

Safety, both during and after construction, is an essential consideration on all tunnel jobs. However, overconservative construction is costly. Instrumentation programs can provide the needed safeguards, while permitting a lower factor of safety or more rapid construction. Continued safety of tunnels in service can be evaluated through long-term monitoring. This is particularly important where loads and deformations change with time, such that the long-term rather than the end of construction is the most critical stage.

Tunnel construction safety records have greatly improved from earlier decades. Part of the credit can be given to instrumentation programs that have helped to develop safer designs and construction techniques. Improved safety records on both the Washington Metro and the Eisenhower second bore have been attributed, in part, to the existence of an extensive instrumentation program.

Documenting As-Built Conditions

The construction of tunnels may affect the development potential of adjacent properties. Information on ground conditions and response of adjacent structures that can be obtained during tunnel construction, and perhaps only then, can be of real value, in the future, to property owners. This value may encourage cooperation.

Future changes in conditions or in system requirements may necessitate modifications to existing tunnels, or repairs. Appropriate instrumentation during original construction will provide data useful for this task, and save cost of later determination of the as-built conditions.

Providing Legal Protection

The availability of monitoring methods may affect owner or contractor liability. If problems develop in the absence of instrumentation that could have been avoided by detection with instrumentation, negligence could be found by the courts.

One section of the Baltimore subway tunnel was driven under two 100-year-old railroad tunnels. One benefit of instrumentation in this case was to document the fact that no damage to these old tunnels resulted from the new construction. Some protection against damage claims was thus provided.

Enhancing Public Relations

The public can obtain reassurance from instrumentation programs which indicate that the construction is being carefully watched. This can expedite the approval of the project. The owner in one rock tunnel project specified extensive instrumentation, more than was needed for technical reasons, to reassure the public that safety would be enhanced and damage potential or adverse problems would be minimized. This resulted in more rapid approval of the project and removed many of the political obstacles. Because of inflation and other cost of delays, the higher than normal instrumentation cost in this case could still have resulted in a cost savings.

General Considerations

When the need for instrumentation is properly and correctly established, and when the program is properly planned, instrumentation will be cost effective. Cost savings may directly result, as indicated by previous examples. However, instrumentation does not have to cut costs to be justified. In some cases, instrumentation has proved that the design is correct. This is valuable, but not cost saving. In other cases, instrumentation might show that the design is inadequate. In this event, the construction cost will be increased. However, the value of added safety and the avoidance of failure will make the instrumentation program cost effective.

Although the potential cost effectiveness of instrumentation has been established, a considerable portion of our instrumentation dollars have not been effectively used. The reasons are, for example, failure to identify the need, use of unreliable instruments, rigid adherence to the predetermined instrumentation plan, improper installation, delay in getting the results back in time, and not having a plan for interpreting the results and making action decisions.

With the need for instrumentation established, the issue then becomes implementation, or the "how." This topic is the focus of the remainder of the paper.

TUNNEL INSTRUMENTATION: HOW?

The discussion of how to instrument will begin with examples of types of instruments and typical applications. Steps in planning and implementing an instrumentation program will then be given. Finally, and very importantly, is a review of contractual arrangements.

Instrument Applications

Tunnel measurements have been divided into eight categories. These are: subsurface settlement, subsurface horizontal movement, diameter or width change, tilt, load or stress in structural support, groundwater level, pore water pressure, and vibration. The types of instruments used for each of these categories are indicated in Table 1, along with typical applications relevant to tunnel projects.

STEPS IN PLANNING AND IMPLEMENTING AN INSTRUMENTATION PROGRAM

The various steps necessary in conducting a tunnel instrumentation program, from conception to implementation, are outlined in Table 2. If an instrumentation program is conducted without following these steps, it will probably not achieve its purpose. The planning and implementation of tunnel instrumentation programs require special effort and dedication on the part of responsible personnel (others have used the words "tender loving care"). It is necessary to establish this point as a prelude to the later discussion, in this paper, on methods of establishing contractual arrangements for instrumentation work.

Three quotes will emphasize the need for a thorough and systematic approach when conducting an instrumentation program: "A well-planned instrumentation program is the key to the whole process," Dr. D.A. Linger. "The purpose of this meeting is to place emphasis on the need for a well thought out, well planned instrumentation program," Dr. G.D. Love. "We need to carry out a vast amount of observational work, but what we do should be done for a purpose, and be done well" (Peck, 1970). This "and be done well" is the key point. How do you "do it well"? If instrumentation is, in fact, to serve as a valuable tool for the tunneling industry, any such instrumentation program needs to address the specific questions that have arisen on the particular project, and the program needs to be conducted in an extremely systematic way.

Table 1. Typical Applications for Various Measuring Instruments.

Measurement	Instrument	Typical Applications
Subsurface settlement	Single point borehole extensometer	Forewarning of surface settlement.
	Multi-point borehole extensometer	Verifying adequacy of tail void filling.
	Vertical pipe or tube settlement gage	Monitoring basal stability of open cut excavations in clay.
Subsurface horizontal movement	Inclinometer Borehole extensometer	Forewarning of surface settlement or tunnel instability by monitoring ground movement towards excavation or heading.
		Verifying adequacy of rock bolting and other support.
Diameter or width change	Tape extensometer	Monitoring changing width of open cut as indication of stability.
		Monitoring lining distortion.
Tilt	Tiltmeter	Monitoring tilting of buildings.
Load or stress in structural support	Load cell Strain gage	Verifying adequacy of structural support (rock bolts, ribs, liner plates, precast concrete liners, cross-lot bracing, tie-backs).
		Determining factor of safety on shoving stresses in soft ground shield tunneling.
		Increasing knowledge of support behavior as input to improved design procedures.
Groundwater level	Observation well	Monitoring drawdown of groundwater table due to tunneling.
Pore water pressure	Piezometer	Forewarning of distress to buildings due to movement of soil or water towards soft ground tunnel.
Vibration	Engineering seismograph	Verifying that ground and building vibrations due to blasting do not exceed an acceptable limit.

TABLE 2. Steps in Conducting a Tunnel Instrumentation Program.

	Steps	Remarks
1.	Define project conditions	e.g. construction method, geotechnical conditions.
2.	Define purpose of instrumentation	A clear answer to "Why instrumentation?"
3.	Select Variables to be monitored	Which variables are key to the problem?
4.	Make predictions of behavior	To determine required measurement range and accuracy.
5.	Decide who will perform all subsequent tasks	To identify possible future staffing or funding gaps.
6.	Select instruments	Overriding desirable feature is reliability.
7.	Write instrument procurement specifications	Negotiation preferable to bidding.
8.	Determine what factors may influence data	These must be recorded to permit analysis of cause and effect.
9.	Plan procedures for ensuring reading correctness	The question "How do we know the instrument is working correctly?" must be answerable.
10.	Plan instrument layout	Determine critical zones.
11.	Write installation specifications	Negotiated contract preferable to bidding.
12.	Plan installation methods	Write detailed installation procedure and list of materials.
13.	Plan data collection, processing, transmittal, portrayal, analytical and interpretation procedures	Prepare data sheets and plots. Plan reading schedule.
14.	Plan implementation or remedial measures	Determine a course of action in event data indicate adverse event.
15.	Procure instruments	
16.	Calibrate instruments	Verify all manufacturer's calibrations.
17.	Install and maintain instruments	Establish cooperation with tunnel contractor.
18.	Collect data, process, analyze, interpret	Update reading schedule in accordance with measured changes. Interpret very soon after collection.
19.	Implement	

Contractual Arrangements

The goals of contractual arrangements are:

- The work should be of maximum quality.
- The work must be done at minimum cost.
- The contractual relations should create maximum flexibility to permit changes as geology is revealed during construction.
- There should be maximum cooperation between instrumentation personnel and the contractor.

For "one-shot deal" instrumentation work, i.e., a single assignment on a single project, the person with the greatest interest in the data should have responsibility for the entire monitoring program. For multiple needs on a single project, or for multi-section projects, many methods are in use. The following contractual arrangments are most suitable for each of the steps identified in Table 2.

The steps in planning an instrumentation program are Items 1 through 14 in Table 2. The task of planning the instrumentation program should be performed by engineers with specialist expertise in applications of geotechnical instrumentation. If the project is subdivided into a series of section designs, these engineers should have a system-wide responsibility, so that uniformity exists throughout the system and so that equipment and measurement results on one section can be used for the benefit of other sections. The words "team player" are applicable. He should obviously work for the owner. He should obviously not be retained on a bid basis. He should work closely with the general design consultant if there is one. He should work closely with and in a coordinated manner with the separate section designers, if there are separate section designers. Whether he is invovled with a section designer or with the general design consultant, he should work closely with their engineering geologists and the entire design team. This instrumentation team player may already be on the staff of the owner or the general design consultant. If neither has that in-house expertise he perhaps may be retained as a consultant to one of them.

Collecting, processing, analyzing, and interpreting data are represented by Item 18 in Table 2. These tasks should be the responsibility of the same "team player" involved in planning. If the project is a multi-section tunnel project, and if there are separate section designers, clearly this effort will be in close cooperation with all of them.

Implementing the program is designated by Item 19 in Table 2. There is no preferred way of establishing contractual arrangements for implementation of instrumentation data, because implementation depends on the purpose of the instrumentation. If the data are intended to benefit the project under construction, clearly the owner, designer and contractor will all be involved in implementation, and payment for any extra work by the contractor will normally be made on a time and materials basis. If the data are intended to benefit future projects rather than the project under construction, responsibility for implementation will depend on who initiated the instrumentation.

Procuring, calibrating, installing and maintaining instrumentation are indicated by Items 15 to 17 in Table 2. There are two possibilities for contracting these tasks. First, if the owner has appropriate in-house skills, he can do this himself. If that is so, then the same "team player" would supervise the work. The major problem with this approach is cooperation and scheduling with the contractor, and there needs to be a strong effort to develop an atmosphere of mutual respect and cooperation. The key word is "communication," and communication between all parties involved at all levels, and well ahead of time.

The second possibility, if the owner does not have necessary in-house skills, is to hire a specialty subcontractor or subconsultant to perform the work. There are three methods of doing this:

1. The work is included as unit price or lump sum bid items in the general contract, with or without prequalification requirements, and with or without the requirement that responsible personnel be subject to the approval of the owner.

2. The owner or designer selects a specialty subconsultant, in accordance with conventional practices for engagement of engineering services (ASCE, 1975). The owner or designer negotiates payment method and enters into a contract for all work requiring specialist skill. Associated support work that is within the capability of the average tunnel contractor's work force is performed by the general contractor.

3. The owner or designer selects a specialist, in accordance with conventional practices for engagement of engineering services, with the approval of the general contractor. The owner or designer negotiates payment and arranges for the specialist to enter into a subcontract with the general contractor for all work requiring specialist skill. The specialist subcontractor is paid by the contractor under an allowance item in the bid schedule. Associated support work that is within the capability of the average tunnel

contractor's work force is performed by the general contractor.

During presentations at the New Orleans conference the writers advocated that procuring, calibrating, installing and maintaining instrumentation should be considered as a professional service rather than a routine construction item, believing this to be the surest way of achieving the needed level of purism (dedication, tender loving care). Hence, they do not favor the first of the above three methods. They prefer the third method because it is most likely to permit cooperation between specialist and contractor. This is an essential feature in a tunnel environment where working space is limited and mining cycle schedules are critical. However, recognizing that others may have different points of view, appropriate questions were asked of a panel representing the owner, designer, and contractor. Questions and a summary of answers are shown in Table 3.

As can be seen from Table 3, it was agreed by all panelists that neither the owner nor the contractor should select the subcontractor on his own; that some way must be found whereby both the owner and the contractor are happy with the selection. Agreement was reached that specialist personnel should be under contract to the contractor rather than the owner, so that cooperation is possible. All agreed that the support work--drilling instrument holes, grouting, physical protection, manholes, and so on--should be bid. Agreement was not reached on whether the task of furnishing and installing sophisticated instrumentation such as strain gages and multiple position extensometers should be paid for on a bid or on a time and materials basis, but it was agreed that if the bid method is used a comprehensive specification is essential. Such a specification should address all the items in Table 4. This list is based on Cording et al. (1975), but additional items have been added by the writers.

SUMMARY

The objective of the March 1980 conference, and of this paper, has been to present to decision makers in the tunneling and underground construction community the need, application, and payoff of a comprehensive instrumentation program, and to outline how such programs should be accomplished. Only time will tell whether this objective has been met. If so, hopefully, the success will be reflected in lower construction costs and an increased demand for tunneling and, in the long run, a viable, long-range, energy-efficient, alternative solution to the current urban transportation crisis.

TABLE 3. Summary of Questions and Answers on Contractual Arrangements for Installation of Sophisticated Instrumentation.

Question	Wallace H. Baker (Specialty Contractor)	Gustave Fleischer (Tunnel Contractor)	Joseph D. Guertin, Jr. (Consulting Geotechnical Engineer)	Larry H. Heflin (Transit Agency)	Douglas J. Mansfield (Consulting Engineer)
Should installation of sophisticated instrumentation be viewed as a routine construction item?					
No		•	•		•
Yes	•			•	
How should specialist personnel be paid for installation of sophisticated instrumentation?					
Bid				•	•
Time and materials		•	•		
Who should select a specialist for installation of sophisticated instrumentation?					
Owner					
Contractor					
Contractor with owner approval	•		•	•	
Owner with contractor approval		•			•
Should specialist personnel hired for installation of sophisticated instrumentation be under contract to the owner or the contractor?					
Owner			•		
Contractor	•	•	•	•	•

Table 4. Items to be Included in Instrumentation if Bid Method is Used.

Purpose of the observation program

Division of responsibilities between owner, designer, resident engineer, instrumentation specialist, contractor for:

- Procuring hardware
- Calibrating hardware
- Installing instruments
- Maintaining instruments
- Establishing and updating reading schedule
- Reading instruments
- Reducing and plotting data
- Interpreting data

Qualifications of specialty field personnel

Need for technical submittal to Engineer

Availability of data to Contractor and Engineer

Contractor cooperation

General requirements for hardware

Procedure for approval of hardware

Specifications for hardware

Quality control of hardware

Factory calibration of hardware

Hardware spare parts

Warranty on hardware

Hardware instruction manual requirements

Locations of instruments

Installation schedule

Delay of construction caused by instrumentation field work

Need for technical advisors

Installation procedures

Access for installation

Work restrictions

Contractor support services

Protection of instruments

Maintenance of instruments

Responsibility for instrument damage

Responsibility for instrument malfunction

Reading instruments

Reducing and plotting data

Disposition of instruments

Ground surface restoration

Interpretation of data

Who acts (and how) when something unforeseen happens

Measurement and payment

Instrumentation: Why?

During the conference both highway and transit owner-agencies described payoffs and uses of instrumentation, and tunnel contractors described cost savings resulting from instrumentation. This evidence of "why instrumentation" is summarized in this paper.

If we ask ourselves, for each new project, what measurements are important during construction, there is always going to be at least one good answer. Hence, there is always a "why." It is time that we designate instrumentation as an essential part of the design/construction process, not just an option. Instrumentation is a tool to be used, just like a computer, and should be a part of all future tunnel projects. To not consider it so is no longer excusable, no longer a responsible position for us, whether we're the owner, the engineer, or the contractor.

Thus the conference concluded that the main question is not whether a need exists, but how the need is identified and implemented. This issue was illustrated very succinctly by Dr. Wallace Hayward Baker in his conference presentation:

> "When we were teenagers we were concerned with the philosophical argument that if a tree falls in the forest and nobody is around to hear it happen, is there a noise? As a corollary to that, I think we can ask ourselves: If instrumentation devices are installed in an underground construction project and nobody is available to analyze the data, is there an instrumentation program? I have seen a lot of trees fall without there being a noise by the people who would respond and get out of the way or change them."

Instrumentation: HOW?

An instrumentation program must be conducted in a series of carefully thought out steps, beginning with conception and ending in implementation. These steps have been outlined. The planning effort should be undertaken by engineers with specialist expertise in applications of geotechnical instrumentation. They should have system-wide responsibility, and should be capable "team-players" authorized to work with the general design consultant, section designers, their engineering geologists and the entire design team. These same "team-players" should also have a responsible role in collecting, processing, analyzing and interpreting data.

The remaining major task, instrument installation, was discussed at length during the conference and is summarized in this paper. It was unanimous that it should be an owner-contractor coordinated effort, and that specialist personnel hired for installation of sophisticated instrumentation should, in order to facilitate cooperation in the tunnel, be under contract to the contractor rather than the owner. However, there was divided opinion on the issue of whether installation contracts should be awarded by competitive bidding or whether contracts should be negotiated. The writers advocate negotiation. To support this view, in his closing remarks at the conference, Dr. Don A. Linger said:

> "From my own experience, I have observed that if installation work is bid, there is a very real possibility the contractor will shop around to fulfill a contractual requirement for instrumentation installation. He will tend to obtain the lowest cost services, that will in fact produce cost cutting in a sophisticated type of technology (which is still an art by today's standards) with resulting severe impact on the accuracy, sensitivity and useability of the instrumentation. The question of "How Instrumentation?" must consider that instrumentation hardware and transducer placement is quite different from the placement of a cubic yard of concrete or 211 lb/ft steel sets and this must be considered by the owner and the designer whose concepts are to be verified or modified by the instrumentation program."

In the event that the bid method is used for installation contracts, a comprehensive specification is essential. The items to be addressed in such specifications are listed in the paper.

A second quotation from Dr. Wallace Hayward Baker's conference presentation will identify the key issue in assigning responsibility for instrumentation work:

> "Who has the motivation? Who cares about the data? The person with the greatest vested interest in the data should have direct line responsibility for producing it accurately."

ACKNOWLEDGEMENTS

The writers wish to express their thanks to the Implementation Division, Office of Development of the U.S. Department of Transportation, Federal Highway Administration, for permission to present this paper. Appreciation is also expressed to the following for their contributions during the conference, all of which have played a part in assembling material for this paper: Dr. Wallace H. Baker, Dr. Tor L. Brekke, Mr. Gilbert L. Butler, Dr. Edward J. Cording, Mr. Gustave Fleischer, Mr. George A. Fox, Mr. Vernon K. Garrett, Mr. Jack Gay, Mr. Joseph D. Guertin, Jr., Mr. Larry H. Heflin, Mr. Frank Hoppe, Dr. Don A. Linger, Dr. Gerald D. Love, Mr. Douglas J. Mansfield, Mr. Phillip R. McOllough, Mr. William C. Shepherd, Jr.

REFERENCES

American Society of Civil Engineers (1975), "Consulting Engineering, A Guide for the Engagement of Engineering Services," Manual No. 45.

Cording, et al. (1975), "Methods for Geotechnical Observations and Instrumentation in Tunneling," Report No. UILU-ENG 75 2022, Department of Civil Engineering, University of Illinois at Urbana-Champaign, Urbana, Illinois.

Hampton, D. and Greenfield, E.M., Editors (1980), "Proceedings of a Conference on Tunnel Instrumentation Benefits and Implementation," held in New Orleans, March, 24-25, 1980, U.S. Department of Transportation Report No. FHWA-TS-81-201, 241 pp.

Peck, R.B. (1970), "Observation and Instrumentation: Some Elementary Considerations," Met. Section ASCE Seminar on Field Observations in Foundation Design and Construction, April.

Chapter 89

A LARGE UNDERGROUND OPENING
MEASURED VERSUS PREDICTED ROCK DEFORMATIONS

by
Norman F. Sweeney and H. John Hovland

Geotechnical Engineer, Pacific Gas and Electric Company
Senior Civil Engineer, Pacific Gas and Electric Company

ABSTRACT

Over one million yards of granite were excavated for the Helms Pumped Storage Project, including a large underground powerhouse complex. Site investigations and in situ stress measurements were essential elements of the project design and provided the necessary geologic parameters for executing a finite element study of the powerhouse. A construction monitoring program, of geologic mapping, field instrumentation, and rock mechanics testing was then designed and has been successfully implemented. This paper reports on the scope of this construction monitoring program and explicitly compares the measured deformations to those predicted. As a result of this recent field experience the assumptions used in the finite element program are reexamined.

INTRODUCTION

Pacific Gas and Electric Company (PGandE) is constructing the Helms Pumped Storage Project. This large underground construction project is located 60 kilometers east of Fresno, California, and is in the high Sierra Nevada (Figure 1 - Location Map). When completed in 1982, the project's three reversible pump-turbines will contribute 1,050 megawatts of electrical peaking capacity to PGandE's system.

This paper describes the numerous geologic investigations and programs conducted throughout the Helms project. The results of the construction monitoring program will be summarized and used to re-examine the assumptions in the project's finite element program.

The Helms project includes the excavation of over 8 kilometers of large-diameter tunnels. Other major underground excavations include the powerhouse and connecting transformer vault, two surge chambers, an elevator shaft and a gate shaft. The powerhouse complex will be excavated 300 meters underground. A plan and profile of the powerhouse complex are shown in Figure 2.

The project will connect two existing reservoirs. Water from the upper reservoir, Courtright Lake, El. 2,500 meters, will be released to generate power during PGandE's peak electrical demand periods. During off-peak periods, the units will be reversed and water pumped from Lake Wishon, El. 1,980 meters, back up to Courtright.

The two large reservoirs, more than $1.5 \times 10^8 m^3$ storage capacity each, were constructed by PGandE in 1956-58. Their close proximity (Figure 1) and large elevation difference were primary factors in their selection as a potential site for a large pumped storage facility. A site reconnaissance and review of aerial photographs confirmed favorable geologic and topographic conditions. Preliminary analyses used these factors in conjunction with hydraulic and environmental constraints to produce a design which locates the major facilities underground.

GEOLOGY

The entire project is situated within the Sierra Nevada geomorphic province. The Sierra Nevada is 80 to 130 kilometers wide and trends northwest for over 640 kilometers. The province consists of Mesozoic granitic batholiths that have broken free along its eastern flank on the Sierra Nevada fault system, tilted westward, and become overlain by the Great Valley sedimentary sequence to the west.

The project is situated predominately in blocky to massive granodiorite or quartz monzonite. Other rock types encountered are quartz diorite, granite, aplite, and a roof pendant of metasedimentary rocks.

There are three predominant joint sets. Two joint sets are steeply dipping and strike northwest and northeast. In addition, there is a near horizontal joint set.

PROJECT INVESTIGATIONS

The project was first conceptualized in 1971. It was evident from the start that an underground construction project of this magnitude required a comprehensive rock mechanics program. A detailed site investigation began in 1973. During the summer months of 1973 and 1974, more than 7,700 feet (2,300 m) of NX core was drilled at 14 hole locations. The boreholes were distributed along the project's tunnel alignment, with special attention given to the proposed major facility locations. Detailed geologic mapping along the tunnel alignment was conducted at the same time. This information was compiled and subsurface conditions were extrapolated.

In addition to compiling visual and descriptive drill logs, core samples were selected for laboratory testing. Samples were taken at representative intervals of each distinguishing rock type. Standard physical tests were performed to determine mohr hardness, compressive tensile strength, specific gravity, adsorption, Poisson's ratio and chord modulus. In addition, downhole seismic measurements and hydrofracturing stress measurements were conducted in selected boreholes. These data, collected and compiled in various reports, provided quantitative data on the rock. This information in turn was used to prepare a project design.

Part of the early site investigation program included hydrofracturing stress measurements in the vicinity of the powerhouse complex.[1,2] This new stress measurement technique was brought to the attention of the designers during the preliminary design phase. The advantage of early stress measurements was weighed against cost and novelty and it was decided to proceed. Helms became the first underground powerhouse design utilizing hydrofracturing stress measurements.[2]

Nine hydrofracturing stress measurement tests were conducted in two of the existing boreholes located in the vicinity of the powerhouse. The magnitude of σHMAX oriented at N25°E in the horizontal plane, ranged from

5.4 MPa to 10.0 MPa and displayed a linear rate of increase with depth (Figure 3). The vertical stress was calculated from the weight of the overlying rock. The minimum principal stress, σHMIN, also in the horizontal plane, ranged in value between 4.5 MPa and 5.5 MPa in a N65°W direction. Figure 4 shows that the long axis of the powerhouse chamber and transformer vault is oriented at N85°E. This illustrates that the maximum horizontal stress would be perpendicular to the long axis of the powerhouse complex.

These stress values were then used in the preliminary project design. Two significant questions were discussed when these results were presented. The first question involves the effects of high water pressures on the rock surrounding the concrete lined penstocks. Calculations indicated that transient water pressures in excess of 7.5 MPa would occur. This is considerably greater than the calculated minimum principal stress of 5.0 MPa. Therefore, water pressures exceeding the minimum principal stress could potentially open or expand existing rock discontinuities. Unrestrained, these could lead to excessive leakage and eventual structural degradation of the rock mass. The project design and field instrumentation program made provisions for this condition. A drainage gallery and weep holes were strategically positioned to cut off the migration of high pressure water and field instrumentation has been designed to monitor actual field conditions.

A second consideration was the impact of the in situ stress state on the stability of the powerhouse complex excavations. A finite element program based on the hydrofracturing results and measured rock properties was run to predict deformation and stress concentrations in and around the powerhouse.[3,4]

FINITE ELEMENT ANALYSIS

Various finite element models were developed for the Helms project. Our discussions will use the plane strain finite element model developed for the powerhouse complex. The mesh, consisting of 717 elements and 771 nodes, is illustrated in Figure 5 .

An initial stress finite element technique was used. The in situ stresses were determined by the field hydrofracturing tests. Initial stresses are applied to each element. The program simulates an excavation sequence, and the stresses and deformation associated with the rock relaxation are computed.

The model assumed an initial isotropic stress field of 8.3 MPa. On the basis of field and laboratory tests, a modulus of elasticity of 41.4 x 10^3 MPA and a Poisson's ratio of 0.2 were selected. A lower rock modulus was used for the elements immediately bordering the cavity at each stage. This was an attempt to simulate the effect of weaker fractured rock in the vicinity of the excavation. The weaker rock modulus was 20.7 x 10^3 MPa and the corresponding Poisson's ratio was 0.25.

The analysis was performed in five sequential steps or "stages of excavation" to determine the response of the surrounding rock as the excavation progressed. These stages of excavation are illustrated in Figure 6. Stage 5 represents the completed excavation.

FIELD INSTRUMENTATION

A commitment was made during an early stage of the project to design and implement an economical field instrumentation program that would utilize the results of the finite element analysis. In compliance with this primary goal, the following steps were taken:

An in-house review process minimized the scope of the field instrumentation program to provide only essential information. An approach of explicit justification for each instrument was used; it led to a better understanding of the purpose of the program by all participants. Simple, rugged and reliable instruments were specified and used. Close coordination with the contractor and his cooperation minimized field installation expenses. Program implementation was directed from the field. This last point turned out to be critical. Any construction project, especially one of this magnitude, experiences continuous changes in its schedule and construction methods. Field supervision of the instrumentation program provided the flexibility needed to respond to changes.

Other goals of the program were to confirm design assumptions, monitor rock conditions and identify potential construction problems, document field conditions for future reference, and enhance construction safety through an improved knowledge and understanding of the construction media. Since the program is now essentially complete, it provides an additional function in the form of documentation to be used in future designs.

The field instrumentation program made use of tape extensometers, borehole extensometers (manual and remote readout), strain gages and piezometers.[6] Most of this instrumentation was used in the powerhouse complex (Figure 4). Results from instruments installed in this area are summarized below. Of special interest is a comparison between the measured deformations and those predicted by the finite element study.

The powerhouse and transformer vaults are elongated, large underground openings (Plan View, Figure 7). This configuration was in response to the fact that the powerhouse contains three pump-turbine units. As a result of this configuration, the largest deformations were anticipated in the transverse direction. Three transverse sections were selected (shown in Figure 7) and a majority of the field instruments were clustered into them. Figure 8 shows a typical section and the approximate instrument locations and depths. The section shows that some form of instrumentation spans the entire width of the powerhouse complex, a distance of 81 m. This instrument arrangement allows one to integrate the cumulative movement from one side of the powerhouse complex to the other.

An instrument was installed as soon as the proposed location was accessible. This early installation increased the chance of blast damage but ensured the most complete record of deformations. Recessed or protected instruments were designed to minimize blast damage.

Field readings were taken repeatedly after an instrument was installed and again when there were excavation activities in the area. Very good correlations were made between the recorded deformations and the size and distance to blasting operations. The rock deformations were primarily instantaneous, except in areas of identified high stress concentrations. The prime example of high stress was the rock pillar between the powerhouse and transformer vault. Relatively large instantaneous deformations would be measured immediately after a blast, but then smaller, gradual deformations, would be measured with time (creep). One possible explanation for this "creep" movement would be the time dependent nature of the stress re-distribution as a result of rock relaxation.

COMPARISON OF PREDICTED VERSUS MEASURED DEFORMATIONS

The predicted deformations are plotted in Figure 9 along with the measured deformations. The measurements are quite close in magnitude but there are several factors or assumptions that must be looked at more closely. The first one deals with the assumption that the rear or deepest anchor of a borehole extensometer is outside the zone of movement. One possibility is that it is not deep enough to capture all of the rock deformation. A few deep anchors were successfully installed and minimal deep movement was recorded. Therefore, deep movement does not appear to have been a significant factor at Helms. A more important factor deals with the time of installation. In most cases, each instrument was installed as early as possible near the advancing heading, but even so, the rock had already deformed an appreciable amount. Therefore, the maximum deformations shown on Figure 9 may not have captured the entire rock movement. This is especially true for rod extensometers installed in the crown. If a correction factor was applied it would increase the magnitude of the measured deformations, but not significantly enough to affect the value of the predicted movements.

Another parameter is the magnitude of the in situ stresses. After rock bursts were encountered on the project, it was decided to proceed with a series of conventional in situ stress measurements. A test drift was excavated off to the side of the powerhouse access tunnel (Figure 10). The drift was located as close to the powerhouse as feasible so the tests could be run and the results made available prior to excavation of the powerhouse. Thirteen USBM type overcoring tests were run in three boreholes. Biaxial modulus tests were run in tandem with them. These tests, as well as three flatjack tests, were performed in the test drift.[8]

The following conclusions were reached, based on analysis of the test results.[5] Based on a complete data set, the principal in situ stresses are:

	Stress (psi)	Bearing (degree clockwise from north)	Inclination (degrees, 0° = vertical down
σMAX.	2,170	187	69
σINTER.	1,050	65	37
σMIN.	880	109	118

Using the results from the nine tests, which were run at depths greater than 5 m (to avoid near surface stress concentrations), resulted in the following in situ stresses:

	Stress (psi)	Bearing (degrees)	Inclination (degrees)
σMAX.	2,230	189	65
σINTER.	1,100	43	29
σMIN.	970	106	104

These data sets along with others gave consistent results. The results appear valid and no unusual difficulties were encountered in the field. For comparison the hydrofracturing results will be reported in the same format. Remember that, for hydrofracturing tests, the intermediate stress value is assumed to be equal to the calculated weight of rock and is oriented vertically.

	Stress (psi)	Bearing (degrees)	Inclination (degrees)
σMAX.	1,380	205	90
σINTER.	1,190	-	0
σMIN.	780	115	90

The overcoring tests gave in situ stress values that were 10 to 60 percent higher than the hydrofracturing tests. The orientation of the principal stresses and their relative magnitudes were close. It appears that for the Helms project the hydrofracturing stress measurement technique provided realistic values.

The flatjack tests on the other hand were inconclusive. They did not compare well with either of the other stress measurement techniques and appear to have been heavily influenced by local geologic discontinuities and near-field stress concentrations.

At this time the finite element analysis was reexamined. Was it necessary to run the program again on the basis of the modified input? Our answer was no. The purpose of the analysis was to define the qualitative response of the rock, identify potential problem areas, and give some quantitative data on stress concentrations and rock deformations. No special effort was made to accurately predict rock stresses and deformations, especially since our literature review indicated that the predicted values were seldom in close agreement with those measured. Another purpose for generating some quantitative data was to develop some guideline information for the field monitoring program.

FIELD OBSERVATIONS

The Helms project provided numerous educational experiences related to the fields of rock mechanics and geological engineering. Only those experiences directly related to this paper's subject matter will be recounted at this time.

The finite element analysis and the field instrumentation program dealt primarily with the powerhouse complex, Figure 4. One important consideration was the fact that the finite element analysis not only modeled the dimensions of the major excavations and used field and laboratory measured geologic properties, but that it also modeled the stages of excavation. This provided pertinent information on when the various deformation were to be expected. This approximate time history of rock deformations (Figure 6) provided useful information for developing the field instrumentation program. One example in particular illustrates the usefulness of this information. The rock pillar between the powerhouse chamber and transformer vault deflected. Stage three, four and five of the finite element analysis excavation sequence provided data on how the rock pillar would be deforming and the resulting stress changes. During excavation some unusual rock fractures were observed in the powerhouse chamber on the surface of this rock pillar. Unlike other blast surfaces this rock had conchoidal fractures that were fresh, closely spaced, and open.

These fractures were only found on the rock pillar side of the powerhouse chamber. This evidence indicated that the unusual rock fracture phenomena was related to the predicted deflection of the rock pillar.

Several other areas within the powerhouse complex had what were considered to be "stress induced" fracture surfaces. They were usually associated with tunnel entries into the powerhouse chambers, corners, or rock benches. The majority of these features were observed in locales where the finite element study predicted the higher stress concentrations. Understanding this correlation was useful more than once when questions arose regarding the reaction of the rock.

SUMMARY

A finite element analysis of the Helms Pumped Storage Project underground powerhouse complex was performed prior to construction. The program provided information on the predicted rock behavior including deformations and the resulting state of stress. Based on this data and the project characteristics a construction monitoring program was developed. The monitoring program included field instrumentation to measure rock deformations in the powerhouse complex. The construction monitoring program has been successfully implemented, and there was good agreement between the predicted and measured rock deformations.

REFERENCES

1. Haimson, B. C., Design of Underground Powerhouses and the Importance of Preexcavation Stress Measurements, in Proceedings 16th U.S. Symposium on Rock Mechanics, American Society of Civil Engineers, New York, 1977.

2. Haimson, B. C., Hydrofracturing Stress Measurements - Helms Pupmed Storage Project, Report for PGandE, January 1975.

3. Willoughby, D. F. and Hovland, H. J., Finite Element Analysis of Stages of Excavation of Helms Underground Powerhouse, in Proceedings 19th U.S. Symposium on Rock Mechanics, University of Nevada, Reno, 1978.

4. Hovland, H. J., Helms Pumped Storage Project Finite Element Analyses of Underground Powerhouse and Other Pertinent Rock Excavations, Report for Pacific Gas and Electric Company, September 1976.

5. Woodward Clyde Consultants, Report on Overcoring Tests for In Situ Stress Measurements at Helms Project, prepared for Pacific Gas and Electric Company, July 21, 1978.

6. Sweeney, N. F., Helms Pumped Storage Project's In Situ Rock Instrumentation and Monitoring Program, Report for Pacific Gas and Electric.

7. Obert, L., Duvall, W. I., Rock Mechanics and the Design of Structures in Rock, John Wiley & Sons, New York 1967.

8. Sweeney, N. F., et al., 1980, "A Practical/Economic Rock Mechanics Program", in Proceedings of the 21st U.S. Rock Mechanics Symposium, Rolla, Missouri, 1980, (in press).

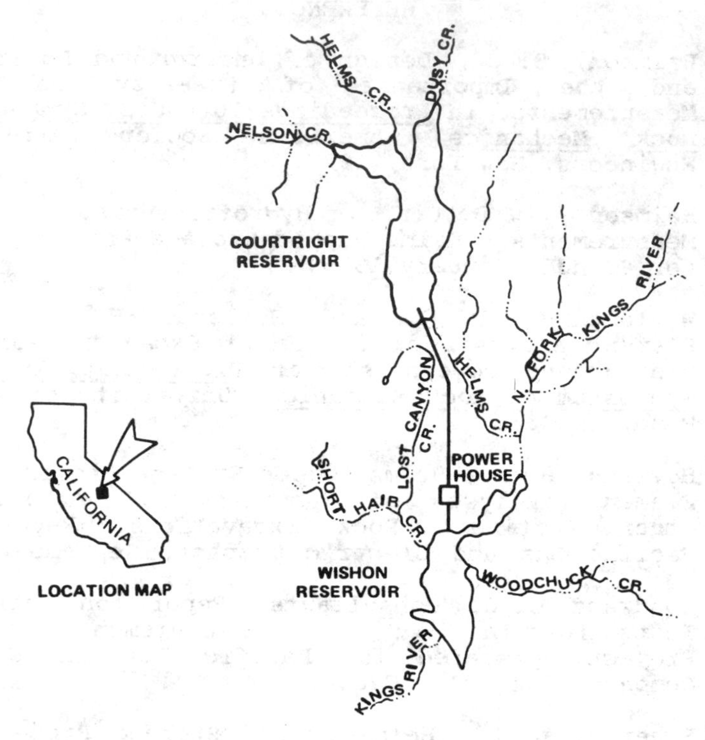

FIGURE 1

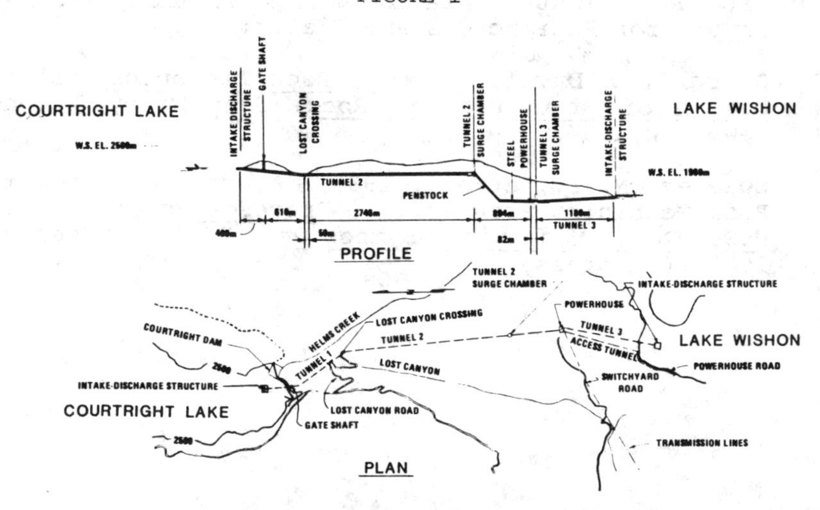

HELMS PUMPED STORAGE PROJECT

Figure 2

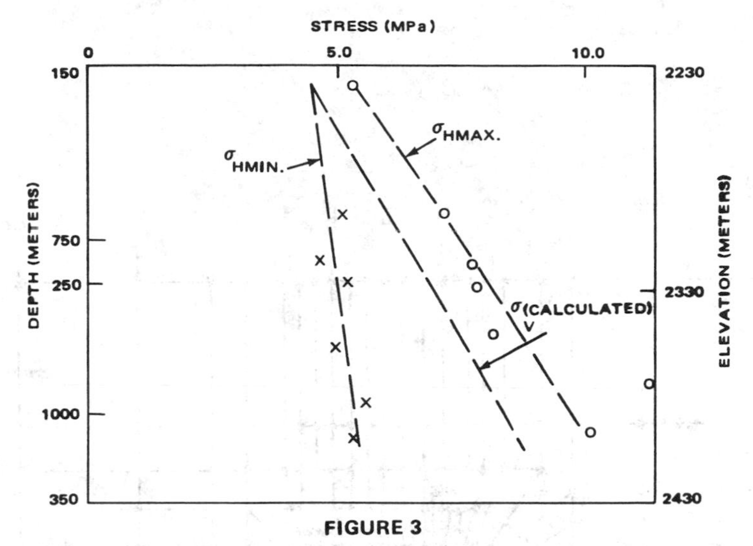

FIGURE 3

STRESS VARIATION WITH DEPTH (WITH RESPECT TO SURFACE ELEVATION OF HOLE D-1).

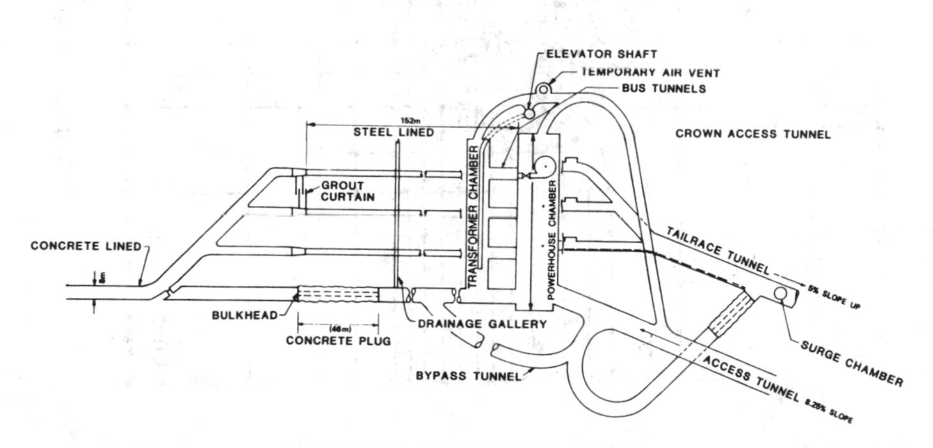

EXCAVATION POWERHOUSE COMPLEX

FIGURE 4

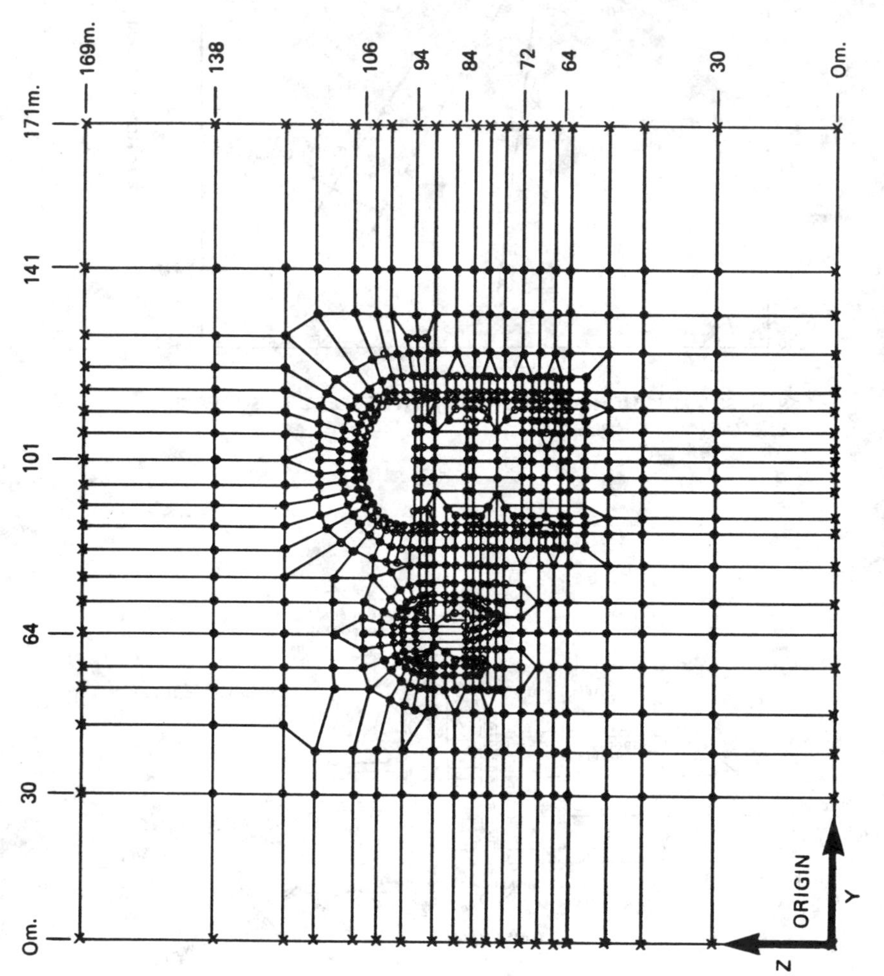

FIGURE 5 - FINITE ELEMENT MODEL

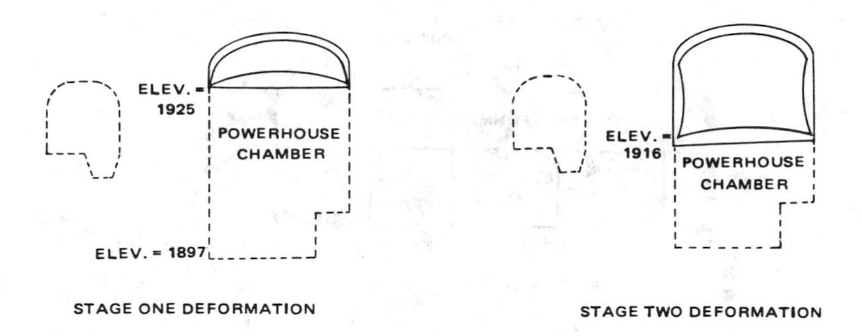

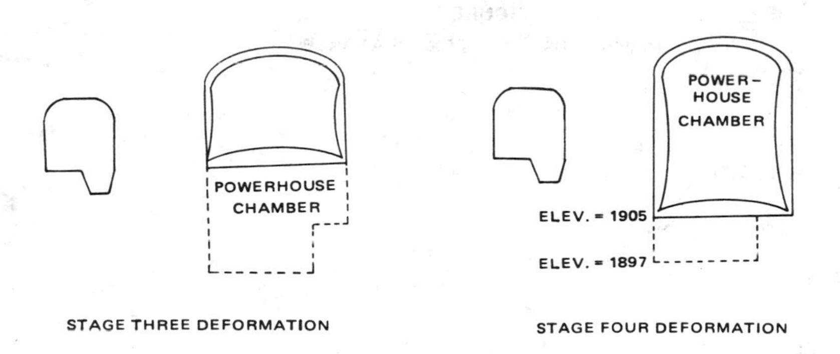

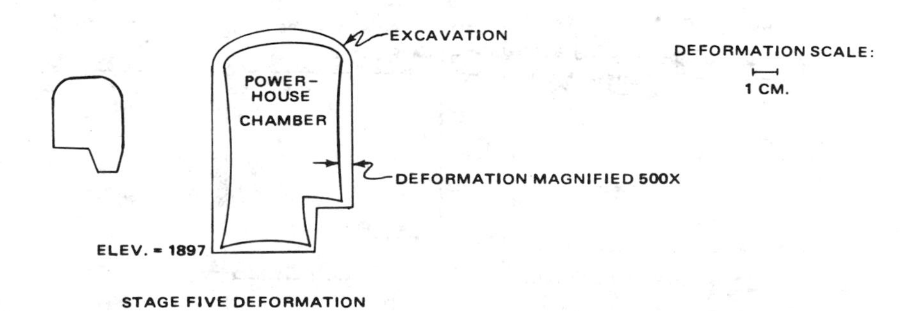

FIGURE 6 - STAGES OF EXCAVATION

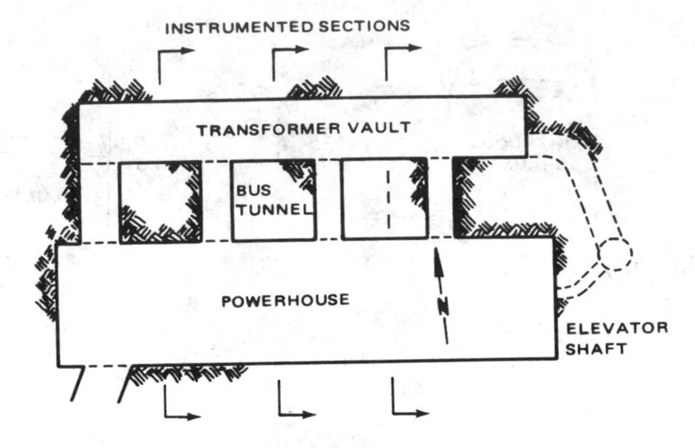

FIGURE 7
POWERHOUSE COMPLEX - PLAN VIEW

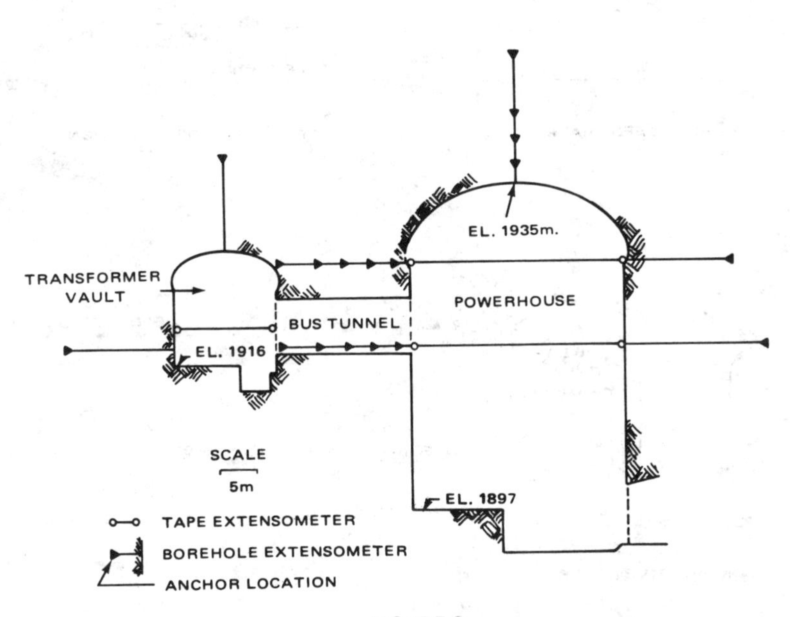

FIGURE 8
POWERHOUSE COMPLEX INSTRUMENTATION

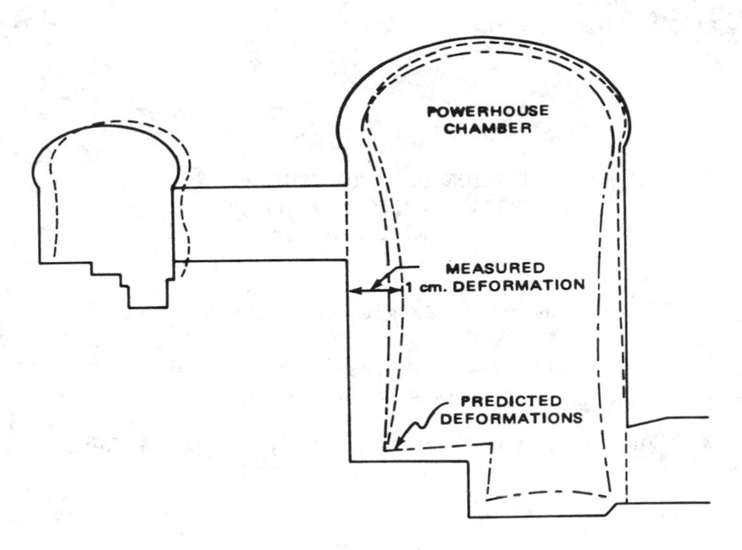

FIGURE 9 - POWERHOUSE COMPLEX DEFORMATIONS

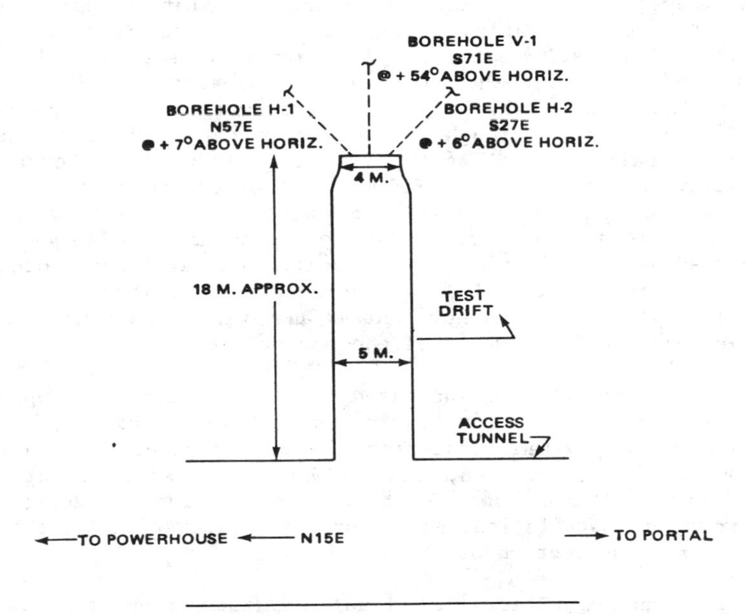

FIGURE 10 - SCHEMATIC OF THE TEST DRIFT

Chapter 90

INSTRUMENTATION USED TO CONTROL EXCAVATION AND ROCK BOLTING FOR UNDERGROUND SUBWAY STATION

By: Edward J. Zeigler and John T. Miller

Associate, Rummel, Klepper & Kahl
Baltimore Maryland

Engineering Geologist, Rummel, Klepper & Kahl
Baltimore, Maryland

INTRODUCTION

Construction of Phase I, Section A, of the Baltimore Region Rapid Transit System required that six underground stations be built using a cut and cover excavation technique. For five of these stations, soldier piles, used as support of excavation, were installed with tip elevations well below the bottom of the excavation. However, in the case of the sixth subway station, the Mondawmin Station, soldier piles were installed only through soil and decomposed rock, with the tips of the piles being stopped well above the bottom of the excavation in partially decomposed rock. Below the tips of the soldier piles, and below a cut slope where piles were not installed, the sides of the excavation consisted of partially weathered and fresh rock and were supported by a combination of rock bolts, wire mesh and shotcrete. An extensive installation of geotechnical instrumentation permitted detailed monitoring of horizontal and vertical movements of the soldier piles and the walls of the excavation.

Preliminary studies indicated that the excavation support system selected for the Mondawmin Station would have several advantages over a conventional system consisting of soldier piles extending to the bottom of the excavation, braced with prestressed struts. These advantages included lower cost of installation, a decreased time required for installation, and a more open excavation for the contractor during construction of the station.

The Mondawmin Station is situated in the northwestern quadrant of Baltimore City, approximately 6.4 km (4 miles) from the center of the City. The station lies midway in a project 12.9 km (8 miles) long identified as Phase I, Section A, of the Baltimore Region Rapid Transit

System. The excavation for the station is approximately 183 m (600 ft) long, 16 m (52 ft) wide and 27 to 29 m (90 to 95 ft) deep. Figure 1 shows a plan of the station excavation and Figure 2 is a photograph showing the nearly completed excavation.

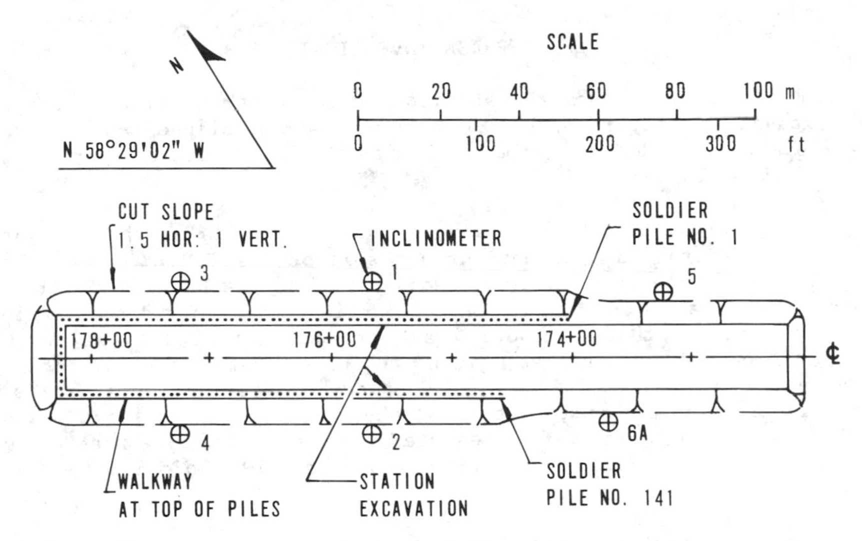

Fig. 1. Plan of station excavation.

Fig. 2.

Excavation complete except for ramp in foreground. Initial concrete pours visible at far end of station.

It is the purpose of this paper to summarize the data obtained from the instrumentation program and to show how the data were used to control excavation procedures and the installation of rock bolts.

DESIGN PHASE INVESTIGATIONS

For final design of the station and the determination of support of excavation requirements, 24 vertical and inclined borings were drilled within the approximate limits of construction during the period 1973 to 1976.

In general, the borings showed that 20 to 25% of the excavated depth of the station would be through soil or residual material which could usually be sampled with soil sampling techniques, with the remaining 75% to 80% through rock and partially decomposed rock. Since it was apparent that a majority of the excavation would be through rock, close attention was given to core sampling and detailed examination of the recovered core samples. Special efforts were made to determine the presence of shears, shear zones, joints, coatings and fillings. All data were presented in detail in a three volume Geotechnical Data Report and summarized in a Geotechnical Data Review Report.

To supplement the geotechnical reports, a Design Summary Report was written. This report described the geotechnical aspects of the design of the Mondawmin Station and the design philosophy and procedures used in designing the excavation, its support system, and the permanent structure.

GEOTECHNICAL SETTING

Zones of earth material designated above rock for the project are defined below as Residual Zone No. 1 (RZ-1) and Residual Zone No. 2 (RZ-2) from the contract documents.

RZ-1 material is a transition zone between Residual Soil and Residual Zone 2 and consists of material derived from the in-situ decomposition of the parent rock with soil-like components and partially weathered and/or fresh rock components. This material, in-situ, usually retains some of the cohesion of the parent rock and exhibits visible remnant rock structure such as schistosity and relict joints.

RZ-2 material is clearly rock-like, having been derived from partial decomposition of the parent rock with partially weathered and/or fresh rock components. This material, in-situ, usually retains rock structure and considerable strength of the parent rock. RZ-2 is commonly heterogeneous with respect to weathering ranging from decomposition throughout the entire body to partial decomposition throughout the material.

A generalized geologic centerline profile of the earth material zones is illustrated in Figure 3. Soil materials are not shown, since they comprise less than 3m (10 ft) of depth, and posed no special problems.

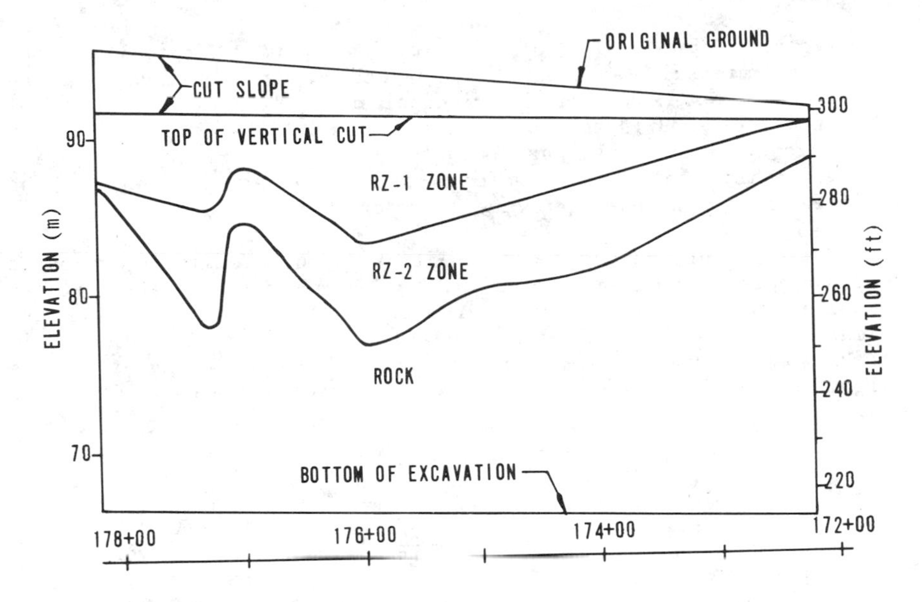

Fig. 3. Geologic section along centerline of station.

The residual zone contact between RZ-1 and RZ-2, and the RZ-2 contact with rock, are roughly parallel although somewhat gradational in detail. The contacts vary in elevation between the right and left walls to a maximum of 6.1m (20 ft.) in the mid-length portion and far (ahead) end of the excavation. Along the profile, a locally pronounced change in elevation occurs in the vicinity of Station 177+00, where a principal shear zone crosses the excavation along azimuth 90°, assuming zero azimuth to be upstation along the centerline.

Rock Characteristics.

The majority rock type comprises an amphibolite, and the minority rock type comprises varieties of gneiss which occur sporadically in the middle 2/3 of the excavation length.

The amphibolite is dark medium gray, fine to coarse grained, and composed of amphiboles and plagioclase feldspars in various percentages with retrograde metamorphism to chlorite along shear planes. Mineral layering is subtle on fresh surfaces. The gneiss is light colored, fine to coarse grained, and composed of quartz and feldspars, with orthoclase locally prominent, having one known biotite concentration, which adds an incipient schistose texture. Mineral layering is commonly banded.

Discontinuities.

Figure 4 is a plan of the Station showing typical discontinuities, mineral layering, and shear zones observed in the excavation. No less than 5 principal discontinuities or sets of discontinuities and three subsets are determinable. A principal set of discontinuities is parallel to apparent primary foliation (stratigraphic foliation) which strikes generally across the alignment, and dips ahead on line at moderate to steep angles.

The signature of the discontinuities, though seemingly myriad at first glance, resolved logically. The essence of the pattern comprises two conjugate pairs, with one pair striking parallel to primary foliation and across the excavation, and the other pair striking transverse to primary foliation and 30° to 45° diagonal to the alignment, plus a set and subsets which bisect the second conjugate pair.

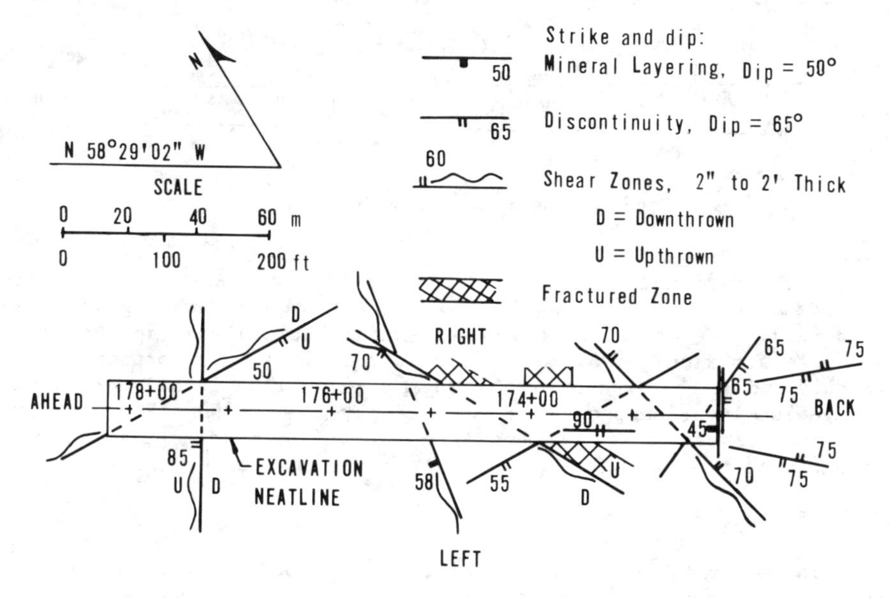

Fig. 4. Plan of station showing typical discontinuities

Stability

Contacts between the host amphibolite and irregularly tabular gneissic intrusives were commonly sheared and faulted, reflecting the multiple generations of metamorphic history. Considering simultaneously the type of discontinuity orientation shown in the photograph of Figure 5, and the multiple directions of discontinuity orientations, as well as the average discontinuity spacing which is less than 1½ ft, it is apparent that the rock would not be self supportive in a vertical wall under any circumstance.

Fig. 5. View of discontinuities in right wall, Station 177.

A typical destabilizing characteristic of the wall areas requiring supplemental support resulted from geological shear zones (late stage faults). The zones were accompanied by an increased density of discontinuities geometrically conjugate to the shear zones and multiple discontinuities parallel to the shear zones, with lenticular and semi-continuous lenses braided with chlorite along the zones. The chlorite braids enclosed teardrop shaped amphibolite inclusions to lengths of several inches (boudinage). Commonly, faulting occurred at the intrusive boundaries of brittle quartzitic or feldspathic gneiss. The differential geologic response to deformation of the brittle material adjacent to the more elastic amphibolite caused the gneiss to fracture intensely to fragments less than 15 cm (6 in.) average size.

CONTRACT REQUIREMENTS

During design of the project it was decided to specify in the contract documents the requirements for installation of a support of excavation system consisting of soldier piles, lagging and rock reinforcement. The contract documents also required that a specific excavation procedure be followed, and that an extensive program of instrumentation be installed.

Soil Support System

Soldier piles and lagging were required around approximately two-thirds of the periphery of the station excavation. The soldier piles were to extend from the ground surface through soil, the RZ-1 zone material, and the more weathered portion of the RZ-2 zone material. Tips of the soldier piles were required to extend at least 0.6m (2 ft) into the less weathered portion of the RZ-2 zone material. Tiebacks were recommended for anchoring the soldier piles and were used by the Contractor, although struts were permitted.

Around the remaining one-third of the excavation, the soil, the RZ-1 zone material and the more weathered portion of the RZ-2 zone material were required to be cut back on a 1½:1 slope. No soldier piles were to be placed in this portion of the excavation.

Rock Support System

The rock support system was comprised of rock bolts, supplemented by rock surface reinforcement below the soldier piles in the RZ-2 material and where fractures in the rock caused concern for the stability of the excavation because of surface raveling. Rock surface reinforcement was specified as two layers of shotcrete, each 5cm (2 in.) thick, reinforced with welded wire fabric.

Rock bolts were specified to be steel reinforcing bars conforming to the requirements of ASTM A615, Grade 60. The minimum rock bolt density was indicated on the contract drawings and by tabulation which showed the required bolt size, length, location, spacing and angle of installation. The specified rock bolt density reflected the design requirements for the most probable condition at the site based on all available data as contained in the geotechnical reports. The specified rock bolts were as follows:

1. No. 8 bars, 4.6 m (15 ft) long, inclined downward 60 degrees from the horizontal. These bolts were to be installed below the bottom of each lift of the excavation for the purpose of doweling the rock together prior to excavation of that particular lift and were to be untensioned, either fully resin grouted or fully cement grouted.

2. No. 11 bars, in lengths ranging from 3.0 m (10 ft) to 11.6 m (38 ft), inclined downward from the horizontal at 0, 5 or 10 degrees as specified on the drawings. These bolts were to be untensioned and fully resin grouted.

It was recognized that supplemental rock bolting could be required, as determined by the Engineer at the time of construction. Therefore, the contractor was required to provide and install additional bolts, other than those shown on the drawings, when directed by the Engineer. These bolts, No. 11 bars, were to be furnished with accessories so that they could be assembled in lengths of up to 24 m (80 ft) without welding and were to be resin anchored, tensioned, and fully grouted.

Figure 6 is a cross section of the excavation at Station 174+35 and indicates the details of the temporary support of excavation at this location. Since the cross section is taken at a focal point of maximum movement in the left wall, the density of the supplemental rock bolts required to stabilize the left wall is considerably higher than at other locations.

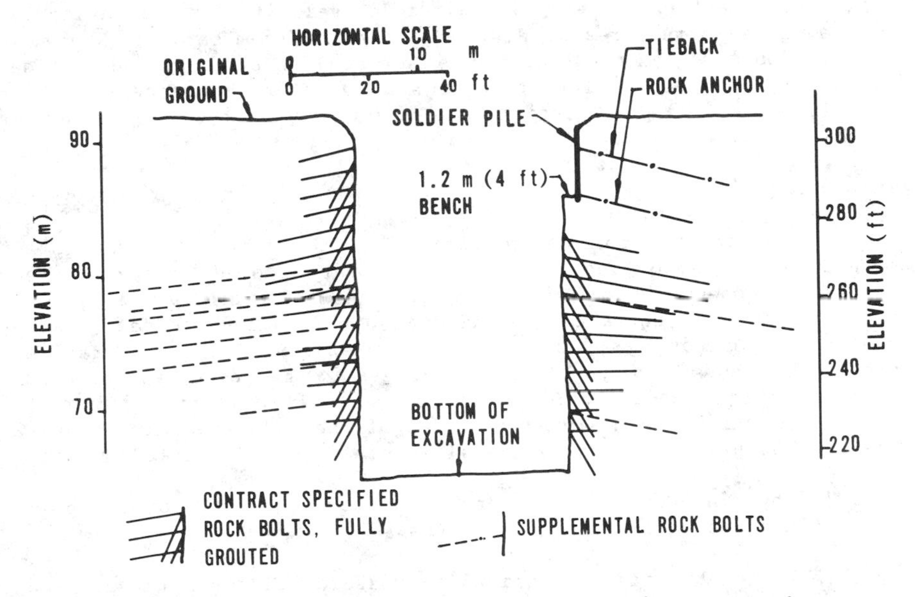

Fig. 6. Cross section looking ahead on line at Station 174+35, showing the support of excavation.

Excavation Procedures

Recognizing that the adequacy of the specified temporary support of excavation system depended to a considerable extent on the excavation procedures used by the contractor, the contract documents detailed a very specific procedure to be followed in excavating rock. Basically, the contract requirements were as follows:

1. The maximum height of each excavated lift was to be no more than 1.5 m (5 ft).

2. A 1.5 m (5 ft) wide safe zone, extending around the perimeter of the excavation was required for each lift. The safe zone could not be removed until the central portion of the lift had been excavated from the safe zone for at least a length of 6 m (20 ft).

3. Safe zone removal in highly fractured rock was limited to a maximum panel length of 6 m (20 ft) or that area which could be covered with a nominal 5 cm (2 in.) layer of shotcrete within 2 hours of exposure.

4. Excavation of more than one lift could proceed simultaneously only if the slope between the lowest point on the neatline and the deepest point excavated was not steeper than 1 horizontal to 1 vertical (45 degrees).

5. When blasting, the peak particle velocity at vibrationally affected structures at distances ranging from zero to 38 m (125 ft) outside the construction limits could not exceed 5 cm per sec (2 in. per sec). For structures at greater distances than 38 m (125 ft), the peak particle velocity was limited to one cm per sec (0.4 in. per sec).

Instrumentation

The contract documents required that the contractor install an extensive program of instrumentation to be monitored by the Engineer for the purpose of determining the adequacy of the temporary support of excavation. The contractor was also required to furnish safe instrumentation monitoring platforms, access stairs and guard railings around the excavation and to provide access for geologic mapping by the Engineer during construction. The access platforms provided by the contractor can be seen along the sides of the excavation in Figure 2. The instrumentation actually installed consisted of the following:

1. Twenty-nine pairs of reference lines of tape extensometer points to measure excavation convergence.

2. Thirty-eight reference points to measure soldier pile settlement.

3. One hundred thirty-nine single point, rod type, mechanical borehole extensometers, installed with anchors ranging from 3 m (10 ft) to 24 m (80 ft) into the rock from the face of the excavation.

4. Six standard inclinometer casings installed an average of approximately 6 m (20 ft) back of the face of the excavation.

5. Five groundwater observation wells.

6. Reference points to measure horizontal and vertical movements of the ground surface.

EXCAVATION FOR THE STATION

History of the Excavation

Excavation for the Mondawmin Station began in mid-December 1978 with the removal of an average of approximately 3m (10 ft) of soil from the entire 183m (600 ft) length of the station. Installation of soldier piles commenced in mid-January 1979 and continued until mid-March, at which time all 141 soldier piles had been installed around the approximate two thirds of the periphery where soldier piles were required by the contract documents. In mid-March 1979 the contractor resumed excavation of soil from in front of the soldier piles, placing timber lagging between the soldier piles and earth anchor tie backs at the soldier pile locations as the excavation was deepened.

Early in April 1979, material requiring blasting was encountered and by the end of April the contractor had begun installing the contract specified rock bolts. Excavation of RZ-2 material and rock continued until September 19, 1980 at which time the excavation phase of the contractor's work was complete. Figure 7 shows the configuration of the bottom of the excavation at various times. Reference to this figure shows that the contractor generally excavated the bottom in horizontal lifts, except for a ramp located at the back wall of the excavation, Stations 172 to 174. This ramp was used as a haul road until it became too steep, at which time material was lifted from the excavation by a crane.

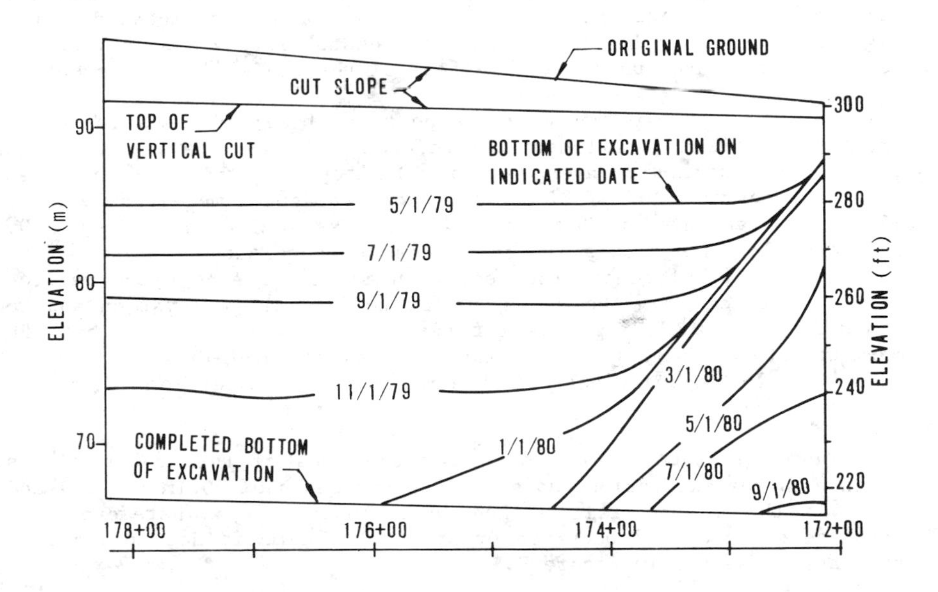

Fig. 7. Excavation of station vs. time.

Soldier Pile Installation and Instrumentation

The contract documents required that the soldier piles be installed in pre-bored holes with the pile tips extending at least 0.6 m (2 ft) into the less weathered portion of the RZ-2 zone materials. This resulted in the tips of the piles being 5.2 m (17 ft) to 12.5 m (41 ft) below original ground, or 2 m (7 ft) to 9.4 m (31 ft) below the bottom of the initial cut.

During excavation for the station, the majority of the soldier piles settled and the tops of the piles moved toward the excavation. Thirty-eight settlement reference points which were installed on the tops of selected soldier piles indicated settlement of the piles ranging from a maximum of 3.4 cm (1.35 in.) to no recorded settlement. The settlement curves for four typical reference points installed on June 1, 1979 are plotted in Figure 8. Reference to excavation records and blasting data indicates that pile settlement was related to some extent to the continuation and location of excavation activities, but to a greater extent to the intensity of blasting, as measured by the maximum charge of powder per delay. The settlement curves for Piles 44, 51 and 106 are steep during the period in September and early October 1979 when blasting was being done with 20 to 27 kg (45 to 60 lb) of powder per delay. Blasting was stopped on October 11, 1979 while supplemental rock bolts were installed, and was resumed on November 9, 1979 with a maximum of 9 kg (20 lb) of powder per delay. Rates of pile settlement were markedly diminished following the decrease in powder per delay and the installation of rock bolts. It should be noted that Pile 65, which experienced a minimum of settlement, was located in the right far corner of the excavation where destabilizing discontinuities were absent and the buttressing effect of the end wall was present.

To measure inward movement of the tops of selected soldier piles (convergence) 29 tape extensometer reference points were welded to the piles. The maximum convergence of the tops of the soldier piles occurred between Piles 31 and 120, located approximately at Station 175+80, and amounted to 8.8 cm (3.45 in.) as indicated in Figure 9. Reference to this figure indicates lesser convergence for the other three lines of reference, the reduction in convergence being related to the distance from the ahead or far wall of the excavation and to other factors, including site geology. It should be noted that the maximum rate of convergence for two lines of measurement (Piles 40-112 and Piles 31-120) coincides with the maximum rate of settlement for the soldier piles.

Tape extensometer monitoring of the tops of the soldier piles began when the excavation was at an average depth of 10.1m (33 ft) and most of the timber lagging had been installed. Therefore, any convergence which had occurred prior to this time is not included in the data presented in Figure 9.

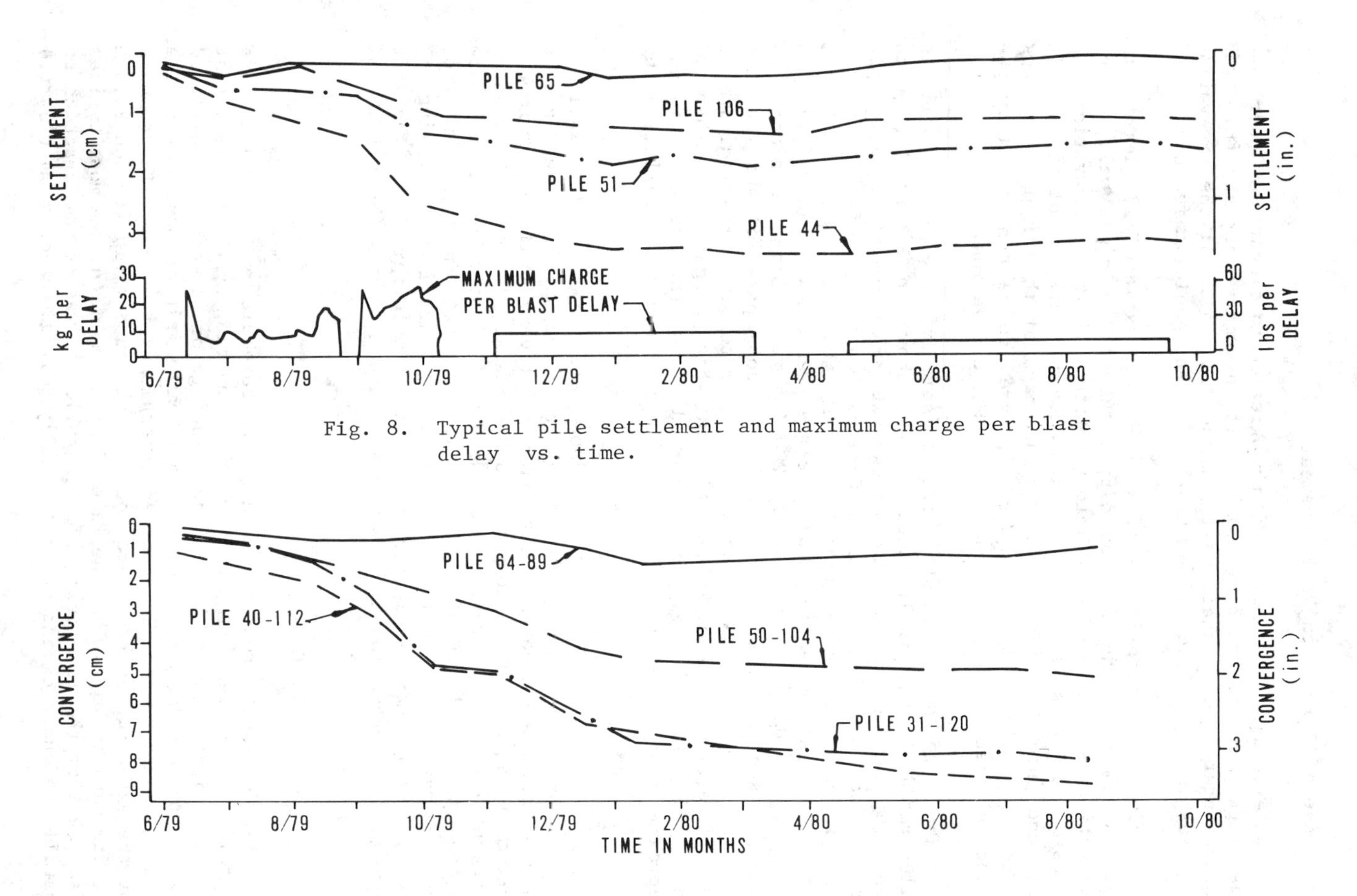

Fig. 8. Typical pile settlement and maximum charge per blast delay vs. time.

Fig. 9. Typical pile convergence vs. time.

Influence of Geology on Wall Movement

As excavation for the station progressed to elevations lower than the tips of the soldier piles, it became apparent from the instrumentation data that the right and left walls of the excavation were responding to the influence of different geologic features.

Principal discontinuities, striking approximately 30 degrees to the centerline of the station dipped out of the right wall of the excavation (See Figure 5) and into the left wall of the excavation. To a lesser extent, some discontinuities dipped inversely out of the left wall and into the right wall. In the case of the right wall, rock movement to a considerable extent appeared to be controlled by the principal discontinuities dipping into the excavation.

The type of movement characteristic of the right wall is illustrated by the inclinometer graphs shown in Figure 10, which represent rock movements with the excavation completed to full depth at the location of Inclinometer Casings 1 and 3. Reference to the graph for movement in Inclinometer Casing 1 both into and parallel to the face of the excavation indicates the presence of a principal slip plane at a depth of approximately 20m (65 ft). Slippage along this plane is approximately 1.3 cm (0.5 in.) both parallel and into the excavation. The plotted data for Inclinometer Casing 3 indicates a slip plane at a depth of 9m (30 ft) along which slightly more than 1.9 cm (0.75 in.) of slippage occurred into the excavation and approximately 0.7 cm (0.25 in.) of slippage occurred parallel to the excavation.

A second type of movement was characteristic of the left wall and is illustrated by the inclinometer graphs of Figure 11. These graphs show incremental movements extending relatively uniformly from the bottom of the excavation to the ground surface. The total horizontal movement into the excavation, excluding what is attributable to loose casing above a depth of 1.5 m (5 ft), is 4.4 cm (1.75 in.) for Inclinometer Casing 2 and 2.5 cm (1.0 in.) for Inclinometer Casing 6A. The type of movement indicated by the inclinometer graph for the left side of the excavation is a movement which combines the effects of toppling and collapse of a column.

Borehole Extensometer Data

Single point, rod-type mechanical borehole extensometers were installed in the vertical walls of the excavation by the contractor at locations indicated on the contract drawings or selected in the field based upon observation of the types of materials encountered in the excavation and previously recorded instrumentation data. The anchors for the extensometer rods were located between 3 m (10 ft) and 24.3 m (80 ft) into the rock from the face of the excavation, the most typical distance from the face being 12m (40 ft.). It was common practice to install one short extensometer typically with the anchor 6m (20 ft.)

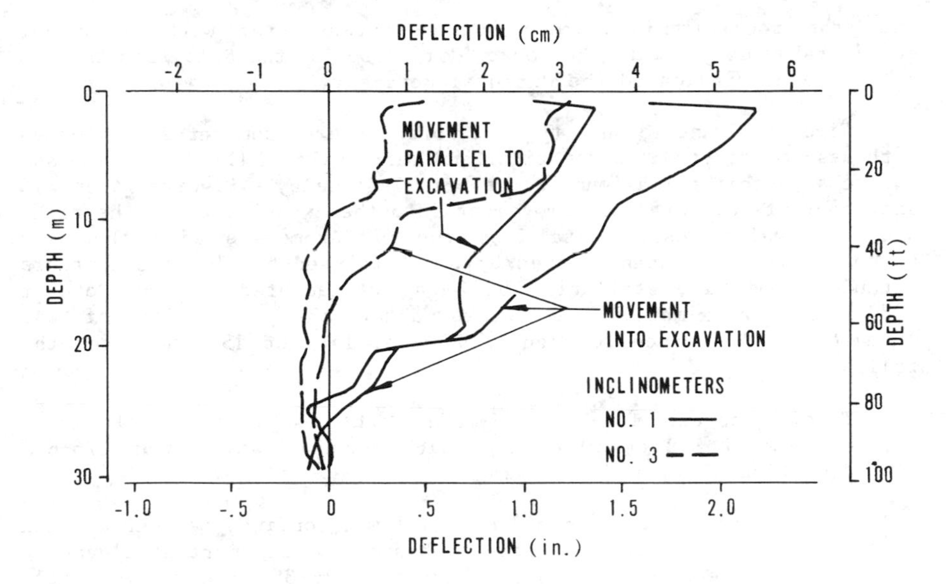

Fig. 10. Horizontal movement behind the right wall as recorded by inclinometers.

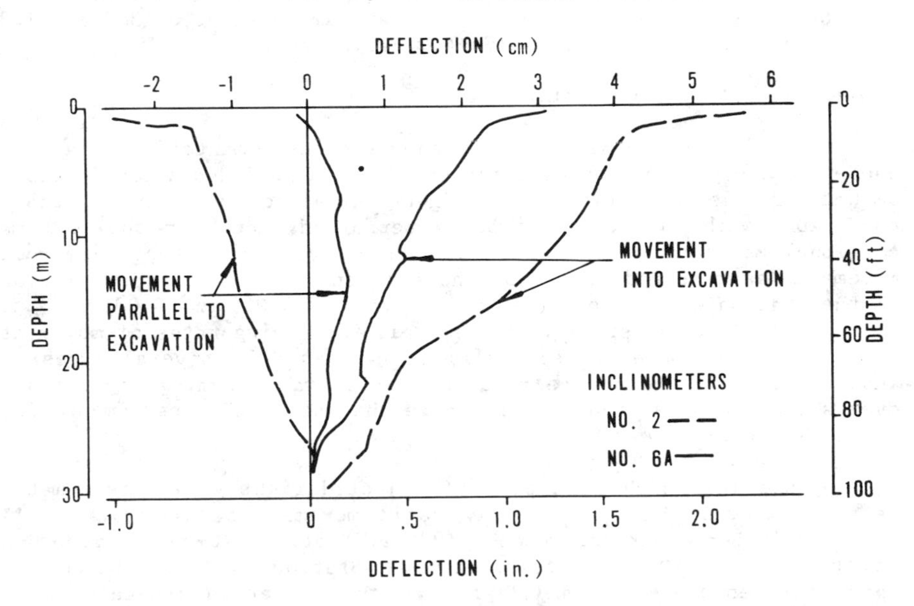

Fig. 11. Horizontal movement behind the left wall, as recorded by inclinometers.

into the rock within a meter of an extensometer with an anchor considerably deeper into the rock. Comparison of the data from the two extensometers indicated the depth of movement.

Figures 12 and 13 show typical borehole extensometer data plotted with respect to time for the right and left walls of the excavation and the relationship to maximum charge per blast delay. Figures 14 and 15 show contours of total wall movement into the excavation for the right and left walls, using data from the extensometers with the deep anchors. The time span covered by the data used to plot the contours extends from the installation of each extensometer through October 1980, or approximately six weeks after the completion of all excavation. Reference to Figures 12, 13, 14, and 15, indicates the following:

1. Total recorded movement of the right excavation wall was a maximum of 1.8 cm (0.7 in.) which occurred at Station 176+65, Elevation 283.

2. In the right wall principal movement was confined between Station 173+50 and 177+00. Localized high spots of movement at Elevation 250 occurred at Stations 175+50 and 176+35, and are directly related to principal discontinuities in the rock mass.

3. In the left wall, the zone of principal movement occurred between Stations 173+00 and 175+50. The maximum movement of 3.3 cm (1.3 in.) occurred at Station 174+40, Elevation 282.

Application of Instrumentation Data

Criteria used to determine whether the instrumentation data were cause for concern were necessarily complex and included a considerable amount of interpretation and judgement, since even under stable conditions with no excavation being performed, the data showed some continual movement of the walls of the excavation. Long term rock movement, as measured in the borehole extensometers after completion of the station excavation, are in the range of 0.025 mm (0.001 in.) to 0.05 mm (0.002 in.) per day. In general, increasing rates of movement were cause for concern, especially if confirmed by several types of instrumentation, and if the total magnitude was becoming significant over a considerable area. To indicate the use of the instrumentation data, two specific examples are given.

Figure 12, which is a plot of selected right wall extensometer data, indicates that relatively rapid movement of the right wall occurred in September and October 1979 at Station 176+65, as recorded in the 12.2 m (40 ft) extensometer at Station 176+65. Since the shorter extensometer 6.1m (20 ft) at this location indicated very little movement, it was concluded that most of the recorded movement was occurring at distances of 6.1 to 12.2m (20 to 40 ft.) behind the face of the wall. Because the rate of movement as recorded in the

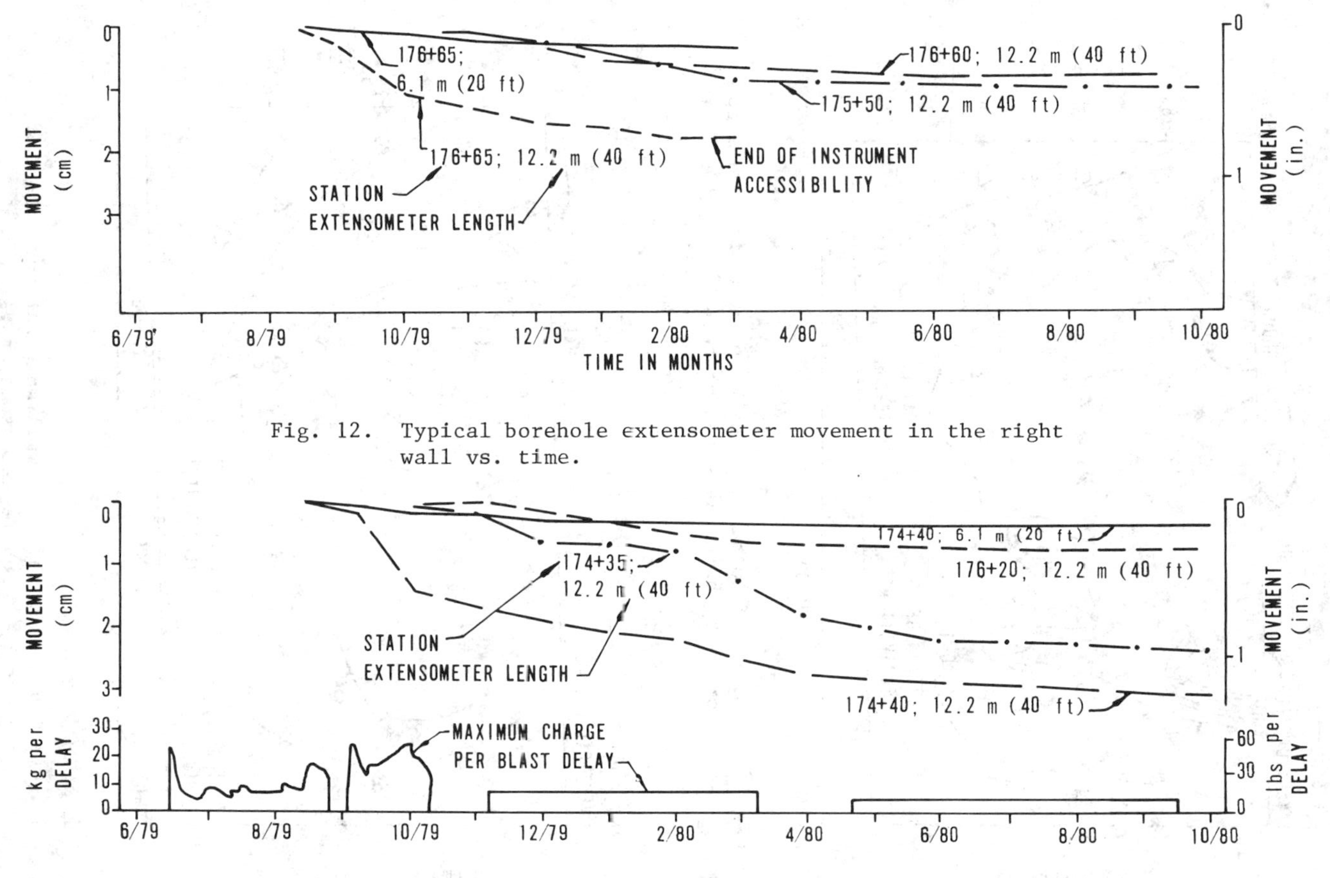

Fig. 12. Typical borehole extensometer movement in the right wall vs. time.

Fig. 13. Typical borehole extensometer movement in the left wall and maximum charge per blast delay vs. time.

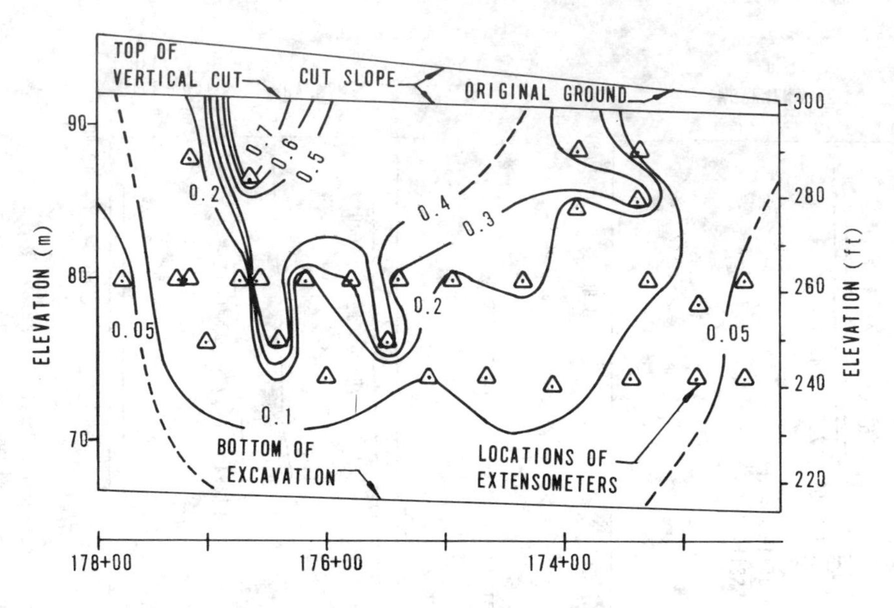

Fig. 14. Contours of total right wall movement in inches as recorded by borehole extensometers.

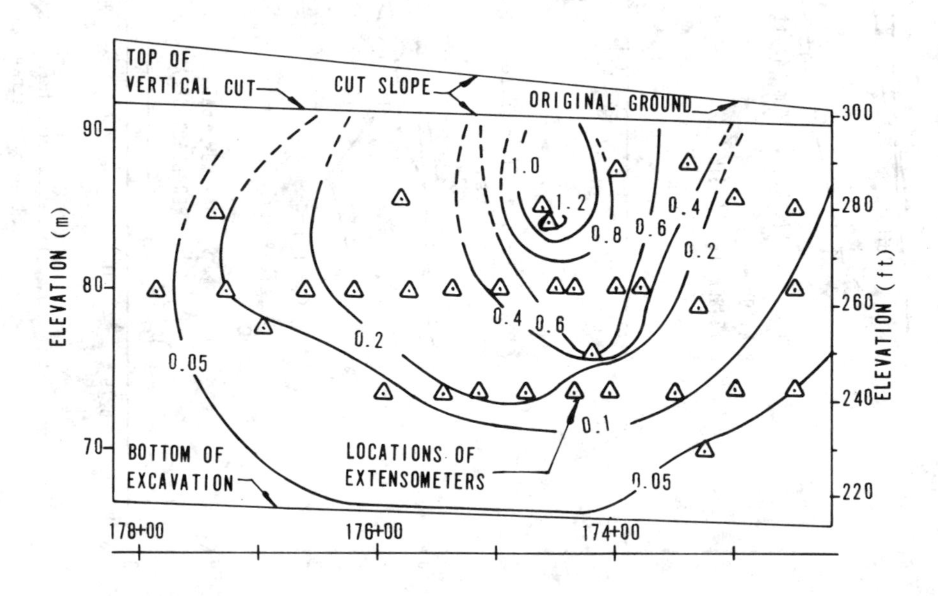

Fig. 15. Contours of total left wall movement in inches as recorded by borehole extensometers.

12.2 m (40 ft) extensometers was of concern, contours of rock movement were plotted as indicated in Figure 16 for the two weeks October 15 to 29, 1979, when no excavation was in progress.

After a study of the extensometer data, as well as other instrumentation data, it was concluded that the movement of the right wall was a cause for concern and that remedial measures were required to decrease the rate of movement to acceptable levels. Consequently, the contractor was directed to cease blasting and to install supplemental rock bolts at locations directed by the Engineer. Using the instrumentation data, it was determined that the supplemental bolts should be longer than 12.2 m (40 ft) and should be concentrated in an area defined by the movement contours of Figure 16. Using seismograph data obtained from within the excavation, it was also determined that when blasting resumed after completion of the installation of the supplemental rock bolts, the maximum charge of powder per delay should be limited to 9.1 kg (20 lbs), as indicated in Figure 13. Subsequent instrumentation data revealed that the area of concern in the right wall had been successfully stabilized.

The second example of the use of instrumentation data to control the work occurred in March 1980 when it was observed that borehole extensometers in the left wall in the vicinity of Station 174+35 at Elevation 265 were showing a rapid increase in rate of movement. Data from extensometers at Stations 174+35 and 174+40 are plotted in Figure 13, showing the increase in rate of movement during March 1980 by the 12.2 m (40 ft) extensometers and the relatively small movement being measured by the 6.1m (20 ft.) long extensometer, again indicating that the recorded movement was primarily occurring at distances of 6.1 to 12.2m (20 to 40 ft.) back of the face of the excavation. This was confirmed by the occurrence of ground cracks as far as 15.2 m (50 ft) back of the face. A plot of the contours of equal movement, Figure 17, showed a focal point of movement at Station 174+35, Elev. 265, with a two week movement at the focal point of at least 0.5 cm (0.2 in.). The instrumentation data were judged to be a cause for concern and the contractor was directed to cease blasting and to install supplemental tensioned rock bolts as directed by the Engineer. Figure 6 is a cross section of the excavation at the focal point of movement, Station 174+35, and indicates the extent of the supplemental rock bolts which were required to reduce the rate of rock movement to acceptable levels. Upon resumption of blasting, the maximum charge of powder per delay was limited to 4.5 kg (10 lbs). Frequent monitoring of the geotechnical instrumentation indicated that the combination of corrective measures had successfully stabilized the left wall in the area of concern.

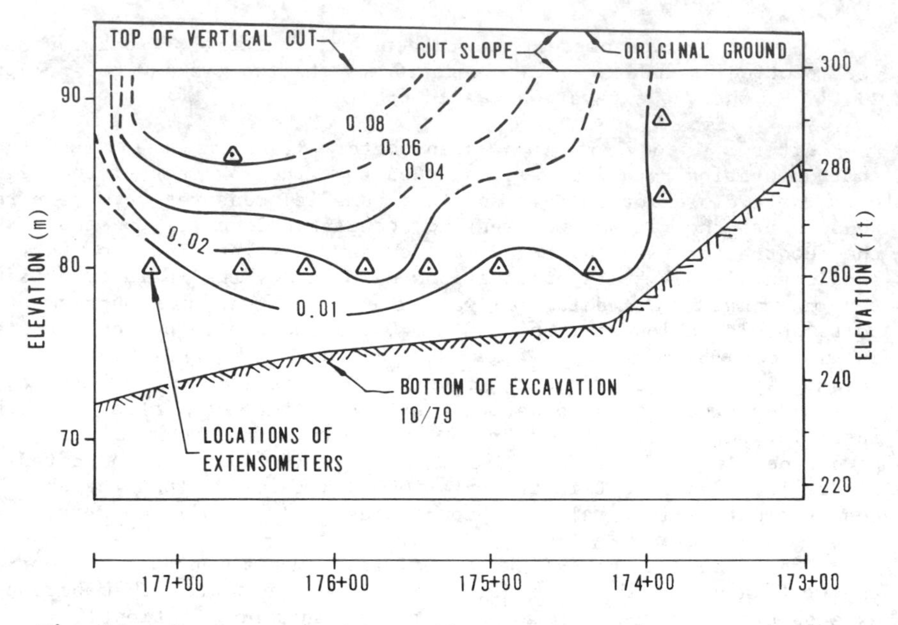

Fig. 16. Contours of right wall movement in inches, Oct. 15 to 29, 1979, recorded by borehole extensometers.

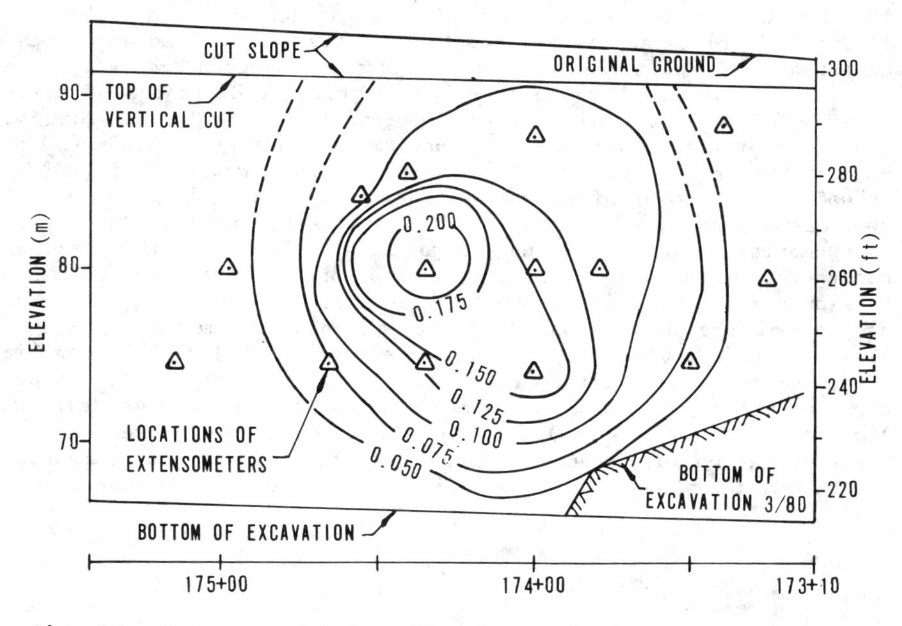

Fig. 17. Contours of left wall movement in inches, Feb. 22 to Mar. 8, 1979, recorded by borehole extensometers.

SUMMARY

The contract documents for construction of the Mondawmin Station specified a support of excvation system consisting of soldier piles and timber lagging to resist soil pressures. Rock bolts, shotcrete and wire mesh were specified to stabilize the rock walls. Recognizing that the adequacy of the support of excavation system depended to a considerable extent on excavation procedures, the contract documents detailed a very specific procedure to be followed by the contractor. In addition, the contract required an extensive installation of geotechnical instrumentation for the purpose of determining the performance of the excavation support system and the need for additional support measures.

Interpretation of the monitoring data, based on geologic mapping of the excavation, enabled excavation procedures to be controlled and the need for additional rock bolting to be defined, thereby making possible the successful completion of a deep open cut excavation in complex metamorphic rock cut by multiple discontinuities.

ACKNOWLEDGEMENTS

The authors wish to express appreciation to the Mass Transit Administration of the State of Maryland for granting permission to use the data acquired during construction of the Mondawmin Station. In particular, thanks are given to Mr. L. A. Kimball, Administrator, Mr. Robert J. Murray, Project Manager and Mr. Frank A. Hoppe, Director of Construction, for their cooperation.

Chapter 91

GEOTECHNICAL PERFORMANCE OF A LARGE MACHINE-BORED PRECAST CONCRETE LINED TUNNEL

by Joseph G. Engels, James T. Cahill and Edwin A. Blackey, Jr.

Project Engineer, Geotechnical Engineers Inc.
Winchester, Massachusetts
Engineer, Geotechnical Engineers Inc.
Winchester, Massachusetts
Division Geologist, New England Division
U. S. Army Corps of Engineers
Waltham, Massachusetts

ABSTRACT

An extensive geotechnical instrumentation program was undertaken during the construction of a 6.7 m (22 ft) inside diameter tunnel to monitor the ground-structure response and to check assumptions made for design. The tunnel was advanced through sedimentary and igneous rock using a fully shielded tunnel boring machine (TBM) with both temporary support and final lining provided by precast concrete liner plates erected in the tail section of the TBM. The parameters measured and evaluated include rock deformation, strain in the precast concrete liner, changes in tunnel cross section and groundwater response. In addition, an automated camera system is described which was mounted on the TBM to provide a continuous photographic record of the bedrock conditions exposed at the tunnel springline. The performance of various types of instrumentation equipment in an underground construction environment is also evaluated.

INTRODUCTION

The Park River Auxiliary Tunnel is a 2,800 meter (9200 ft) long, 6.7 meter (22 ft) inside diameter inverted siphon-shaped tunnel designed to bypass floodwaters beneath the City of Hartford, Connecticut. Fig. 1 is a profile of the tunnel route. The tunnel was designed by and is being constructed for the New England Division of the U. S. Army Corps of Engineers.

During the planning process a computerized tunnel design and construction program was used to select the least cost alignment

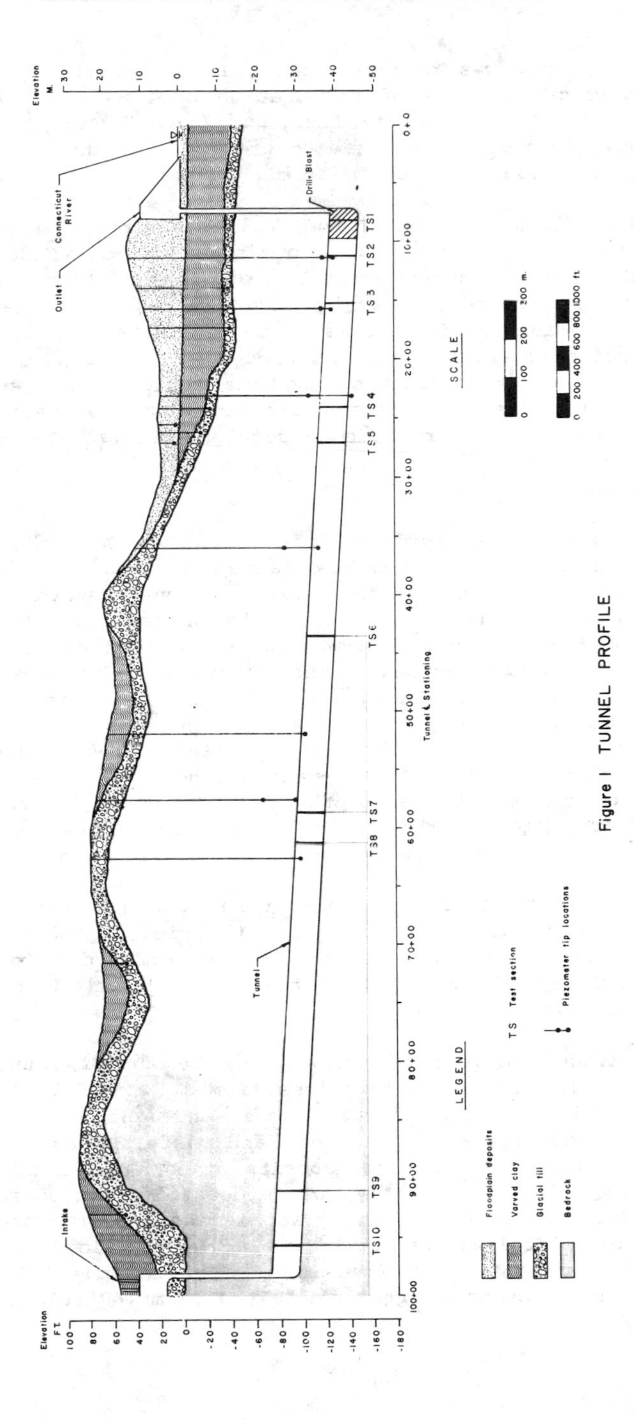

Figure I TUNNEL PROFILE

and the tunnel was designed using rock classification techniques and empirical methods of calculation such as a modified Terzaghi system[1] and the Barton, Lien and Lunde System.[2] Use of an intergraphic computer program to predict ultimate rock loads on the lining was utilized to optimize the design.

A significant portion of the design assumptions was evaluated by an instrumentation and visual observation program during and subsequent to the construction. The purposes of this program were to validate the theoretical design assumptions, to refine the calculations for future designs and to evaluate the safety of the construction operation as work proceeded. This paper will discuss some of the instrumentation systems employed and evaluate their results and effectiveness in obtaining data for validation of the design assumptions for the construction condition.

Geology

The City of Hartford is located in the Connecticut Valley, a broad generally North-South oriented lowland basin underlain by bedrock of Triassic age consisting of conglomerate, sandstone and shale with included dikes and sills of basalt. The sedimentary rocks of the valley have been faulted and tilted to the east at a dip of 15 to 20 degrees. The tunnel was driven at a slope of approximately .6 percent into the dip of the sedimentary structures for a distance of approximately 2,620 m (8600 ft) and 152 m (500 ft) through a basalt dike and two fault zones. The tunnel was constructed on nearly an east-west alignment, roughly normal to the strike of the beds and at depths of up to 60 m (200 ft) beneath the city. The RQD of the bedrock measured during the exploration program averaged over 80 for about 88% of the tunnel length.

The largest fault zone encountered along the tunnel alignment occurred near the tunnel intake in the vicinity of Sta 95+50. The rock in the fault zone displayed anomalously high bedding angles, and consisted of thin zones of clayey "gouge" interspersed with zones of severe brecciation.

Overlying the bedrock for the entire tunnel route is a dense glacial till varying in thickness from 1.5 to 10.7 m (5 to 35 ft). Glacial lake deposits of varved clay and silt are found overlying the till deposits at the western and eastern ends of the project. The thicknesses of the lake deposits at each shaft are about 12.2 m (45 ft) and are lightly to moderately overconsolidated and compressible. Overlying the glacial lake deposits and/or till are areas of miscellaneous fill and granular flood plain deposits generally consisting of fine sand. The maximum thickness of the floodplain deposits is approximately 12.2 m (40 ft) near the outlet shaft.

Groundwater levels measured prior to construction of the tunnel indicate that the piezometric level in the bedrock is normally 47 to 58 m (155 to 190 ft) above the invert of the tunnel.

Construction

Three different tunnel sections were designed and offered as bid options:

1. Drill and blast with a reinforced, cast-in-place liner.

2. Machine excavation with a reinforced cast-in-place lining.

3. Machine excavation with a reinforced precast lining.

The five lowest bidders (out of seven) chose the third option and construction was begun employing this method in November 1977.

The tunnel was advanced upgrade from the outlet shaft adjacent to the Connecticut River. Upon completion of the outlet shaft, approximatey the first 71.6 m (235 ft) of the tunnel was advanced using drill and blast excavation techniques to form a U-shaped chamber approximately 7.9 m x 7.9 m (26 ft x 26 ft). The roof of the tunnel in the drill and blast section of the project was supported with both 3 m (10 ft) long fully encapsulated resin rock bolts installed on approximately 1.2 to 1.5 m (4 to 5 ft) centers and shotcrete.

After completion of the drill and blast section, the tunnel boring machine (TBM) was assembled in the excavated chamber and the tunnel advance using the TBM was begun. The TBM was a fully shielded, rotary hard-rock machine manufactured by the Robbins Company, Seattle, WA, which cut a 7.4 m (24 ft, 3 in.) diameter bore. The temporary support and final lining are provided by four-segment precast concrete liner rings which were erected in the tail shield of the TBM approximately 10.7 to 12.2 m (35 to 40 ft) behind the cutter face. Each of the four segments is 22.9 cm (9-in.) thick and about 1.8 m, (6 ft) wide. A completed ring provides a finished inside diameter of 6.7 m (22 ft). Circumferential sponge rubber O-rings were provided between rings and neoprene pad gaskets and a hydraulic cement sealant (Preco-Crete) were used between segments. The invert segment was set on a bed of peastone and the annular space between the excavated rock surface and outside surface of the crown and side segments was backfilled with 1.3 cm (0.5-in.) peastone, generally two to three rings behind the last ring installed. Cement grouting of the peastone was generally accomplished in the invert between the second and seventh ring and at the crown and sides from an independent grout gantry about 60 to 150 m (200 to 500 ft) behind the last installed ring.

TUNNEL DESIGN FACTORS

The assumed load predictions made during the design were computed by various methods as noted above and as more completely described by Blackey.[3] The load factors varied with the method of construction, a factor which was largely determined by excavation methods and the time required to install the temporary support. In the elected design, the precast segments served as both temporary support and final lining. Load factors were varied based on the quality of the rock structure and ranged from 24.8 kN/m^2 (0.26 tsf) for the best average condition to 167.6 kN/m^2 (1.75 tsf) for the fault zones. The precast liner segments were designed for the fault zones. Worst average conditions were estimated to occur in approximately 10 percent of the tunnel. Load configuration was considered to be uniform on the cross section based on the tunnel excavation being normal to the strike of the rock structure at a relatively uniform dip. Load computations were computed based on a density of 2.66 BSSD (801 kg/m^2) for the shale and 2.75 BSSD (829 kg/m^2) for the basalt.

Groundwater inflow in the tunnel was predicted during design based on data from both zone pressure testing and falling head permeability tests. Rates of water inflow during tunneling were predicted for the various rock conditions. Inflow was calculated in terms of gallons per minute per lineal foot of tunnel based on the excavated diameter.[4] Best average conditions related to rock with an RQD of 80 and an average inflow of 0.0001m^3/sec/m (0.5 gpm/lf) of unsealed tunnel. The worst average condition rock with an RQD of 40 was calculated to have an inflow of 0.0012m^3/sec/m (6.0 gpm/lf) of unsealed tunnel. Fault zones were estimated at a higher value of up to 0.01m^3/sec/m (50 gpm/lf) of unsealed tunnel for very short distances.

INSTRUMENTATION PROGRAM

Design

The earliest phase of the instrumentations program was initiated prior to construction and consisted of an in-situ stress measurement program in rock and the establishment of groundwater measuring devices to obtain an evaluation of the site conditions prior to the start of construction. The in-situ stress measurement programs will not be discussed in this paper. Maximum principal stresses averaged 3.1 $\pm$ .9 MPa (450 $\pm$ 130 psi) in compression or about twice the overburden stress.

The instrumentation program during construction was not specified at the time of bidding since the construction method was not fixed but was to be one of three options discussed earlier. The specifications required that the prime contractor retain an independent geotechnical firm to select, install and monitor contract specified instrument systems. The contractor submitted for approval his choice of firms to perform the specified work. The cost of the instrumentation program was bid as a line item of the main contract and the methods of installation and types of instruments were submitted for approval by the prime contractor. Payment was lump sum, which included all labor, equipment, materials and services specified. Contractor bids for the line item ranged from $300,00 to $350,000 on six bids for the selected systems under Option 3. Portions of the instrumentation program not contained in the geotechnical service contract included reading of instruments prior to and following the actual tunneling operation and vibration monitoring.

A monitoring program was developed by the geotechnical consultant (Geotechnical Engineers Inc.) in conjunction with the Corps of Engineers and the contractor (Roger J. Au & Son, Inc.) to measure rock movement and water pressure at selected locations along the tunnel route together with structural liner performance data consisting of strain and diametrical deformations at the same locations. In all, ten test sections were chosen, one in the drill and blast section and nine in the TBM driven, precast-concrete-lined section.

Test Section #1 in the drill and blast portion of the tunnel consisted of a six-anchor multiple position borehole extensometer (MPBX) installed over the crown of the tunnel from the ground surface and twelve rock bolt load cells installed on selected roof bolts in the immediate vicinity of the MPBX. The remaining nine test sections in the TBM portion of the project each consisted of a six-anchor MPBX installed over the crown of the tunnel from the ground surface. The four-segment precast-concrete-liner ring directly below each MPBX was instrumented with four embedded vibrating wire strain gages (one in each segment) and three surface-mounted vibrating wire strain gages (on the crown and two side segments). In addition, tape extensometer reference points were located on each strain gaged ring to measure possible length changes in various chord distances for the ring. A vibrating wire piezometer was also installed through the precast concrete liner into the adjacent bedrock to monitor the hydrostatic pressure on each test ring. See Fig. 1 for the location of these test sections along the tunnel route.

The location of the instrumented test sections was based on one or more of the following considerations: to provide a comparison between different tunneling methods in similar geology; to provide a comparison of the tunnel performance in different geologic structures and lithology; to monitor the rock movements and structural performance of the tunnel in areas of key buildings located over the tunnel at the ground surface; and to provide access at the ground surface for the MPBX's.

Installation and Data Collection Procedures

It has often been observed in other rock tunnel projects that a major portion of the rock movement over the crown of the tunnel occurs during the time the tunnel heading is advancing to about two to three tunnel diameters past the measurement location (5,6,7,8). Since the TBM used for this project was about 12.2 m (40 ft) long and fully shielded, it was not possible to gain access to the tunnel crown until the heading had progressed at least two tunnel diameters past the intended measuring point. In addition, the installation of an MPBX from within the tunnel would have delayed the TBM progress during the instrument installation. Therefore, it was decided that the MPBX's would be installed from the ground surface in advance of the tunnel heading.

The MPBX's used were untensioned rod extensometers with six grouted anchors. The instrument reference head was attached to flush joint steel drilling casing which was installed through the overburden soils and seated in the underlying bedrock in an attempt to provide a fixed reference point to compute the relative anchor movements. Prior to installing the instrument hardware down the borehole, a verticality survey of each boring was made using inclinometer techniques so that deviation of the borehole from vertical could be determined. See Table 1 for the approximate location of the reference anchors above the tunnel crown. Measurements of the depth to the top of each stainless steel rod relative to the brass reference plate in the instrument head were made using a digital depth micrometer, with a resolution of 0.003 cm (0.001 in.). Nine of the MPBX's were monitored on a daily basis when the tunnel heading was in a position of 30.5 m (100 ft) before to 45.7 m (150 ft) past the instrument location. Readings were then decreased to twice weekly or weekly for approximately the next four weeks, after which they were decreased to about monthly until the end of the tunnel advance. The brass reference plate was optically surveyed periodically using standard surveying equipment.

The rock bolt load cells used during this program in the drill and blast section of the tunnel were 534 kN (60-ton) capacity, full bridge, hollow center cells, supplied with 9 m (30 ft) of armored cable. The instrumented rock bolts were 3.1 m (10 ft) long steel reinforcing rods, which were installed with a resin grouted length of approximately 0.6 m (2 ft), allowing for about 2.4 m (8 ft) of free anchor length. Steel bearing plates were placed on both sides of the load cells and wedges were used between the plate and the rock to make the load applied to the cells as uniform as possible. The cells were placed at approximately the 1, 2, 10 and 11 o'clock positions in an array below MPBX-1. The load cells were installed approximately 6.1 to 9.1 m (20 to 30 ft) behind the heading and were monitored on an approximate daily basis when the tunnel heading was within 30.5 m (100 ft) of each cell. The readings were then decreased to approximately three times a week until the cells were removed prior to shotcreteing.

Vibrating wire strain gages were selected due to their comparatively robust nature, relative ease of installation and repair, and good performance in dirty, wet environments. The embedded strain gages were installed in the precast liner segments at the casting yard. The gages were suspended on the rebar cage using 24-gage steel wire and were generally located as close to the center of the segment as possible, midway between the inner and outer circumferential rebar. Concrete cylinders were obtained during the instrumented ring pours. These cylinders were then cured under environmental conditions similar to those experienced by the liner segments and then tested to obtain representative concrete moduli for the various liner segments. The surface-mounted strain gages were installed on the instrumented liner rings immediately following ring erection. The mounting end blocks were welded to 15 cm (6 in.)-long #6 rebars, which were inserted into two mortar-filled holes drilled in the precast concrete lining, placing the gage approximately 1.2 cm (0.5 in.) from the segment surface. After the mortar had cured, the gages were set at midrange. Surface-mounted strain gages were generally installed at the tunnel springline and tunnel crown adjacent to the embedded gages and were located at the same locus circumferentially but approximately 0.3 m (1 ft) ahead of the embedded gages to avoid damaging the embedded gage during installation. The initial readings for the embedded gages were obtained immediately after the ring was erected, prior to installation of pea gravel behind the crown and side segments. The initial readings for the surface gages were obtained approximately two days after the erection of the ring, following gage placement and mounting cement cure. The gages for each ring were then generally monitored on a daily basis for about two to three weeks after which the monitoring frequency was reduced to about once a week.

Vibrating wire piezometers were also selected at each test ring to provide a system compatible with the strain gages and to allow for ease of monitoring as only one type of readout device was required. Tunnel piezometers were installed in 6.3 cm (2.5 in.)-dia. holes drilled by percussion air drills approximately 1.8 m (6 ft) into rock adjacent to the tunnel lining at each test section. Three holes were drilled at or near each test section to intercept water-bearing joints in the rock. Those holes exhibiting the greatest amount of water flow were chosen and the piezometer was inserted and surrounded by Ottawa sand. The remainder of the hole was filled with bentonite and plugged with styrofoam. The tunnel piezometers were usually monitored on a weekly basis from the day of installation until the completion of the tunnel advance.

Tape extensometer measurements of selected tunnel chords were made using a commercially available tape extensometer unit. Anchors were typically located in the same vertical plane as the surface strain gages. This was primarily done so that should any appreciable movements occur, possible correlations could be made with respect to strain gage data and chord measurements in the same plane. The anchors were located adjacent to the upper and lower grout holes in side segments #2 and #3. Anchors were not located in the crown segments because of poor accessibility during construction nor were they located in the invert segment due to interference with the grout gantry and muck train. The chord distances were measured on approximately a weekly schedule after the trailing gear had passed since it was not possible to obtain these dimensions or other meaningful chord lengths because of interference when the trailing equipment was present. Ambient temperature was also measured at the time of each reading, as it was for all of the instruments, and appropriate corrections made to the measured distances.

Fig. 2 is a cross-sectional sketch of a typical instrumented ring at each of the precast lining test sections showing the approximate strain gage and tunnel piezometer locations and the cross-section chord lengths which were monitored.

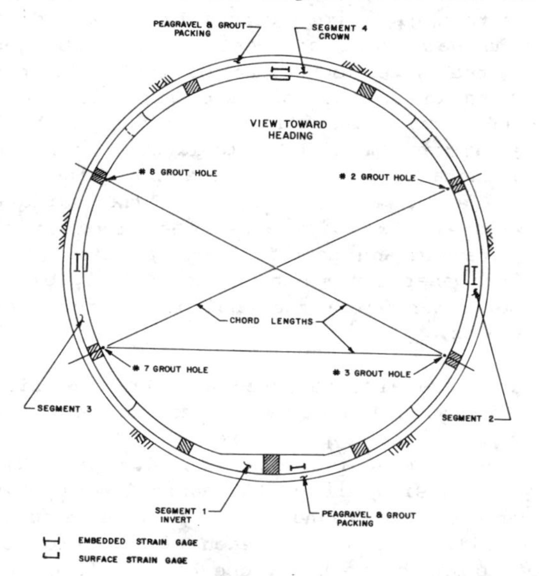

Fig. 2 - Instrumented Ring Cross Section

Thirteen open standpipe piezometers were installed from the ground surface into the bedrock adjacent to the tunnel alignment prior to the award of the construction contract. An additional six open standpipe piezometers and two observation wells were installed in the overlying glacial till and flood plain deposits a minimum of 60 days prior to the start of construction. The locations and porous tip elevations of these instruments are shown on Fig. 1. All of the piezometers and observation wells were generally monitored on a monthly basis using an electronic sounding device.

Settlement measurements were performed on critical structures and at various stations along the alignment. Twenty-five markers were established and tied to two permanent benchmarks, one of which extended to bedrock. All markers were read monthly except when more frequent readings were directed. Settlement readings throughout the construction of the project were read by a surveying subcontractor retained by the prime contractor.

To estimate groundwater inflows during tunnel construction, measurements were made of the total tunnel discharge by the use of a calibrated weir at the outlet portal discharge shaft. Adjustments were made for the volume of water being used by the mole operations and inflow from unsealed portions of the tunnel.

Data Obtained

It should be noted that the instrument measurements obtained for this project were subject to a range of error depending on the instrument type and monitoring procedure used. The accuracy and repeatability of the measurements is controlled by the instrument or instrument component in the measuring system with the lowest resolution or subject to the most operator error during the measurement procedure. Thus, the data that are summarized below are considered accurate to within the following ranges:

Type of Instrument	Probable Range of Error
MPBX	$\pm$ 0.008 cm ($\pm$ 0.003 in.)
Load Cell	$\pm$ 512 N ($\pm$ 115 lb)
Strain Gage	$\pm$ 5$\mu\varepsilon$ (1$\mu\varepsilon$ = 10^{-6} cm/cm)
Tape Extensometer	$\pm$ .025 cm ($\pm$ 0.01 in.)
Tunnel Piezometers	$\pm$ 0.03 m H_2O ($\pm$ .05 psi)
Ground Surface Piezometers	$\pm$ 1.3 cm ($\pm$ 0.5 in.)
Settlement Survey	$\pm$ 0.3 cm ($\pm$ 0.12 in.)

Rock Movement - The maximum rock movements measured by the MPBX's during construction are summarized in Table 1. The measurements presented for MPBX's 1, 2 and 3 are relative to anchor #6 which was considered out of the zone of rock movement and therefore fixed. This was necessary since it appeared that the reference heads for these three instruments settled slightly during the monitoring period even though they were attached to steel casings seated in rock. The other instruments did not appear to be affected by reference head settlement and these movement data are relative to the reference head.

TABLE 1 - MAXIMUM MEASURED MPBX MOVEMENT

MPBX No.	Maximum Downward Movement, cm (in.)					
	Anchor 1	Anchor 2	Anchor 3	Anchor 4	Anchor 5	Anchor 6
1 (TS-1)[1)]	0.073 (0.029)	0.066 (0.026)	0.048 (0.019)	0.041 (0.016)	0.013 (0.05)	-
2 (TS-2)[1)]	0.665 (0.262)	0.594 (0.234)	0.528 (0.208)	0.307 (0.121)	0.056 (0.022)	-
3 (TS-3)[1)]	0.411 (0.162)	0.414 (0.163)	0.371 (0.146)	0.335 (0.132)	0.046 (0.018)	-
4 (TS-4)[2)]	0.165 (0.065)	0.079 (0.031)	0.063 (0.025)	0.046 (0.018)	0	0
5 (TS-5)[2)]	-0.084 (-0.033)	-0.084 (-0.033)	-0.063 (-0.025)	-0.063 (-0.025)	-0.038 (-0.015)	0.025 (0.010)
6 (TS-6)[2)]	0.170 (0.067)	0.003 (0.001)[4)]	0.063 (0.025)	0.058 (0.023)	0.038 (0.015)	0.013 (0.005)
7 (TS-7)[2)]	0.457 (0.180)	0.297 (0.117)	0.180 (0.071)	0.196 (0.077)	0.109 (0.043)	0.033 (0.013)
8 (TS-8)[2,3)]	-0.038 (-0.015)	-0.033 (-0.013)	-0.010 (-0.013)	0.028 (0.011)	0.033 (0.013)	-0.015 (-0.006)
9 (TS-9)[2)]	0.526 (0.207)	0.455 (0.179)	0.455 (0.179)	-0.010 (0.004)	-0.046 (-0.018)	-0.036 (-0.014)
10 (TS-10)[2)]	1.585 (0.624)	0.714 (0.281)	0.462 (0.182)	0.165 (0.065)	0.107 (0.042)	0.048 (0.019)

NOTES: 1) Relative to Anchor #6
2) Relative to Reference Plate
3) Installation completed and initial reading obtained after passage of tunnel heading
4) Probable instrument malfunction

- up
+ down

Anchor Locations Above Crown

Anchor #1: 0.6 to 1.1m (2.0 to 3.7 ft)
Anchor #2: 1.2 to 1.6m (3.9 to 5.3 ft)
Anchor #3: 2.1 to 2.7m (6.8 to 9.0 ft)
Anchor #4: 3.3 to 4.8m (10.9 to 15.7 ft)
Anchor #5: 6.0 to 8.1m (19.8 to 26.7 ft)
Anchor #6: 14.2 to 18.8m (46.7 to 61.6 ft)

Based on the MPBX data, the rock movement measured over the crown of the tunnel excavation was relatively small in the areas of competent shale and sandstone bedrock. The movement recorded 0.6 to 1.2 m (2 to 4 ft) above the crown at the first nine test section locations, except TS-8, ranged from 0.08 to 0.66 cm (0.03 to 0.26 in.). (Note: MPBX-8 is not included since its installation was completed after the passage of the tunnel heading.) The movements recorded at MPBX-1 in the drill and blast section were the smallest observed during the project which would not generally be expected due to the greater anticipated disturbance resulting from drill and blast methods. This may be partially due to the fact that the top portion of this section of tunnel was first excavated (approximately 4.9 m [16 ft] high) and the roof bolts were installed before the lower bench was removed. Since the initial opening was smaller than in the TBM driven tunnel, the stress redistribution around the tunnel and resulting rock movement may have been smaller. When the bench was removed, the transfer of the additional stresses was probably accomplished more uniformly and distributed further into the rock mass due to the rock bolts.

The larger rock movements (MPBX-7 and 9) were measured in areas that were identified as possible fault zones. (The large movements recorded in MPBX-10 will be discussed below.) The relatively large movements measured at MPBX-2, where no apparent fault zone was determined, may be partially due to TBM start-up procedures.

The rate of the measured rock movement at the first nine MPBX locations appeared to be somewhat dependent on the rate of heading advance in the zone approximately 15 to 30 m (50 to 100 ft) past the respective instrument locations. At all of these locations practically all of the measured rock movement at the six anchor locations above the crown occurred as the heading passed through the 30 m (100 ft) zone, with most of the movement measured as the heading advanced through the first 15 m (50 ft) of the zone. For example, at MPBX-2 the tunnel heading advance was slower than at MPBX-7 and the measured rock movement also seemed to develop more slowly. While the rate of movement seemed somewhat dependent on the rate of heading advance, there was no apparent correlation of the magnitude of rock movement at the various instrument locations and the rate of tunnel advance.

The reason for the apparent upward rock movement recorded at MPBX-5 is not readily apparent. The movement appears to be attenuating toward the ground surface, and therefore, it is unlikely that the reference head is settling as in MPBX-1, 2 and 3. This upward movement may have resulted from the existence of lateral rock stresses being somewhat higher than vertical stresses at this location. This stress condition was observed in some in-situ stress measurements at other locations. Similar phenomena have been reported in other rock tunnels.[6,9]

The rock movements which were measured over the tunnel crown were the most substantial at Test Section 10 as measured by MPBX-10. While a large percentage (approximately 80%) of the measured movement occurred as the heading progressed 30 m (100 ft) past the instrument, there was some additional movement measured up to 1.5 months after the heading exited this zone. A small upward movement of about 0.038 cm (0.015 in.) could also be observed as the tunnel heading approached within 15 m (50 ft) of MPBX-10. These phenomena were not present or not as pronounced at the other MPBX locations and are most likely a result of the highly fractured and weathered nature of the fault zone. The clay infilling in the numerous joints and apparent decomposition of a large portion of the shale rock mass would account for the larger movements and "creep" of the rock mass above the tunnel opening.

All ten of the MPBX's indicted that the measured rock movements attenuated in an upward direction from the tunnel opening.

In general, the load indicated by the instrumented rock bolts increased very little, if at all, above the lock off load during the monitoring period. This is also an indication of the relatively small rock movement and redistribution of most of the rock stresses fairly close to the advancing face. The lack of load pickup by the instrumented rock bolts may be a result of installing the cells approximately one tunnel diameter behind the face, after most of the rock movement had taken place. This hypothesis is supported by the data from MPBX-1 which indicated that most of the downward rock movement had occurred by the time the face had reached Sta 8+50, 9 m (30 ft) past this instrument location. In addition, the data from MPBX-1 also indicated that the rock movement at the roof of the tunnel was very small (on the order of 0.08 cm [0.03 in.]) and, thus, most of the rock load was probably redistributed by arching in the rock mass with very little load transferred to the rock bolts.

Structural Liner Response - For the most part the maximum strains measured for the nine instrumented rings were less than 200με (microstrain [με] = 10^{-6} cm/cm). The ranges of measured maximum strain and percentages of gages within that range are summarized in Table 2. The maximum strain readings obtained for each gage are presented in Table 3. The negative strain values which were measured are a reflection of the bending stresses which were induced in the liner.

TABLE 2

Range of Maximum Measured Strain (με)

	Percentage of Gages					
	0-100	100-200	200-300	300-400	400+	Damaged
Embedded	39.1	7.8	1.6	1.6	1.6	4.6
Surface	23.4	14.1	0	0	4.6	1.6
Total	62.5	21.9	1.6	1.6	6.2	6.2

Based upon an average of the elastic moduli measured in the concrete cylinders tested in this program, a factor of 28 kPa/με(4 psi/με) can be applied to the strain measurements to obtain an approximation of stress.

Preliminary structural analyses have been performed using the strain gage data obtained taking into account the hydrostatic load applied to the rings at the time of measurement. These analyses have indicated that the maximum developed rock loads on the instrumented rings were slightly less than those assumed during design for the various loading conditions.

TABLE 3 - MAXIMUM MEASURED STRAIN ($\mu\varepsilon$ cm/cm)[5]

Test Section No.	Strain Gage Designation[1]						
	1E	2S	2E	3S	3E	4S	4E
2	-19 +52	+157	-57 +41	-126 + 18	- 66 + 23	+538	- 26 + 54
3	+109	- 45 + 31	+237	- 37 + 75	+155	- 13 +168	+ 87[2]
4	+ 28	- 50	- 3 + 22	- 53 +136	- 13 + 18	-[4]	- 5 + 54
5	-351	- 26 + 53	- 29	- 31 + 24	- 32	+129	+ 44 (+229)[3]
6	- 68 + 34	- 42 + 34	-[4]	+ 52	+105	+514	+165
7	- 38 + 91	- 56 + 50	+ 78	- 14 +162	- 4 + 61	+152	+ 95
8	- 6 + 14	+164	- 49 + 5	+131	+ 23	+ 99	+ 43
9	-142 + 56	- 66	- 31 + 9	- 59	- 51	+ 90	- 37
10	-429	- 43 + 10	- 18 + 16	- 5	- 22	+1609	-[4]

NOTES: 1) Gages designated as follows: 1 - Invert; 2 - Right; 3 - Left; 4 - Crown; S - Surface; E - Embedded; (2E - Embedded gage, right segment).
2) Gage damaged, not monitored for complete period.
3) Questionable reading.
4) Gage damaged.
5) Approximate equivalence = $28 kP_a/\mu\varepsilon$ (4 psi/$\mu\varepsilon$)

+ Compression
- Tension

The rock movements imposing these loads at seven of the instrumented ring locations were fairly small. Rock movements of 0.02 to 0.08 cm (0.01 to 0.03 in.) were measured in the rock 0.6 to 1.1 m (2.0 to 3.7 ft) above the crown after ring installation and peastone placement at all but Test Sections 8 and 10. These movements were approximately 10 to 35% of the total measured rock movement at these locations. No correlation can be made at TS-8, since the delay in MPBX installation did not permit measurement of total rock movement after liner installation. Approximately 0.7 cm (0.28 in.) of movement was measured 0.6 m (2 ft) above the tunnel crown at TS-10 after ring installation, which was about 50% of the total measured movement at this location. This relatively large movement evidently produced substantial load transfer to the ring, resulting in the high strains and resulting stresses measured in the crown segment. Although the cause of the relatively high strains measured in the TS-2 and 6 crown segments is not readily apparent, the rock movement measured above the liner crown in these areas was at the high end of the range given above. The high tensile strains measured in the TS-5 and 10 invert segments may have been due to stress concentrations produced by the wood blocking used to align the rings during installation.

A trend which was generally noted in most of the strain gages was a decrease in tensile strain, which was initially acquired after ring erection, or an increase in compressive strain with time. By the end of the monitoring period, most of the gages were indicating compressive strain or were moving in that direction as the loads were redistributed around the ring and the relatively uniform hydrostatic load increased. The ring at Test Section 3, which had a different installation procedure than the other eight instrumented rings in that it was grouted immediately after erection, responded somewhat differently than the other rings during the early period following ring erection. It appeared as though the installation of the grout at the earlier stage caused the ring to develop a more compressive load distribution sooner than the other instrumented rings. The earlier grouting did not seem to have an effect on the relative magnitude of the strains which were measured.

Another indication of load redistribution in the instrumented rings was observed in the tape extensometer measurements. Slight bending and/or shifting of the side segments is evident from the chord measurements, probably due to changes in the load distribution in the ring. Generally, with a few exceptions, the measured changes in the three chord lengths monitored at each test ring (18 total) were all less than ± 0.15 cm (± 0.10 in.) based on the initial readings obtained after passage of the trailing sled.

Groundwater Response - All of the surface piezometers installed in bedrock measured very large drops, 30 to 40 m (100 to 130 ft), in the bedrock piezometric level as the tunnel heading approached and passed their locations. The piezometric level in the glacial till stratum was also found to decrease, but to a much lesser amount (6 to 8 m [20 to 25 ft]) as the tunnel heading passed in the vicinity of an instrument. The observation wells in the flood plain deposits did not appear to be significantly influenced by the tunnel construction. The groundwater drawdown due to tunnel construction typically occurred 300 to 500 ft ahead of the tunnel heading. The magnitude of the piezometric drawdown over the tunnel was also observed to decrease proceeding to the ground surface, similar to the drawdown adjacent to a pumped well.

Groundwater recovery after passage of the tunnel heading and installation of the precast lining has been quite slow. Recoveries of 9 to 18 m (30 to 60 ft) have been recorded in many of the rock piezometers 10 to 14 months after the passage of the tunnel heading and lowest measured level. The largest recoveries have been measured in those piezometers closest to the Connecticut River. The data from the vibrating wire piezometers installed through the tunnel lining concur with the surface rock piezometer measurements. The piezometers located in the glacial till stratum have indicated recoveries of about 1.8 to 3 m (6 to 10 ft) over the same time period.

The measured amounts of groundwater inflow have indicated that the design calculations were valid and generally conservative for the conditions encountered, averaging less than 0.0001 m^3/sec/m (0.5 gpm/lf) of unsealed tunnel.

Surface Settlement - The measured settlements of structures adjacent to the tunnel route, resulting from compression of the overburden soils due to the increased effective stresses produced by groundwater drawdown, have been very small. No readings have exceeded the allowable established by the government during the design, with the maximum settlements being recorded in the range of 1.52 cm (0.6 in.).

Instrument Performance - All of the MPBX instruments performed satisfactorily during the life of the project. In three of the instruments, apparent reference head settlements were observed, probably due to elastic compression of the attached steel casing. Because of the relatively small rock movements measured and the fact that the resolution of the optical surveys of the head were about two orders of magnitude smaller than the MPBX resolution, it was necessary to reference the lower anchor movements to the top anchors in each instrument.

The rock bolt load cells were quite prone to damage or disturbance due to flyrock during the tunnel advance. Ten of the twelve cells required repair and/or reinstallation during the monitoring period. In addition the electrical resistance measuring system employed in the cells was not very compatible with the wet, dirty tunnel enviornment since dry, clean connections were essential to obtaining reliable measurements.

Of the 64 vibrating wire strain gages installed, four were damaged or otherwise failed to function properly during the life of the project. The vibrating wire system performed very well in the adverse tunnel environment in that they were easy to install, modify, repair and monitor.

Interference from the trailing equipment on this project did not permit the tape extensometer measurements of the cross sectional chord lengths to be made until the tunnel heading had progressed about 300 ft past the instrumented area. However, even though total liner deflection following installation could not be determined, any long-term changes in dimension were monitored. The measurements were found to be laborious and time consuming to perform.

All of the vibrating wire piezometer instruments performed satisfactorily. However, four of the piezometers were apparently installed in boreholes which were not in communication with the surrounding groundwater since there was little agreement with these four piezometers and nearby piezometers installed from the ground surface.

AUTOMATED CAMERA SYSTEM

The excavation of the Park River Auxiliary Conduit employed the use of a fully shielded tunnel boring machine in whose shielded tail precast-concrete-tunnel-liner rings were erected before the tail shield was advanced. As a result, the excavated bedrock surface could only be observed along the invert of the tunnel prior to the installation of the invert segment for each precast liner ring. At best, this would permit a geologist, who would need to be present at the tail of the TBM at all times during tunnel advance, to briefly view the muck-coated rock surface at the invert and perhaps sketch or photograph any observable features before an invert segment was placed. Therefore, at the start of the project it was decided by the project team to design and operate an automatic system to photographically record a small portion of the geology which was encountered along the tunnel route, near the tunnel springline.

Design and Installation

The photographic system which was used was composed of two separate but dependent systems: the protective and external power system and the actual photographic equipment which recorded an image of the exposed rock surface.

The protective housing and power system were designed and built by the Robbins Co. in conjunction with GEI. The protective housing basically consisted of a two-section, steel box about 0.6 m high x 0.9 m wide x 1.0 m long (2 ft x 3 ft x 3.3 ft) fabricated of 6.4 mm (0.25 in.) thick steel plate. The housing was welded to the inside skin of the TBM near the front right side at approximately the tunnel springline. An approximate 0.6 m x 0.9 m (2 ft x 3 ft) opening was cut in the shield prior to the housing installation to provide visual access to the rock surface. Fig. 3 is a cross sectional sketch of the camera system.

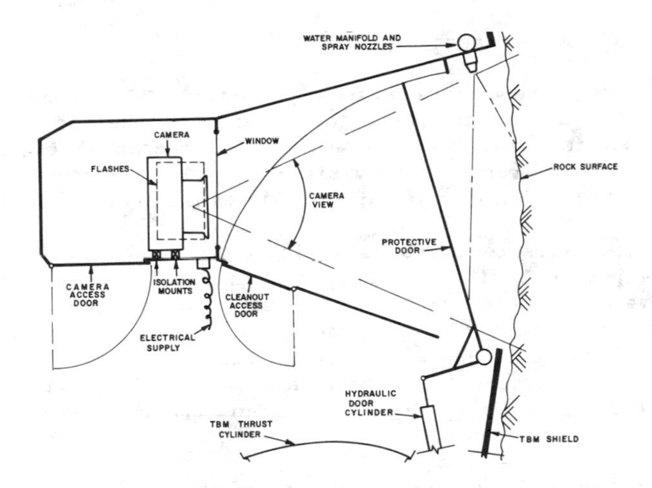

Fig. 3 - Camera System Housing

The front portion of the housing included a hydraulically operated steel door in front of the opening in the shield to keep the inside of the housing free of TBM cuttings when photographs were not being taken. Water spray jets were provided to wash the rock surface just prior to obtaining a photograph.

The rear portion of the housing was sealed from the front portion and the surrounding environment so that it was essentially dust and moisture proof. This is where the photographic equipment was located. The front face of the rear housing was plate glass through which the photographs were taken. A locking trap door permitted access to the photographic equipment.

The advance of the TBM was monitored by a telescoping proximity switch with a 1.8 m (6 ft) stroke. As the TBM advanced every 0.6 m (2 ft), the camera system would be triggered by the proximity switch and a photograph would be taken.

The photographic equipment used was a commercially available automated Nikon system with a 250 frame film magazine. Lighting was provided with dual Sunpac electronic flashes. The system was triggered at 0.6 (2ft) intervals by means of a telescoping proximity switch attached to the forward and rear sections of the TBM.

Operation and Maintenance

In general, the camera system performed well, considering the environment and the fact that the camera was checked on the order of only two to three times a week. The operation of the system involved three basic activities: (1) reference exposure stationing, (2) film changing, and (3) maintenance.

Reference exposures were established by means of taking several exposures per roll with the lens cap in place at a known station. After development and printing, the reference exposures were identified by roll number, date and known station on each contact sheet. Duplicates and overlaps were distinguished and so identified. Stations were then assigned to each frame to the nearest 0.3 m (1 ft). Film changing and stationing generally averaged twice per month.

The maintenance performed on the system during operation primarily involved cleaning the glass window in front of the lens, which was subject to moisture from the water spray and dust generated during TBM operations, and changing the drying desiccant in the housing. Occasionally, TBM cuttings had to be removed from the front portion of the housing.

The photographic system continued operating until soft material from the fault zone at Test Section 10 squeezed past the protective steel door and shattered the glass window in front of the camera.

Results and Interpretation

The automatic photographic system produced aproximately 75% coverage of the exposed bedrock surface at the tunnel springline in the approximately 2680 m (8800 ft) excavated by the TBM.

Using this photographic system, geologic features such as bedding, jointing, fractures and certain lithology, were distinguished. Bedding features were among the most common encountered in the exposures. Where contrasting colors existed in the bedding, apparent dip angles and the thickness of beds were more readily distinguished. Apparent dip angles were measured with respect to the frame of the film which was assumed to be horizontal. Joints and joint sets were visible in many photographs and measurements could be made of the apparent dip angle and other angles of structural significance in the bedrock. Occasional areas of overbreak were also sometimes observed. Distinguishing lithology in the exposures was very difficult and, in most cases, impossible, particularly if no samples were obtained at or near the exposure location to verify interpretations.

Fig. 4 is one of the more interesting exposures obtained. It exemplifies some of the geologic features which were documented by the system. This exposure was obtained at Sta 91+32 and appears to be calcite-healed breccia in contact with gray sandstone at an apparent dip of 19° to the east. Two parallel calcite-healed joint sets appear, one set approximately perpendicular to bedding with an apparent dip of 71° to the west, the other approximately 25° to bedding with an apparent dip of 43° to the east.

It was also possible to distinguish some excavation features resulting from the TBM excavation such as the near-vertical striations due to the gage cutter (outermost on cutterhead) shearing into the rock and leaving behind the imprint of its path.

Some observed features were associated with the automated system used and were generally a result of a malfunction of some system component. The most notable feature appearing in the exposures was the water spray which periodically would remain on during a series of exposures. In two separate instances the welded mount providing the reaction for the cylinder which opens the door (see Fig. 3) failed and resulted in a series of exposures of the door. Another characteristic intrinsic to the system was the result of not fully extending the TBM to its 1.8 m (6 ft) stroke. The proper operation of the proximity triggering switch was based upon the assumption that three exposures would be taken and a full 1.8 m (6 ft) stroke would be completed before regripping. Due to alignment corrections and to facilitate ring placement, occasional short stroking would occur resulting in overlaps and duplicates.

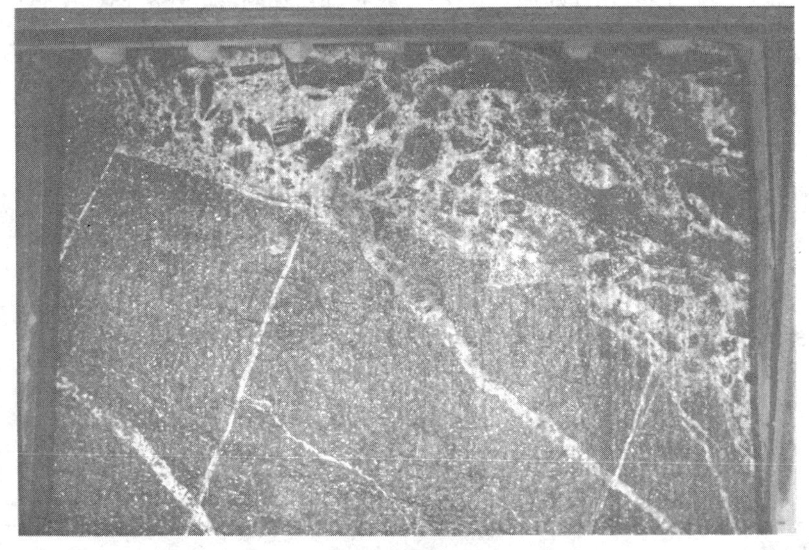

Fig. 4 - Example Photograph

Conclusions

Based upon viewing approximately 4500 contact print frames of the exposed bedrock surface at the tunnel springline, the following conclusions can be made in regard to the geologic photo documentation system used for this project.

1. Automated photo documentation is better suited in identifying structural characteristics of exposed bedrock rather than identifying specific lithology. Certain structure can be distinguished and apparent dip angles of joints, joint sets, fractures and faults can be measured.

2. The color of the exposed bedrock can be misleading and is particularly vulnerable to inconsistencies in development processes.

3. Water spray jets are an effective means to rid the exposed bedrock surface of fines which may conceal structural features.

4. The use of automatic photo documentation to record geologic features encountered during advancement of machine-bored tunnels is feasible.

SUMMARY AND CONCLUSION

Based on the instrumentation data obtained during the construction of the Park River Auxiliary Conduit the following observations and conclusions can be made relative to the response of the geologic medium, structural response of the precast concrete liner and performance of the instrumentation systems.

Geologic Response

1. The sedimentary and igneous rock through which the tunnel was constructed responded as anticipated during design in that it was generally stable with relatively small measured deformations.

2. The rate and magnitude of rock deformation depended on the rock quality. Measured rock movements were largest in areas of poorer quality rock, such as in the encountered fault zones. Depending on the rock conditions, downward movements from 0.08 to 1.6 cm (0.03 to 0.6 in.) were measured within approximately 0.6 m (2 ft) of the crown. In most cases, the maximum downward movement near the crown in sound rock was less than 0.25 cm (0.1 in.). The major portion of the rock movement under all conditions occurred as the heading advanced about 30 m (100 ft) beyond the instrument location.

3. Small upward movements of up to 0.08 cm (0.03 in.) were measured in one MPBX, possibly indicating lateral rock stresses higher than vertical at this location.

4. All rock movement attenuated upward from the tunnel opening with no significant movement measured beyond two diameters above the tunnel crown. The rate of rock movement appeared to be dependent on the rate of heading advance. However, there was no apparent correlation between the magnitude of rock movement and the rate of heading advance.

5. The groundwater drawdown in the surrounding rock and overlying soils was relatively large (35 m and 7 m, respectively) and recoveries were slow. Improved liner grouting techniques could improve this condition in future projects.

6. Groundwater inflow averaged less than 0.0001 m^3/sec/m (0.5 gpm/lf) for unsealed portions of the tunnel.

Structural Liner Response

1. Preliminary analyses of the strain data indicates that the maximum developed rock loads were slightly less than those assumed during design.

2. At seven of the nine test sections, the rock movements imposing the structural loads were small. Rock movements of 0.02 to 0.08 cm (0.01 to 0.03 in.) were measured near the crown after ring installation, which were 10 to 35% of the total rock movements measured at these locations. The relatively high rock movement (0.7 cm [0.28 in.]) measured above the crown after ring installation in a fault zone imposed the highest measured strain and resulting stress (approximately 44.8 MPa [6400 psi] compression) measured during the project.

3. Strain in the precast segments measured as a result of rock loading were non-uniform in the four liner ring segments with the largest strains generally measured in the crown. Tension stresses generally decreased with time as the load on the rings became redistributed. Tensile strain was less where the ring was grouted soon after installation.

4. Long-term changes in the tunnel cross section measurements relative to initial measurements obtained 92 m (300 ft) behind the face were very small ($\pm$ 0.15 cm [$\pm$ 0.10 in.]).

Instrument Performance

1. Instrument survival rate was high. Less than 7% of lost data in the precast portion of the tunnel was due to instrument failure.

2. Whenever possible, instrumentation should be installed well in advance of the construction to be monitored. Extensometers installed from within the tunnel would have been totally ineffective in measuring rock deformation due to the tunnel excavation since practically all of the movement would have occurred before the instrument could have been installed. In addition, extensometer installation from within the tunnel causes delay for the contractor and instrument damage is much more likely.

3. Electronic monitoring equipment employing vibrating wire technology seemed well suited to the adverse environment found in a tunnel.

4. Machine excavation methods, such as those used on this project in which extensive trailing equipment follows directly behind the heading and extends back for a substantial distnce, do not allow for measurements of total changes in dimension of interior diameters and chord lengths because of interference.

5. Instrumentation can provide valid criteria for construction monitoring and future design of tunnels. Types of instrumentation must be adjusted to the construction operation.

6. The use of a photograhpic log provides a valuable record of ground condition for post-construction appraisal.

7. Making the prime contractor contractually responsible for the gathering of the geotechnical data through an approved geotechnical consultant can be advantageous to the designer.

REFERENCES

1. "Tunnels and Shafts In Rock," EM 1110-2-2901, U. S. Army Corps of Engineers, Office of the Chief of Engineers, Department of the Army, 1973.

2. Barton, N., Lien, R., and Lunde, J., 1974, "Engineering Classification of Rock Masses for the Design of Tunnel Support," Rock Mechanics, Vol. 6, No. 4.

3. Blackey, E. A., Jr., December 1979, "Park River Auxiliary Tunnel," ASCE, Journal of Construction Division, Vol. 105, No. C04.

4. Goodman, R. E., January 1965, "Groundwater Inflows During Tunnel Driving," Bulletin of the Association of Engineering Geologists, Vol 2, No. 1.

5. Austin, W. G. and Fabry, J. W., 1974, "Rock Behavior Studies During Drill-Blast and Machine-Bored Tunneling,." Third International Conference on Rock Mechanics, Denver.

6. Guertin, J. and Plotkin, E. S., 1979, "Observation of Construction Behavior of a Major Rock Tunnel," Proceedings, 1979 Rapid Excavation and Tunneling Conference, Atlanta.

7. Deere, D. U., et al., February 1969, "Design of Tunnel Liners and Support Systems," Report for Office of High Speed Ground Transporation, USDOT, NTIS-PB/83799.

8. Mahar, J. W., Gau, F. L., and Cording, E. J., 1972, "Observations During Construction of Rock Tunnels for the Washington, D. C. Subway," Proceedings, 1972 North American Rapid Excavation and Tunneling Conference.

9. Guertin, J. D. and Flanagan, R. F., Sepember 1979, "Construction Behavior of a Shallow Tunnel in Highly Stressed Sedimentary Rock," Proceedings, 4th International Conference on Rock Mechanics, Montreux, Switzerland.

Chapter 92

NEW DEVELOPMENTS IN LASER-NUMERICAL ANALYSIS INSTRUMENTATION

by Prof. Dr. Manuel Diaz del Rio

Assistant Director, Spanish National Railway (RENFE)
Madrid, Spain

ABSTRACT

At the present time there are over 5,000 Kms of railway tunnels in existence throughout the world. In many cases these tunnels were built over a century ago using techniques obsolete today.

Supervision and maintenance of these tunnels is essential to the economy of each country involved. For this purpose an electro-optical measuring system has been designed incorporating highly complex soft and hardware (15 mW laser, high resolution TV camera and processing computer), mounted on a vehicle. Its job is to scan, record and compare sectional gauge values (profiles) and strains inside tunnels both momentarily in situ and on permanent record, as an aid to the supervision work.

From the state of the strains observed, in conjunction with an infrared spectrum of the tunnel lining and soil involved, the mechanical stresses in the tunnel can be deduced by applying the boundary elements method.

INTRODUCTION

Where railways are concerned, operation in tunnels represents a unique case. This stems from the impossibility of establishing variations in the layout if failures in fact appear and the difficulty involved in altering the gauge when exceptional loads have to pass through; it is well-known that railways are being increasingly used for the transport of over-size and indivisible loads such as nuclear reactors, parts for refineries and cement factories, etc.

The fact that over 5,000 Km of tunnels exist in the main railway networks of the world is a patent indication of the importance of the study and control of the gauges and strains in tunnels in all the networks and especially in those built in countries with highly irregular orographic conditions.

The majority of the railway tunnels were built over a century ago according to techniques today considered outdated and in some cases actually awesome.

It is commonplace in all railway networks for a considerable portion of the maintenance budget to be assigned to reinforcement and reconstruction work of small stretches of tunnels that have suffered damage as a result of faulty stability, in order to maintain an acceptable level of reliability. (2)

The drilling of a tunnel disturbs the previous balance of the soil; it can be appreciated therefore that if special precautions were not taken in the past during the boring process, slow or indeed fast changes are to be feared in the water pattern existing in the surrounding ground and in the structure of the tunnel itself, since it must not be forgotten that certain types of soil can alter owing to their actual nature, especially those of eruptive or metamorphic and sedimentary rock types. It is equally obvious that the tunnel lining itself is subject to similar phenomena.

This article will not refer to reinforcement and reconstruction techniques for tunnels already built nor to the work involved prior to the construction of new galleries since in both cases there is a set of acceptable technical solutions available which experience has proved to be correct. The idea behind this paper is to study techniques enabling us to make constant supervision of the geometrical properties of tunnel sections and by complex algorithms to be able to compare profiles taken at different times, thereby deducing from this comparison the stresses and strains that have occurred in the lining and/or in the ground.

VEHICLE AND APPARATUS USED FOR THE MEASUREMENTS

It is obvious that the measuring equipment must be mounted on a standard railway vehicle which will allow the following procedures to take place:

- the tunnel sections, and if necessary other outside masonry work also, to be scanned and recorded on magnetic support systems,
- the circulation gauge to be carefully inspected both on the spot and for permanent record.

The vehicle that the Spanish National Railways (RENFE) has been using since the end of 1980 is 16.04 m long and weighs 30 t in all. It can therefore circulate in radiuses of up to 150 m and it has been designed to couple to conventional trains travelling up to 100 Km/h.

A flexion- and torque-rigid metal frame resting on three points is fixed solid with the wagon platform; these three points eliminating any possible torque effect.

Fixed at various points to this metal frame is a metal girder which serves as an optical bench, supporting at each of its ends the electro-optical devices:

- the laser emitting device
- the TV camera for scanning data.

A laser-emitting device of 15 mW starting power sends out a beam of between 488 and 633 μm wavelengths which continually illuminates a stretch of the tunnel wall. This beam is fan-shaped with the maximum angle of 280°.

The plane of this beam takes in the turning axis of the first bogie and is fitted with a device to ensure perpendicularity at the tangent of the curve at this point.

The electro-optical scanner consists of a high resolution television camera.

The lens of the optical system has a variable focal length designed to select the necessary field for the best use of the system on altering the focal length.

A 90° rotation in the camera group round the optical axis allows the image to be analysed in the best direction in relation to the part of the tunnel in question.

A device that makes discriminations in the amplitude of video signal shown distinguishes which are the first two points to be illuminated in each line.

The resolving power and precision of the electro-optical device is set according to the following parameters:

- Resolution of the electronic device at mesh level .... 20 μm
- Precision of the electronic device at mesh level ..... 40 μm
- Amplification of the optical device for a 5-m diameter tunnel .... g = 1/500
- Resolution of the electro-optical device at tunnel level .... 10 mm
- Relative precision of the electro-optical device at tunnel profile level (static case, wagon stopped) . 0.4% tunnel Ø
- For the scanning and recording of each point in the profile a maximum standard speed for the vehicle has been established of .... 1 m/s

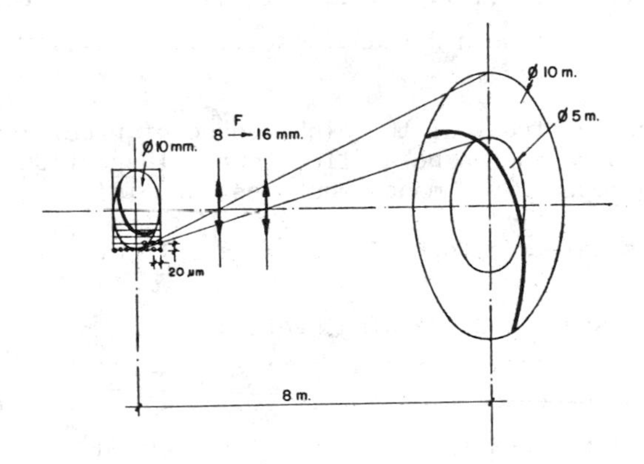

Fig. 1. Camera mesh surface of scanner

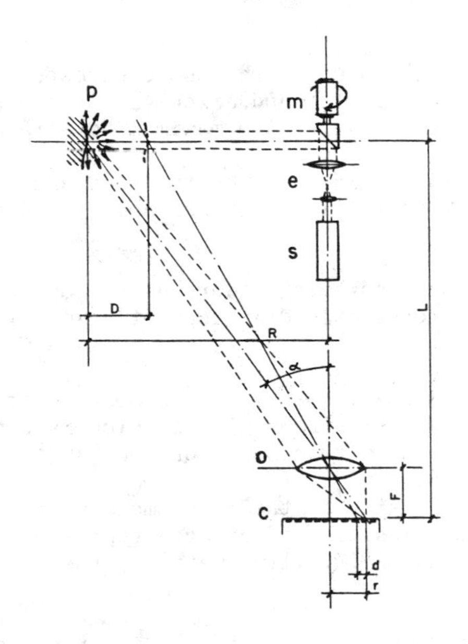

Fig. 2. Flowsheet of optical process

- Maximum scanning cadence .... 4 profiles/sec
- Minimum space between two scannings (for a speed of 1 m/s) .... 0.25 m
- Average dispersion between 2 scannings .... 0.2% of tunnel Ø measured

It will be appreciated that the high degree of precision developed for the study of strains can be applied to the inspection of circulation gauges which logically demands much less precision.

The properties selected for this work are reflected in the following details:

- Maximum vehicle speed for scanning profile recordings .... 10 m/s
- Maximum scanning cadence .... 4 profiles
- Minimum interval between two scannings for a speed of 10 m/s .... 2.5 m
- Average dispersion between two scannings .... 0.2% tunnel Ø

The camera mesh surface (Fig. 1) has a working diameter of 10 mm. This surface has 500 horizontal lines each divided into 500 dots. This gives a metrological mesh of 250,000 points with the basic increment being 20 mm. This increment in theory represents the separating power of the camera.

Single or double track tunnels are recorded respectively in these circles of 5- and 10-m diameter and a zoom lens is needed to be able to use the mesh surface always to the maximum advantage.

Each time the light beam is swept by the camera an analogical signal is obtained which is immediately digitized and stored in the system's memory.

As a function of the separating power and the optical amplifications selected, the maximum recordable displacement value of the tunnel wall can be deduced.

The inspection of circulation gauges is a most important operation in view of the increase in over-size vehicles which is constantly reducing the admissible margin of tolerance for the gauge.

The computer with the aid of its programme memorizes the essential gauge values. When the inside surface area represented by the gauge is not distorted by an abnormality illuminated by the optical system, no warning is given.

If the opposite is true, a siren rings and warns the operator. By stopping the wagon it is possible to return to the position indicated by the linear dial at the spot where the alarm was set off and measure precisely the importance of the obstacle. In the two main functions of the apparatus, inspection of circulation gauges and dimensional measurement, the area inspected covers a 280° section.

According to the flowsheet of Fig. 2, a laser ray S whose beam concentrates at E is directed towards a mirror that revolves at great speed. This beam illuminates the wall P in a continuous manner and produces the image of this area on the surface C of a photo-electronic receiver which allows distance R to be digitized. The irregularities D in the wall P will be shown on the surface C of the receiver by a simple optical process.

BOUNDARY INTEGRAL EQUATION METHOD (B.I.E.M.)

For any technical solution involved in the maintenance of tunnels the state of stress must constantly be known; there is no easy way to obtain this state of stresses directly.

It is obvious that with modern techniques as they stand the only procedure that is practically possible is the continual measurement of strain values and the use of calculations to deduce the state of the stresses.

With the arrival of fast computers with extensive memories, several methods have been developed among which the Finite Elements Method (F.E.M.) is outstanding and has enjoyed a spectacular field of application in technological media. However, in the specific case of tunnels, this has not proved to be very practical because of the need for a laborious preparation and checking of input data and the problems derived from optimizing the nodes, plus the difficulty involved in obtaining a degree of precision that is important in determining stresses.

The Boundary Element Method appears to be the logical alternative for reducing these problems. In synthesis this method, also known as Integral Equations in the boundary, consists of transforming the field equations of the problem that describe the behaviour of the functions within the domain and in the boundary of this into an integral equation that relates the unknown factors in this boundary to known functions of the same. A reciprocal theorem and the existence of fundamental solutions in the field equation allows the treatment of the problem to proceed from the domain solution to the boundary solution.

At this first stage of study we have assumed that a stress/strain linear-elastic law will be sufficiently exact.

There follows a summary of the results obtained during the Boundary Element Method after the studies of Zienkiewicz (6), Tsuji (5), Sokolnikoff (4), Alarcon (1) and Jaswon (3).

In elasticity the balancing equation in terms of movements, that is Navier's equation, is:

$$\frac{\lambda + G}{G} \nabla \; (\nabla u) + \nabla^2 u + \frac{1}{G} X_i = \rho \ddot{u} \tag{1}$$

In matrix notation and for a static case it becomes:

$$\frac{1}{1-2\,\nu} u_{j,ji} + u_{i,jj} + \frac{1}{G} X_i = 0 \tag{2}$$

Therefore the elastic problem is reduced to finding a displacement function $\underline{u}$ that will satisfy the previous equation under certain circumstances, or a linear combination of those.

Applying Betti's second theorem, or the reciprocal theorem, to the fundamental solution of Navier's equation, after Kelvin, we obtain:

$$u_i = \frac{1}{16\,\pi\,\mu \;\; (1-\nu) \;\; r} \left\{(3-4\nu)\; \delta_{ij} + r_{,i}\, r_{,j}\right\} e_j \tag{3}$$

this solution can also be expressed as:

$$u_i(y) = U_{ji}\;(x,y)\, e_j \tag{4}$$

To find the expression for the stresses in the coordinates we only need to remember:

$$t_i = \sigma_{ij}\; n_j$$

$$\sigma_{ij} = \frac{2\mu\nu}{1-2\nu} \varepsilon_{mm} \;\; \delta_{ij} + 2\mu\, \varepsilon_{ij} \tag{5}$$

with

$$\varepsilon_{ij} = \frac{1}{2} \;\left(\frac{\partial\mu i}{\partial x_j} \;\; \frac{\partial\mu j}{\partial x_i}\right) \tag{6}$$

from whence

$$t_i = \mu \left(\frac{\partial ui}{\partial n} + u_{j,i}\, n_j + \frac{2\,\nu}{1-2\nu}\, u_{j,j}\, n_i \right) \tag{7}$$

and equally we obtain the expression t_i.

$$t_i = -\frac{1}{r^2} \left[\frac{\partial r}{\partial n} \left[(1-2\nu)\delta_{ij} + 3_{r,i\,r,j} \right] + (1-2\nu) \right.$$

$$\left. (n_j r_i \; - n_i r,j) \right] \frac{ej}{8\,(1-\nu)} \tag{8}$$

By analogy with how we arrived at the displacement

$$t_i\,(y) = T_{ji}\,(x,y)\; ej. \tag{9}$$

From Somigliana's identity we can proceed to calculate the movements and stresses at all points in the domain.

The tensor of stresses at an internal point can be expressed as follows:

$$\sigma_{ij} = \frac{2\pi\nu}{1-2\nu}\, \delta_{ij} \frac{\partial u_m}{\partial x_m} + \mu \left(\frac{\partial u_i}{\partial x_j} + \frac{\partial u_j}{\partial x_i} \right) \tag{10}$$

which can also be given as:

$$\sigma_{ij} = \int_{\partial D} t_k \left[\frac{2\,\mu\nu}{1-2\,\nu}\, \delta_{ij} \frac{\partial U_{mk}}{\partial x_m} + \mu \left(\frac{\partial U_{ik}}{\partial x_j} \quad \frac{\partial U_{jk}}{\partial x_i} \right) \right] ds -$$

$$- \int_{\partial D} u_k \left[\frac{2\,\mu\nu}{(1-\nu)}\, \delta_{ij} \frac{\partial T_{mk}}{\partial x_m} + \mu \left(\frac{\partial T_{ik}}{\partial x_j} + \frac{\partial T_{jk}}{\partial x_i} \right) \right] ds \tag{11}$$

This expression can be abbreviated as follows:

$$\sigma_{ij} = \int_{\partial D} t_k\, D_{kij}\, ds - \int_{\partial D} u_k\, S_{kij}\, ds \tag{12}$$

where:

$$D_{kij} = \frac{1}{r^{\alpha}} (1-2\nu)(\delta_{ki} r,_j + \delta_{kj} r,_i - \delta_{ij} r,_k) + \beta r,_i r,_j r,_k /$$

$$/ 4\alpha\pi(1-\nu) \tag{13}$$

$$S_{kij} = \frac{2\mu}{r^{\beta}} \beta \frac{\partial r}{\partial n} (1-2\nu)\delta_{ij} r,_k + \nu(\delta_{ik} r,_j + \delta_{jk} r,_i -$$

$$- \gamma r,_i r,_j r,_k) + \beta\nu (n_i r,_j r,_k + n_j r,_i r,_k) + (1-2\nu)$$

$$(\beta n_k r,_i r, + n_j \delta_{ik} + n_i \delta_{jk}) - (1-4\nu) n_k \delta_{ij} /$$

$$/4\alpha\pi (1-\nu) \tag{14}$$

For two dimensions:

$\alpha = 1, \quad \beta = 2, \quad \gamma = 4$

For three dimensions:

$\alpha = 2, \quad \beta = 3, \quad \gamma = 5$

ADDITIONAL INFRARED TECHNIQUES

It is well known that infrared radiations extend from dark red (333 tcps) to the field of microwaves (0.1 tcps).

In the inside of tunnels and under certain conditions the quasi-theoretical conditions can occur of a black body in a cavity impermeable to heat, or an adiabatic wall.

Planck's law determines the spectrum distribution of energy radiated by the black body. Initially this law is expressed as:

$$N_l = 2Kc \frac{T}{l^4} \tag{15}$$

where:

N_1 = Energy radiated by the black body for a specific wavelength $\underline{1}$

K = Boltzmann's constant

c = speed of light

T = absolute temperature

By integration in relation to the wavelength Stefan's Law is obtained which gives the total energy radiated by a body at a temperature T.

$$E = s\,T^4 \quad W/cm^2 \tag{16}$$

$$S = 5.73 \,.\, 10^{-12} \; W/cm^2 \; ({}^{o}K)^4 \tag{17}$$

These laws allow the temperature of the black body to be deduced from the radiation.

Infrared auscultation in the case of tunnels is sufficiently precise owing to the low absorption of the radiations by diatomic molecules, or more complex ones, and to the low diffusion rate produced where tunnels are concerned.

According to Stefan's Law, a black surface of 1 m^2 at 300°K emits approximately 480 W, consequently a tunnel can have a considerable identification effect which is perfectly measurable.

Experiments carried out in Spain (Valos Tunnel near to Vigo and the Meridiana Tunnel in Barcelona) have even allowed small areas of discontinuity to be detected, which proves extremely interesting in determining the physical parameters that identify the different ground properties, values that will subsequently be included in the calculation process summed up earlier in the Boundary Integral Equation Method.

The infrared analysis mechanism used consists of a revolving mirror describing an 80° angle at a speed of 16 turns per second and a spacial resolution of 5 mrad. The focus is adjustable.

The precision obtained is 0.1^{o}C at a temperature of 25°C.

The infrared thermal radiations are converted into an electric signal at the end of the wavelengths from 2 to 5.5 μm.

SYMBOLS

ν = Poisson coefficient

G = rigidity modulus

λ = Lamé's constant

X_i = forces per unit of volume

δD = boundary of a domain D

ε_{ij} = strain tensor in Cartesian coordinates

G_{ij} = stress tensor in Cartesian coordinates

u_i (y) = displacement in the direction i at point y

$U_{ji}(x,y)$ = displacement in the direction i at point y owing to a unit load at point x in the direction j

e_j = unit vectors in the coordinated directions

δ_{ij} = Kronecker's delta

r(x,y) = distance between points x and y

r,i(x,y) = derivative of r with respect to the direction

t_i (y) = stress at point y in the direction i

T_{ji} (x,y) = stress at point y at the surface in the direction i owing to a unit load at point x in the direction j

REFERENCES

Alarcon, E., et al., 1979, "Boundary Elements in Potential and Elasticity Theory", Computers and Structures, Vol. 10, No. 1/2, Apr., pp. 351-362.

Diaz del Rio, M., 1980, "Fiabilidad y Conservación de las Instalaciones Fijas Ferroviarias en los Países no Industrializados", Revista de Obras Públicas, Oct., pp. 757-766.

Jaswon, M.A., and Symm, G.T., 1977 "Integral Equation Method in Potential and Elastostatics", Academic Press, New York.

Sokolnikoff, I.S., 1956, Mathematical Theory of Elasticity, McGraw Hill New York.

Tsuji, M., 1958, Potential Theory in Modern Function Theory, Chelsea, London.

Zienkiewicz, O.C., 1977, The Finite Element Method, McGraw Hill, New York.

Chapter 93

CONSTRUCTION AND PERFORMANCE OF A MIXED FACE TUNNEL EXCAVATION

by William R. Beloff, David E. Puza, and Franklin M. Grynkewicz

Chief Engineer; Soil and Rock Instrumentation Division, Goldberg -Zoino and Associates, Newton, MA

Project Engineer; Perini Corporation. Davis Square, Somerville to Porter Square, Cambridge, Tunnels and Shafts Project

Field Engineer; Soil and Rock Instrumentation Division, Goldberg -Zoino and Associates, Newton, MA

Construction of the MBTA Red Line Extension through Somerville, MA, called for driving twin tube tunnels through a zone of approximately 83m (273 ft) with mixed face conditions. While the majority of the tunnels were driven through competent hard rock using drill and blast techniques, the mixed face zone was advanced using floating crown bars for primary support. The overburden consisted of medium clay, underlain by water bearing glacial till, over a sloping bedrock surface. Due to the unusual nature of the construction techniques, a program was undertaken by the Contractor to monitor ground movement and stresses in the temporary steel supports. This paper presents a description of the instrumentation employed, as well as the measured ground movements and support stresses. Additionally, the tunneling techniques are briefly presented and commented upon.

PROJECT DESCRIPTION

The Davis Square to Porter Square Tunnel Contract is part of the Massachusetts Bay Transportation Authorities (MBTA) Red Line Extension from Harvard Square in Cambridge to the Alewife Brook Parkway via Somerville. The 5.1km (17,000 ft) Red Line Extension consists of four major new stations, three of which will be interlinked via tunnel construction, and the remaining station will be the last link of an open cut portion, and a terminal point for this phase of the extension. This 866m (2,790 ft) portion began at Porter Square in Cambridge and rose at a 4% slope through Somerville, terminating at the new Davis Square Station. Twin tube tunnels were constructed through 763m (2,517 ft) of rock and 83m (273 ft) of mixed face conditions at the Davis Square end. Figure 1 presents a plan view of the entire contract.

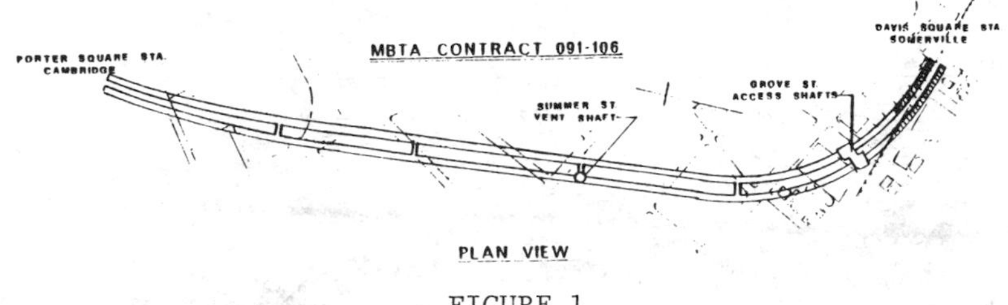

FIGURE 1

MIXED FACE DESCRIPTION

Tunneling operations progressed from the Grove Street access Shafts toward Davis Square Station. Forty-two meters (139 ft) of 6.7m (22 ft) diameter horseshoe shape tunnel was driven before the mixed face area was encountered. At this point, the excavated diameter was then increased to a 7.16m (23.5 ft) circular section, to allow adequate support at the invert. Cover over the mixed face tunnels varied from 11.9m to 9.5m (39 ft to 31 ft) as excavation advanced up the 4% incline. The three materials encountered during the mixed face excavation were:

Marine Clays (Boston Blue Clay): consisting primarily of medium stiff to stiff, gray silty Clays found beneath fill and glacial outwash deposits approximately 3.96m to 15.24m (13 ft to 50 ft) below the surface. The average physical properties of the clay at tunnel depth are presented in Table 1.

Glacial Till: consisting of dense to very dense gray, coarse to fine Sand, coarse gravel, silt and clay averaging 10.6m to 18.29m (35 ft to 60 ft) beneath the surface. Permeability varied considerably.

Bedrock: consisting of moderately hard, to hard black silty Argillite (Cambridge Argillite), extremely fractured at the till and rock interface, very pervious. Top of rock 10m to 18.29m (33 ft to 60.36 ft). Figure 2 shows an idealized view of the mixed face profile.

TOTAL UNIT WEIGHT KN/m³ (lb/Ft³)	EFFECTIVE ANGLE OF FRICTION DEGREES	UNDRAINED SHEAR STRENG KN/m² (lb/Ft²)	OVER CONSOLIDATION RATIO O.C.R	ATTERBERG LIMITS			SENSITIVITY RATIO S.R	COMPRESSIBILITY RATIO $C_c/1+e_o$	RECOMPRESSIBILITY RATIO, $C_R/1+e_o$	EARTH PRESSURE COEFFICIENT		
				PL	LL	W				K_o	K_A	K_P
19.6 (125)	22	48 (1000)	2.5	22	35	42	6	0.017	0.155	0.8	0.4	1.6

ENGINEERING PROPERTIES OF MARINE CLAY

TABLE 1

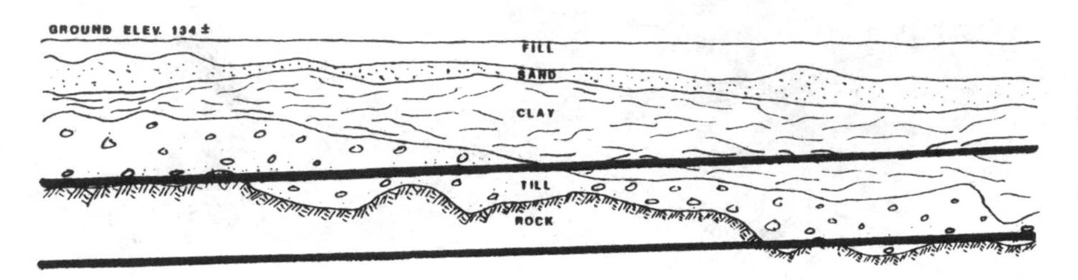

MIXED FACE PROFILE

FIGURE 2

CONSTRUCTION METHOD AND PROCEDURES

Mining of the mixed face tunnel was to be accomplished beneath an active railroad in a heavily commercialized business district. The floating crown bar method coupled with circular steel rib sets and timber blocking was selected and felt to be the most economical and efficient method considered. For a discussion of this method refer to the companion paper presented by Puza, Borggaard, Bhore (RETC 1981). Additionally, it was considered necessary to provide a means of controlling groundwater inflow through the glacial till. This was to be accomplished with a two phase program of pumping from a deep well installed at the down slope end of the sloping till, and a cement grouting program aimed at lowering the permeability over the entire length of glacial till. Hayward Baker Company of Odenton, Maryland designed and executed the grouting program. The deep well was installed and pumping prior to the implementation of the grouting program. The pattern of grout holes advanced towards the deep well, and the well proved to be beneficial in lowering the static water levels in the till prior to grouting. A detailed description of the grouting program employed is discussed in the paper presented by Puza et al (1981).

Floating Crown Bars: The floating crown bar method provided the temporary earth support needed to install the W8 x 35 support rings. It consisted of seventeen 12.7cm x 17.8cm x 3m (5 in x 7 in x 10 ft) steel box beams with a closed wedge leading edge. The crown bars were spaced approximately 61cm (2 ft) on center around the outside circumference of the steel support rings, which were installed at a maximum spacing of 1.2m (4 ft). A detailed analysis and description of the floating crown bar method is presented by Puza et al (1981)

PREDICTED GROUND MOVEMENT

Prior to advancing the tunnel through the mixed face condition, an estimate of the amount of the ground deformation was made. As discussed below, the estimates were based on emperical procedures and the geotechnical data available at the time of bidding. No additional geotechnical explorations or testing was performed. The assumed critical soil profile was taken to as shown on Figure 3, and the engineering properties were assumed to be the average values shown on Table No. 1.

The commonly used index for the stability of a tunnel in plastic clays, originally developed by Broms and Bennermark (1967), is the following ratio:

$$N = \frac{P_z - P_a}{S_u}$$

where: N = Stability Ratio
P_z = Total vertical pressure at springline
P_a = Air pressure above atmosphere
S_u = Undrained shear strength of clay

Broms and Bennermark suggest that this ratio should not exceed about 6, while Cording, et al (1975) suggests that the ratio should not exceed about 5. It should be noted that these suggestions assume very little over excavation and proper void filling. The stability ratio for the critical profile computed to be 5.9, hence, it was recognized that some difficulties could be encountered, however, the potential was not high enough to rule out an attempt at tunneling.

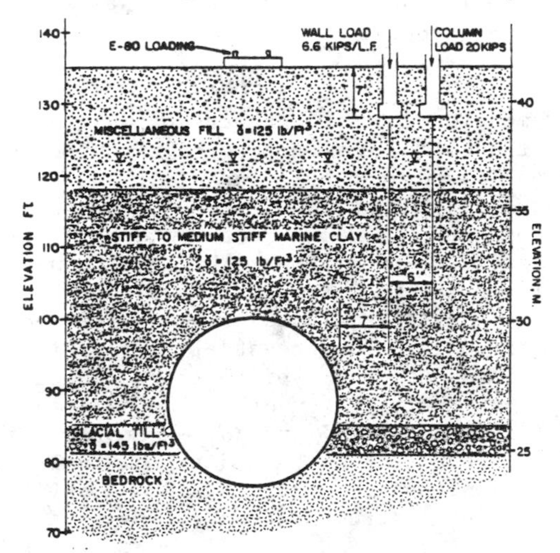

FIGURE 3

Cording, et al (1975) present a summary of available data concerning the shape of the settlement trough over soft ground tunnels and give ranges for the typical volume of lost ground as a function of the stability ratio. The research shows that the volume of the surface settlement trough may be 2 to 5 percent of the excavated tunnel volume. It was determined that a value of 4 percent would be assumed and that since only 75 percent of the heading was in the clay, this would be lowered to 3 percent.

Using the planned excavated diameter of 7.1m (23.6 ft), the anticipated volume of the settlement trough was $0.37m^3$ ($13.1 ft^3$). The expression to estimate the maximum surface settlement is:

$$S_{max} = \frac{V_s}{2.5i}$$

S_{max} = Maximum surface settlement

V_s = Volume of settlement trough

i = Point of inflection on the anticipated trough

Using the relationship proposed by Peck (1969) and a Z/2R equal to 2, i was estimated to be 7.1m (23.5 ft). The maximum surface settlement computed out to 6.6cm (2.6 in). Additional surface settlement was anticipated due to localized lowering of the ground water table. This settlement was estimated at 2.5cm (1 in) over an 8 month time span.

Based upon the planned efforts to control the mining activity and to provide immediate blocking of overcut areas, no allowance was made in the settlement predictions for loss of ground due to excessive over excavation.

MONITORING PROGRAM

Instrumented monitoring sections were established along the route of the outbound tunnel for the purpose of measuring ground movements, and to observe any associated building distress. Five instrumented sections were located as shown on Figure 4. Essentially, the instrumented sections were laid out on a 15m (50 ft) interval over the length of the mixed face condition. The instrumentation employed consisted of surface settlement points, deep settlement points, inclinometer casings, multi-level subsurface settlement points, and vibrating wire strain gages on the steel ribs. Figure 5 shows the general instrument layout at a typical instrumented section. This layout is similar to that used by others on numerous projects, and has been shown to provide a fairly good understanding of the soil mass movement. At test sections 4 and 5, the inclinometers and multi-level settlement points were deleted. A brief description of the ground movement instrumentation follows.

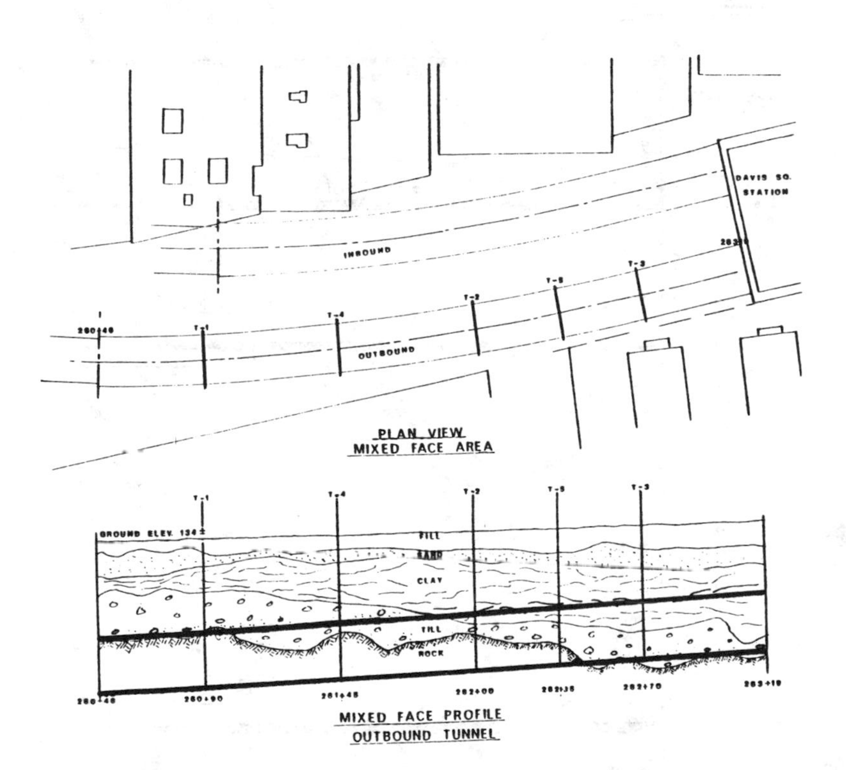
DAVIS SQ.
STATION
INBOUND
260+40
T-1
T-4
T-2
T-5
T-3
OUTBOUND
PLAN VIEW
MIXED FACE AREA
T-1
T-4
T-2
T-5
T-3
GROUND ELEV. 134±
FILL
SAND
CLAY
TILL
ROCK
260+90
261+45
282+00
282+35
282+70
283+10
MIXED FACE PROFILE
OUTBOUND TUNNEL

FIGURE 4

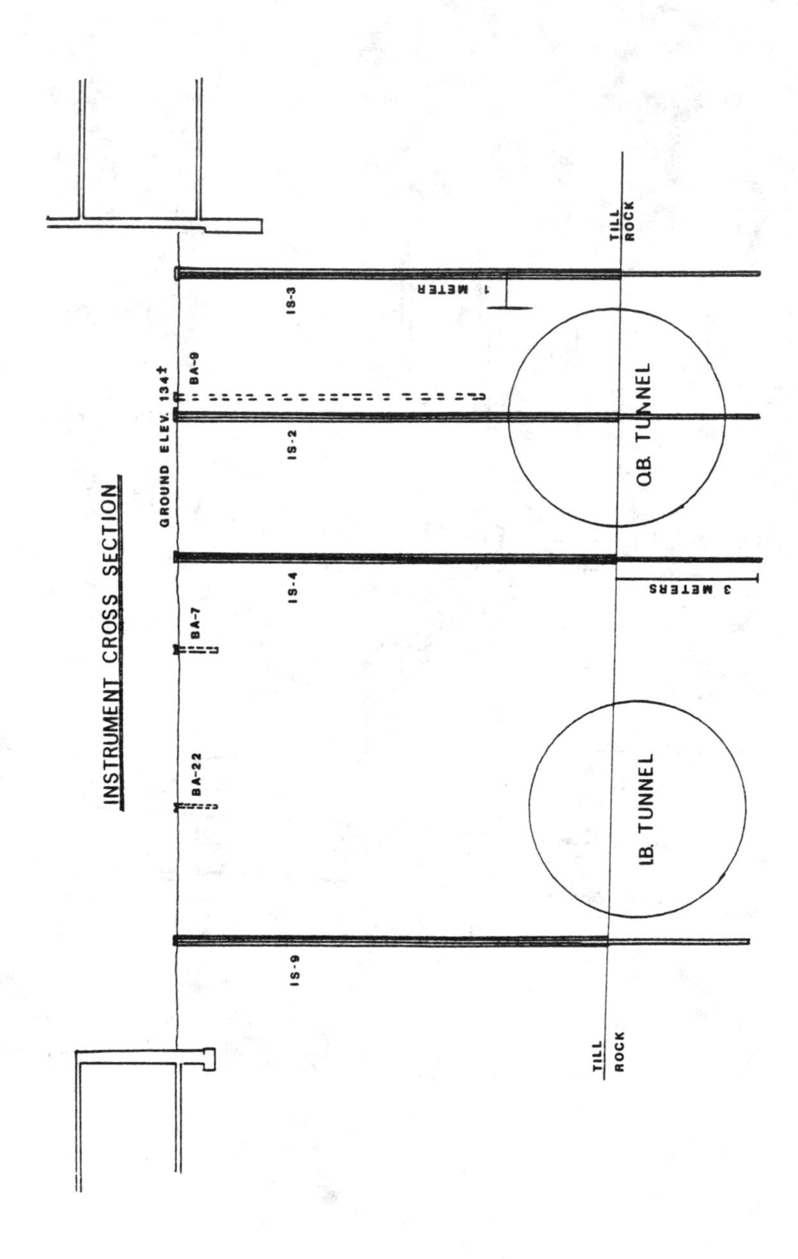
INSTRUMENT CROSS SECTION
GROUND ELEV. 134±
BA-9
IS-3
1 METER
IS-2
Q.B. TUNNEL
IS-4
3 METERS
BA-7
BA-22
I.B. TUNNEL
IS-9
TILL
ROCK
TILL
ROCK

FIGURE 5

Surface Settlement Points: As discussed previously, the upper .95m (3 ft) of material over the tunnel consisted of crushed basalt ballast for the active railroad tracks. Since this material is prone to a great deal of shifting, it was necessary to measure the surface settlements at a level below the ballast, or roughly 1.2m (4 ft) below existing grade. The instrument consisted of a "Borros Anchor", originally manufactured by Borros Company, Ltd., Sweden, and now available through A & S Company, Milford, MA. The anchor consists of a steel housing approximately 30cm (12 in) long containing three prongs, which are mechanically extended into the soil. The prongs are connected to a 0.64cm (0.25 in) steel pipe which serves to extend the prongs and acts as a riser onto which elevations are taken. A 2.54cm (1 in) steel pipe fits over the smaller pipe and serves to isolate it from the surrounding ground. The pipes were slightly recessed below grade and access was provided by a standard valve gate box. The in-place cost of these settlement points, including the gage box, was approximately $175.00 each. Figure 6 shows a detail of the "Borros Anchor."

Deep Settlement Points: "Borros Anchors" were also used as the deep settlement points. Of interest, is the fact that it was possible to push the anchors through the clay with the weight of two people. This allowed the installation to be accomplished without the use of a drill rig, and the work proceeded rapidly at a fairly low cost. The in-place cost of a typical 7.5m (25 ft) deep installation was approximately $250.00.

Inclinometer Casing and Multi-Level Subsurface Settlement Points: These two instruments are grouped together since the two measuring systems were combined and installed in a single borehole. Standard 7cm (2.79 in) ABS plastic casing, manufactured by Slope Indicator Company, Seattle, Washington, was used as the inclinometer guide casing. Based upon previous experience with movements of the magnitude anticipated on this project, rigid couplings were employed in lieu of telescopic couplings at the casing joints. The inclinometer casings were installed with a minimum embedment of 3m (10 ft) into competent rock to ensure bottom fixity and to allow for data analysis working from that point upward through the moving soil mass. The readout unit consisted of the Slope Indicator Company biaxial digitilt probe and manual readout box. This unit offers an accuracy of approximately 0.64cm (0.25 in) of horizontal movement per 30m (100 ft) of casing depth. The guide groove in the inclinometer were aligned for measuring movement parallel and perpendicular to the heading advance. Due to the relatively short installed lengths of guide casing, no groove spiral measurements were taken.

Subsurface settlement points were established at 1.2m (5 ft) intervals over the guide casing length by attaching sections of flexible corrugated plastic pipe onto the guide casing. Each section of plastic pipe was fitted with a single wrap of stainless steel wire. The position of this wire is then sensed by an electrical inductance circuit, encased in a portable probe. The sensing system is called the "Sondex" system and is manufactured by Slope Indicator Company. Figure 6 shows a detail of the plastic pipe attached to the guide casing. Laboratory tests indicated that the plastic pipe could accommodate up to 18cm (7 in) of vertical movement and this appeared acceptable based upon the anticipated movements.

The assemblies were installed in 10cm (4 in) boreholes through use of a grout check valve system installed through the guide casing bottom cap. The borehole grout consisted of a mixture of water, cement, and bentonite proportioned to yield a stiffness slightly less than the surrounding clay. Once again, the deepest sensing ring was located in competent rock, allowing for data analysis working from the bottom upward.

The standard Slope Indicator "Sondex" probe was modified to accept a digital height gage mounted on a portable work stand. This allowed for recording data to 0.01mm (0.004 in) with an overall accuracy of approximately 0.15mm (0.060 in).

The in-place cost of each assembly was approximated $70.00 per linear foot, and the combined readout units rented for approximately $600.00 per month with a one time cost of $900.00 for the digital height gage work stand assembly. The field time for monitoring each assembly was approximately 2 hours and all data reduction was performed using a mini-computer. Alternately the data reduction could be performed by hand in roughly 1.5 hours.

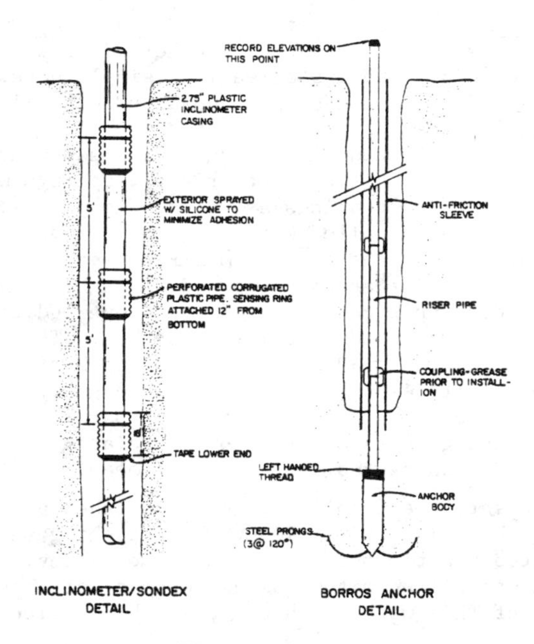

FIGURE 6

Strain Gages on Steel Ribs: Originally, it was felt that stresses in the steel would not be a significant problem, and, therefore, no strain gages were planned as part of this study. However, as tunneling progressed the steel ribs began to show a noticeable amount of deformation and vibrating wire type strain gages were installed on three ribs.

Ribs No. 37 and 38 at outbound Station 261+94 and 261+98 were two of the more deformed ribs and Model No. SM-2W strain gages, manufactured by Irad Gage, Lebanon, New Hampshire, were installed on the ribs underground. These gages were attached with a portable spot welder, following surface grinding with a number 300 high speed disc. At each measuring location, four gages were installed on the flanges to provide sufficient data to analyze biaxial bending of the rib. Since these gages would provide only the stress change subsequent to gage installation, another rib (No. 48) was instrumented above ground and installed at Station 262+38. It was planned that these gages would provide the full stress history. Due to several factors, two types of strain gages were installed on Rib 48, the SM-2W mentioned above and the more popular Irad Model SM-5A were employed, with double coverage at three locations. Of particular interest is the fact that the SM-5A is a more rugged gage employing a gage length roughly 5 times that of the SM-2W. All gages were read with an Irad Model MB-6 portable readout unit and all data reduction was performed manually.

The in-place cost of these strain gages was approximately $250.00 per gage, and the readout unit was obtained on a rental basis of $185.00 per month.

CONSTRUCTION PERFORMANCE

The sloping rock profile, coupled with the rising tunnel alignment created distinctly different heading conditions along the short mixed face section. For ease of analysis, the section has been divided into three generalized zones, defined by face conditions as follows:

Zone 1 - Station 260+46 to 261+85: Throughout this zone the crown showed the cemented till with the underlying bedrock composing the remainder of the face. No marine clay appeared in the heading in this zone.

Zone 2 - Station 261+85 to 262+75: Marine clay appeared at the crown and gradually dipped to slightly above springline.

Zone 3 - Station 262+75 to 263+19: Marine Clay at Springline or below and composing over 50% of the face.

As would be expected, the construction performance varied in relation to the face condition, with increasing difficulties occurring with increasing amount of marine clay. The following presents a view on the performance in each of the zones.

Zone 1: The cement grouting program was very effective in tightening the glacial till. In effect, the grouted till exhibited the characteristics of a soft rock. This created very favorable conditions for the floating crown bar tunneling method. The heading was advanced through this zone at an average rate of 0.4m (1.2 ft) per shift with steel ribs set on 1.2m (4 ft) centers. Timber blocking was installed between ribs, as required, and the grouted till was removed with negligible over excavation using the methods described by Puza et al, (1981).

In addition to strengthening the till, the grouting program also sealed the contact surface between the till and bedrock. This successfully prevented water in-flow, and the entire zone was passed with no noticeable wet areas.

Centerline surface settlements were less than 2.5cm (1 in) throughout the zone and settlement directly over the crown were of the same magnitude. Surface settlements at a 10m (33 ft) offset, i.e. at the location of the surface structures, were approximately 1.3cm (0.5 in) and no distress was noted in any of the structures. Additionally, inclinometer measurements showed negligible movements into the face.

The crown deflection of the steel rib sets was generally less than 2.5cm (1 in) and appeared to occur as the floating crown bars passed over the rib. This was most likely due to the increased loading caused by the cantilever action of the crown bars. These deflections were not large enough to require any resetting of the steel.

Zone 2: As the marine clay began to appear in the crown, conditions changed also immediately. Although the till remained very tight and no water inflow was encountered, the marine clay acted quite differently than had been assumed. Significant surface settlements began very early on in this zone, and the crown deflections of the third and fourth ribs continued to increase after the crown bars had passed.

Strain gages installed underground on these two ribs were functional after the ninth rib was positioned in this zone. The stress build up from then on was on the order of 82.8MPa (12,000 psi) and the total crown deflection was approximately 10cm (4 in) with associated opening of the butt plates.

Although there appeared to be no significant over excavation, except at one isolated area, in the early parts of this zone, centerline surface settlements were approximately 20cm (8 in) by the time the clay had dipped to the midpoint between the crown and springline. Surface settlements in this area at an offset of 8m (25.5 ft) were approximately 6cm (2.5 in) and some minor distress was noted in one adjoining structure.

As described by Puza et al (1981) a program of compaction grouting was undertaken at this stage to try to raise the distressed structure. The grouting holes were offset approximately 3m (10 ft) from the tunnel side walls and were to a depth of approximately 4m (13 ft) above the tunnel crown. The grout pressures applied varies between 1.4 and 2.8 MPa (200 to 400 psi) and did provide some uplift to the structure. However, the subsequent applied loadings on the timber lagging were large enough to actually cause flexural failures at the mid points between the steel rib sets. The damaged lagging was reinforced with new lagging installed after the completion of the compaction grouting program.

With further advancement of the heading, the clay surface continued to dip until it occupied the upper 50% of the face. Surface settlement increased correspondingly, reaching a maximum of approximately 45cm (18 in) at one centerline location. The cross-sectional shape of the settlement trough reassembled the anticipated probability distribution, however, not as well as has been the case, on numerous other projects. The cross sectional pattern of settlements is believed to have been influenced by the sloping clay/till contact throughout the entire zone. In general, this surface was inclined at roughly 20 degrees, sloping from the right to the left as one looks at the face. Surface settlements generally leveled off after the heading had advanced approximately 18m (60 ft) as shown on Figure 7.

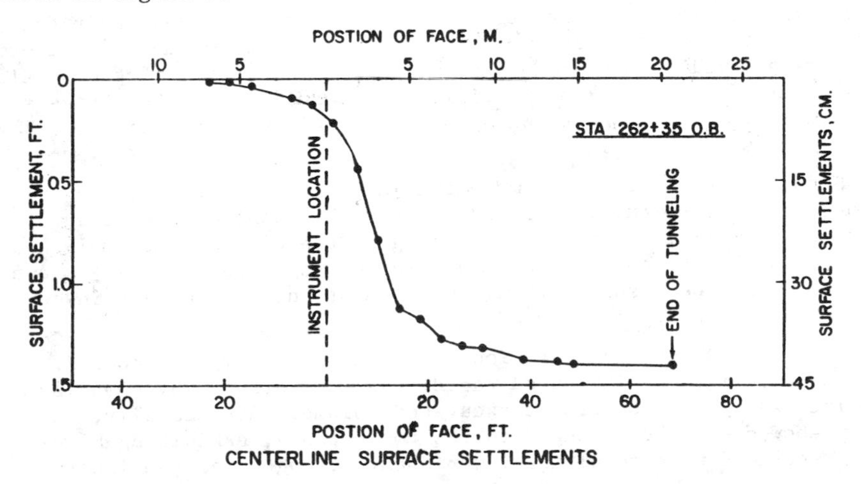

CENTERLINE SURFACE SETTLEMENTS

FIGURE 7

Graphical methods were used to calculate the volume of the surface settlement trough. Although these attempts were hampered by the lack of undisturbed monuments in the areas of high settlements, the volume of the trough was estimated at $1.9 m^3/m$ ($65 ft^3/ft$), or roughly 30% of the excavated clay volume. Settlements of the railroad tracks, which were offset approximately 3m (10 ft) to the left approached 15cm (6 in) in this area. Once again, the subsurface settlements as measured by the deep settlement points and the sondex system, were only slightly larger than the surface settlements. This appears to indicate the general yielding of the marine clay.

Subsurface horizontal movements, as measured by the inclinometer casings installed adjacent to the tunnel, occurred quite rapidly as the heading passed the instrument, and indicated a yielding of the clay just above clay/till contact surface. Movements on the order of 15cm (6 in) were observed before increasing to a level high enough to crimp the plastic inclinometer casing, making it impossible to gather further data. Furthermore, inclinometer casings installed along the centerline indicated a significant amount of squeezing into the face. At one location the squeezing had amounted to approximately 5cm (2 in), or a volume of roughly 8% of the excavated clay volume. Relating this to the total volume of surface settlement, it appears that 25-30% of the loss ground occurred due to yielding at the face.

The vertical crown deflections of the steel rib sets tended to increase over this zone and at some points approached 28mm (11 in). As one would expect, this created very high stresses in the steel and the strain gages installed at Station 262+38 indicated bending stresses approaching the yield limit of the steel. Additionally, the strain gages indicated a large degree of biaxial bending and this was verified by visual observations of the deformed shape of the loaded steel ribs. This is believed to have been caused by the eccentrically applied concentrated point loads developed under the extensive timber blocking, which is in sharp contrast to the uniform loading generally assumed in design. Although several of the strain gages were damaged, making it difficult to fully evaluate stresses in the rib, they proved to be a valuable tool in forewarning of high stress build ups.

Despite the large ground movements and rib deflections, the tunnel was successfully advanced through this zone at an average rate of 0.3m (1 ft) per shift. Mining of the clay was accomplished by hand with very nominal apparent overcutting. The floating crown bars did provide a safe working environment in that no cave-ins or instabilities were encountered.

Zone 3: As described previously in the discussion of Zone 2, ground deformations increased rapidly as the marine clay comprised an increasing portion of the excavated volume. Additionally, the clay showed a marked changed in its consistency, exhibiting higher water content with resulting lower shear strengths as the inclined heading tended towards the midpoint of the clay layer. Lower shear strengths in the clay created excessive loadings on the steel rib sets and instability of the open face, resulting in a substantial loss of ground into the excavation and rib deflections in excess of 30cm (12 in). Since these difficulties occurred within 8m (25 ft) of the contract limits; the remaining length was excavated by open cut methods, rather than jepordizing the safety of the tunneling crews. Furthermore, the open cut allowed removal of adjacent ribs which had exhibited deflections beyond acceptable limits.

As discussed, the clay in this zone exhibited significantly lower shear strengths than had previously been encountered. It is felt that one contributing factor to the lower shear strengths may have been the vibrations from nearby construction which could be felt in the heading.

SUMMARY AND CONCLUSIONS

The instrumentation program employed on this project was independent of contract requirements. The contractor retained an independent consulting engineering firm to study subsurface conditions, determine ground behavior and estimate ground settlements based on the floating crown bar method of excavation.

As a result, the instrumentation program which was established provided the contractor with settlement data, subsurface horizontal deflection data, and stresses in the ground support system.

In general, ground deformations and stresses on the support system were larger than anticipated, however, the floating crown bar method proved successful in advancing the heading through the difficult mixed conditions.

The data obtained alerted the contractor to potential surface and building settlements allowing adequate time for mobilization of compaction grouting equipment and implementation of his building protection programs. The instrumentation data further demonstrated the potential problems that could be encountered in the excavation of the inbound tunnel and provided the contractor with the information needed to alter his methods of excavation. It should be noted that following completion of the outbound tunnel, modifications were made to the method of excavation, and the contractor excavated the adjacent inbound tunnel with total surface settlements less than 7.5cm (3 in).

All measurement systems performed as expected with the following noteworthy points.

1. Although the "Sondex" settlement rings were designed to accommodate only 18cm (7 in) of vertical movements, comparisons between the rings and nearby Borros Anchor points indicate that the rings moved with the soil for at least

35cm (14 in). It is believed that the taped end broke free, allowing the ring to move with the grout backfill.

2. The data from the Model SM-5A strain gages was much more consistent than the data from the Model SM-2W strain gages. As stated previously, all gages were mounted on the curved flanges on the steel rings. It is believed that the sharp curvature of the mounting surfaces contributed to this fact.
3. The crimping of the inclinometer guide casing, which blocked passage of the sensing probe, greatly limited the data gathered from these important instruments. It is believed that positioning the instruments within 1m (3 ft) of the side walls is unwarranted in future similar studies.
4. The deep Borros Anchor points proved to be a very reliable and economical measuring system.

REFERENCES

Broms, B.B. and H. Bennermark, (1967). "Stability of Clay at Vertical Openings." Transactions, ASCE, Vol. 93, No. SM 1, pp. 71-94.

Cording, E.J., A.J. Henderson, Jr., W.H. Hansmire, J.W. Mahar, H.H. MacPherson, R.A. Jones, and T.D. O'Rourke, (1975). "Methods for Geotechnical Observations and Instrumentation in Tunneling," Final Report Contract No. NSF-RA-T-75-076A NTIS Paper No. PB 252-585.

Peck, R.B., (1969). "Deep Excavations and Tunneling in Soft Ground," Proceedings, Seventh International Conference on Soil Mechanics and Foundation Engineering, Mexico City, State-of-the-Art Volume, pp. 225-290.

Puza, D.E., Borggaard, R.C., and J.S. Bhore, (1981). "Mixed Face Tunnel Excavation Using Floating Crown Bar and Modified Spiling Methods," Preprint, Rapid Excavation and Tunneling Conference, San Francisco, California.

22

Increasing Productivity Through Better Contractual Arrangements & Management

Chairman: D.G. Hammond

Daniel, Mann, Johnson & Mendenhall, Baltimore, MD

Chapter 94

BETTER CONTRACTING & BETTER MANAGEMENT
FOR MAJOR UNDERGROUND CONSTRUCTION PROJECTS

by Erland A. Tillman

Associate Vice President and Project Director
Daniel, Mann, Johnson, & Mendenhall

ABSTRACT

The U.S. National Committee on Tunneling Technology under the aegis of the National Academy of Sciences has long recognized that productivity in major underground construction projects could be increased through better contracting practices and better management. Between 1974 and 1978, this Committee has prepared three reports on these subjects. This paper reviews these reports and their recommendations. It covers the extensive actions by the U.S. National Committee on Tunneling Technology to bring the recommendations to the attention of leaders in the underground construction industry and thus further their adoption and implementation. These activities are continuing. Visibility in this session will give these reports and recommendations increased exposure.

PRESENTATION

The cornerstone of the larger subject "Increasing Productivity through Better Contractual Arrangements and Management", is probably this subject "Better Contracting & Better Management for Major Underground Construction Projects" since certainly better contracting and better management provide the two areas where the greatest increase in productivity in heavy construction is achievable. Innovations in design and innovations in construction are, of course, areas which have an impact on increased productivity, but so much emphasis has already been placed on these two areas that the opportunities for further improvements there are nowhere near as great as the opportunities which exist in the better contracting and better management areas.

The need for better contracting practices in the United States in the area of heavy construction, and particularly underground construction, has been recognized for many years. It has been felt that contracting practices in the United States are inadequate even for past methods of construction and certainly constitute a serious barrier to the application of new technology and to the most economical development of underground space.

In light of this, the U.S. National Committee on Tunneling Technology acting under the aegis of the National Academy of Sciences established in 1973 a Standing Subcommittee No. 4, Contracting Practices, and charged them with making a study and developing recommendations for the improvement of contracting practices in the United States. This project was approved by the governing board of the National Research Council acting on behalf of the National Academy of Sciences and the National Academy of Engineering. It was the first step by the U.S. National Committee on Tunneling Technology, leading to 3 reports since then--all on the subject of Better Contracting and Better Management for Major Underground Construction Projects. All of these reports have been published by the National Academy of Sciences which sponsors the U.S. National Committee on Tunneling Technology.

The first of these was the report, "Better Contracting for Underground Construction" published in 1974. It resulted in 17 recommendations, all for the improvement of contracting practices in the United States. The second report, "Recommended Procedures for Settlement of Underground Construction Disputes" was published in 1977 and was developed as a follow-on report dealing in more detail with one of the recommendations of the previous report, that of "Arbitration". A third report, "Better Management of Major Underground Construction Projects", was published in 1978. This report resulted in 34 recommendations dealing with the management of any large underground construction work but with emphasis on public projects that generally involve a large number of participants and more complicated funding and approval processes than major private projects. These recommendations were grouped under six major objectives identified in the report.

These three reports are available from the National Technical Information Service, 5285 Port Royal Road, Springfield, Virginia, 22161. "Better Contracting for Underground Construction" is Accession No. PB 236 973; "Recommended Procedures for Settlement of Underground Construction Disputes" is Accession No. PB 272 964/AS; and "Better Management of Major Underground Construction Projects" is Accession No. PB 290 855/AS.

Before proceeding with the discussion of these reports produced by the U.S. National Committee on Tunneling Technology, it should be noted that there are also others who are concerned about the broad subject of better management of construction projects. The

Committee on Management of Urban Construction Programs of the National Research Council Building Research Advisory Board has recently completed a study on this subject. This study has resulted in a two-volume report entitled "Management of Urban Construction Programs" published in 1980.

The first report, "Better Contracting for Underground Construction", was the result of the activities of Standing Committee No.4-Contracting Practices. The subcommittee headed by A. A. Mathews, then president of A. A. Mathews, Inc., was composed of 24 members. It had the assistance of two consultants, Solomon Ribakoff, a lawyer highly qualified in construction contract law, who is presenting a paper at this conference entitled "European vs. United States Construction Contracting Practices" which discusses Increasing Productivity from that aspect, and Charles F. Palmetier, an engineer, highly qualified in construction engineering. Evidence of the interest in which this study was held by the engineering and construction industry was the fact that it was supported by five federal government agencies: the National Science Foundation--Research Applied to National Needs (RANN); Department of Transportation--Office of the Secretary; Urban Mass Transportation Administration; Bureau of Reclamation; and Corps of Engineers. It was also supported in part by nine private organizations: the General Contractors Association of New York, Inc.; Brown & Root, Inc.,; Gates & Fox Company; Greenfield Construction Company; Al Johnson, Construction Company; Traylor Brothers, Inc.; S&M Constructors, Inc.; Morrison-Knudsen, Inc.; and S. A. Healy Company.

The project was conducted by means of an intensive study of United States and foreign contracting practices conducted over a period of 9 months. The study was followed by a workshop conference review and analysis of the findings that resulted in the comprehensive report. The consultants guided and assisted by members of Standing Subcommittee No. 4 prepared a questionnaire and other documents for the systematic interrogation of qualified people in all sectors of tunneling and underground construction, both in the U.S. and Europe. Previous experience in construction contracting analysis, particularly the experience of the construction study group of the Commission on Government Procurement and the General Services Administration Consultant Group, was considered in designing the interview documents. The questionnaire was mailed to organizations and individuals representing all segments of the underground construction community and was followed by personal calls from members of the subcommittee. In addition, many experienced people in the United States and in selected foreign countries were personally interviewed by the construction engineering and contract law specialists.

On the basis of the analysis of data and information obtained from the replies to the questionnaire and from personal interviews, the specialists drafted proposed recommendations for improved contracting systems. These recommendations were reviewed and approved or modified, both individually and in workshop conference, by members of the subcommittee and by representatives of other owners, contractors, engineers, lawyers, educators, and contract managers from all sectors of the community interested in tunneling and underground work. Thus a cross section of the views of expected users of the recommendations directly influenced the conduct of the study and the preparation of the report and the recommendations.

The 17 recommendations for improvement of United States contracting practices as contained in this report are summarized as follows:

RIGHTS-OF-WAY, PERMITS, AND OWNER-FURNISHED MATERIALS, PLANT, AND EQUIPMENT. With certain exceptions, the owner should obtain all necessary rights-of-way of a permanent nature and those required for temporary construction, and the contractor should obtain all those associated with his own facilities and equipment. Permanent materials, plant, and equipment to be incorporated in the work should continue usually to be furnished by the contractor, but in certain circumstances the owner should furnish some items.

DISCLOSURE OF ALL SUBSURFACE INFORMATION, PROFESSIONAL INTERPRETATIONS, AND DESIGN CONSIDERATION. All factual subsurface data, professional interpretations thereof, and design considerations thereby raised should be made available to bidders, but with a careful distinction drawn between factual data and interpretation or opinion.

DISCLAIMERS. Whether or not a changed-conditions clause is included in the contract, disclaimers of responsibility for factual data provided should not be made.

CHANGED CONDITIONS (DIFFERING SITE CONDITIONS). A changed-conditions clause (preferably with wording similar to the Federal Differing Site Conditions clause) providing, in essence, for assumption by the owner of the risk concerning unknowns in subsurface physical conditions, should be included in all contracts for underground construction.

EXTRAORDINARY WATER PROBLEMS. Special contractual provision should be made to provide for the contingency of water problems.

TYPES OF CONTRACTS. Under certain circumstances, a cost-reimbursable type of contract is strongly indicated, and this type of contracting should be considered for greater use in underground construction.

BIDDER PREQUALIFICATION. Recommended.

BID PRICING. Improvements are recommended in the selection of bid items, so that contractors will not need to unbalance bids to obtain early recovery of capital investment, and to provide, in the contract as awarded, for possible variations that may be required in the work.

ALTERNATIVE BIDS. Consideration should be given to adoption of a procedure whereby bidders would be permitted to submit alternative bids, provided that the plans and specifications are also bid as advertised. Arguments are presented for and against this recommendation.

ESCALATION. For contracts that will take over 18 months to complete, a provision should be included for the owner to share escalation in the cost of labor, permanent installed equipment, and materials enumerated in the contract.

WRAP-UP INSURANCE. For large, multicontract projects in urban areas where exposure to third-party-liability claims exists, procurement of owner-furnished wrap-up insurance should be considered. Arguments for and against this type of insurance program are presented.

TUNNEL SUPPORT AND ADJACENT SUPPORT SYSTEMS. The owner and engineer should accept responsibility for the design of permanent tunnel support and for the design of support systems for buildings and structures located within or adjacent to the project site, where the necessity for such support is inherent in the project design and where the economics justify provision of the support. Where necessity for, or economics of, support is doubtful, the contractor should be given the responsibility for design and provision of such support as he may determine to be necessary or desirable. The contractor should, in any event, be responsible for design and provision of initial support inherent in his construction method. Where the performance of initial tunnel support is critical to the project, the owner and engineer may design it or may specify minimum criteria for the contractor's design.

CHANGE NEGOTIATIONS. Recommendations are made for inclusion of certain bid items and specification provisions so that effort and time now devoted to negotiation of contract price adjustments for changes can be substantially reduced.

VALUE ENGINEERING. Recommended for inclusion in all construction contracts.

PUBLICATION OF ENGINEER'S ESTIMATE. The engineer's estimate should be disclosed by public agencies with the opening of bids, and if there is a limit on the amount available for contract award, whether for a public or private project, it should be announced in the invitation for bids.

CONTRACTOR FINANCING COSTS. Provision should be made in the contract for contractors to be promptly reimbursed for the cost of premiums for bonds required, mobilization expense, and cost of permanent materials. The amount withheld as retained percentage should be kept to the minimum considered necessary to protect the owner against contracting default or procrastination.

ARBITRATION. An industry-wide system of arbitration with qualified arbitrators is proposed.

Following the publication of the report, "Better Contracting for Underground Construction", Standing Subcommittee No. 4, Contracting Practices, was dissolved, and a subcommittee entitled Subcommittee on Contracting Practices was established to take its place. This subcommittee continued with A. A. Mathews as chairman and was charged with giving the report of its predecessor subcommittee as wide visibility as possible and with further implementing the adoption of the recommendations of the previous report.

As part of this effort, the Subcommittee on Contracting Practices established a task group on arbitration from within the subcommittee and charged them with studying the settlement of disputes. The task group reviewed methods, other than court litigation, currently used for the settlement of disputes in the United States, particularly in the construction industry.

None of the methods currently available in the dispute--settlement process seemed suitable for settling underground construction disputes because they do not provide for participation of individuals skilled in the geotechnical issues that often cause underground construction disputes. Therefore, the task group considered it important to prepare recommended procedures for settlement of disputes and an organizational arrangement under which such procedures could be administered effectively.

The task group recommended that the American Arbitration Association be the organization through which the recommended procedures be implemented. The procedures recommended involve the establishment of a panel of highly qualified experts from which impartial advisors, mediators and arbitrators could be selected. The panel roster should be established and maintained by the American Arbitration Association and should be composed of experts suggested or approved by professional and technical organizations in the fields of mining, civil engineering, engineering geology, and contracting. The panel should be composed of two categories: Category #1 being those experts who are in a position to commit themselves to a long-term assignment whenever such an assignment is offered and accepted by them. Category #2 should be those experts who commit themselves to perform in the same manner as a Category #1 experts, except that such commitment may be only for short-term assignments. The task group then recommended five optional settlement procedures:

IMPARTIAL OR ADVISORY COMMITTEE FOR EMERGING PROBLEMS. Exceptionally large or complicated projects as well as those having unprecedented features are almost certain to encounter unexpected problems during their execution. On such projects an impartial advisor or advisory committee representing various disciplines could not only provide technical assistance but could promote cooperation between the contractor and the owner/engineer in the solution of contractual problems before they become unmanageable at job level. Parties wishing to incorporate provisions for an impartial advisor or advisors in their agreement could incorporate suitable recommended wording in their contract.

MEDIATION. Mediation constitutes the effort of an individual or individuals to assist the party in reaching a settlement of a controversy or claim by direct negotiations between or among themselves. A mediator participates in the negotiations and acts as an impartial advisor and consultant to the various parties involved. He cannot impose a settlement and can only seek to guide the parties to direct settlement between or among themselves.

MEDIATION-ARBITRATION. This method of resolving disputes involves the designation of an impartial expert called a mediator-arbitrator, either in the original contract, through mutual agreement of all parties at the beginning of the contractual relation or by selection by the American Arbitration Association. As agreed to by the parties or incorporated in the original contract, mediator-arbitrator can be given specific powers all tending to assist in the settlement of disputes.

FINAL AND BINDING ARBITRATION. Under final and binding arbitration the award of a tribunal will settle all controversies or claims arising under or relating to the contract or the breach thereof pursuant to the terms and provisions of applicable arbitration law.

NON-BINDING ARBITRATION. Under non-binding arbitration the award of the arbitrator does not legally bind the parties but may be introduced as evidence as a matter of right in any subsequent proceeding.

The report of the task group on arbitration was adopted by the Subcommittee on Contracting Practices and by the U.S. National Committee on Tunneling Technology. The project leading to this report was supported by the National Science Foundation, the Urban Mass Transportation Administration, the Federal Highway Administration, Department of Transportation-Office of the Secretary, U.S. Bureau of Mines, and U.S. Geological Survey.

The third report sponsored by the U.S. National Committee on Tunneling Technology was "Better Management of Major Underground Construction Projects". As part of the investigation done in 1973 and 1974 during the study leading to "Better Contracting for Underground Construction", management problems were looked at and it was noted that many of the problems encountered in the contracting and construction phases of underground projects resulted from actions taken in the development, pre-design, and design phases. That report called for a study to identify the procedures and practices in major projects that contribute to unnecessary increases in costs and to recommend improved procedures that would insure more efficient and economical execution of major underground construction projects. This third report therefore is a sequel to the 1973-74 study.

Following the initial report, the U.S. National Committee on Tunneling Technology continued to be concerned about the management problems in large underground projects, and when in 1976 three federal agencies requested the National Research Council to consider ways in which management of such underground projects could be improved, the U.S. National Committee on Tunneling Technology was considered the logical agency to undertake such a study. They organized a special Subcommittee on Management of Major Underground Construction Projects and assigned this study to them. The subcommittee was headed by David G. Hammond, Vice President, Daniel, Mann, Johnson, & Mendenhall. It was broadly based, consisting of owners' representatives, designers, contractors, geotechnical engineers, a management expert, a labor official, an insurance specialist, a lawyer and a geologist.

The members were selected on the basis of their knowledge and experience in planning, designing, contracting, and managing construction of underground facilities. To assure a broad balance of perspective, the members were selected from both the public and private sectors and from universities. The subcommittee consisted of 21 individuals and to assist them in conducting the study they hired two consultants with broad engineering management backgrounds. These consultants were William A. Bugge, formerly Director of Highways, State of Washington, and Franklin T. Matthias, formerly Vice President for Heavy Construction, Kaiser Engineering Company. In addition, many others in the underground construction community assisted by providing information, expert opinion, and suggestions through interviews, questionnaires and participation in a workshop. The project under which this subcommittee pursued this study was supported by the National Science Foundation, the Urban Mass Transportation Administration, and the Department of Transportation--Office of the Secretary.

The results of the subcommittee efforts was the report, "Better Management of Major Underground Construction Projects", published by the National Academy of Sciences in 1978. A second result of the subcommittee activities was a second publication entitled, "Executive Presentation--Recommendations for Better Management of Major Underground Construction Projects" also published in 1978.

The recommendations contained in this report are presented in the form of six major objectives which the subcommittee concluded were necessary to improve the management of major underground construction projects. Each of the objectives had subordinate recommendations which the subcommittee considered important to good management procedures and practices. There were a total of 34 of these recommendations. The subcommittee considered that the adoption of all of the objectives is feasible and necessary to make the maximum possible improvement in management of a major underground construction project. The recommendations are directed at major public projects which generally involve a larger number of participants than major private projects and hence are usually more complex to manage. However, most of the recommendations are considered appropriate to private projects as well. Each of the management objectives listed is followed by the recommendations which would aid in achieving it. The objectives and recommendations are listed below:

TO ESTABLISH THE PROJECT'S GOALS AND OBJECTIVES AND TO ORGANIZE THE PROJECT TO FACILITATE THEIR ACCOMPLISHMENT:

- Define project purposes, goals, and policies.
- Establish the owner's organization to direct the project.
- Determine the management structure for the project.
- Select consultants, if deemed necessary, to supplement the owner's staff.
- Retain senior consultants, if necessary, to assist the owner in reviewing major decisions.
- Act promptly to identify and solve problems.

TO PLAN THE PROJECT TO ACHIEVE THE OWNER'S OBJECTIVES:

- Establish the owner's objectives to achieve project purpose.
- Make realistic cost estimates.
- Obtain public and political acceptance of the project.
- Establish an understanding with agencies and organizations likely to be involved.
- Expedite approval of the Environmental Impact Statement (EIS).
- Establish the plan for financing the project.
- Obtain firm financial commitments for funding the project.

TO ACHIEVE EFFECTIVE DESIGN ORGANIZATION, SUPERVISION, AND ACCOUNTABILITY:

- Organize and coordinate project design.
- Review designs to assure effective satisfaction of project goals and objectives in a cost effective way.
- Freeze design criteria early.

TO ACHIEVE EFFECTIVE CONSTRUCTION METHODS, PROCEDURES, AND SUPERVISION:

- Plan contract packages for efficiency and economy.
- Minimize urban disruptions.
- Establish problem solving procedures.
- Develop a labor relations plan to assure continuity of work and to avoid labor disputes.
- Establish sound contracting procedures.
- Establish dispute settlement procedures.
- Set up a review board to assist in the settlement of construction contract disputes.

TO ACHIEVE SOUND MANAGEMENT OF THE PROJECT:

- Establish and adhere to a realistic budget.
- Establish and adhere to realistic schedules.
- Adopt sound management and financial reporting systems.
- Exercise strict control of expenditures.
- Grant agencies should revise practices to permit the project management to exercise appropriate authority.
- Prepare a comprehensive risk and liability plan.
- Establish adequate real estate acquisition organization and procedures.
- Foster morale and productivity by strong leadership.

TO ACHIEVE SUCCESSFUL START-UP OF THE PROJECT:

- Select key operations and maintenance personnel early.
- Prepare operations plans early.
- Allow ample time for a thorough testing program prior to scheduled operation.

The U.S. National Committee on Tunneling Technology has realized that the value of these three reports is dependent upon their visibility; i.e., the degree to which owners, engineers, and contractors, everyone who is involved in major heavy construction, are knowledgeable concerning the reports and are willing to follow the recommendations contained in them. Achieving this is no easy task. All too often the people who participate in these studies end up talking to each other with those outside the circle knowing very little about the studies. Also, as time passes, the studies tend to be forgotten. For this reason, the National Committee has continued to have a subcommittee whose primary mission has been to spread knowledge of these reports.

Following the publication of the initial report, a Subcommittee on Contracting Practices was established to work on the implementation of this report. It was that subcommittee which developed the second report, and it was also charged with implementing it after its publication. When the third report was published in 1978, the subcommittee currently headed by Winfield O. Salter, Senior Vice President, Parsons Brinckerhoff Quade and Douglas, Inc., was renamed as the Subcommittee on Contracting and Management Practices and was charged with furthering the implementation of all three of the reports.

The initial Subcommittee on Contracting Practices prepared a printed executive presentation on the recommendations contained in the initial report, "Better Contracting for Underground Construction". In addition, it prepared executive presentations which were given for officials of government agencies and others concerned with planning and developing projects for urban underground transportation. During 1976 three presentations were given in Chicago, Atlanta, and Los Angeles, which were widely advertised through the founding societies and were well attended. In addition, a relatively high level presentation was given to the heads of various government agencies in Washington. The subcommittee also endeavored to publicize the initial report by means of a questionnaire which was sent to a mailing list of top level officials of federal, state and local agencies doing heavy underground construction. This questionnaire elicited information concerning knowledge of the report and the degree to which the recommendations contained in it were being adopted. While the response to the questionnaire was good, it was evident that additional selling of the report is needed.

Those people who were involved in the preparation of the initial report and who are in senior positions where they can influence contracting practices have done quite well at implementing the report's recommendations. Informal information from them indicates that they are pleased with the results. The problem is that they are only a small percentage of the people nationwide who are in senior positions in agencies involved in heavy construction. It is this large number of top level people that need to be reached with information concerning the reports, its recommendations, and the benefits to be achieved by adopting them.

Following the completion of the second report, "Recommended Procedures for Settlement of Underground Construction Disputes", the subcommittee concentrated its efforts on providing the American Arbitration Association with names of experts which the subcommittee considered qualified to be members of the panel called for in the report.

Now that the third report, "Better Management of Underground Construction Projects", has been published, the Subcommittee on Contracting and Management is in the process of preparing new questionnaires covering each of the three reports. These questionnaires will be sent to an extensive mailing list of key officials in agencies performing or about to perform heavy underground construction. In addition to queries about knowledge of the reports and the degree to which their recommendations are being implemented, the questionnaires will also provide information on how to obtain copies of the reports if they are not available to the addressees receiving the questionnaires. As an added effort, the subcommittee is concentrating its efforts to obtain places on founders' societies and other engineering oriented organization programs.

Through these efforts it is hoped that these three reports will become more widely known and that the recommendations contained in them will be more widely adopted. The importance of this seems paramount since the recommendations contained in these reports represent the best thinking of a very, very large cross section of the entire heavy underground construction industry.

Chapter 95

EUROPEAN vs. UNITED STATES CONSTRUCTION CONTRACTING PRACTICES

by Sol Ribakoff

Attorney, Encino, California

Lecturer, California State University at Northridge

In 1973, the Subcommittee on Contracting Practices, U. S. National Committee on Tunneling Technology, National Academy of Sciences, under the able chairmanship of A. A. Mathews, Engineering Consultant, now residing at Kaunakokai, Hawaii, undertook the task of developing recommendations for improving the performance of underground construction work, reducing the costs of such work and minimizing the adverse atmosphere in which owners and contractors were performing their respective functions. The author of this paper and C. F. Palmetier, a highly qualified engineer, were thereupon appointed as staff assistants to the Subcommittee, to conduct a study of existing practices and relationships in Western Europe and in the United States, to formulate recommendations, for consideration by the Subcommittee and the participants in a future workshop, as to desirable improvements in United States contracting practices and relationships.

The study, conducted during 1973 and 1974, involved personal interviews of a total of 162 owners, engineers, contractors, lawyers, and educators throughout the United States and in 7 European countries, the analysis of 178 replies to questionnaires sent to individuals and firms involved directly or indirectly in construction, and a workshop, near Napa, California, attended by 53 representatives of all segments of the construction community. The resulting report, entitled "Better Contracting for Underground Construction", was submitted by the Subcommittee to the National Academy of Sciences, which approved its publication in 1974 by the National Technical Information Service. It may be obtained from that Service at Springfield, Virginia, 22161, as Accession No. PB-236 973.

It was recognized during the course of the study that while contracting practices and owner-contractor relationships were the cause of a number of serious problems they were not the sole cause. In addition to the need for improvements, it became apparent that there was a need, of equal importance, to develop and "sell" better management practices upon the part of the owner. As covered hereinbelow, another Subcommittee addressed itself to the problems in that area.

Following issuance of the "Contracting Practices" report, an Ad Hoc committee of the Subcommittee on Contracting Practices conducted a further study for the purpose of developing dispute settlement procedures which might be utilized as an alternative to court litigation. The study resulted in a report entitled "Recommended Procedures for Settlement of Underground Construction Disputes" which was published in 1977. It is available from the National Technical Information Service, as Report No. PB 272 964/AS. A variety of settlement procedures are described in the Report, viz; Impartial or Advisory Committee for Emerging Problems, Mediation, Mediation-Arbitration, Final and Binding Arbitration and Non-Binding Arbitration. An appropriate contract clause is included in the Report for use as to the particular procedure selected.

In 1976, the Subcommittee on Management of Major Underground Construction Projects, U. S. National Committee on Tunneling Technology, was asked to develop a set of guidelines that could be used by owners to advance management efficiencies and construction economics. As a part of such endeavor, the Subcommittee was requested to develop a descriptive model of a hypothetical urban underground construction project that could be used to examine the ways that current procedures and practices influence the responsiveness, schedules, and costs of underground projects.

The Subcommittee, under the chairmanship, first, of J. Donovan Jacobs, Chairman, Jacobs Associates, San Francisco, California, and, subsequently, of David G. Hammond, Vice President, Daniel, Mann, Johnson & Mendenhall, Baltimore, Maryland, conducted an extensive study and developed a report entitled "Recommendations for Better Management of Major Underground Construction Projects". It is available from the Information Service above referred to, as Accession No. PB 290 855/AS.

The recommendations set forth in the three reports above identified are reviewed in considerable detail in a paper which is being presented at this convention, entitled "Better Contracting and Better Management for Major Underground Projects", by Erland A. Tillman, Associate Vice-President, Daniel, Mann, Johnson & Mendenhall. His background of Subcommittee membership and, particularly, his contribution to the recommendations contained in the reports, eminently qualify him to present a paper on the subjects indicated.

The study of the subject to which the present paper is addressed — European as contrasted with United States construction contracting practices, provided the basis for certain of the recommendations made in the "Better Contracting" report, and were at least of background assistance to those who participated in the "Better Management" study and report. The study as to contracting practices involved personal interviews of owners, contractors and engineers, both in Europe and in the United States and analysis of responses to written questionnaires, as above mentioned. The information received is set forth below, in summary fashion, only. Those interested in a very detailed presentation of the information, including the names of the respondents to questionnaires, as well as the names of those who participated in the workshop, are referred to Appendices 3 to 6, inclusive, of the "Better Contracting" report.

SUMMARY OF PREVAILING EUROPEAN CONTRACTING PRACTICES

In European countries, contracting practices utilized vary from one country to another and even within a country. To some extent, however, certain practices prevail within all countries and are therefore worthy of note. These practices are discussed in detail in Appendix 5 to the "Contracting Practices" report, and are here merely summarized as follows:

. Except in England, consulting engineers are not extensively utilized by owners in the planning of projects and in the preparation of contracts, including drawings and specifications. The same may be said of the monitoring of contract performance and the making of decisions concerning contractor claims.

. Potential contractors are prequalified, i.e., the qualifications and experience of their management personnel, their financial capacity, equipment availability, and their past record of work performance and claims submissions have been investigated. With respect to claims submissions, owners are particularly interested in a potential contractor's past record of resort to arbitration and court litigation.

. Contractors that are found to have satisfactory records in the matters mentioned are placed on a list of qualified bidders, the selection procedure not generally being open to public scrutiny.

. Contractors are preselected for invitation to bid by a two-step procedure. First, they are placed on a prequalified list. Second, a specific number of contractors is selected, from the list, to receive an invitation to bid; however, all on the list may be invited.

. Bidders are, in general, permitted and even invited to submit an alternative design, provided that they fulfill the following requirements:

—A bid is submitted for performance of the job as advertised, so that the owner will have a comparable basis for evaluating all bids received.

—Any alternative proposed must be accompanied by detailed plans and specifications, together with the bidder's written justification for adoption of the alternative. The bidders must also include a bid price schedule covering the alternative submitted, and must be prepared to support his prices for an alternative with his detailed cost estimate.

. Although the attachment of qualifications and restrictions on the bid may be prohibited by the owner, and is certainly discouraged, contractors are, as a practical matter, allowed to attach such qualifications, and qualified bids are considered for award of a contract. These qualifications on the bid usually affect one or more of the following factors: quality, quantity, price or time of performance. Although the owner has the option of rejecting any qualified bid, he will negotiate with such a bidder and with others whose bids are within reach of award. Following such negotiations he will award the contract on the basis of the best price for the job as modified by any alternatives and qualifications that he has accepted.

. Bids are, in general, opened privately, and negotiations may then be conducted with the low apparent bidder and with other bidders, covering bid prices, alternatives, and qualifications on bids. It need hardly be mentioned that this particular procedure represents a radical difference from United States contracting practice, except for jobs awarded by some private owners in the United States.

. An arbitration clause is generally included in the contract, sometimes by requirement of national law. In several countries, however, inclusion of an arbitration clause is specifically prohibited by the national law.

. Contractors are reluctant to resort to arbitration and especially to court litigation because this usually results in their removal from the list of qualified contractors. In any event, the contractor who resorts to such means for collecting on claims acquires the reputation of being a "hard head".

. In one of the countries visited, subsurface conditions are generally thoroughly investigated by owners. The results of this investigation, including interpretations of the basic data, are furnished to bidders more frequently than they are in the United States. The practice varies greatly, however, from country to country and even within a country.

. Owners generally assume the risk concerning changed subsurface conditions.

Owners and contractors appear to work more as a team than they do in the United States, first, because both are reluctant to force a dispute to resolution by arbitration, particulary by court litigation, and, second, because contractors who propose alternatives have an incentive to make them work, whereas owners who adopt them have a stake, at least as far as their reputations are concerned, in their success. As a result, when an alternative has been proposed and adopted, both contractor and owner have a mutual interest in its success. It appears, however, that this relation between contractor and owner is deteriorating, at least compared with the climate that existed a decade ago. The reason given was that stiffer competition is resulting in lower prices, with consequent greater emphasis being placed by contractors on the collection of claims. Another reason, although not as often cited, is that the advent of the tunnel boring machine has resulted in the situation, today, wherein the contractor who encounters difficulties in underground excavation finds himself in a much more serious position in advancing the tunnel that if he had been proceeding by use of conventional methods. This is because a contractor who employs a tunnel boring machine has placed all his eggs in one basket. Consequently, if a changed condition is encountered with a tunnel boring machine, the contractor is much more likely to persevere in a claim, because the additional costs will usually be substantially higher than those incurred when using a conventional method. Despite all these considerations, and on the basis of reports of those people interviewed, the relation between owner and contractor in Europe is still much more conducive to teamwork. Among other beneficial effects of this relationship, it results more often in negotiated settlement of disputes than is the case in the United States.

SUMMARY OF EXISTING UNITED STATES CONTRACTING PRACTICES

. Public agencies, both federal and state, and private owners almost invariably issue contract documents that include detailed plans and specifications, often prepared by engineering organizations. Public agencies usually issue these to all contractors who express an interest as a result of public notices. In the private sector, bidders are usually prequalified; their qualifications to perform the work are investigated and approved before the bidding documents are issued to them.

. The plans and specifications are prepared either by engineers directly employed by the owner (normally the situation with public agencies engaged in a substantial and continuing program of construction) or by an engineering organization engaged by the owner for this purpose. The owner's staff engineers or the engineering organization will perform or secure subsurface investigations, analyze the results or have them analyzed by engineering geologists, and prepare designs, plans and specifications, cost estimates, and performance-time schedules for construction. Staff engineers or separate engineering organization will be employed to perform management and administrative functions on behalf of the owner. These tasks will be in connection with construction performance and the evaluation and determination of the validity of contractor claims for additional money or time for performance. It is obvious that the engineer serves a vital purpose in connection with the accomplishment of the construction project. It may not be as obvious that the expertise and fairness with which he performs the variety of functions indicated will often determine whether the contract will be performed properly and as scheduled, at the best cost to the owner, and with a reasonable profit to the contractor.

. In the invitation to bid, prospective bidders are notified of the form of contract (usually firm-fixed-price) that will be awarded, and are provided with the following documents:

—General contractual provisions, which are included by the owner in all construction contracts of the type named in the invitation.

—Special provisions applying particularly to the specific project being advertised for bids.

—Technical specifications and plans or drawings, which, depending on the particular circumstances involved, have been developed in differing amounts of detail for the particular project.

. The following requirements are either set forth in the invitation to bid or apply as a matter of law:

—Public agencies will require that sealed bids be submitted, accompanied by a bid bond or cash deposit to guarantee execution of the contract documents by the successful bidder. In the private sector, however, bid bonds are seldom required.

—All bids are publicly opened by public agencies at the time and date specified in the invitation. At that time, bid prices are announced with the engineer's estimate, and the bids are immediately made available for inspection by the public. Private owners very seldom open bids publicly, publish the engineer's estimate, or make bids available for public inspection.

—All public agencies and most private owners require that the bid be responsive to the invitation, i.e., that it must not be qualified or restricted concerning quality, quantity, price, or time for performance of the work.

—After bid opening, the low bidder must satisfy the owner, if he has not already done so, that he is responsible, i.e., has a satisfactory record of performance of like work, and the management capability, financial strength, and equipment availability to assure timely performance of the job as specified.

—Award by public agencies is made to that responsible, i.e., qualified bidder who submits the lowest responsive bid. A responsive bid is defined as one that proposed to perform the work in strict accordance with the contract terms and provisions, plans, and specifications as issued, i.e., without qualification as to price, quality, quantity, or time for performance. Private owners are not bound by any such legal requirements concerning acceptability of bids.

—On award of contract, the contractor must, in public agency contracts, furnish performance and payment bonds in the amounts called for in the invitation to bid. Private owners will normally make no such requirement if they have prequalified and preselected bidders for invitation to bid.

United States practice has some aspects that are unquestionably desirable, others that are at least open to question, and still others that appear to be undesirable, as follows:

. Compared with a system used in European countries in which contractors are preselected for invitation to bid, there is little or no opportunity under the United States system for the exercise of favoritism in the bidding stage. This is, of course, desirable.

. The United States system, at least as employed by public agencies, results in the receipt of a greater number of bids than is the case in any other bidding system studied. There are both desirable and undesirable aspects in this situation. It is to the nation's benefit to secure the maximum number of contractors who have a background of experience in the ever-increasing program of underground construction works in the United States, and the first necessity for a background of experience is to have the opportunity to obtain it. On the other hand, it is difficult to justify elimination of the bidder who has submitted the low bid, and who can comply with the bonding requirements, although one or more of the following factors are unsatisfactory: past record of performance, demonstrated inclination to seek extra reimbursement through litigation, existing management capability, financial strength, or equipment availability. Although final cost to the owner has every prospect of being greater than if award were made to another, more acceptable, bidder, it is not practical to demonstrate that another bidder could do the work better or more economically.

. Because more contractors are contending for public-agency jobs, more competition, closer pricing, and hence, lower bid prices result than in any other system studied. It is questionable, however, whether the strong competition engendered by this process always fosters good work, timely performance, and the best final price to the owner.

. No opportunity is afforded to bidders in the public sector to submit an alternative design, even for a portion of the work advertised. This appears to be undesirable since the benefits of innovative designs and techniques that might be proposed by such alternatives are frequently lost. It is true that, after award, the contractor may present an alternative or alternatives through a value engineering proposal, but this does not give the owner the benefit of receiving all likely alternatives prior to award. Consequently, the tremendous fund of ingenuity and experience of construction contractors in the United States is not completely channeled toward the submissions of possibly useful improvements in the owner's design when such improvements might be considered and reflected in the cost of the job.

. Compared with the relation in European countries, less incentive exists under United States practices for contractor and owner to work together as a team in the accomplishment of the project and in the settlement of disputes without resort to litigation. The contractor who obtains a public contract in the United States does not feel that his record of cooperation in solving problems that may involve both design and construction aspects and his record of claims submissions will affect his qualifications to bid on future jobs. Very simply, he proceeds, with considerable and well-placed confidence, on the assumption that he will be awarded a contract if his bid is the lowest and complies with the bonding requirements. On the other side of the coin, contract documents almost invariably contain provisions that are partial to the owner. Owners continue to insert such provisions, and even strengthen them, on the theory that contractors will be sufficiently eager for business to accept them. Also, there appears to be less incentive here than in European countries for both contractors and owners to settle claims short of litigation. The result is an adversary atmosphere with consequent expenditure by owners, consulting engineers, and contractors alike, of too much time and money in the administration of contracts, particularly in the settlement of claims. The effect is to waste talent and money, and the general public eventually absorbs the cost. Projects are not completed as quickly as possible, and owners, engineers, and contractors are forced to devote the time and attention of top management personnel to the resolution of controversies before administrative boards or in the courts. This is an obviously undesirable aspect of contracting in the United States.

CONCLUSION

I suggest that a conclusion which can properly be drawn from the studies above described, and one which has not been sufficiently emphasized, is that a successful contract, for both owner and contractor, is the product of a marriage between good contracting practices and good management organization. A contract which fails to distribute construction risks equitably will breed an adversary relationship with the result that the owner's management, both field and home office, and their opposite numbers in the contractor's camp, will be occupied too much of the time in prosecuting or defending against claims, with inevitable adverse effect upon job progress. Conversely, a contract which does distribute the risks equitably but which is poorly managed by the owner, will also breed an adversary relationship, with the same result.

It makes sense, then, for owners, engineers and contractors to evaluate their existing practices in the light of what others are doing, both in Europe and the United States, and to adopt such of the recommendations, contained in the three reports, as appropriate to their contracting position. Since owners write the contracts and therefore make the decisions as to what goes into them, and since they establish the management teams, it follows that we shall see major improvements in contracting practices, dispute settlement procedures and owner management organization to the extent that owners recognize existing inequities in the drafting of contracts, and existing deficiencies in management organization, and set about doing what is necessary to correct both.

In sum, better contracting and better management go hand-in-hand. To borrow words from an old song: "You can't have one without the other".

Chapter 96

A NEW APPROACH TO THE MANAGEMENT AND EXECUTION OF MAJOR PUBLIC WORK PROJECTS

Richard Gallagher and Russell K. McFarland

Manager/Chief Engineer SCRTD Metro Rail Project
Urban Mass Transportation Administration

INTRODUCTION

The Southern California Rapid Transit District has commenced Preliminary Engineering for an 18-mile Metro Rail Project. This initial line will consist of approximate 36 miles of single track tunnel and 16 subsurface stations. The estimated cost of $1.2 Billion in 1978 dollars, places it in the category of a major public works project.

During the planning phase of this project, particular attention was paid to the National Academy of Science Reports, "Better Contracting for Underground Construction" (1974), "Better Management of Major Underground Construction Projects" (1978), and "Management of Urban Construction Programs" (1980). The improved transportation service that this project will furnish the Los Angeles Metropolitan Area will result in significant benefits that will add immensely to the economic well being of the community-which is one of Webster's definitions of improved productivity.

RAPID TRANSIT PROJECT BACKGROUND

Rapid Transit studies have been going on in the Los Angeles area since 1925. In 1968 and 1974, sales tax ballot issues were not adopted by the electorate of the County mainly because the preponderous of County voters are outside the City of Los Angeles.

In 1974, the District was funded by UMTA to evaluate some 16 transit corridors in the metropolitan region. Representatives of all interested local and state agencies were invited to, and did, participate in a Rapid Transit Advisory Committee (RTAC). Over the next year and a half, the RTAC group evaluated the 16 corridors and some 64 combinations or portions of those corridors for both rail and bus transit. The top-rated rail corridors was one which extended from the westerly end of the San Fernando Valley easterly and southerly through the heart of the downtown region and on down to the Harbor area.

Further detailed evaluation and interagency discussion led to the adoption in September, 1976 of a 4-Element Regional Transit Development Program (something for everybody) consisting of:

1. Transit (Bus) System Managment Improvements with nominal funds.

2. A Free Transit Program to be funded by Cal-Trans and the FHWA.

3. A Downtown People Mover Demonstration Project to be funded by UMTA with the City and State supplying the local funds.

4. An initial segment of rail rapid transit - approximately the center one-third of the the First Priority Rail Corridor selected in 1974, to be funded by UMTA and State Proposition 5 funds (i.e., funds derived from gasoline sales tax) as approved by the voters of the County in June, 1974.

On December 22, 1976, the Secretary, U.S. Department of Transportation, informed the Mayor of Los Angeles and the President of the SCRTD Board of his approval of Preliminary Engineering on the 4-Element Regional Transit Development Program, but with the provision that "further study of fixed guideway alternatives . . . is marited" in the corridor extending from Downtown Los Angeles to North Hollywood, on a line to be determined from a detailed study of Alternatives. Therefore, from August 1977 to May 1980, the District conducted an in-depth Alternatives Analysis/Environmental Impact Study of bus and rail rapid transit options in the Regional Core.

In October of 1979, the District Board identified the "preferred alternative" as being a rail rapid transit line extending from the central district westerly along the Wilshire Corridor to Fairfax Avenue and thence northerly through Hollywood and into the San Fernando Valley.

In June of 1980, UMTA approved this proposal and authorized and funded the start of the Preliminary Engineering Phase of the Project. It is significant to note that on November 4, 1980, a 1/2¢ sales tax to provide local funds "for bus and rapid transit systems" was adopted by the electorate of Los Angeles County by a 54 percent vote, which means that in the central city areas the plurality was as high as 80 percent. This indicated that the people of the entire country and finally realized the importance of improved public transit to the economic and social health of this metropolitan region. We are hoping this recognition has not come too late.

DETAILED PROJECT DESCRIPTION

The Metro Rail Project, when placed into revenue operation, hopefully by 1990, will be the basic building block of SCRTD's integrated bus/rail metro system serving Los Angeles County. This will enable a rearrangement of bus service which not only will result in much better service, but will require some 200 fewer busses. The revamped bus service will primarily provide a feeder network to the rail rapid transit line. A map of the proposed system is shown in Figure 1.

Physical features and elements are as follows:

- Corridor - A 55 square mile areas covering Downtown Los Angeles, Wilshire, Fairfax, Hollywood and North Hollywood Districts, with an average population density of over 110000 people per square mile (over 22,000 in the denser portion).

- Technology - Standard gauge conventional rail rapid transit.

- Horizontal Alignment - Passes through or near the following points: From Union Station out Broadway and Seventh Street to Wilshire Boulevard, thence north along Fairfax Avenue through Cahuenga Pass, thence north along Vineland Avenue to a terminal at Chandler and Lankershim Streets in the San Fernando Valley.

It is significant to note that the Valley terminal is located on the right-of-way of the Southern Pacific Railroad's Burbank line which extends westerly to Canoga Park and then up to Chattsworth, travelling the heart of the entire San Fernando Valley.

- Vertical Alignment - All inbored subway, 40-200 feet underground. The feasibility of a "rolling" profile between stations to save propulsion energy and reduce braking energy losses is being evaluated. Cut-and-cover configuration will be considered for some sections of line where construction costs would so indicate.

- Grade Separation - Totally grade-separated.

- Stations - Will be mined or by cut-and-cover construction, depending on local conditions. A total of 16 stations along the corridor are presently being considered at the approximate locations set forth below. Additions to or deletions from this list may be recommended as a result of Preliminary Engineering studies.

  (1) Union Station
  (2) First and Broadway (Civic Center)
  (3) Fifth and Broadway
  (4) Seventh and Flower
  (5) Wilshire and Alvarado
  (6) Wilshire and Vermont
  (7) Wilshire and Normandie
  (8) Wilshire and Western
  (9) Wilshire and La Brea
  (10) Wilshire and Fairfax
  (11) Fairfax and Beverly
  (12) Fairfax and Santa Monica
  (13) Hollywood and Cahuenga
  (14) Hollywood Bowl
  (15) Universal City
  (16) Lankershim and Chandler

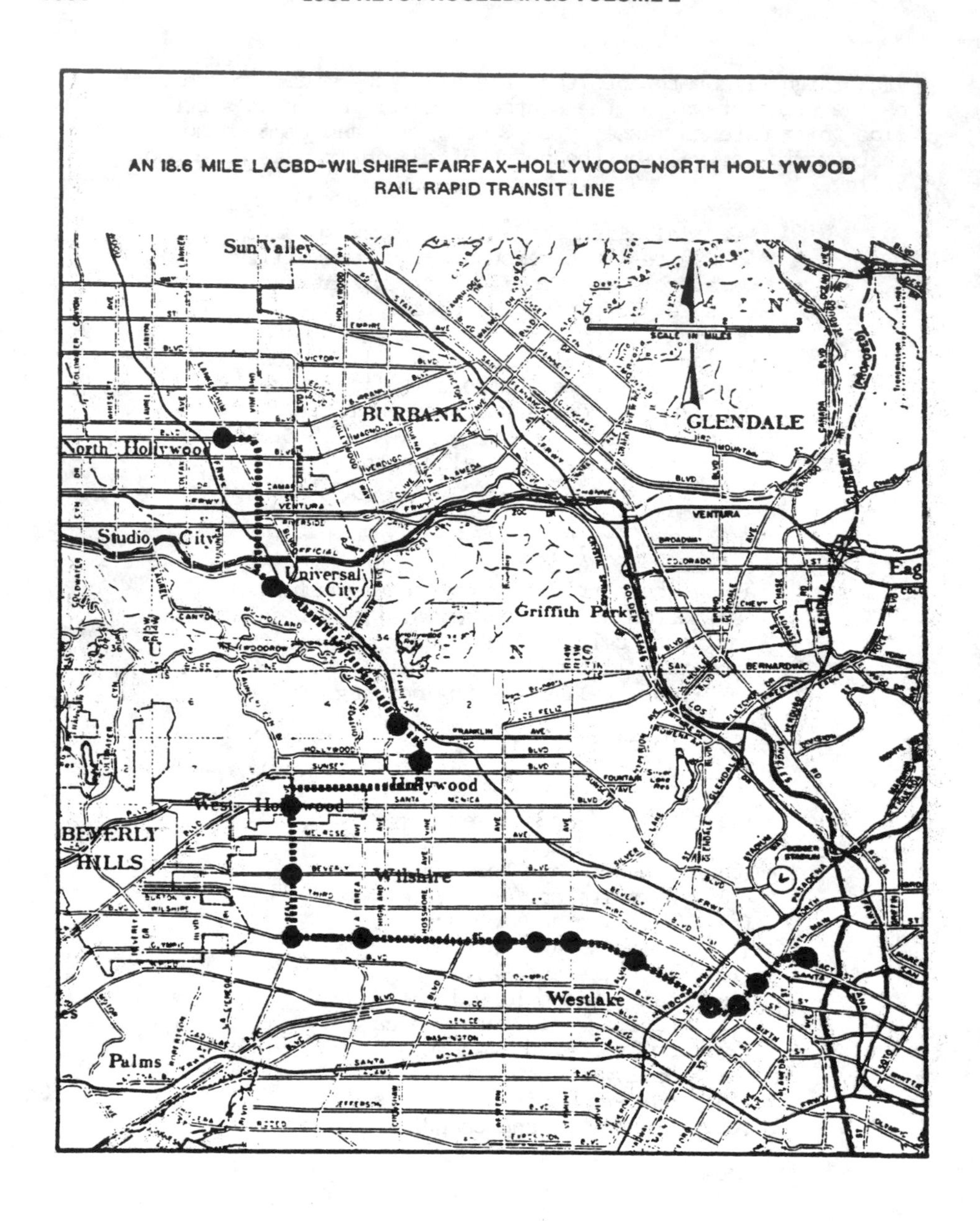
AN 18.6 MILE LACBD-WILSHIRE-FAIRFAX-HOLLYWOOD-NORTH HOLLYWOOD
RAIL RAPID TRANSIT LINE
Sun Valley
BURBANK
GLENDALE
SCALE IN MILES
N
North Hollywood
Studio City
Universal City
Griffith Park
Hollywood
West Hollywood
BEVERLY HILLS
Wilshire
Westlake
Palms
VENTURA
FRANKLIN
HOLLYWOOD
SUNSET
SANTA MONICA
MELROSE
BEVERLY
OLYMPIC
(PROPOSED)

FIGURE 1

- Yard & Shops - Two locations, main yard and repair facility in the Los Angeles Downtown area, and a minor yard located in the San Fernando Valley, adjacent to the terminal section.

- Estimated Cost - $1.2 Billion in 1978 dollars.

- Rapid Transit Vehicles - Approximately 120 rail transit cars will be required. The exact number and size are yet to be fixed. A married-pair configuration with all cars identical is likely.

- Train Control - The train control system will include trackside and train-carried equipment, route interlockings, central control and localized station control. A basic building block approach that incorporates automatic train protection, and allows for more sophisticated options as the system grows is preferred. Included in such a perferred system will be automatic train protection (ATP) throughout the system, manual train operation (MTO) and manual train supervision (MTS) assisted by automatic devices.

- Communication - The related communications network will provide for a public address system and communication between the Operations Control Center, stations and revenue vehicles. Security communications will be designed to enhance passenger safety.

- Electrification - This element includes rectifier substations and appurtenances for a complete electrification system to furnish third rail power for train propulsion. The industry standard 750V nominal will be used, with dual utility supply lines to each substation, solid state rectification and high conductivity third rail.

- Safety/Security System - Particular attention will be paid to Fire and Operational Safety and Passenger Security.

PROJECT ORGANIZATION AND MANAGEMENT

The Management Structure for this project is somewhat different than what has been used by other urban rail projects. It has been the practice of other rail properties to obtain the services of a single "Umbrella" Design Consultant, usually consisting of a joint venture, which for all practical purposes made all critical decisions, primarily because they could staff up at a much faster rate and level than the public owner agency. In our case, over the last 14 years, we have had an opportunity to study the various management structures and we now know what is needed and how best to obtain the desired results for the community, and we have an experienced staff on board, therefore, this project will be managed by the SCRTD's Metro Rail Project Staff, assisted by three General and a number of Special Consultants. Figure 2 shows the general relationship between the Project Staff and the Consultants. The three line divisions provide functional design capabilities with a General Consultant associated with each division. The Systems Engineering and Analysis Section will provide system wide criteria, coordination between the design divisions, and assure the compatability and most efficient interrelationship between all of the subsystems that make-up the Rapid Transit Project.

A key responsibility of the System Engineering and Analysis Section will be to develop a computer simulation of the proposed rail line. The simulation model will be improved in detail through the various stages of Preliminary Engineering, and will be used to examine all possible operating and configuration options available, to provide a rail system configuration which best meets the needs of the Los Angeles community.

The primary role of the Program Control Section will be to operate the project control and management information system, which includes the development and maintenance of project budget and schedules and provides current and accurate information on project progress and status. An additional role of Program Control will be to keep management aware of the exceptions or variances that are occurring in the project, especially those that are on the critical path. Program Control will take an active role in working with project personnel to develop recommendations for fixing or minimizing the impact of cost and schedule variances, which will require a constant interface with project as well as consulting personnel.

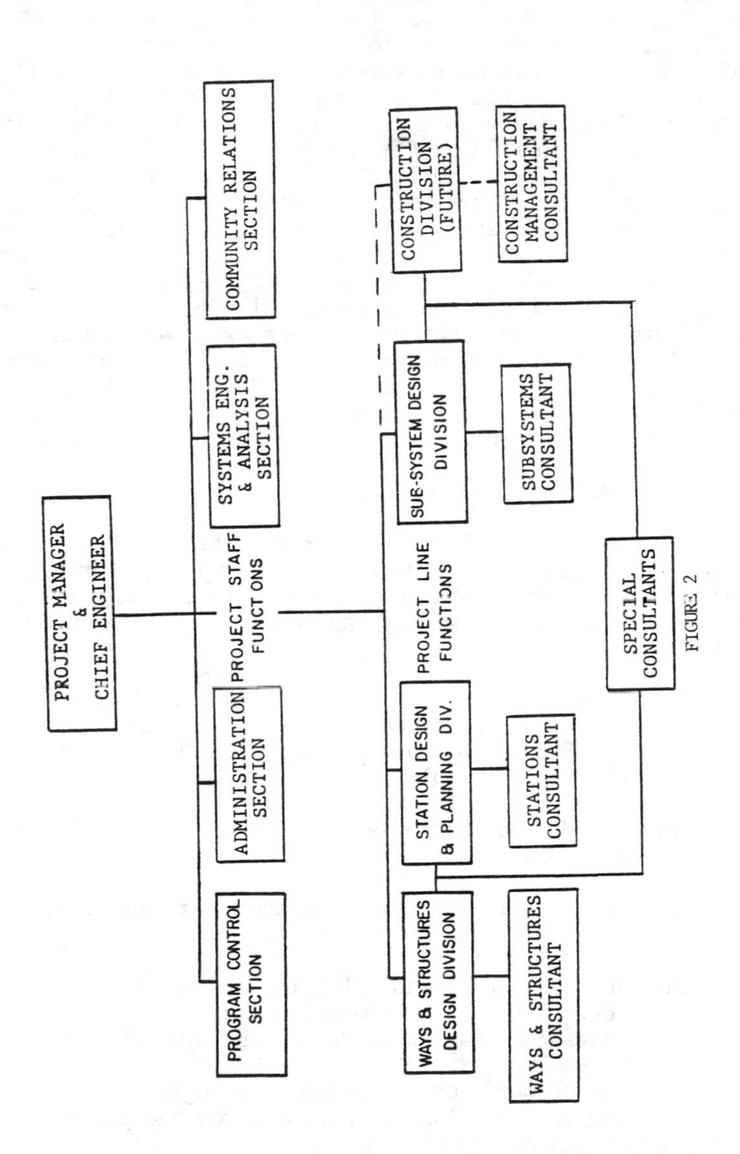
PROJECT MANAGER & CHIEF ENGINEER
PROJECT STAFF FUNCTIONS
PROGRAM CONTROL SECTION
ADMINISTRATION SECTION
SYSTEMS ENG. & ANALYSIS SECTION
COMMUNITY RELATIONS SECTION
PROJECT LINE FUNCTIONS
WAYS & STRUCTURES DESIGN DIVISION
STATION DESIGN & PLANNING DIV.
SUB-SYSTEM DESIGN DIVISION
CONSTRUCTION DIVISION (FUTURE)
WAYS & STRUCTURES CONSULTANT
STATIONS CONSULTANT
SUBSYSTEMS CONSULTANT
CONSTRUCTION MANAGEMENT CONSULTANT
SPECIAL CONSULTANTS

FIGURE 2

To effect overall design control for the project, a Board of Control woll be established, composed of the Manager of each design division, The Manager of Systems Engineering and Analysis Section, General Designs Consultants as appropriated, and chaired by the Manager/Chief Engineer of the Metro Rail Project. The function of the Board will be to establish design policy, to notify the consultants as to which design alternatives will be investigated and to monitor and control all Preliminary Engineering tasks. In addition to the Board of Control, the District, in cooperation with UMTA staff, has established Peer Review Boards, to assist in providing technical guidance. The Peer Review Boards consist of experienced key personnel from other operating transit properties, and are chaired by the Metro Rail Project Manager and the UMTA Program Manager. The Boards will meet on an as required basis during Preliminary Engineering, with membership of the Board reflecting the particular technical issues to be reviewed by the Board. With the support of these two Boards, the District staff will exercise judgment on critical issues and decisions of Metro Rail Project design. The staff will seek council from all possible sources on critical issues, but the resulting decision will be made by the project staff on behalf of the general public.

WORK PROGRAM FOR PRELIMINARY ENGINEERING

In cooperation with the Urban Mass Transportation (UMTA) Office of Transit Assistance, a detailed Preliminary Engineering Work Statement (PEWS) was generated which sets forth the tasks to be completed during Preliminary Engineering. Key features of the PEWS are:

(a) Cost estimates for the Metro Rail Project based on a completed Preliminary Engineering Program which will represent 30% overall design completion;

(b) The development of a detailed project management plan;

(c) The definition of the configuration/design alterantive to be evaluated;

(d) The evaluation and selection of the preferred system configuration that best meets the transit needs of Los Angeles;

(e) The preparation of Preliminary Engineering design, plan and estimate for the preferred configuration;

(f) The completion of a Second Phase EIS, concurrent with the completion of Preliminary Engineering.

A more detailed discussion of each of these key features of the Preliminary Engineering Work Statement follows:

A. COST ESTIMATE:

Until the development of the Preliminary Engineering Work Statement for the Metro Rail Project, UMTA had no guidelines for scoping the Preliminary Engineering effort for new rail system starts. Each new start Preliminary Engineering was funded essentially on a funds available basis. With the adoption of the UMTA Full Funding Policy, wherein a local transit property would agree to build a specified rail system at a given total cost, and agree to absorb any overruns in return for funding commitment from UMTA with minimal oversight, the need for a more accurate cost estimate became paramount. Therefore, our work statement specifies that the completed Preliminary Engineering Program would represent 30% overall design completion. To do this, UMTA agreed to provide up to $36 Million for Preliminary Engineering. With matching funds based on a 80/20 split, a total of $45 Million will be available to SCRTD for the Preliminary Engineering efforts. The State of California is providing the local funds in accordance with pre-existing legislation.

B. THE PROJECT MANAGEMENT PLAN:

The most recent National Academy of Sciences Report, "Management of Urban Construction Programs" defines in detail the need for and scope of a project management plan. The following paragraph was taken from this report:

"A written project management plan serves a multitude of management purposes. Initially, it demonstrates that the owner has analyzed the management and execution needs for a project and has considered the methods to be used and the interface problems that will be created among the various participants.

A written plan also is a mechanism for communicating the objectives of a project to all project participants (including those whose interests or roles are outside the direct performance of the project) and the methods and resources proposed to be used in meeting these objectives.

Further, the report identifies the following as the Content of Project Management Plan for an Urban Construction Program:

A. Parameters and Constraints
B. Organization and Staffing
C. Management Control System
D. Human Resources and Labor Relations Policy
E. Risk Management
F. Dispute Resolution
G. Procurement
H. Design Program
I. Real Estate Acquisition
J. Communications Program
K. Construction Program
L. Legal Requirements
M. Safety Program
N. Operation and Maintenance Interface
O. Communication Interface Management
P. Maintenance of the Plan

At the completion of Preliminary Engineering, we expect to have a Project Management Plan that will clearly meet the objectives of the National Academy of Sciences Report, and provide a precedence for other urban public works projects.

C. ALTERNATIVE CONFIGURATIONS

With the realization that the Los Angeles basin has demographic and topographic characteristics considerably different from those of other U.S. cities, it became apparent that considerable thought and analysis must be given to the operational and physical characteristics of a rapid transit system to serve the urban area.

As such, considerable effort will be expended in defining system configuration and design alternatives. For example, a "rolling" profile, wherein the vertical alignment would dip between stations, to reduce traction energy requirements, is being considered. Operational constraints may eliminate this configuration option, however, design alternatives such as this will be examined in detail, where warranted.

D. PREFERRED SYSTEM CONFIGURATION:

Once the approved alternative layouts and designs have been developed, a perferred system configuration will be selected that best meets the transit needs of the Los Angeles basin. This selection process will utilize the computer simulation model previously developed, and we will be able to demonstrate by use of this model, those system characteristics, layouts, and designs that best meet our needs.

E. PRELIMINARY ENGINEERING DESIGNS, PLANS AND COST ESTIMATES:

Once the preferred configuration has been specified, and all system and design criteria identified, design and plans will be developed to a 30% overall design completion. Some element such as stations will not be at 30% completion, however, sufficient detail will be available to provide a cost estimate with a sufficient level of confidence that the District would be willing to enter into a full funding agreement with UMTA.

F. TIERED ENVIRONMENTAL IMPACT STATEMENT:

On transit development programs prior to the Los Angeles Project, UMTA's EIS regulations specified a classic "Catch-22" situation wherein no Preliminary Engineering could be conducted on a proposed system until EIS had been completed. However, to define the environmental impacts in sufficient detail to be meaningful, a system configuration had to be defined. Hence, a great number of technical assumptions had to be made, and once documented in the EIA, they could not be changed, regardless of cost, without re-opening the EIS Fortunately, the EIS regulations have been modified such that the EIS can be tiered, or phased. The first EIS which SCRTD completed in connection with its Project Alternatives Analysis, addressed the general corridor impacts, patronage projections, and through the alternatives analysis process showed the relative cost effectiveness of various transportation improvement alternatives, and identified a preferred mode, a rail rapid transit system. With the approval of the AA/EIS/EIR, SCRTD was allowed to proceed into Preliminary Engineering, however, a key task to be preformed during Preliminary Engineering is the 2nd Tier EIS. This document will be completed at the completion of Preliminary Engineering, and contain detailed information on the transit system based on 30% overall design completion. In this manner, we hope to avoid much of the continuous litigation experienced by other urban transportation construction projects, wherein the public was unaware of the nature of specific changes to the community resulting from the construction program.

PRESENT STATUS OF THE SCRTD METRO RAIL PROJECT

Progress made to date in the start-up of the Metro Rail Project Preliminary Engineering is as follows:

- The City of Los Angeles has set all 1st order survey control points that will be needed by the project.
- A consultant has been retained to check the patronage estimates for the starter line to determine increased patronage demands on the starter line when various extensions are made in the future.
- A consultant has been retained to evaluate joint development possibilities at each of our proposed stations.
- A consultant has been retained to develop a project control plan and a management information system.

- A Board of Special Geotechnical Consultants has been retained to develop an RFP for Subsurface exploration surveys.

- We have commenced Peer Review Board Meetings. Peer Boards on System Operations, Signalling and Communications and Ways and Structures have met.

- In cooperation with the management consultant, the project staff has developed a Work-Breakdown - Structure and Network Diagram for Preliminary Engineering.

- The Project staff has developed work statements and initiated contracts with the City of Los Angeles Planning, Traffic, Police and Fire Departments.

- The Project staff has prepared and issued RFP's for a General Engineering Consultant Ways and Structures, General Engineering Consultant Subsystems, General Architectual Consultant, and a Systems Engineering and Analysis Consultant.

- The project staff is in the process of being expanded and should total 35-40 people by mid 1981.

CONCLUSIONS

A recent article in the Civil Engineering Magazine featured the Baltimore Mass Transit System, and enumerated the progress and improvement in the State-of-the-Art made during the engineering and construction of this system. We in Los Angeles expect to pick up where Baltimore left off and institute improvements in project management, in contracting practices, in construction techniques and technology and in the operating equipment used in our metro rail system. We fully expect to have the privilege to address the RETC at their bi-annual meeting in 1989, the year that the SCRTD Metro Rail System will start operations, and report to you on the innovation, progress and improvments in productivity and in the State-of-the Art brought about by the SCRTD Metro Rail Project.

Chapter 97

IMPROVEMENTS IN CONTRACTING PRACTICES AND MANAGEMENT

by William L. Barnes and Maurice Leiser

Vice President, Perkins & Will, Chicago, Illinois
(formerly Assistant General Manager, MARTA)

Detroit Area Manager, Parsons Brinckerhoff, Michigan, Inc.,
Detroit, Michigan

INTRODUCTION

The literature on project management considerations and techniques for large rail rapid transit projects in mid-1979 was fairly large and getting larger. UMTA was establishing special organizational elements to deal with the subject as it related to those properties requesting capital assistance, and comprehensive project management plans were being requested from those properties as an early step to build confidence in UMTA that the particular project could be planned, designed, and executed efficiently and effectively, thereby using critically short capital assistance funds to best advantage.

In the late 60's and early 70's, the choices of models for heavy rail construction would have been quite limited... and perhaps much simpler than was the case in 1979. One of the writers was with an agency in 1979 in the process of finalizing its organization for project implementation after several years of study and had the opportunity to review the experiences of others at length, presumably to build on the success and to try to avoid the pitfalls and failures. The properties that were surveyed all reported more or less success stories. One could only conclude that there are many ways to organize for a major transit (construction) project and that there is a great variety of viable management structures, but it seemed that chances for success were best where the executing property had prepared a comprehensive project management plan, then resolved to follow it. Perhaps more important, a commitment or prior approval had been sought from UMTA as to the validity of the project management plan, and the property was allowed to proceed without detailed prior UMTA review or approval of all specific intermediate steps. Most important, however, an early overall UMTA funding commitment had been obtained that permitted some reasonable expectation of the rate of funding, perhaps by commitment to an ultimate amount of financial support that would be forthcoming, and definitive planning could proceed.

The most notable and apparently successful property in these respects was the Metropolitan Atlanta Rapid Transit Authority (MARTA), which seemed to be a happy compromise in many respects. The management technique for the Authority had been selected early to facilitate decision-making, a comprehensive project management plan had been prepared and approved by UMTA, which eliminated the intermediate reviews and approvals by UMTA at the regional and headquarters levels that tended to retard project execution, and MARTA had a funding commitment from UMTA of a $800 million plus Federal share. Even staffing levels for the project staff had been held to compromise numbers (somewhere between the BART and WMATA levels) and a competent and experienced general consultant had been engaged and was firmly in place to manage all design and construction for the owner. (It was, therefore, professionally rewarding for one of the writers of this paper, when the Chicago Central Area Transit Project was dropped sharply in priority by a new regime in city government, to move in mid-1979 to the ongoing MARTA project to observe and participate in these management philosophies at first hand. He found a truly dynamic situation and an evolving approach to overall project management and the execution of design and construction, an attitude that had been actively in effect since the first contract.)

For some at MARTA, the amount of truth arrived on June 30, 1979. The skeptics were poised with pen and barbed tongue to attack in case of failure. But the MARTA Board, the General Manager and his staff, the general engineering consultant, the designers, constructors, and operators all beamed proudly as the U.S. Secretary of Transportation, Brock Adams, cited the beginning of an era of "class transportation" rather than "mass transportation" with the opening of the MARTA System. Six miles of the planned $4 billion, 53 mile system was opened to revenue services that day (Fig. A)...six months behind schedule, but very close to the 1975 budget. Another five mile segment was opened on schedule in late December, 1979, and more will open next winter.

Customer satisfaction has been high - the MARTA rail vehicle (Fig. B) is a superb car with smooth, quiet ride; the system is fast, efficient, safe, cheap at 50 cents to go anywhere, and has well-planned stations designed to complement the growing adjacent communities and provide clean, aesthetic, grafitti-dissuading surroundings. Early critics have become supportive, communities previously refusing to participate now wish to be included in the system, and Georgians are proud.

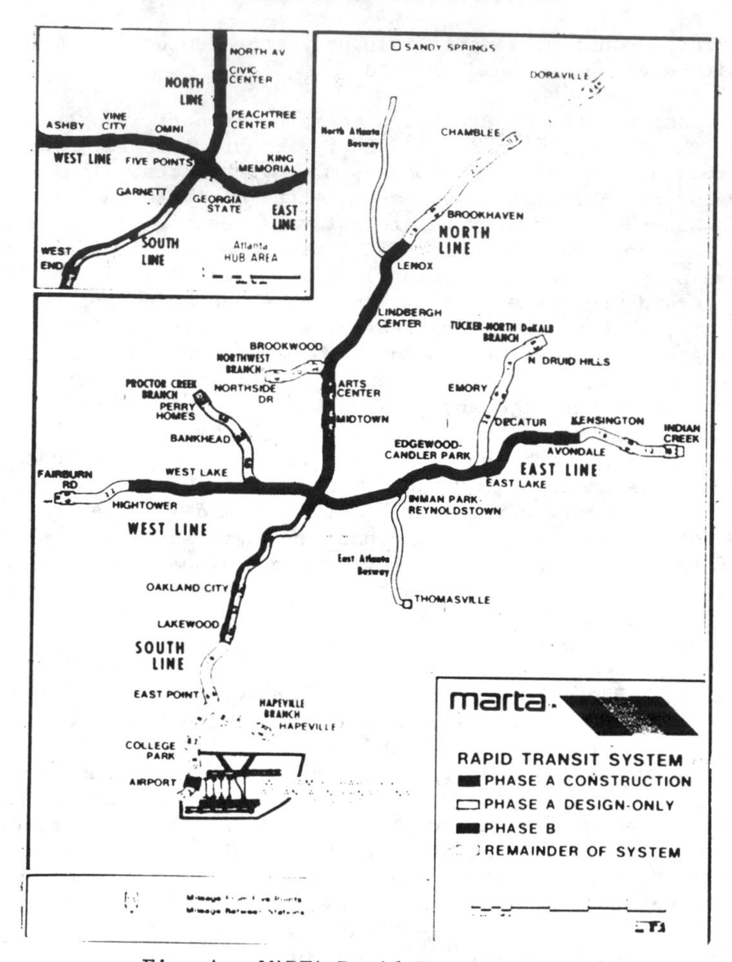

Fig. A. MARTA Rapid Transit System

Fig. B. MARTA Rail Vehicle

This is truly a success story, but the story is far from complete, and it has certainly had its full share of design problems, construction and operating dilemmas; personalities, agencies, laws, rules that affect the outcome - even villains - and scenarios that change confusingly as the story progresses. The theme, however, for MARTA and its General Engineering Consultant, Parsons, Brinckerhoff/Tudor, has been "Find a way to move ahead," and jointly they have always succeeded.

This paper gives observations as to the transition in management methods, organization structure, and contract nature, during the 5-6 years of MARTA project execution, and outlines the rationale for change in order to "move ahead," noting good and bad results.

PROJECT ENVIRONMENT

Fifteen to 20 years of planning, discussions with civic groups, businessmen, city, state, and national governmental officials finally led to a coalescing of support and eventually a Federal commitment of $800 million for the Federal share of the initial 13.7 miles (Phase A) of the system. The 53 mile rail rapid transit system, approved by voter referendum in November, 1971, called for aerial, ground level, or underground lines and stations as appropriate for grade, or as necessary to avoid congestion or preserve certain surroundings and facilities, such as historic structures, perhaps involving cut and cover or tunneling methods to achieve the necessary profile. Much of the system was aligned adjacent to various existing railroads, thereby making use of historic transportation corridors to a considerable extent.

Early commitments were made to Equal Employment Opportunity practices, to provide real opportunities for minorities and small businesses, stimulate employment, investment, growth, and dollars spent in the Atlanta area, and to upgrade facilities in the vicinity of, or associated with, the MARTA rail alignment to current standards. The MARTA Board of Directors, appointed to represent the areas to be served, guided the project and undertook considered decisions on major policy issues in these and all other areas. To actually accomplish the job, during the 5-6 years there were as many as 120 contractors working at one time, with 2500 people on site and as many as 5000 or more off site in manufacturing and design activities. Obviously, three to four times those numbers of people could also benefit in some monetary manner from the project and as evidence of its wide effects, materials and equipment have been assembled from Germany, France, Italy, Mexico, as well as the United States and Canada.

THE CHALLENGE

It is a professional juggler's challenge for public officials to balance outside interests, legalities, personalities, achieve goals mentioned previously, and still get the job done. Only idealistic engineers can wish away such influencing, frustrating, demobilizing, sometimes contributory impacts. But we learn to live within our constraints, not wish them away, and instead plan and manage our projects with both creativity and realism. We must dampen adverse program impacts by appropriate planning, permitting adequate lead time for decisions, assuring early development of acceptable criteria, educating all who have interests, developing procedures acceptable to all to assure uniformity in problem solving, providing information where needed and guidance to the uninformed, and always citing proven methods for accomplishing the job. --Then, updating all to currency.

The balancing act is shown here (Fig. C).

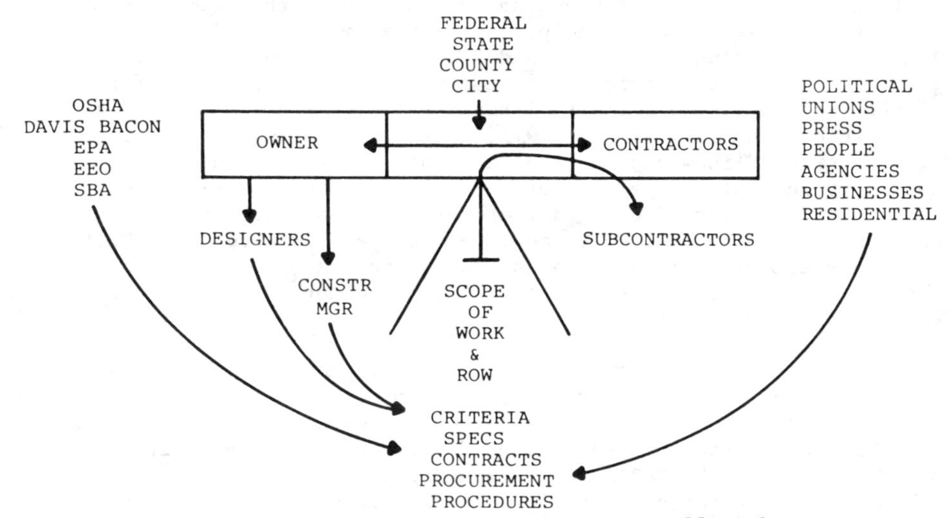

Fig. C. Balancing Problem for MARTA Officials

In MARTA's case, balance has been maintained by what has seemed to be continuous negotiation of desired changes among the participants over the years. The owner guided the designers and construction manager in observing Federal, State, County, and City laws, regulations, codes, and specified the points of interface and methods of communication. Applicable factors then were reflected in the scopes of work, right of way agreements, criteria, specifications, procurement procedures and products, safety, and hiring practices. Union positions, agreements with business interests, political groups, utilities agencies, and residential groups then also had to be reflected solidly in the fulcrum base.

Only then could appropriate guidance be provided contractors to assure the balance in the job and maintenance of progress. During construction, of course, unforeseen impacts because of changes in rules or positions or "new inspirations" could still force the situation out of balance, realizing that many of the external influences impact on either or both of the owner and contractors. Because of these factors, MARTA has tried to control the controllable and cope with the uncontrollable! Designs must be determined to be buildable. Competent materials and systems must be specified properly and procured. Complete and proper scopes and contracts must be prepared, negotiated, and arbitrated, so reasonable schedules and budgets can be set and met. By doing these things, impacts of the uncontrollable have been minimized.

MARTA SINCE 1975

How much has MARTA management improved since 1975 and what has MARTA management done? One could say that success is in the eye of the beholder. The riders see the finished facilities, measure the service, the cost, and the comfort. The government measures cost against service provided, adherence to schedule, and whether regulations were observed in the process. Businessmen consider construction adversely affecting their sales vs. longer term benefits upon completion. The Press measures all and seeks issues or headlines, good or bad. MARTA's engineers, managers, and auditors believe in self-flagellation and criticize themselves in-house for not having done it better, cheaper, and closer to schedule! However, lessons learned are hopefully retained so that the hard-learned wisdom can be spread freely to others, and that has always been the policy. Besides, MARTA management can share credit with first, Parsons, Brinckerhoff/Tudor/Bechtel for the early planning period, and with Parsons Brinckerhoff/Tudor since 1976, during the construction management phase. Actually, without such professional help, the project never would have been so successful.

CONCEPT EVALUATION

The early concept, dreamed in a dollar vacuum, was for a functional, 50 mile or so total system to be completed in just a few years. It was realized very early in the game that funding would not be unrestrained, that outside influences might upset the calculations. To meet all needs, MARTA required current - in this case, assured - dollars in a regular manner and from solid sources to develop reasonable schedules, scopes, and alternatives. Plans were scaled back initially to reflect realistic funding for Phase A, involving UMTA funding of $800 million. Phases B and C were set up for later funding, then MARTA expanded beyond Phase A with local funds from bond sales and sales taxes to take economic advantage of building early the facilities and systems contributing to the total project but located in or near Phase A territory.

CONCURRENCY

Even so, to utilize funds then available, to reduce inflationary impacts on design, construction, and procurement costs, a conscious decision was made to utilize evolutionary detailed design, on concurrency, methods. This, naturally, has resulted in some claims of significance, but project cost growth since 1975 has only been about 8.5 percent - a miraculous figure considering that only 7 percent inflation was programmed originally for procurement and construction for each year. Perhaps inflation of everything should have been planned for 10-13 percent and there would have been no difficulty with the budget.

To save time, gain the benefits of an underemployed construction industry, and turn the dream quickly into a reality to gain greater public support and additional revenue, the MARTA stations were designed and built in stages, first the shell, then the more detailed finish work. This provided the needed time for detailed design and associated construction. Single contractors were used to install systemwide items such as communications, train control, trackway, escalators, elevators, etc.

The major problems encountered, of course, were contractor project access, contractor cooperation and coordination with each other, project coordination, and the chain reaction impact of delays, either on the part of MARTA or one or two slow contractors. Use of such contracts and early bulk buying of systemwide items did achieve procurement savings and standardization not easily accomplished otherwise.

Now that about 12 miles of the system are in use and there is more breathing time and understanding, designing and contracting single-stage work has become the preferred procedure. New contractors will perform all of the shell and most of the finish work, and incorporate most of the systems, some still centrally procured, however, to assure standardization and enhance maintenance activities.

INDIVIDUAL AE'S FOR STATIONS

Another initial policy was use of a different design firm for each station. This was done to spread business opportunities, gain greater community participation, assure originality and differing appearance for each station, and gain political/public support for the MARTA system. This, of course, also has had its inefficiencies: greater individual cost rather than for one or two basic designs, a larger learning curve for multiple designers, greater administrative/management problems in overseeing multiple designs and construction of each differing type, and finally a higher construction cost reflecting uniqueness, unforeseen design corrections for each, and the need for assuring that independently installed systems will fit each station.

In the future, the plan is to utilize many of the same designers, eliminating any prohibition against repeat assignments, taking advantage of MARTA's knowledge as to which are the best, most reliable, and the cheapest for top quality.

CPFF AE CONTRACTS

In the beginning, to match the concurrency mode, design contracts had to be cost-plus-fixed-fee (CPFF). Criteria development was still under way and had to be fed into the design as it became available. Management of CPFF contracts usually requires more people, more expertise on the management staff, more money, involves less certainty of high quality work, more time, and encourages ultimate operators of the system to feed in more "nice to have" changes, sometimes at the last minute.

Happily, the policy changed in favor of lump sum design contracts, and consequently, costs have been reduced as well as numbers of management people. Design and progress are still checked at various points, but in-house concept design and preliminary engineering are performed only to the extent that a fixed price for final design can be negotiated. Now there are model stations for the designer to examine, and everyone has more experience. Inexperience and increases in the size of the MARTA staff have permitted MARTA takeover of station concept design as well as more technical design from PB/T. This is normal and was expected as the organization grew.

CONTRACT IMPROVEMENTS

Additional breathing time on the project also has led to better refinement of the language in the contracts to assure proper understanding by all, to obtain the product aimed for, to reduce the contractors' risks to the extent possible and MARTA costs as well, and to obtain compliance with EEO and small/minority business governmental regulations and MARTA's developed policy in this regard.

A truly professional project manual is now produced for each construction contract. From a computer bank, the applicable contract specifications are selected, most of which follow GSA standards and those of the Construction Specifications Institute. Redundancies are purged, the contracts are made readable, confusion is minimized, specifications used are those common to the industry, and inapplicable provisions do not appear. In addition, through systems engineering methods, the required reliability, maintainability, dependability, and safety performance for the major systems involved have been spelled out clearly. Moreover, a range of acceptable types of hardware is now specified rather than a rather vague performance standard which required item testing for quality control. Much more complete soils and geological information, obtained from more extensive geotechnical investigations, is now included for each project (Fig. D). For MARTA's major tunneling project, for instance, a million dollar pilot tunnel was driven to secure maximum information in order to reduce the contractor's risk and to obtain the best possible contract price. MARTA contracts are covered by an overall wrap up insurance policy which covers the contractor's general liability (personal injury and property damage), workmen's compensation, property insurance, including builder's all-risk, errors and omissions, and business interruptions, and Safety Program Supervision. This insurance has contributed to a better coordinated safety program, with proper coverage for all major risks, and have saved MARTA some higher contract costs. Overall, these contract improvements have attracted more contractors to bid the jobs, helped to obtain lower bids, and have reduced claim and change order activity.

As mentioned previously, MARTA and its general consultant, PB/T, were committed early to EEO goals. Hiring practices of both stressed these, and results were enviable for the industry. In addition, goals were set for minority business commitment of 14 to 19 percent for properly qualified engineer design firms. Through MARTA's early negotiations with construction contractors, about 17 percent of the contract dollar value was allotted to minority owned firms against a goal of 16 to 21 percent. Where non-minority firms were the successful bidders on the smaller projects, they normally had in-house work forces sufficient for these jobs. The larger contracts that drew prime contractors from outside the Atlanta area relied more on subcontract work and provided the best opportunities for local minority subcontractors. Contractors who were unable to meet their minority commitments in a specific area were required to substitute in another area, such as procurement of items from a minority firm to make up a construction subcontractor shortfall, perhaps. Contract payments were stopped if a contractor failed to keep his commitments until his plan was reviewed and mutually agreeable commitments were renegotiated. No construction firms have defaulted under these procedures; however, one design firm did. Since UMTA developed a new policy in 1979, MARTA's contracts now cite the minimum minority contracting goals: 15 percent for architecture and engineering, 17 percent for construction, 13 percent for manufacturing and equipment, 14 percent for professional services, and 6 percent for service and supply. Specific commitments are required, however, with bid submittals for all construction and procurement contracts.

One last remark about contracts, as much of the utility relocation work as possible was done under our agreements by the utility itself. The power lines were moved by the power company, telephone lines by Ma Bell, etc., in advance of the construction contract for that section. This reduced disruptions, simplified problems, and assured all that "experts" were performing this work.

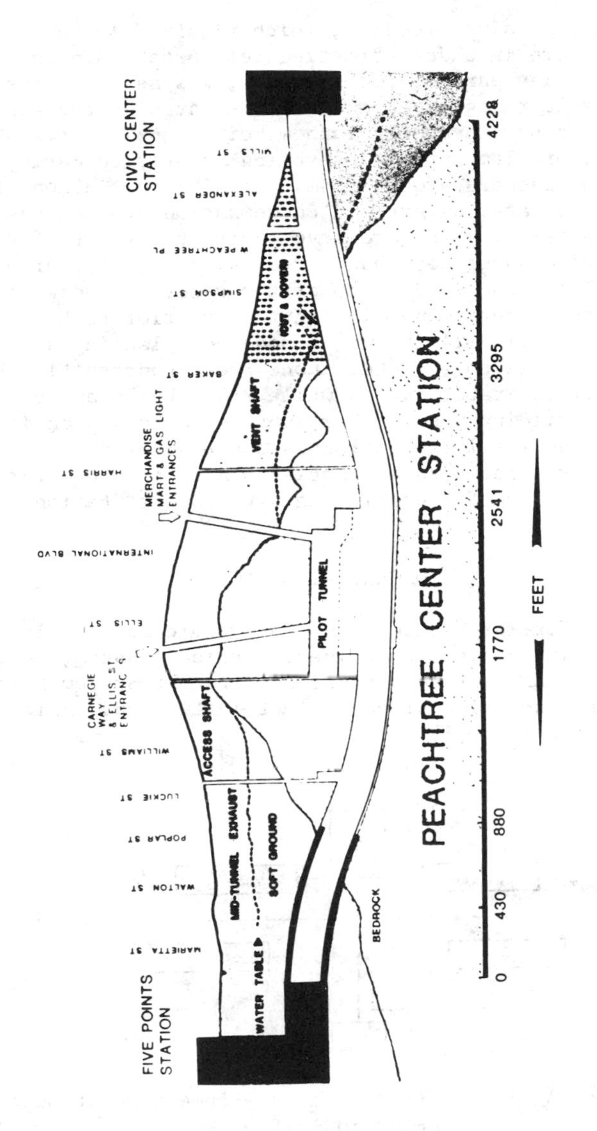

Fig. D. MARTA Tunnel

REAL ESTATE

MARTA's most expensive blunders, which resulted in "chain reaction" claims actions, were in underestimating real estate acquisition time. The delay for one key parcel, for instance, was seven months! This was an expensive learning experience, exacerbated by the concurrency mode. Needless to say, property is now being acquired far ahead of detailed design, problem parcels are being identified early, and the system or design proceeds around them. If ROW negotiations falter, MARTA does not hesitate to initiate condemnation proceedings immediately, if the parcel is vital, to move obstructions out of the way. There are many more successes than horror stories, of course. MARTA's work with Bell Telephone to do much of the necessary work on North Avenue Station and underground line entrances prior to Bell's construction of their new building was a model of planning and cooperation MARTA still tries to emulate. Concurrent construction by the State of the Georgia State Station while MARTA built and opened its station in that building was another success. The lesson is to plan early for entrances for large buildings and businesses directly into stations; MARTA even included entrances to Atlanta's Underground as well as Rich's Department Store in its Five Points Station.

ORGANIZATION

Organizations for large endeavors are dynamic and complex in nature and reflect changing goals, objectives, outside impacts, and, certainly personalities. MARTA's Department for Transit System Development (TSD) has been no exception since project initiation. Prior to 1975, it looked like this (Fig. E).

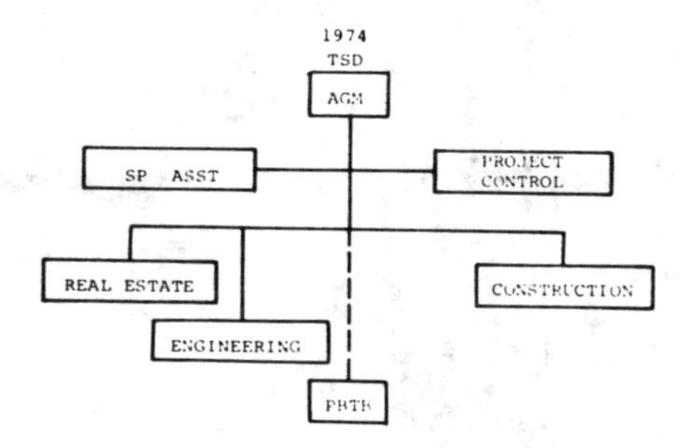

Fig. E. MARTA Transit System Development Department Prior to 1975

Very simple. The Construction Division was one man! TSD strength was a total of about 50 "carefully chosen" people. Complete reliance was vested in PBTB for system concept design, management of Design AE's, contracting, early procurements, etc. MARTA's General Manager planned, however, to develop the TSD staff into a force that could appropriately oversee the General Engineer Consultant and provide him management control and in-house recommendations for decision rather than depending solely on the GEC. In 1975, TSD was reorganized (Fig. F) to split the local agreements people out of Engineering to assure direct access to the AGM.

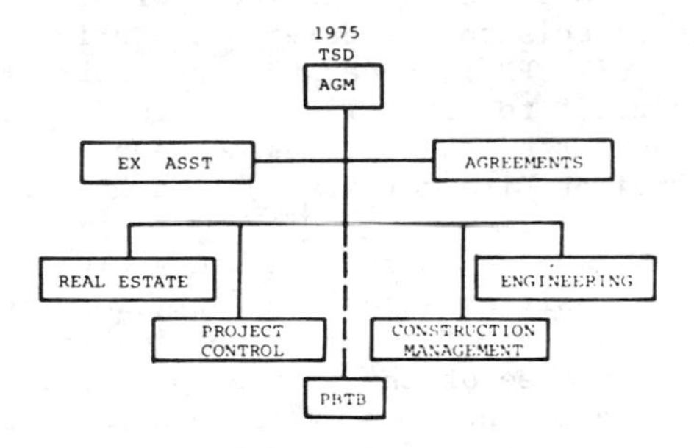

Fig. F. MARTA TSD Department, 1975

During 1976, (Fig. G) the program managers similarly were moved out of Engineering, and in December, 1976, finally, Rail Activation split out (Fig. H).

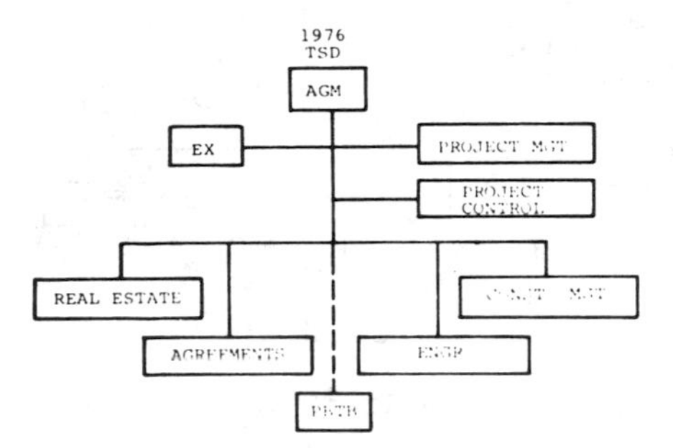

Fig. G. MARTA TSD Department
Prior to December, 1976

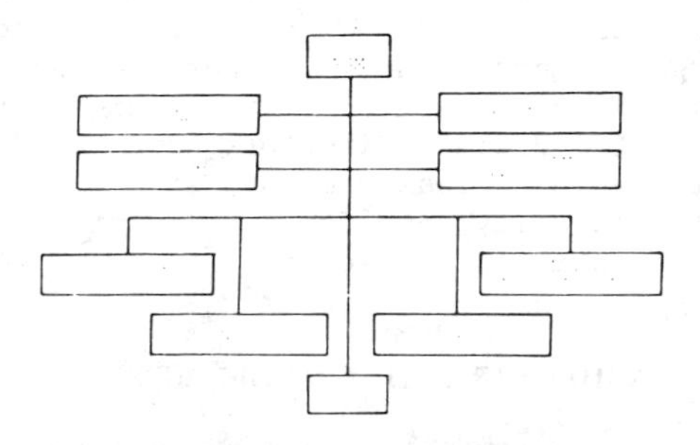

Fig. H. MARTA TSD Department, December, 1976

There was some thought, then, of the TSD assuming functions of the construction manager with an in-house inspection force and complete contract administration capabilities. However, because of the equitable contract terms arranged with PB/T, the excellent relationships with that GEC, and the spectre of owning 600 or so engineers on a temporary basis, that decision was deferred. During 1976, TSD grew to nearly 133 folks while PB/T, under the new contract without Bechtel, dropped from 605 to 480. TSD did assume a greater role in the process, which permitted PB/T to reduce people, but more significantly, the PB/T Project Director streamlined his organization.

By the end of 1976, a close interface had evolved between PB/T and TSD that had not previously existed. In fact, some integration in the Systems area took place. This close working relationship improved through 1980 largely because of the various personalities on both sides that successfully nurtured the relationships and the joint respect that developed among professionals. Agreements responsibilities returned to Engineering as the load lightened and (Fig. I) program management fused back into Engineering in 1977.

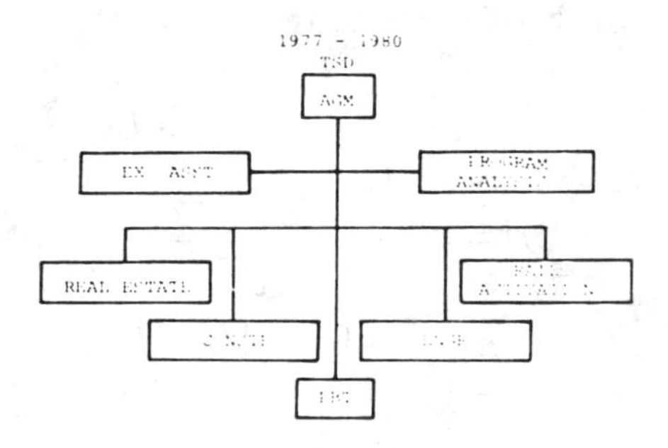

Fig. I. MARTA TSD Department, 1977

Essentially, the TSD had remained in this configuration since 1977. As TSD matured, the AGM in 1979 became the contracting officer for all contracts including design, although PB/T has continued to monitor and review the work. Change order actions, claims handling, and concept design were assumed by TSD with input and recommendations from PB/T. All legal counsel since 1976 has been provided by MARTA, augmented by general legal consultants from a highly reputed firm. The AGM/TSD and the PB/T Project Directors have tried continuously to assure that both organizations remained streamlined to prevent bureaucratic attitudes, delay, and duplication of effort. Despite human nature, that effort has succeeded.

RELATIONSHIP WITH OUTSIDE AGENCIES

There are, of course, many other management lessons that could be tracked. Although space is limited, the changing relationships with outside agencies is worthy of a quick mention. It is certainly necessary to gain rapport and support quickly for such a traumatic, disruptive project from businessmen, utilities companies (particularly to reduce public impacts), railroad companies whose right of way is needed, the State Department of Transportation and City organizations whose roads and traffic are disrupted, the Power People, civic groups, et al. MARTA recognized the importance of those groups early after running into stone walls and moved to educate and sell them on the project. Perhaps the project was oversold by MARTA's demonstrating its willingness to go beyond normal, or more reasonable, expectations. New track and new road segments were rebuilt to current standards rather than to the existing conditions, sewer lines extended well beyond project boundaries, conveniences put in for business interests that had to be paid from the existing budget, and on and on. What has happened is, of course, they have learned to expect the best and more, and the demands from all have increased! One can only hope that the project support increased proportionally because the job became more difficult and required more time and dollars as a result. Agreements with outside agencies and groups are always difficult but where property, particularly, is involved, the builder is clearly disadvantaged. To gain badly needed access to retain the schedule, sometimes it is better to give, and receive (Fig. J).

Fig. J. MARTA Vehicle, Georgia Capitol

Chapter 98

CONSTRUCTION MANAGEMENT OF WASHINGTON METRO

JOHN S. EGBERT

WASHINGTON METROPOLITAN AREA TRANSIT AUTHORITY

Many of you are familiar with the Washington Metro Project. However, inasmuch as some may not be, and others may want to refresh their memories regarding certain facets of the project, I will cite a few summary details about the rail transit system we are constructing. That summary will also give each of us a common point for departure as I develop the principal thoughts that I want to leave with you.

The Washington Metropolitan Area Transit Authority (WMATA) is an interstate agency established by Compact between the District of Columbia, Maryland and Virginia and approved by the United States Congress. Currently, the Authority has approval to build and operate a 101-mile (162.5 km) regional rapid rail transit system as shown on Appendix A. Of that total, 38 miles (61.2 km) will be in D. C., 32 miles (51.5 km) in Maryland and 30 miles (48.3 km) in Virginia. (Mileage figures, because of rounding error, do not add to 101 miles.) Referring again to the 101-mile total, 48 miles (77.2 km) will be underground, 42 miles (67.6 km) on the surface and 10 miles (16.1 km) on aerial structures. Of the 48 miles (77.2 km) that are underground, 15 miles (24.1 km) are rock tunnel, 14 miles (22.5 km) are earth tunnel, 0.5 miles (0.8 km) is sunken tube and 19 miles (30.6 km) are cut-and-cover construction. The system will include 86 stations, with 51 of them underground. Referring again to the full 86 stations, 43 will be in D. C., 23 in Maryland and 20 in Virginia.

We currently have 37 miles (59.5 km) of line and 41 stations in operations as shown on Appendix B. Also shown on Appendix B is another 16 mile (25.7 km) increment and 13 stations which have been substantially completed, but are not yet in service. Additionally, another 19.3 miles (31.1 km) of double-track line and 12 stations are identified as presently under construction. Of those 13 miles (20.9 km), 1 mile (1.6 km) is rock tunnel, 2 miles (3.2 km) are cut-and-cover, 9 miles (14.5 km) are on the surface and 1 mile (1.6 km) is on aerial structures. Of the 17 stations, 2 are cut-and-cover construction, 8 are in rock tunnel and 7 are on the surface.

Passenger comfort was an important consideration in the design of the system. All underground stations will be air-conditioned, using both envelope and spot cooling techniques, and passengers will ride in air-conditioned 2, 4, 6 and 8-car trains. The cars are also constructed and outfitted for the passenger's acoustic comfort.

Each car in the existing fleet seats 81 people and has room for an additional 94 standees, for a maximum capacity of 175 passengers per car. Each car is 75 feet (22.9 m) long, 10 feet (3 m) wide, 10 feet 8 inches (3.3 m) high, with inside headroom of 6 feet 10 inches (2.1 m). These transit cars have steel-wheeled trucks, with air-cushioned suspension and power on each axle. Trains will operate on continuously welded 115 lbs/yard (47.7 kg/m) steel rails and, to reduce vibrations, are mounted either on neoprene-cushioned track fasteners or ballasted wood ties. To further dampen vibrations at critical points, such as in close proximity to buildings, floating concrete slabs, supported on neoprene pads, are used.

Trains have a maximum speed of 75 mph (120.7 km/hr), can accelerate at 3 mi/hr/sec (4.8 km/hr/sec) and decelerate at 3.3 mi/hr/sec (5.3 km/hr/sec), and can maintain an average speed of 35 mph (56.3 km/hr), including stops. Trains will operate on a 2-minute rush hour headway on main routes and 4 to 8 minutes on branch lines. An automatic train control system regulates train speed and headway, starts and stops trains, operates doors and monitors train performance. An on-board operator can override the automatic controls. The system also has extensive communications, including independent telephone, mobile radio, teleprinter, public address and closed-circuit TV. Fare collection is completely automatic, using a stored-value, magnetic fare card about the size of a credit card.

Construction valued at $2.6 million has been placed to date. The total value, either completed or under construction, and including $182.4 million for transit cars and $146.9 million for automatic train control and communications, totals $4.0 billion. Dollar value of construction placement peaked in 1976 at a figure in excess of $2 million per working day. During the peak construction placement period, there were 85 prime construction contractors working on Metro with an on-site construction force of over 8,000 people. Currently, there are 50 prime construction contractors with forces on site of over 2,000.

Having given you some feel for the scope of the Metro project, I would like now to transition to the main topic of my address - that of our organization for managing construction of this immense and complex project, how our current organizational posture evolved, and what I would recommend for future projects of similar scope and duration.

In the early phases of planning for the Washington Metropolitan Area's rapid transit system, the jurisdictions and system's planners did not envision as comprehensive a system as we are now constructing. For example, when WMATA was established in 1966, the total approved system measured only 25 miles (40.2 km), as compared to today's 101 mile (162.5 km) system.

Construction of the 25 mile (40.2 km) system was projected to span a relatively short duration -- about 5 years -- and that duration would not justify building up a large in-house technical organization. Further, because of that limited duration, it would have been difficult to attract personnel with the proper professional expertise. Consequently, the Authority elected to follow the procedure commonly used in construction wherein each architect-engineer firm that furnished design services also provided the construction management services for the projects that it had designed. This system was used during construction of Phase I -- those projects comprising the first increment of the Metro rail system to be placed into revenue service. Consequently, each of those construction projects were managed and inspected under a separate contract between the Authority and the respective design firm.

In order to provide some basic continuity to the overall construction management effort, our General Engineering Consultant established a construction branch with the mission of overall coordination of construction projects. For a time this system worked satisfactorily; but, as the number of active contracts increased, the task of coordinating increasing numbers of construction management organizations, often from different architect-engineer firms, became progressively more unwieldy. Recognizing this problem, and at the same time realizing that the system would expand to a full 101 mile (162.5 km) length, it was apparent that major changes would be necessary in managing the expanding construction effort. Specifically, the Authority would be forced either to employ a single construction management consultant to manage all of the construction work or to provide that management through an entirely in-house -- but greatly expanded -- staff.

The Authority carefully considered the advantages and disadvantages of managing the construction effort with an in-house staff. Again, however, the projected duration of the project was an overriding consideration. The 101 mile (162.5 km) system, as then planned, would require about ten years to construct. To acquire the in-house expertise needed for this still relatively short period would place the Authority and many large, well established construction management firms in direct competition for the limited construction management resources that would be available. Those firms maintained large, relatively mobile work forces, and could accommodate the rapid build-up and subsequent fluctuations in construction workload and eventual demobilization of the large, highly skilled workforce, principally through transfer of its personnel. For the Authority to compete for qualified and available personnel, in the numbers needed and with the salary structure available, would involve great risk that it would have to settle for less talented, less experienced and less motivated personnel. The Authority elected, therefore, to employ a General Construction Consultant (GCC) to manage all construction projects and to abandon the system it had used during Phase I construction.

Accordingly, in the Fall of 1970, the Authority convened a Contract Evaluation Board to select and recommend a General Construction Consultant (GCC). Many firms submitted proposals; and, after a keen competition, the Authority awarded the work to Bechtel Associates. Bechtel assumed management of all construction contracts awarded after May 1971. Its responsibilities include the conventional construction management duties relating to construction inspection, contract administration, field engineering and safety enforcement. Additionally, the GCC provides other important services, such as certain engineering services (over and above those normally included in the field engineering function), materials testing services, contracting for outside laboratory services, supervising Authority-furnished materials procurement contracts and furnishing associated warehousing services. It also accomplishes certain start-up and testing, instrumentation and monumentation, and project support functions. I will discuss most of these functions in more detail later.

To date, our GCC has managed roughly 730 contracts and agreements, 293 of which have been completed. The GCC's organization for managing the Authority's projects is necessarily a relatively large one, one of over 400 personnel.

Annually, the manning level for the forthcoming year is established after careful evaluation of contracts to be supervised during the coming year. A new contract is then negotiated to cover the upcoming one year period.

I will digress for just a moment to describe the categories into which the Authority divides its construction contracts. That will facilitate a better understanding of how the GCC is organized to perform its mission and why it is organized that way.

The Authority's construction contracts fall into two major categories -- line and station contracts, and systemwide contracts. The line and station work (comprising both structural and finish contracts) includes soft ground and hard rock tunnel, cut-and-cover subways, at-grade trackway, aerial structures and underpinning. The systemwide contracts pertain to work which is common to the entire system, including trackwork, electrification, train control, communications, fire protection, escalators, elevators, graphics, station furniture and ancillary construction services.

I will return now to the GCC's functions and organization, describing first the Resident Engineer/Area Manager responsibilities and hierarchy. Basically, the Contracting Officer designates a Resident Engineer for each construction contract. In some instances, an individual may be designated a Resident Engineer on more than one contract. This is determined by contract size, geographic dispersion (or concentration) of work, type of work, and any other factors that may weigh importantly.

The Resident Engineer, although an employee of the GCC, is designated in writing as the Authorized Representative of the Contracting Officer. He is personally charged with certain responsibilities for contract administration that no one other than the Contracting Officer himself has authority to perform. In his special capacity, the Resident Engineer represents both the Authority and the GCC and is the focal point for discharging the responsibilities of both. The Resident Engineer has authority to take such actions as may be delegated by the Contracting Officer; and his responsibilities include, but are not limited to, the following:

a. Inspection of construction work and enforcement of contract specifications.

b. Issuance of orders to stop, and/or resume, work in the event of serious safety violations.

c. Preparation of Authority estimates for contract modifications.

d. Modification of contracts in accordance with the Change Article when the value of the modification does not exceed $25,000.

e. Negotiation with contractors relative to Proposed Change Orders and Contract Modifications as to adjustment for price and time.

f. Approval of contractor's shop drawings.

g. Approval of contractor's progress schedule and checking of actual progress.

h. Preparation of progress payment estimates.

i. Enforcement of contract safety provisions.

j. Testing of Materials. (The Construction Department operates a materials testing laboratory serving various WMATA contracts; and the Procurement Section supervises contracts for services of outside testing laboratories.)

k. Coordination of surveys.

The Resident Engineer's office is staffed with the number and types of construction inspection, office engineers, and clerical personnel that the Resident Engineer needs to insure that the Authority's interest is properly represented and protected.

Area Managers supervise the work of the Resident Engineers to assure compliance with required standards and directives. They check the contractor's monthly payments and the documentation for contract modifications and claims.

Proper coordination of contract activities which impact upon other contractors involved in Metro construction is critical to the success of the overall construction effort. Work must be scheduled so as to minimize interference between two or more contractors working in the same area. Resident Engineers have this responsibility with respect to contractors working entirely within the confines of projects under their control. The Area Managers have that coordinating responsibility with respect to contractors whose work crosses boundaries between Resident Engineers.

At the present time (February 1981), there are 21 resident offices functioning under the guidance of three Area Managers, two of the latter with geographical orientations and the other with systemwide responsibilities.

The GCC's central office provides for necessary administration support services, quality assurance, safety, engineering capability and other support personnel to manage the overall construction operation.

The engineering support function involves checking and approving the shop drawings which contractors are required to submit. The GCC must insure that the drawings conform to the Section Designer's specifications. Additionally, the GCC must check certain designs which contractors may be required to prepare and submit. Examples are designs for support of excavations and Category II underpinnings (those underpinnings which are not specifically called for in contract drawings and which the contractor, at his option, may elect to provide or elect to provide another suitable means of support). The contractor submits the pertinent calculations along with the designs in order that the GCC can check them against specified criteria.

As a measure of this workload, an overage (during 1980) of 45 submittal packages were made per week, with submittals ranging from simple catalog cuts to several hundred drawings each. Individually, contracts average between 25 and 225 drawings, catalog cuts and calculations; for large structural contracts, the average per contract exceeds 60; and for train control, it exceeds 20.

The engineering support staff also provides technical assistance to the Resident Engineers. For example, if major engineering problems arise, technical personnel visit the job site to gather data that the designers will need to resolve those problems. Also, that staff expends considerable effort in clarifying conflicts and inconsistencies between contract documents and in keeping the "failure recording and feedback" system viable.

The engineering support function also includes responsibility for updating contract drawings and specifications to reflect "as-built" status.

To perform the above functions, the engineering support staff has representatives from all disciplines: Civil/Structural, Mechanical, Electrical (this includes train control, communications, station electrical, electrification and fare collection), Architectural, Trackwork, Utilities and Corrosion, Soils and Geology, Agronomy and Materials.

The project support function encompasses estimating, scheduling and procurement support, in addition to the normal administrative functions of accounting, personnel and office services. The estimating group has functional responsibility for all estimates used in negotiating change orders and claims. The scheduling group coordinates all construction schedules specified in the various contracts and reviews all contractor claims involving extensions of time. The procurement group provides administrative and warehousing support for WMATA-awarded procurement contracts and supervises "in-plant inspection" of manufactured items that are used in the project. The procurement group also awards subcontracts for surveys, specialized lab services, and other required services.

The test and start-up support function includes coordinating and witnessing static and dynamic testing of each system and the interfaces between the various subsystems that comprise the total rail system. Operations are simulated during the testing that precedes the placing of a facility into service. The GCC also provides recommendations to the Authority in the latter's development of an integrated system test plan and the orderly testing and start-up of each system. System testing and start-up is a complex process and safety and schedule constraints, of course, are major considerations.

The quality assurance function assumes significance when contract specifications require quality assurance programs of contractors or suppliers. The GCC assures the proper development of the quality assurance programs, reviews proposed procedures for compliance with project criteria, and monitors implementation of the programs. The GCC conducts field inspections and quality audits, and submits appropriate reports to the Authority.

The GCC also performs a crucial liaison function. Construction in a central city is very disruptive to normal travel and local access. To reduce the impact of construction activities on affected individuals and businesses, the GCC maintains liaison with property owners, tenants, merchants and others to advise them of impending construction plans and physical obstructions. They also receive and act on complaints from whatever source.

The Authority is especially concerned about safety and devotes a concerted effort to the Safety Program. Safety, of course, includes the physical welfare of workers, as well as the public using the finished product and those exposed to hazards during the construction phase. Safety includes consideration of impacts on surrounding properties. Attention to safety during construction impacts on construction time and cost. However, it cannot be compromised. The GCC staff, the WMATA Safety staff, and the Resident Engineers work as a team to assure compliance with all applicable safety standards. Those staffs use a broad range of formal and on-the-job training, regular inspections, special surveys and investigations in furtherance of the Authority's safety goals. Preventive safety measures are the dominant features of the Program.

In 1979, in a concerted effort to improve safety and reduce rising claims for Workmen's Compensation, the Authority instituted the Safety Awareness Program (SAP). That Program provides incentives to focus the contractor's attention upon worker safety. The Authority, based on the type of contract and the estimated manhours that are projected to be expended over the contract performance period, includes a safety performance goal and associated incentives in the bid documents. The incentive can be either rewarding or punitive, depending upon safety performance. The contractor can earn a payment at the end of the contract if he keeps his incident rate to the minimum specified in the contract or he can lose a considerable amount of money if his incident rate rises above the established goal. Results of Metro's SAP are gratifying.

In Fiscal Year 1979, the Authority realized a 22% reduction in incurred and paid Workmen's Compensation from that of the previous year; and, in Fiscal Year 1980, it realized an additional 24% reduction, or a total reduction over the two year period of 46%.

Reportable accidents, including both lost time and non-lost time injuries, have decreased 30% in the same time frame. We now have 31 contractors working under contracts with SAP provisions and only 2 of the 31 are in a "penalty" status. As a further measure of the program's effectiveness, a lost time accident occurs, on average, every 22,300 manhours for non-SAP contracts as compared to every 47,500 manhours in SAP contracts. We are enjoying this success within reasonable financial outlays -- 4 contracts with SAP provisions have been closed out at a total payment of $159,000.

As of November 30, 1980, our combined index of 5.5 lost time cases (SAP and non-SAP) was 2.3 below (index-value-wise) the 1979 figure and 1.1 below the national average.

Now let us turn to the subject of risks in construction work and the responsibility, liability and accountability involved. A major construction project has many attendant risks, many of which are difficult to categorize or describe in general terms. When viewed from an overall standpoint, however, it would appear that they all stem from three basic factors. These are safety, time, and cost, with the first two eventually impacting on the last -- cost.

I will return to another aspect of safety a little further on; however, for the moment, I want to talk about other risks -- risks which when taken, have no safety implications whatsoever. These are economic risks which, if they have successful outcomes, save time and money; but which, if they do not, can cause excessive costs. Practices, policies, and procedures for dealing with these risks on large public projects must be developed with a view toward their effect upon competitive bidding. Competitive bidding dictates a set of contract documents which specify what is required with a degree of finiteness that provides each bidder an equal opportunity in preparing his bid. In the competitive bidding process, many questions as to allocation or responsibility, accountability and liability for various risk factors arise and each requires resolution. Therefore, the Owner, working through his Engineer, must establish rules which assess risks and anticipate and deal with any temptation on the part of a contractor to take risks which the owner considers to be unacceptable. These rules, as implemented by contract documents, govern the relationship as to risks between the Owner and the Contractor during the prosecution of the work. Unfortunately, the creation of an adversary relationship is inherent to some degree -- that degree being inversely related to the quality of the contract documents.

I view the following as a basic principle of risk relationships:

> The party that takes the risk should assume the liability and either suffer the consequences or reap the benefits therefrom, depending on the outcome of the endeavor.

An outstanding example of this principle occurs when the contractor encounters Differing Site Conditions. The sharing of risks for differing site conditions, particularly in underground construction, has received considerable attention over the years. The standard Federal clause on this subject was designed to place a considerable degree of liability on the Owner for unforeseen conditions. This was done with a two-fold purpose in mind -- providing equity and obtaining bids with fewer contingencies.

Decisions involving an assessment and assignment of risks take place at every level. For example, choices concerning Owner or contractor-designed underpinning or grouting, or whether protection is required at all, must be made many times during the routine preparation of subway plans and specifications.

With regard to risks in implementing innovative concepts or involving new materials, products, systems or procedures, the risk devolves principally upon the contractor by virtue of his familiarity with the particular construction and the general rule of associating liability with those responsible for the work. Both fixed-price and unit-price type contracts offer incentives to the contractor to innovate, as do value engineering provisions. Indeed, contractors historically have been great innovators. However, this risk assignment procedure undoubtedly slows advancement of the state of the art.

The Owner can, of course, specify innovative concepts; but, in doing so, he must assume at least some responsibility, accountability and/or liability. Therefore, research and development should be held to realistic levels in most major construction projects where time and resources are at a premium.

Activities of others can also affect construction in many ways and introduce risks. For example, project opponents have used certain laws to delay projects and cause costly litigation. Approvals by others, whether required by virtue of the particular funding arrangements or the effect of the proposed project on existing facilities or other parties, can also be difficult to obtain and can cause delay. Social concerns of the public concerning public projects cannot, of course, be ignored; and, the time required to respond to and alleviate those concerns can cause delay. You may well ask, "Where should we place our emphasis in seeking to alleviate the foregoing problems?" My response to that is:

First -- Streamline the procedures and requirements for studies, environmental statements, permit requirements, etc., which agencies and private enterprise must comply with before a project can get underway and which plague every project in ways that make it difficult to maintain a schedule.

Second -- Continue to refine contract provisions so as to clearly assign risk responsibilities and minimize disputes as the work progresses.

Turning now to the matter of risk insurance, WMATA uses a "wrap-up" insurance concept wherein its construction contractors need provide only automotive vehicle insurance and such special coverage as they may want. It is our Coordinated Insurance Program (CIP) which provides our "wrap-up" insurance. I do not intend to get into a discussion here of which system is better -- wrap-up or non-wrap-up. Suffice it to say that a year ago, after a considerable period of complaints from one of our major structural contractors about our "wrap-up" program, we told him he could withdraw if he wished, provided he got the same coverage for the Authority, the Public, and his workers as provided under the CIP and at no increase in contract amount. Today, that contractor still has the Authority's CIP coverage, but he is complaining no more.

Incidentally, the General Construction Consultant is also covered under the Coordinated Insurance Program.

I would like to discuss one innovation that the Authority has introduced into its contractual relationship with the GCC. The Authority was motivated by a desire to focus the attention of the General Construction Consultant's (GCC) management personnel on critical field activities. Accordingly, in 1979, we introduced a performance incentive program into the contract. The program provides for an intensive management review of field operations and establishes associated monetary incentives. Five Resident Engineer Offices are evaluated during each quarter of the contract year. A team of senior members from the Department of Design and Construction examines the Resident Engineer's performance with respect to four categories of responsibility. These are knowledge of the contract, field inspection and enforcement, contract administration, and safety. The various elements of each category are weighted as to importance and the team awards grades for each, with grades ranging from unsatisfactory to superior. The incentive fee, either rewarding or punitive, for the quarter is based on the average rating for the five categories. The incentive focuses management's attention, induces competition, and improves field office performance.

I should mention a contract management technique which we in the Authority have used with considerable success. I am referring to our employment of formally constituted negotiating teams in our concerted efforts to close out contracts which have defied resolution by more routine methods. On subway construction contracts, it often happens that physical work will have been completed long ago; but, because of complex claims disputes or appeals of the Contracting Officer's Final Decisions, the contract will not have been closed out financially. Formally constituted negotiating teams can be effective in closing out such contracts, particularly when several fields of expertise are needed in negotiating the financial settlement. Examples of some of the disciplines that are often involved are audit, critical path analysis, cost estimating, engineering, contract administration, counsel, and construction management. Our experience confirms that the best results are obtained when the following simple principles are adhered to:

- The Contracting Officer should appoint the team members and designate the team leader. (Normally, the Authority's team leaders are selected either from the staff of its Office of Construction or from the General Construction Consultant's construction management organization.)

- A professional contract administrator, who is thoroughly acquainted with the instant contract, is always a valuable team member.

- Beyond the team leader and the contract administrator, the team should be constituted to provide the specific disciplines that will be needed in negotiating the issues. (On our contracts, we have found that CPM analysts and cost estimators are generally needed. If design intent or specifications are at issue, the project design engineer should also be a member of the team.)

- The audit representative, although normally a formal member of the team, often is not required at all head-to-head negotiating sessions and should be excused, as appropriate.

- The Contracting Officer's legal counsel should not normally be a member of the team. However, counsel should be acquainted thoroughly with the closeout issues, abreast of the progress in the negotiations, and immediately available to advice the team in caucus.

- The Contracting Officer, his counsel, and the Chief Auditor should be briefed on the various issues at the outset. Recommended courses of action, as appropriate, should be presented in the briefing and specific guidance, if needed, should be sought. The team leader should keep the Contracting Officer (and his counsel) informed as to progress of negotiations. If negotiations reach an impasse, the Contracting Officer needs to know this immediately. As the situation changes, or as issues become clearer, recommendations should be revised, as appropriate, and new guidance sought. In other words, the Contracting Officer should never be placed in the position of being surprised by a negotiating team's proposed settlement.

Because there may be some contractor personnel in the audience, a few words would be advisable about contract payments, changes, cost proposals, time extensions and disputes. The Authority's standard contract specifications contain articles that permit cost and/or time adjustments for changes, differing site conditions, suspension of work, and value engineering. The tendency toward bureaucratic inertia in an organization like the Authority is quite real and requires constant attention to preclude unreasonable delays in settling on contract adjustments that will permit contractor payment. The

Authority is well aware of the need to expedite "paper work", but the very number of actions being handled almost guarantees some delays, especially where there are legitmate differences of opinion. To compensate for these situations where delays seem inevitable, the Authority has established a policy of using a two-part modification. Under this procedure, certain costs are paid under Part 1 as they become known and agreed upon. Other less tangible costs, and profits, are included later in a Part 2 of the modification. It would be a tremendous help in speeding up payment if the contractors would submit their cost proposals promptly and in complete detail as called for by the contract change provisions.

Monthly progress payments could also be expedited if preparation of pay estimates were begun a few days before the cutoff date. In this way, the pay estimate could be mutually agreed to by the contractor and the Resident Engineer early-on and the pay estimate could be signed by both parties and forwarded to the Authority within a day or two following the estimate cutoff date. The Authority fully realizes its financial responsibilities; and, while at times it may seem to the contrary, the Authority has no desire nor intention for its contractors to "finance" Metro construction. Every reasonable action to speed up proposals, negotiations, settlements and payment is being implemented by the Authority. We ask the cooperation of our contractors in this regard.

In summary, for a large construction project similar to our rapid transit project in Washington, I would advise construction management by either one of two means: In-house forces or a single construction consultant. Construction management by designers, where a great number of individual designers are involved, becomes impractical from a coordination standpoint. Whether to go with in-house forces depends a great deal on the project duration. If construction will continue for many years at a fairly even rate, then it would be practical to establish and maintain a built-in organization to manage the effort. That situation would enable employees to look foward to a long-term job with the normal opportunities for job growth and advancement. Short of that, it would be best to do as the Authority has done - establish a small key staff of construction experts and contract for the field inspection personnel with a company having experienced personnel available.

APPENDIX A

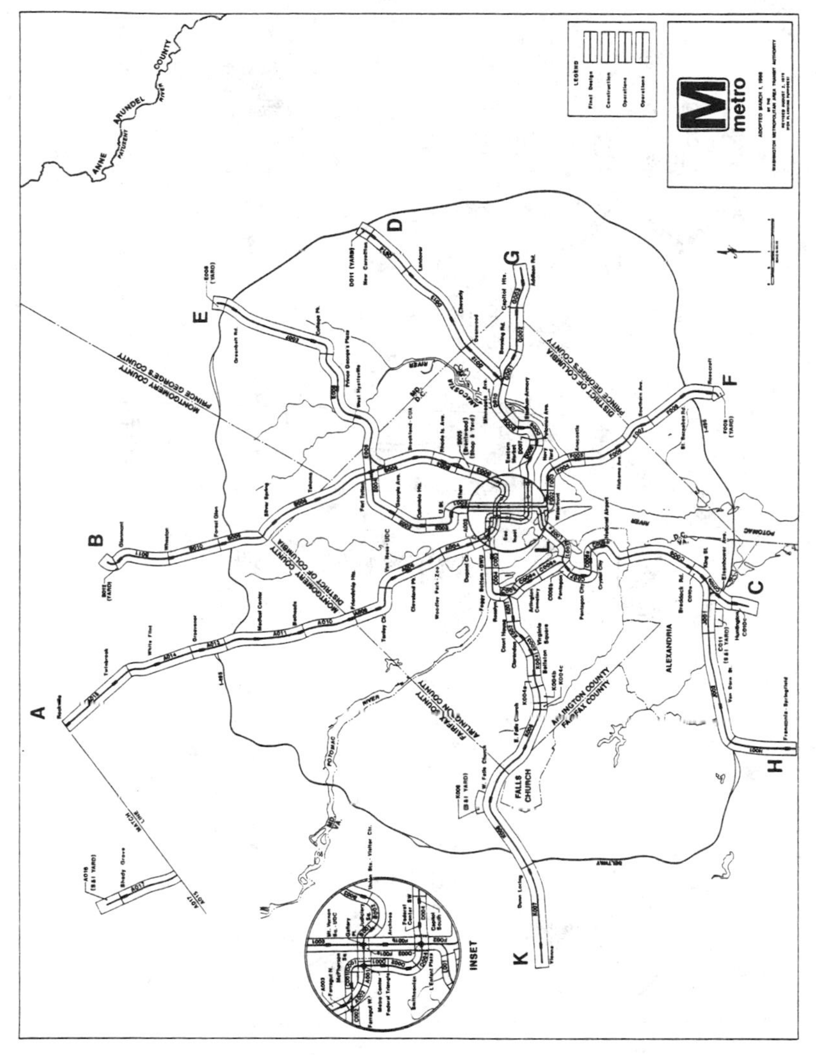

WASHINGTON METRORAIL SYSTEM

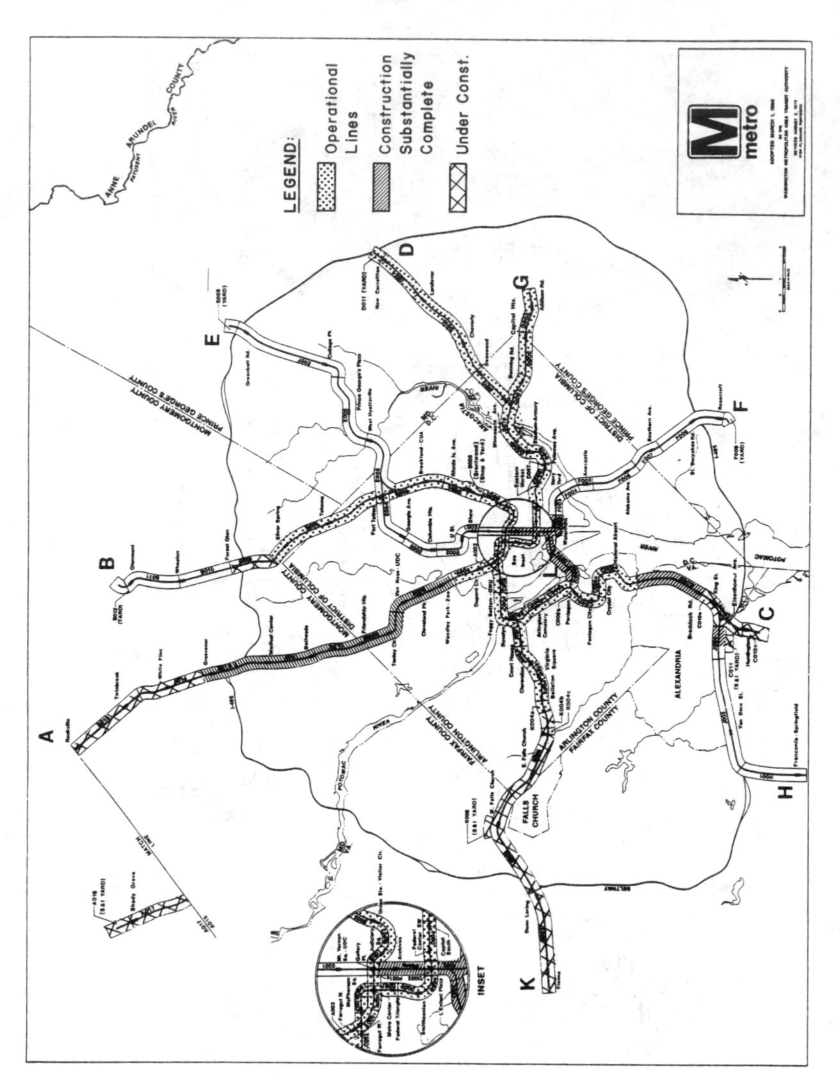

STATUS OF CONSTRUCTION & OPERATIONS

APPENDIX B

Chapter 99

BUILDING THE TUNNEL AND RESERVOIR PLAN USING THE CONTRACTING PRACTICES OF THE METROPOLITAN SANITARY DISTRICT OF GREATER CHICAGO

Forrest C. Neil, Chief Engineer
and
Frank E. Dalton, Deputy Chief Engineer

The Metropolitan Sanitary District of Greater Chicago
Chicago, Illinois

INTRODUCTION

The Tunnel and Reservoir Plan (TARP) (Figure 1) was adopted in 1972 as the most cost-effective way to bring Chicago area waterways up to Federal and State water quality standards. TARP will significantly reduce pollution of these waterways and provide flood relief for Chicago and 53 adjacent suburban communities.

These communities, covering an area of 971 sq km (375 sq miles), are at present served by combined sewers, which carry both raw sewage and stormwater. Because porous ground surfaces have been covered over in recent years by buildings, streets, and parking lots, stormwater runoff into sewers frequently exceeds the capacity of the sewers. When this happens, sewers back-up into hundreds of thousands of basements, and the overflows on the combined sewers discharge rainwater mixed with raw sewage directly into the area's waterways at 645 overflow points. The result is severe pollution of the waterways and flooding in 53 communities. During particularly heavy rains, overloaded rivers have to be relieved by opening the locks and allowing the polluted waterways to flow into Lake Michigan, the region's water source.

<u>Goals of TARP</u>

1. PREVENT BACKFLOWS INTO LAKE MICHIGAN.
2. ELIMINATE WATERWAY POLLUTION CAUSED BY COMBINED SEWER OVERFLOWS.
3. PROVIDE AN OUTLET FOR FLOOD WATERS.

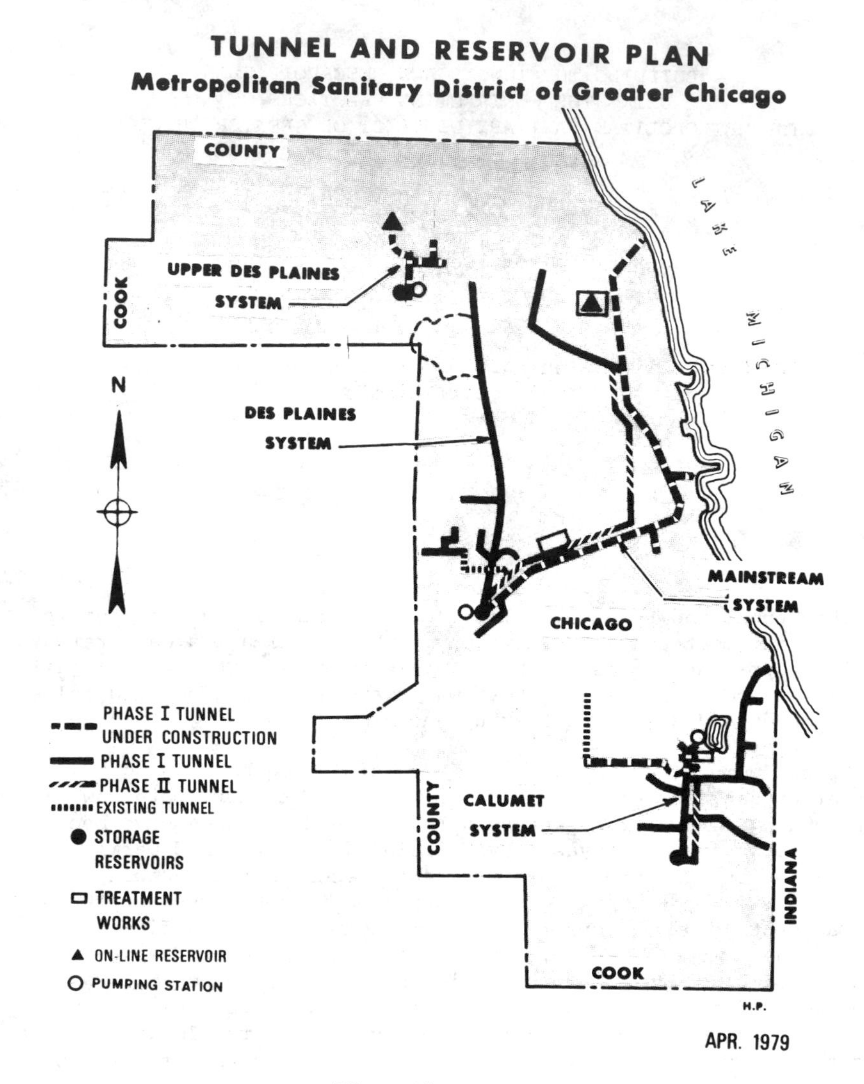
TUNNEL AND RESERVOIR PLAN
Metropolitan Sanitary District of Greater Chicago
COUNTY
COOK
LAKE MICHIGAN
UPPER DES PLAINES
SYSTEM
N
DES PLAINES
SYSTEM
MAINSTREAM
SYSTEM
CHICAGO
PHASE I TUNNEL
UNDER CONSTRUCTION
PHASE I TUNNEL
PHASE II TUNNEL
EXISTING TUNNEL
STORAGE
RESERVOIRS
TREATMENT
WORKS
ON-LINE RESERVOIR
PUMPING STATION
COUNTY
CALUMET
SYSTEM
INDIANA
COOK
H.P.
APR. 1979

Figure I.

1. PREVENT BACKFLOWS INTO LAKE MICHIGAN.

   A. TARP PHASES I and II will prevent the rivers from back-flowing into Lake Michigan.

   B. *The present river system can handle flows up to 283.20 cu m/s (10,000 cfs) before they must be reversed to the lake. Communities have installed relief sewers which overflow during rainstorms. The relief sewers impose flows in excess of 1699.20 cu m/s (60,000 cfs); therefore, reversals to the lake are more frequent in recent years. These river reversals to the lake contaminate the lake, thereby adversely affecting the area water supply and adversely affecting the recreational use of the lake. Preventing the discharge of all wastes of any kind to Lake Michigan is a public policy and enforced by law. This goal is non-negotiable.*

2. ELIMINATE WATERWAY POLLUTION CAUSED BY COMBINED SEWER OVERFLOWS.

   A. TARP PHASES I and II eliminate waterway pollution from combined sewer overflows.

   B. *After analyzing 26 years of records, it has been established that the waterway pollution problem is equivalent to raw sewage being discharged to the rivers by a population of 1,000,000 people each and every day.*

   C. TARP PHASE I eliminates raw sewage discharges to the rivers by a population of 850,000 people each and every day.

   TARP PHASE II eliminates raw sewage discharges to the rivers by a population of 150,000 people each and every day.

3. PROVIDE AN OUTLET FOR FLOOD WATERS.

   A. TARP PHASES I and II eliminate raw sewage back-up in basements in approximately 260,000 dwellings. Raw sewage back-up in the remaining 140,000 dwellings will be prevented when the local communities make local sewer improvements.

   B. *Over 400,000 dwellings have raw sewage back-up into basements several times each year.*

   C. TARP PHASE I will eliminate raw sewage back-up in basements in approximately 40,000 dwellings.

   TARP PHASE II will eliminate raw sewage back-up in basements in an additional 220,000 dwellings.

SUBSURFACE STUDIES

Seismic Surveys

Seismic surveys comprising 453 km (281.5 miles) of seismic profiles were performed to provide data on the configuration of the top of bedrock, the top of Galena Formation and the top of the St. Peter Formation, and to indicate the location, orientation, and magnitude of faults throughout the greater Chicago area. Limits of accuracy of the seismic surveys precluded indication of faults with vertical displacements less than about 6.1 m (20 feet). The results, including structure contour maps and seismic profiles, are given completely in the Report on a Vibroseis Survey Phases I, II, III, 1968.

Geotechnical Studies

The geotechnical studies conducted and reported in this stage of work consisted of the following:

- Final horizontal tunnel alignment
- Final vertical tunnel alignment
- Final determination of tunnel sizes and shapes
- Construction contract sizes and schedules
- Aquifer and potable water tunnel protection requirements
- Construction shaft locations
- Excavation methods and disposal of excavated materials
- Noise and damage prevention criteria for blasting
- Tunnel lining requirements
- Tunnel support and rock reinforcement requirements
- Tunnel grouting
- Ventilation
- Safety
- Detailed cost estimates

These geotechnical studies were supported by a data acquisition program consisting of field exploration, field testing, and laboratory testing. This program was conducted during the latter half of 1974 and early 1975. Sixty exploration holes were drilled for a total of 6,096 m (20,000 feet) through overburden and rock. The data obtained, combined with that obtained from the several prior exploration programs, were used in the final report.

Pilot Tunnels

Forecasting of project tunneling conditions and design requirements was greatly enhanced by inspection of the construction of two "pilot scale" rock tunneling projects: the LaGrange-Brookfield Sewer Tunnel in the southwest and the Crawford Avenue Sewer Tunnel in the southeast. Significant data concerning these two projects is given in Table 1.

Table 1

PILOT SCALE PROJECT DATA

Project	Construction Period	Tunnel Length	Tunnel Diameter	Compressive Strength of Rock	Average per hr.	Maximum per week	Machine Use Coefficient
Crawford Av (18E, Ext A)	1968 to 1971	5584 m (18,320 ft)	5.1 m (16.83 ft)	1652-2742 kgf/sq cm (23,500-39,000 psi)	2.0 m (6.4 ft)	185.0 m (607 ft)	35.2%
LaGrange-Brookfield (13-A)	1968 to 1971	5344 m (17,533 ft)	4.2 m (13.83 ft)	1055-1750 kgf/sq cm (15,000-24,900 psi)	3.7 m (12 ft)	180.1 m (591 ft)	50%

Relationship between Subsurface Studies and Tunnel Boring Machines

It was desired that as much of the tunnel as possible be constructed by tunnel boring machine (TBM) methods. Transporting and using explosives associated with the drill-and-blast method was considered unacceptable for so large and lengthy a project as TARP. Early analyses and discussions with manufacturers led to the conclusion that the maximum diameter that could be machine bored in this rock at this time would be approximately 11.0 m (36 feet).

Conveyance capacity requirements for the full project would have necessitated 12.8 m and 13.7 m (42 and 45 foot) diameter tunnels through about 50 percent of the system. Additionally, identified funding levels indicated that only a portion of the project could be constructed in a first phase of approximately a ten-year duration.

Since a second phase was therefore required for ultimate completion, an apportunity was provided for subsequent construction of an increment of conveyeance capacity. Accordingly, the maximum tunnel diameter was established as 11.0 m (36 feet), allowing the entire Phase I project to be developed around the tunnel boring machine and circular tunnel cross section.

From the point of view of underground construction, greatest interest lies in the strata in the upper 152.4 m (500 feet), particularly in dolomites and shales.

Underlying the surficial soil and any artificial fill material in the project area are the Pleistocene Series of deposits. These consist of a variety of materials transported by, or directly related to, the continental glaciers that covered the Chicago area. These deposits range in thickness from o to over 61 m (0 to 200 feet) locally. The depth range of the glacial deposits at most places is perhaps 18.3 to 27.4 m (60 to 90 feet).

The Racine Dolomite, the youngest, most variable, and topographically highest of the bedrock formations of the Chicago area, consists of dolomite with some chert and shale.

Laboratory drillability tests on core samples indicated rates of progress of tunneling machines ranging from 1.6 m (5.1 feet) per hour to 3.4 m (11.0 feet) per hour for a 3.1 m (10 foot) diameter tunnel. These values reduce to 0.6 m (1.9 feet) per hour and 1.4 m (4.7 feet) per hour for a 9.1 m (30 foot) diameter tunnel. Laboratory tests were performed by the Reed Tool Division of the G. W. Murphy Industries, Houston, and are keyed to specific tunnel diameters, bit types, machine models, bit pressures and similar parameters.

COMPARISON OF EXCAVATION TECHNIQUES STUDIED

Excavation by Tunnel Boring Machine

ADVANTAGES:

1) Reduced overbreak.
2) Option of eliminating lining; the decision of whether or not to leave the tunnel unlined can be delayed until after excavation is complete.
3) Reduced support requirements compared to drill-and-blast excavation.
4) Hydraulically efficient surface.
5) Elimination of blast damage.
6) Minimized interruption of grouting rock-bolting, lining operations.
7) A smooth excavation surface.
8) Minimal disturbance of surrounding rock.
9) Little or no disturbance to people at the surface.
10) Safer to construction personnel - SAFETY.
11) Fewer personnel required and less reliance on skill of crews.
12) Speed of construction for comparable distance of tunnel.

DISADVANTAGES:

1) Requires lead time to design, build, and erect the mole
2) Cross sections limited to a circular shape.
3) Diameter limitations.
4) High capital investment.
5) Limited flexibility in changing diameter and dimension.
6) Limited capability to accommodate variable rock conditions.
7) Excavation locations limited to the number of moles per contract.

Excavation by Drill-and-Blast

ADVANTAGES:

1) Excavating large size tunnel does not extend present state-of-the-art.
2) Lower excavation cost for large size tunnel.
3) No cross section limitations.
4) Short lead time for delivery and mobilization.
5) Low capital investment.
6) Good flexibility in both diameter and direction - variable rock conditions.
7) Good capability to accommodate variable rock conditions.

DISADVANTAGES:

1) Overbreak of about 0.61 m (2 ft) would occur unless presplitting were employed. This results in greater muck and concrete volume.
2) Added ventilation problems.
3) Interference with auxiliary operations.
4) A rough excavation surface, requiring lining for good hydraulics.
5) Disturbance of surrounding rock, requiring much ground support.
6) Explosion vibrations.
7) Safety limitations.
8) Greater requirements for skilled labor.

THE SUCCESSFUL USE OF TUNNEL BORING MACHINES AS A PART OF THE TARP CONTRACTS

Early Reservations

In earlier stages of design and prior to advertising of TARP projects, the District had several reservations in specifying TBM as mandatory requirement for tunnel excavation. Key questions were 1) will the "mole" cause restrictive competition?, and 2) will the bids be higher because of higher costs of this specialized TBM equipment?

The first question was answered as bids were received; the two contracts - 59th Street to Central Avenue and Central Avenue to Damen Avenue - each had three consortiums of contractors bidding, involving a total of nine different contractors. Other parts of TARP have attracted additional contractors in the bidding. In addition, there have been at least six pre-bid conferences held which were open to the public, and no contractor attending these conferences suggested that tunnel boring machine excavation would be more costly or could not be used, nor was it ever proposed that the drill-and-blast method be substituted for moling. This indicates that the many contractors attending the pre-bid conferences accept the tunnel boring machine method of excavation without significant reservations.

It is interesting to note that on five large diameter tunnels for the Washington Metro project, contractors chose the boring machine method even when permitted to make independent selection of tunneling techniques. In one situation, where the machine bored option was not specified, the contractor requested same and was authorized to redesign the tunnel section.

In answer to the second question, we have found that higher costs are not associated with the use of TBM's. Table 2 is a comparison of engineer's estimate versus actual bids received on TARP tunnel

Table 2

TARP TUNNEL CONTRACTS
COMPARISON OF ENGINEER'S ESTIMATE VS BIDS RECEIVED

Contract Number	Engineer's Estimate	Bid Price	Percent + or -
72-049-2H	$ 65,529,302	$ 63,140,480	- 3.6
73-317-2S	31,000,000	35,749,664	+15.3
73-320-2S	18,000,000	21,371,607	+18.7
73-287-2H	64,083,000	79,256,370	+23.7
73-160-2H	80,800,000	86,493,975	+ 7.0
75-126-2H	111,500,000	98,985,250	-11.2
75-125-2H	102,800,000	107,837,300	+ 4.9
75-124-2H	93,300,000	101,970,680	+ 9.3
75-123-2H	90,000,000	85,205,910	- 5.3
TOTAL	$657,012,302	$680,011,236	
Weighted Average			+ 3.5

Note: Pump station and connecting structures not included.

contracts. We believe that the increased productivity of TBM's has kept cost increases to a minimum.

Comparison of estimated costs for a) tunnel excavation, and b) total tunnel excavation using TBM and drill-and-blast methods are given on Figures 2 and 3. These estimates were obtained in 1975 when the Geotechnical Design Report for Mainstream Tunnel System of TARP was prepared. Moling costs were developed as follows. The cost of mole excavation is dependent on capital (purchase) cost and its write off, maintenance and replacement parts, instantaneous advance rates and machine availability. Cost data used are based on preliminary estimates made by manufacturers using past experience in the Chicago area and rock core samples from representative strata. The unconfined compressive strength of rock samples used was about 1758 kgf/cm^2 (25,000 psi).

Capital costs for 4.6 m to 10.7 m (15 to 35 foot) diameter moles vary from about $2,000,000 to about $5,500,000.

The usual practice is for a contractor to completely write off the capital cost of the mole against the tunnel for which it was purchased. Therefore, the capital cost of the mole, per meter (foot) of tunnel, is dependent on the tunnel length. For the larger size tunnels that will be used on this project, the amortization of the mole was based on a tunnel length of 8047 m (5 miles). The cost of the initial stock of replacement parts amounts to 10 percent of the capital cost of the machine. Cutter costs are practically independent of tunnel diameter and are assumed to be about $6.54 per cu m ($5.00 per cubic yard) of excavated rock. Average cutter life is about 200 hours actual excavating time.

Estimated advance rates used in preparing estimates are shown on Figure 4. These rates are based on data provided by Robbins Company and an assumed machine utilization of 45 percent for tunnel larger than 9.1 m (30 ft) in excavated diameter and 50 percent for tunnels 9.1 m (30 ft) or smaller. The boring machine is typically available for work about 80 to 85 percent of total working time. Maintenance and cutter replacement are done simultaneously during such operations as track laying and extension of the power supply and ventilation systems that are required every shift. These operations account for part of the above reduction in machine availability (15 to 20 percent). In addition, muck haulage delays, belt conveyor interruptions, shaft availability and similar work stoppage further reduce the mole's utilization as indicated above. Robbins Company believes that the larger machines may have a greater usage than the smaller machines used to date because material handling problems are more easily solved in larger tunnels, but since little experience exists with moles as great as 9.1 m (30 ft) in diameter, a more conservative machine utilization percentage was used. Machine usage rates of up to 60 percent have been achieved with the smaller machines. Actual machine use will depend on the experience and coordination of the

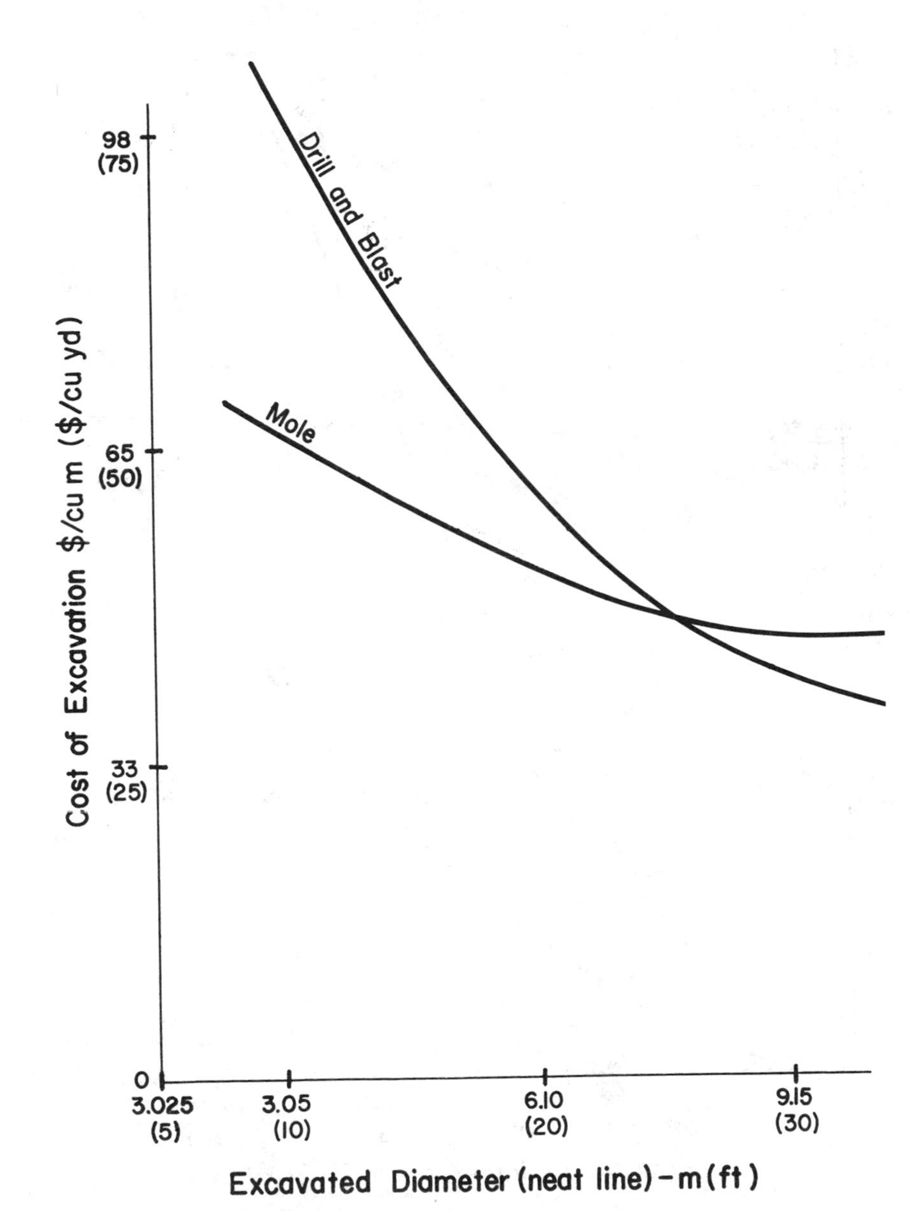

Figure 2. ESTIMATED TUNNEL EXCAVATION COSTS

Reference: Geotechnical Design Report, Mainstream Tunnel System Tunnel and Reservoir Plan, August 1975

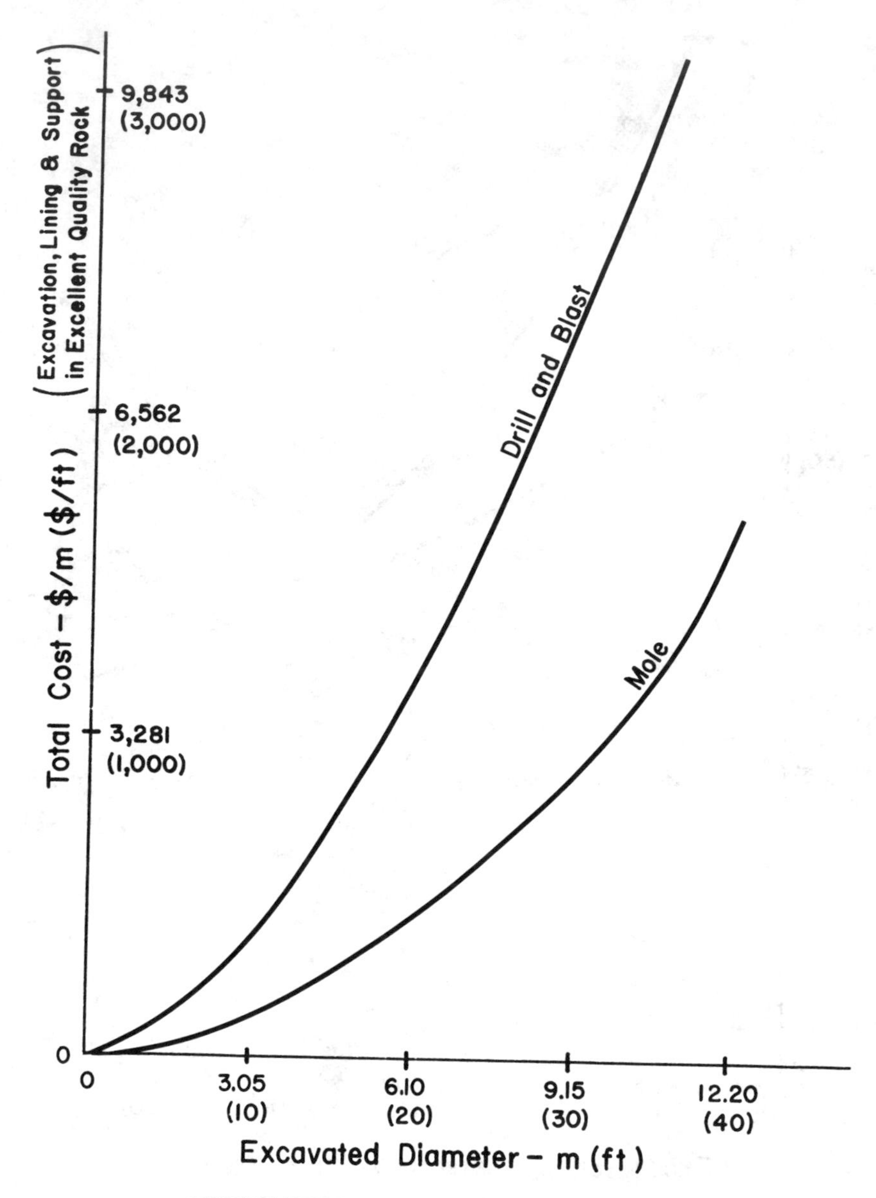

Figure 3. **ESTIMATED TOTAL TUNNEL COSTS**

Reference: Geotechnical Design Report, Mainstream Tunnel System Tunnel and Reservoir Plan, August 1975

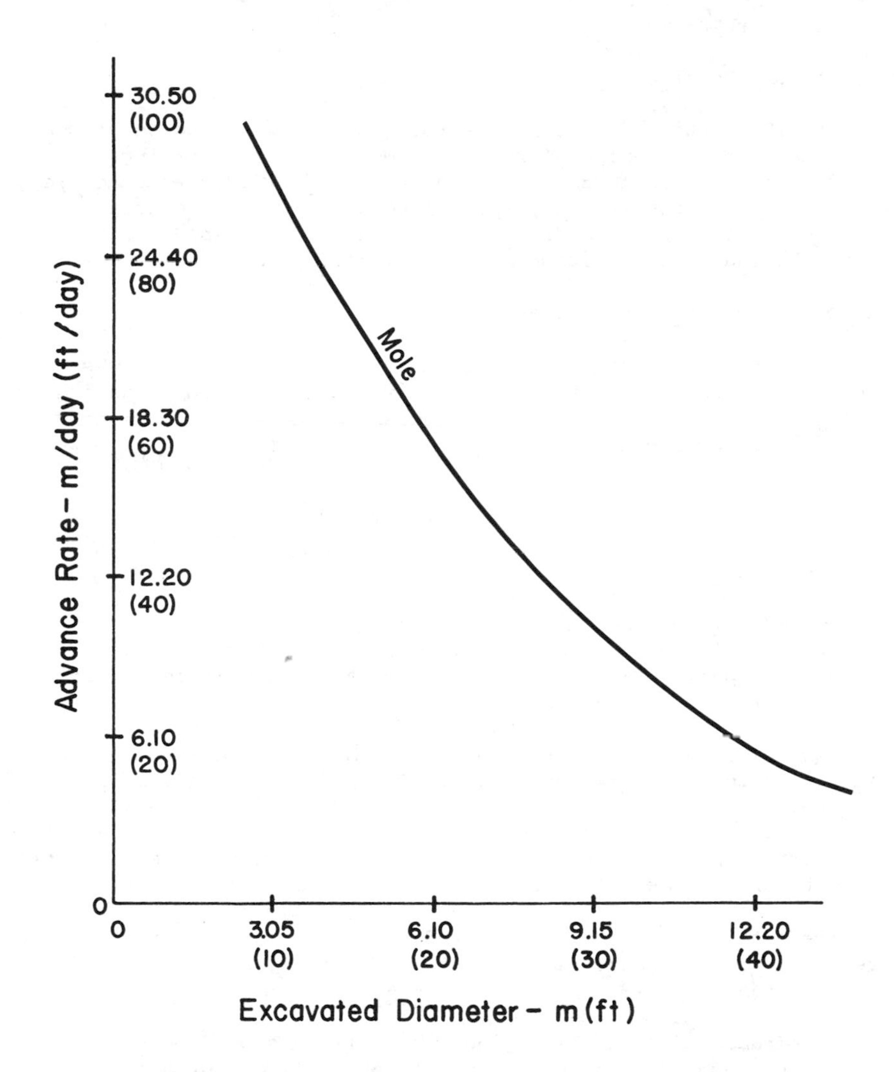

Figure 4. **ESTIMATED AVERAGE DAILY ADVANCE RATE IN MOLED TUNNEL**

Reference: Geotechnical Design Report, Mainstream Tunnel System Tunnel and Reservoir Plan, August 1975

various work crews.

Actual TBM Rates of Progress

The TBM method of tunnel construction has proven to be of special advantage in cost and construction time savings, providing there is a high quality homogeneous rock structure and sufficient tunnel length. During actual construction, average advance rates have been higher than estimated. This is indicated by Table 3, which depicts TARP projects under construction and/or completed.

Actual Crew Size for Excavation with TBM

The actual crew size per shift used by the contractors was smaller for most of TARP projects than the crew size used in preparing estimates. Table 4 is a summary of crew sizes per shift, estimated vs. actual for TARP contracts.

CONTRACT ADMINISTRATION

Size of Contracts

In 1976, it was decided to combine 33.8 km (21 miles) of tunnel along with 79 drop shafts and all related high level sewers into a single bid pacakge. This decision was based in part on the availability of a dormant quarry which was located midpoint of the tunnel alignment. It was assumed that the successful contractor would use the quarry as a staging area, use two TBM's, and fill the quarry with muck from the tunneling operation. The project was advertised, 125 companies took out bid documents, and only one joint venture submitted a bid. The bid was non-responsive, because it lacked the mandatory 100 percent performance bond and exceeded the engineer's estimate. It, therefore, was rejected.

The entire contract was reviewed in detail, and contractors were requested to furnish their comments. The following points were made by most contractors:

1) Indicated that the engineer's estimate should be higher by about 25 percent, to about $500 million for the entire 33.8 km (21 mile) contract.
2) Requested smaller contracts and shorter time durations.
3) Requested relief on the 100 percent performance bond requirements.
4) Requested a changed conditions clause.

Table 3
SUMMARY OF RATE OF PROGRESS
ESTIMATED VS. ACTUAL

CONTRACT NUMBER	TUNNEL SIZE EXC. DIA. m(ft.)	RATE OF PROGRESS LINEAL m(ft.)/DAY ESTIMATED	ACTUAL	CONTRACTOR AND TBM MANUFACTURER	
72-049-2H	9.17 (30.08) 6.73 (22.08)	9.75 (32) 11.58 (38)	16.76 (55) 20.73 (68)	Kenny-Paschen-S&M "	Jarva Jarva
75-123-2H	9.85 (32.33)	13.11 (43	19.51 (64)	Ball-Healy-Horn	Robbins
75-124-2H	9.85 (32.33) 4.65 (15.25)	14.33 (47) 16.46 (54)	18.29 (60) 14.94 (49)	Kiewit-Shea-Shea "	Robbins Jarva
75-125-2H	9.83 (32.25)	17.10 (56)	12.19 (40)	Paschen, M-K, Kenny	Jarva
75-126-2H	10.74 (35.25)	15.54 (51)	17.37 (57)	Healy-Ball-Horn	Robbins
73-160-2H	10.77 (35.33)	13.41 (44)	18.59 (61)	M-K, Kenny, Paschen, S&M	Robbins
73-287-2H	6.48 (21.25) 2.74 (9.00)	10.06 (33) 16.15 (53)	18.90 (62) 5.49 (18)	Traylor-Ferrara-Resco "	Robbins Special
73-317-2S	6.73 (22.08)	6.71 (22)	22.86 (75)	Healy, Ball, Greenfield	Robbins
73-320-2S	5.54 (18.17) 2.74 (9.00)	6.71 (22) 4.57 (15)	22.56 (74) (N.A.)	McHugh Constr. Co. "	Robbins N.A.

Estimated rate of progress extracted from Engineer's Estimate.
Rates of progress based on data received until end of November, 1980.

$$\text{Actual rate of progress} = \frac{\text{total length moled}}{\text{total no. of days worked}}$$

Total number of days worked includes machine downtime and maintenance time.

Table 4

SUMMARY OF CREW SIZE PER SHIFT
ESTIMATED VS. ACTUAL

CONTRACT NUMBER	TUNNEL SIZE EXC. DIA. m(ft.)	CREW SIZE/SHIFT		ACTUAL LABOR		CONTRACTOR AND TBM MANUFACTURER	
		ESTIMATED	ACTUAL	MH/cu yd	MH/cu m		
72-049-2H	9.17 (30.08) 6.73 (22.08)	24 22	13 12	0.210 0.304	0.274 .398	Kenny-Paschen-S&M "	Jarva Jarva
75-123-2H	9.85 (32.33)	31	22	0.246	.322	Ball-Healy-Horn	Robbins
75-124-2H	9.85 (32.33) 4.65 (15.25)	31 17	18 23	0.234 1.529	.306 2.000	Kiewit-Shea-Shea "	Robbins Jarva
75-125-2H	9.83 (32.25)	31	23	0.432	.565	Paschen, M-K, Kenny	Jarva
75-126-2H	10.74 (35.25)	32	17	0.198	.259	Healy-Ball-Horn	Robbins
73-160-2H	10.77 (35.33)	32	27	0.273	.357	M-K,Kenny,Paschen,S&M	Robbins
73-287-2H	6.48 (21.25) 2.74 (9.00)	14 10	21 11	0.563 3.529	.736 4.616	Traylor-Ferrara-Resco "	Robbins Special
73-317-2S	6.73 (22.08)	33	25	0.590	.772	Healy,Ball,Greenfield	Robbins
73-320-2S	5.54 (18.17) 2.74 (9.00)	33 39	20 N.A.	0.420	.549	McHugh Constr. Co. "	Robbins N.A.

Estimated crew size/shift obtained from Engineer's Estimate.

Actual crew size utilized/shift obtained from computer printout based on weekly tunnel excavation report submitted by resident Engineers.

$$\text{Labor MH/cu m (MH/cu yd)} = \frac{\text{Total Man Hours}}{\text{Total Solid Volume Bored}}$$

Our review resulted in the following conclusions:

1) The contracts were too large in physical scope and too long in time duration and, therefore, contractors had to assign a substantial risk factor.
2) Because of the size of the estimate, with its high risk factor, many elements of the construction industry found it difficult to obtain the 100 percent performance bond and, therefore, were precluded from bidding.

The following recommendations were made:

1) Separate the 33.8 km (21 mile) contract into 5 tunnel and drop shaft contracts and 31 connecting structures contracts, and commence advertising no later than July 13, 1977.
2) Include in the subject contracts all of the recently mandated USEPA construction contract general conditions, which include the changed conditions clause.
3) Continue to pursue reduction in the performance bond requirements with the USEPA. If such change is permitted by the USEPA, it will be included in all future District contracts as a requirement.
4) Review insurance and bonding requirements.
5) Do not obtain additional construction estimates by any other parties. The District has rock tunnel work under way, has received bids on approximately 14.5 km (9 miles) of the 10.7 m (35 feet) diameter tunnel and has independent estimates on elements of TARP from many consultants.
6) Do not contact construction management firms at this time since design is already completed, and obtain bids for multiple contracts from the construction industry.
7) All rock becomes the property of the contractor. A meeting was held with City of Chicago representatives to determine what conditions should be included in all subsequent contract documents so that Stearns Quarry will be a viable option as a rock disposal location for all contractors.

The two most critical factors that governed contract sizes were:

1) Life of TBM. It is anticipated that after about 8047 m (5 miles) of tunnel excavation, considerable amount of rehabilitation or rebuilding work has to be done on a TBM in order to obtain similar rate of output.

2) Availability of sites for construction shafts and staging area. The contractor uses construction shaft for lowering equipment and building underground plant.

The cost and size of tunnel also played a key role in segmentation process. For example, if at certain points along the route of the tunnel a change in diameter was warranted hydraulically, and also if enough staging area was available, then this location was considered as limit for one contract. The estimated cost played a key role in the sense that it helped in determining limits of a contract, thus making it biddable by more consortiums. Increased biddability invited competitive bidding and avoided restrictive competition because of financial limitations of any group or joint venture.

A summary of TARP contracts by tunnel diameter, total lengths, and contract duration is provided in Table 5, and a progress chart for TARP tunnel contracts is provided in Table 6.

Rights-of-Way and Permits obtained by the District and Printed in the Contract Documents

The District obtains all necessary rights-of-way for the permanent structures and those which we feel are necessary for temporary construction. The contractor is required to obtain all rights-of-way and permits for his own facilities and is further required to comply with all local laws and the obtaining of permits to open streets in the public rights-of-way.

Full Disclosure of Subsurface Information

The advertising for the contract states that all subsurface information is available and gives the location where it is available. The District further indicates that the bidders are encouraged to contact consulting engineers who have performed the subsurface investigation program and review information they have used in developing the subsurface investigation report.

Temporary Support Systems

We assume responsibility for the design of permanent structures; however, the contractor is responsible for design of all temporary structures. All designs must be submitted to the District for approval.

Owner's Estimate is Published in Advertisement

The value of the project is made public at the time the project is authorized and then updated annually during each of our budget hearings. By the time the contract documents are completed, we do the final cost estimate in the advertisement.

Table 5

SUMMARY OF TARP CONTRACTS

CONTRACT NUMBER	TUNNEL DIAMETER IN m(ft.)	TOTAL LENGTH IN m(ft.)	CONTRACT DURATION IN YEARS
72-049-2H	9.17 (30.08) 6.73 (22.08)	8458 (27,750) 7326 (24,036)	4.4
75-123-2H	9.85 (32.33)	6891 (22,607)	5.0
75-124-2H	9.85 (32.33) 4.65 (15.25)	4184 (13,726) 2026 (6,648)	5.0
75-125-2H	9.83 (32.25)	7678 (25,189)	5.2
75-126-2H	10.74 (35.25)	7925 (26,000)	5.4
73-160-2H	10.77 (35.33)	5731 (18,804)	4.6
73-287-2H	6.48 (21.25) 2.74 (9.00)	12966 (42,540) 1681 (5,515)	4.6
73-317-2S	6.73 (22.08)	6724 (22,061)	3.0
73-320-2S	5.54 (18.17)	3252 (10,670)	2.6

*Includes length of drill and blast segment (where required) to set up TBM operation.

Table 6

CONTRACT NO.	MACHINE TYPE/DIA. m (ft)	TUNNEL LENGTH MINED m(ft)	TUNNEL LENGTH TO BE MINED	STATUS
72-049-2H	JARVA 9.14m (30FT.)	8,312m (27,269 FT.)	*	COMPLETED
72-049-2H	JARVA 6.71m (22 FT.)	7,326m (24,036 FT.)		COMPLETED
75-123-2H	ROBBINS 9.75m (32 FT.)	5,103m (16,741 FT.)	6,891 (22,607)	
75-124-2H	ROBBINS 9.75m (32 FT.)	3,573m (11,723 FT.)	4,187 (13,726)	
75-124-2H	JARVA 4.57m (15 FT.)	1,899m (6,230 FT.)	*	COMPLETED
75-125-2H	JARVA 9.75m (32 FT.)	5,038m (16,529 FT.)	* 6,937 (22,789)	
75-126-2H	ROBBINS 10.67m (35 FT.)	4,297m (14,097 FT.)	7,925 (26,000)	
73-160-2H	ROBBINS 10.67m (35 FT.)	5,409m (17,747 FT.)	*	COMPLETED
73-287-2H	ROBBINS 6.40m (21 FT.)	7,376m (24,201 FT.)	12,966 (42,540)	
73-287-2H	ROBBINS 2.74m (9 FT.)	1,248m (4,093 FT.)	1,681 (5,515)	
73-317-2S	ROBBINS 6.10m (20 FT.)	6,724m (22,061 FT.)		COMPLETED
73-320-2S	ROBBINS 4.88m (16 FT.)	3,252m (10,670 FT.)		COMPLETED

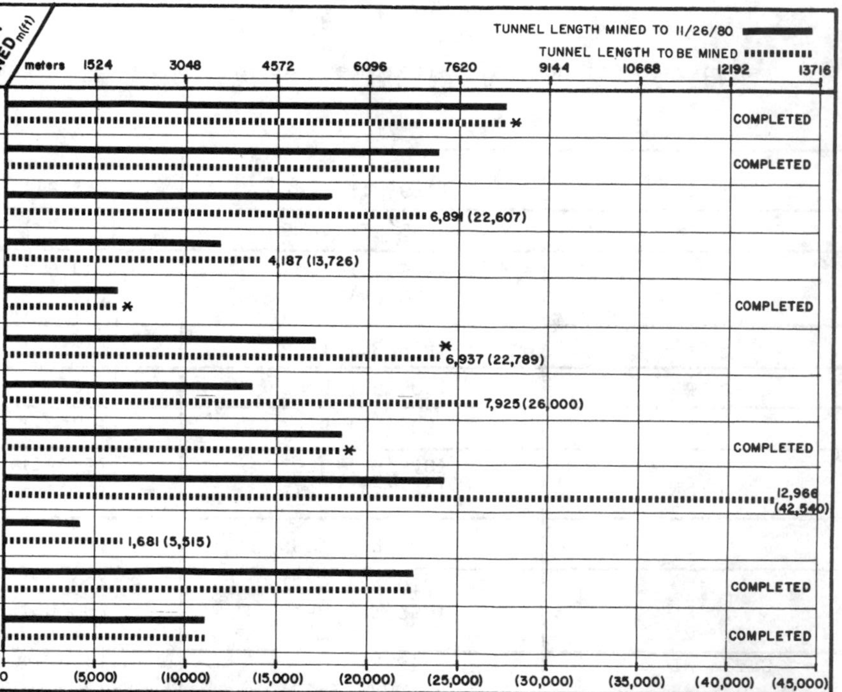

Chart scale: meters 1524, 3048, 4572, 6096, 7620, 9144, 10668, 12192, 13716; (Ft.) 0, (5,000), (10,000), (15,000), (20,000), (25,000), (30,000), (35,000), (40,000), (45,000)

Legend: TUNNEL LENGTH MINED TO 11/26/80 (solid bar); TUNNEL LENGTH TO BE MINED (dashed bar)

TARP PHASE I TUNNEL BORING MACHINE PROGRESS CHART

* Drill & blast segment not included

THE METROPOLITAN SANITARY DISTRICT OF GREATER CHICAGO
ENGINEERING DEPARTMENT
12-80 TUNNEL AND RESERVOIR DK:HP

Unit Price Contracts

All TARP contracts are unit price contracts. The contractor is paid his unit bid price for the work that is installed. For certain items of work, such as dewatering, there is a specific amount of dewatering in the contract; however, if the amount of dewatering exceeds the specified amount, then the contractor will be paid for any additional dewatering at a unit price bid in the contract.

Mobilization Costs

TARP contracts do include an item for mobilization. On some contracts, we have set a mobilization price before the contract is advertised. In other cases, bidders are given an opportunity to bid a mobilization cost. Since USEPA funded contracts do not permit reimbursement for inflation, and since most TARP contracts are for 4 to 5 years with substantial early capital purchases, contractors were permitted to bid mobilization costs and to receive early payment.

Prompt Progress Payments

Contractors are paid monthly. Payments are generally made 15 calendar days after the contractor submits a voucher. After payment to the contractor, the District then requests 75 percent from the USEPA, and the reimbursement is generally received 15 calendar days after the request is made. At the present time, the District is making progress payments to contractors at the rate of $31 million per month.

Progress Payments on Reserves

If the contract value is $10,000,000 or less, an amount shall be withheld of 10 percent of the payment claimed until work is 50 percent complete. When work is 50 percent complete, the withholding shall be reduced to 5 percent of the dollar value of all work satisfactorily completed to date until the work is 90 percent complete. When the work is 90 percent complete, the withholding shall be reduced to 4 percent of all work satisfactorily completed to date.

If the contract value is more than $10,000,000, an amount shall be withheld of 7.5 percent of the payment claimed until the work is 50 percent complete. When work is 50 percent complete, the withholding shall be reduced to 5 percent of the dollar value of all work satisfactorily completed to date until the work is 75 percent complete. When the work is 75 percent complete, the withholding shall be reduced to 4 percent of the dollar value of all work satisfactorily completed to date until the work is 90 percent complete. When the work is 90 percent complete, the withholding shall be reduced to 3 percent of all work satisfactorily completed to date.

For all contracts, when the dollar value of the work satisfactorily completed has reached 90 percent and the Chief Engineer determines that the work under the contract is substantially complete, the Chief Engineer may recommend further reduction in the reserves to 2 percent of the dollar value of the work performed, subject to the approval of the Board of Commissioners.

Formal Written Contract Communications

All claims by the contractor must be in writing and meet the notice requirements of the contract. The District response to all correspondence is through a formalized numbered letter system. Every attempt is made to respond as quickly as possible to all inquiries.

Resolution of Claims through Litigation not Arbitration

TARP contract documents do not permit arbitration as a means of final settlement of any disputes. Any dispute which cannot be settled through administrative channels is settled through litigation.

Differing Site Conditions

The USEPA, which provides 75 percent funds for TARP, has mandated that the following Differing Site Conditions clause be in all contracts:

a) The contractor shall promptly, and before such conditions are disturbed, notify the owner in writing of: 1) Subsurface or latent physical conditions at the site differing materially from those indicated in this contract, or 2) unknown physical conditions at the site, of an unusual nature, differing materially from those ordinarily encountered and generally recognized as inhering in work of the character provided for in this contract. The owner shall promptly investigate the conditions. If he finds that such conditions do materially differ and cause an increase or decrease in the contractor's cost of, or the time required for, performance of any part of the work under this contract, whether or not changed as a result of such condition, an equitable adjustment shall be made and the contract modified in writing accordingly.

b) No claim of the contractor under this clause shall be allowed unless the contractor has given the notice required in paragraph (a) of this clause, except that the owner may extend the prescribed time.

c) No claim by the contractor for an equitable adjustment hereunder shall be allowed if asserted after final payment under this contract.

We have issued the following written interpretation of this clause:

"Contract documents which contain a Differing Site Conditions* Clause state, in part, that differing site conditions are "..... unknown physical conditions at the site, of an unusual nature, differing materially from those ordinarily encountered and generally recognized as inhering in work of the character provided for in this contract."

"It is the interpretation of this office that work necessary to remove any unknown and abandoned structure is work that qualified under the Federal definition of Differing Site Conditions and, therefore, qualifies as extra work.

"*Excerpts from Federal Register dated September 27, 1978, Volume 43, Number 288, Appendix C-2, Required Provisions, Construction Contracts."

This clause has been used and extra costs authorized in the following cases:

a) The contractor had to use a hand-mining procedure instead of the tunnel boring machine because of the absence of rock in the tunnel.
b) Contractor encountered rock where none was shown on the plans.
c) Contractor encountered abandoned manmade structures where none were shown on the plans.

CONCLUSIONS

TARP is being completed on time or slightly ahead of schedule, under the award prices (Table 7), and with an excellent safety record.

There has been significant improvement in the advance rates of the TBM's, which is a tribute to the entire industry, the contractors, and the manufacturers.

In the years ahead, many other owners of rock tunnel works will receive the benefits of what has been learned and developed on the TARP project.

Table 7

FINANCIAL STATUS SUMMARY OF TARP CONTRACTS
AS OF DECEMBER 31, 1980

SYSTEM	BID VALUE	CREDITS/ REDUCTION IN QUANTITIES	EXTRAS	PROGRESS PAYMENTS TO DATE	ESTIMATED FINAL CONTRACT VALUE	LIQUIDATED DAMAGES
Mainstream Tunnels, Shafts & Pump Station	$805,212,295	$10,343,340	$1,825,788	$509,939,628	$796,694,743	--
Mainstream Connecting Structures	168,685,947	677,061	2,058,917	95,644,340	169,441,237	626,566
Calumet Tunnel, Shafts & Pump Station	134,098,195	571	39,600	85,036,742	134,137,224	--
Calument Connecting Structures	19,173,509	22,820	78,366	7,313,805	19,229,055	--
Upper Des Plaines Tunnel & Shafts	57,121,271	2,028,790	37,976	54,484,081	54,522,057	608,400
Upper Des Plaines Connecting Structures	4,598,650	--	147,322	4,500,395	4,745,972	--
TOTAL	$1,188,889,867	$13,072,582	$4,187,969	$756,918,991	$1,178,770,288	$1,234,966

Chapter 100

EISENHOWER MEMORIAL TUNNEL - HOW COLORADO DEPARTMENT OF HIGHWAYS IMPROVED CONTRACTING PRACTICES AND MANAGEMENT

by P. R. McOllough

District Engineer, Colorado Department of Highways
Denver, Colorado

ABSTRACT

The Colorado Department of Highways awarded a contract to construct the Second Bore of the Eisenhower Tunnel in August, 1975. The contract was completed June 29, 1979, nine days ahead of schedule, without major claims or delays. The tunneling involved complex construction through difficult ground conditions.

The contract, plans and specifications were specifically planned to more equitably share the risks involved and to minimize adversary relationships. The Department produced a detailed tunnel design and maintained responsibility for the design. The contract employed some new provisions; e.g., a review board for settlement of claims and disputes; escrow documents (contractor's bid documents) to determine the contractor's basis of bid when determining adjustments.

The tunnel contract, plans and administrative efforts employed by the owner and contractor were very successful in this project.

PROJECT HISTORY

The Eisenhower Memorial Vehicular Tunnel, located on Interstate 70 approximately 95 km (60 miles) west of Denver, passes under the Continental Divide at the elevation of 3350 m (11,000 ft). The twin 2700 m (8900 ft) tunnels carried 8200 average daily traffice in 1973, and it is estimated, will carry 14,000 average daily traffic in the year 2000.

As early as the 1930's, highway planners realized that a vehicular tunnel would be the ultimate answer for handling the projected traffic volume across the Colorado Rockies. Due to steep grades, sharp curves, severe winter conditions and maintenance problems of conventional high mountain passes, the tunnel alternative was investigated. Preliminary sites were examined, and in 1943 a small bore was tunneled beneath Loveland Pass. However, extensive problems arose illustrating the need for further studies. The result of these studies culminated in the selection of the route following the Straight Creek Valley, and a pilot bore along this route was completed in 1964.

Construction of the first bore and ventilation buildings started March 13, 1968 at the west portal. The project was opened to traffic March 8, 1973. The project encountered many difficulties and gained notoriety when construction costs escalated from $54 million to $108 million and completion was delayed approximately two years.

Early in the project, a number of problems were encountered with foundation materials in the west ventilation building. Many claims were submitted during this time from the subcontractor via the prime contractor to the owner.

Tunneling of the west heading proceeded relatively smoothly while the ventilation buildings were under construction. After driving 1325 m (4350 ft) on the west heading, a chamber was constructed for the installation of the shield. Simultaneously, the east heading was started and driven approximately 550 m (1800 ft) before severe structural deformation problems began to occur. On September 5, 1969, the contractor notified the owner that underground conditions existed that were beyond the scope of the contract and claimed that a breach of contract existed.

On December 6, 1969, the east heading advance was halted. Heavy loading resulted in unexpected convergence and deformation of the steel support sets in the east heading. Extensive remedial work such as rock bolting, buttress concrete, shotcrete, grouting, rock reinforcement and jump sets were required to stabilize this heading. Three months prior, excavation using a full face shield was stopped in the central section of the mountain because the shield developed mechanical problems. This method was later abandoned.

For the next year, underground construction was at a standstill while discussion ensued between the owner, contractor, consultants and Federal Highway Administration engineers on methods of resolving the construction problems. A redesign of the tunnel was necessary to accommodate the difficult geological conditions encountered, and the original unit price contract was re-negotiated to a cost type of contract to complete the tunnel portion of the project. As the result of these negotiations, the owner became intimately involved with the contractor's organization and problems. In other words, the owner's supervisory personnel had to expand their attention from payment of bid items and documentation to concern with all aspects of costs and construction methods involved. This negotiated partnership produced the desirable effect of immediately improving relations between the owner and the contractor. On January 7, 1971, construction resumed.

The owner's involvement in the first bore project varied markedly before and after renegotiation of the original contract. The owner's staff became substantially more involved in construction and administrative matters generally and historically assigned to the contractor in the original contract. It was interesting to observe the improved cooperation between the owner and contractor. As a result, the work progressed at a substantially improved rate; and the adversary relationships which had previously existed were, in some cases, greatly diminished or became non-existent.

Due to the success of the re-negotiated contract, the multiple-drift method and other refinements to the tunneling methods, the holing-through occurred on March 1, 1972, and the first bore was officially opened to traffic March 8, 1973.

The tunneling contract for the second bore of the Eisenhower Memorial Tunnel was awarded August 11, 1975 to Peter Kiewit Sons Co.-Brown and Root, Inc. after submitting the low bid of $102,800,00.00. The second bidder submitted a bid of $102,988,770.00. The engineer's estimate was $110,559,806.50. The tunneling contract was completed on June 21, 1979. Upon completion of the finish contract, the second bore was opened to traffic December 21, 1979.

THE SECOND BORE CONTRACTS

Planning and design work started on the second bore of the Eisenhower Tunnel in June of 1973. It was decided to utilize the "in house" capabilities of the Department of Highways to accomplish the planning and design of the second bore. The consulting firm of Leeds, Hill & Jewett of San Francisco was engaged to assist the Department's designers on an "as needed" basis in planning, design, specification preparation and, ultimately, the construction of the project. The author was assigned the task of coordinating planning, design and construction administration of the second bore.

All information relative to the construction history of the first bore was reviewed in considerable detail by the design and planning group. Considerable time was employed in analyzing why the construction of the first bore met with severe difficulty and what factors contributed to those problems. Particular attention was given to the adversary relationships which developed during the construction of the first bore. The planning group concluded the following elements should be addressed in the second bore design, contract and specifications as well as in other contracts which would be utlized to complete the entire facility:

Type and Number of Contracts
Advertising Period
Contract Time and Working Hours
Disclosure
Safety
Prequalification
Contingencies and Exculpatory Language
Payment for Materials on Hand
Mobilization
Labor Adjustments
Adjustment of Material Costs and Changes in Common Carrier Rates
Escrow Documents
Cost Accounting
Dispute Resolution
Detailed Plans
Financing
Other Elements

The planning group separately considered other related elements that were deemed important to the administration of the second bore contract such as:

Staffing of the owner's construction team
Qualification of the owner's construction team
Authority and lines of communication for the construction team
Training of project inspectors

Type of Contract

Several types of contracts running the gamut from a cost type of contract at one extreme to the fixed price contract at the other were considered. It was concluded that the unit price type of contract would be the most appropriate, considering the constraints imposed on governmental agencies. However, it was believed that the historic unit price cost type of contract typically used by government agencies would be modifield to promote more equitable sharing of risks between the owner and contractor. Thus, a more equitable unit price type of contract was employed for the second bore construction.

Number of Contracts

It was noted that considerable difficulty was experienced by both the owner and contractors in handling and coordinating the single large contract employed for construction of the first bore. These difficulties existed in the areas of providing space for each contractor in a very limited work area at the tunnel portals, coordination and sequencing of the work, materials procurement, labor disputes, etc. In light of these types of problems and in recognition of advantages of stage financing to construct the entire second bore facility, the planning group concentrated upon clearly defining and separating the total work necessary to construct the facility. The following contracts were decided upon in the sequence shown:

1. Ventilation and Electrical Equipment Procurement and Installation in the Portal Ventilation Buildings. This project was designated as I 70-3(82).

2. Tunneling, Concrete Lining and Tunnel Drainage. This project was designated as I 70-3(81).

3. Bridge Construction East Portal Tunnel Approach. This project was designated as I 70-3(80).

4. Finish Work in the Tunnel Including Installation of Tile Walls, Suspended Ceiling and Ventilation Ducts, Safety Curbs, Tunnel Paving, Electrical Conduit, Wiring, Cabinetry, Mechanical Equipment (i.e. Carbon Monoxide Sampling Equipment). This project was designated as I 70-3(83).

5. Paving Tunnel Approach Roads. This project was designated as I 70-3(84).

6. Landscaping Work at the Tunnel Portals and the East and West Approaches to the Tunnel along Interstate 70 Highway. This project was designated as I 70-3(85).

Although this paper is principally concerned with the tunneling contract (No. 2), it is important to note that many of the provisions and concepts of the tunneling contract were utilized in contract numbers one and four.

Prospective bidders for the second bore contracts were advised of the number and sequence of all projects planned. This information was listed in the project specifications.

Advertising Period

It was recognized that the shorter advertising period (three to four weeks) customarily used by the owner on highway contracts was not appropriate in considering a tunneling project of this magnitude. Consequently, a six-week advertising period was eventually employed due to the time constraints which had developed by the summer of 1975. However, it was the concensus of opinion of the planning group that a twelve-week advertising period would have been more appropriate and desirable.

Contract Time and Working Hours

The author strongly believes this provision of contracts is one of the most important facets which should be determined through thorough analysis by the designer and construction personnel. It is my opinion that all too often contract times are set based upon little or no analysis.

In the interest of developing realistic, reasonable contract times for the entire project, the owner's design and construction group scheduled all contracts and related work activities on the basis of reasonable construction rates and floattime which were achieved during construction of the first bore. Construction rates available from other tunnels were also considered. Thus, the tunneling contract time for the second bore was established at 940 working days or approximately three and one-half years. This type of procedure was utilized in setting the contract times for all contracts.

In setting contract times for this contract, additional explanation is necessary to convey the owner's reasoning based upon conclusions reached during the construction of the first bore.

The owner noted several circumstances during construction of the first bore which were worthy of consideration in setting the contract time and developing the contract specification provisions.

It was noted during the first bore construction that when the contractor was compelled to conduct many work activities in close proximity to one another, there was a greater exposure of all work force in those congested areas to accident. It was concluded that by being a bit more liberal in setting the contract time, that a contractor could minimize this exposure of the work force by reducing the work activities in a given location, thus reducing the congestion and promoting greater safety for the work force.

Secondly, it was observed that when the first bore contractor worked a three-shift seven-day week, the work force would work the premium time shifts on the weekends and then be absent during the straight time shifts during the week. This was noted particularly on Mondays and Tuesdays when absenteeism would run as high was 45%. A general decrease in productivity was evident on the weekend shifts.

Additionally, it was noted that the contractor, although adequately equipped with the numbers and type of equipment to conduct the work, was hard-pressed to maintain his equipment due to the lack of adequate maintenance time imposed by the scheduled seven-day work week.

A general observation concluded that both the supervisory personnel of the owner and contractor were overly fatigued by the seven-day work week and the adverse environment at this location, i.e., the 3350 m (11,000 ft) elevation and generally nine months of snow and sub-zero temperatures.

Finally, in consideration of the high traffic volumes using the Interstate highway on summer and winter weekends, the resulting traffic congestion produced at the approaches to the two-lane first bore and difficulties of winter highway maintenance at this location, the contract time for the second bore was set at 940 working days based on a specified five-day work week.

Disclosure

It was recognized that prospective bidders for the second bore should have available all information possible relating to the design and construction of the first bore, as well as that developed for design of the second bore.

The design and construction group assembled, filed and recorded two complete copies of virtually every report, photograph, article, "as constructed" plan, and engineering construction record available. This information was made available to all contractors during the pre-bid period at a pre-bid room located at the Division headquarters in Denver.

The owner's pre-bid room was manned by knowledgeable construction personnel and a procedure was employed where a list of available information was provided to the bidders, who then could request to review any of the documents in the pre-bid room and order copies of those documents which they desired.

The pre-bid room also contained one geological model and a construction model depicting the owner's design for the second bore.

All information made available to bidders in the pre-bid room was stored, maintained intact, and was accessible at the project site through the duration of the contract work. A complete listing of this information was included in the project specifications.

One pre-bid conference was scheduled during the bidding period. Prospective bidders were instructed to submit written questions to the owner. These questions were verbally answered at the pre-bid conference. A written response to all questions was also furnished and distributed to conference attendees, plan holders and prospective bidders.

Safety

The planning group unanimously endorsed developing plan specification provisions which would promote safety during construction, such as the workable design details evident in the project plans and specification provisions which would directly pay the contractor for safety related items.

Further, the planning group felt the owner should lead by promoting safety where possible in a direct way, thereby eliminating some of the contingency risks associated with the items of work.

Specification provisions and contract units relating to project safety were incorporated in the second bore contract as follows:

Specification Provision No.		Unit
625	First Aid Attendant	Hour
	Ambulance Driver	Hour
	Ambulance Attendant	Hour
	Furnish Ambulance	Each
614	Traffic Control Supervision	Per Day
614	Flagging	Hour
521	Pedestrian Overpass	Each
211	Rock Reinforcement	Each

One can readily conclude that the construction group employed on the first bore felt that the owner could and should provide greater emphasis on project safety by participating directly in the costs as well as addressing safety aspects in the design of the tunnel structure.

Prequalification

The planning group recognized the need for employing a highly competent contractor with an adequate organization and resources, including personnel to accomplish this difficult project. The group felt that prospective bidders should have a substantial "track record" of successful completion of similar tunnels of this size, length and difficulty to be eligible to bid the second bore work.

The prequalification specification employed in the tunnel contract, quoted in part, required the bidders to satisfy the following requirements:

-Ten years experience in major construction projects involving similar work with at least one major tunnel project within the immediate previous 10 years.

-Each prospective bidder must have satisfactorily completed one construction contract in the amount of at least $30,000,000.00. If in a joint venture, at least one party must comply.

-Tunneling experience to include at least 10,000 ft of tunnel or shaft of diameter greater than 20 ft, in rock, of which at least half was concrete lined. If in joint venture, at least one party must comply.

-Set up and operation of concrete batching plant; placement of concrete for tunnel lining or similar underground experience; one job of at least 10,000 cubic yards of concrete.

-At least 10 key staff personnel, each having at least 5 years of experience acceptable to the Division. The personnel list shall include the names, positions and the individual tunneling experience of each of the supervisory persons who will be available for assignment to the project.

-Quick assets equal to at least $2,000,000.00.

-Serious failure in connection with a previous contract or other unfavorable circumstances of past work as interpreted by the Division will be cause for disqualification.

-Each prospective bidder must submit his bonding record or show proof of his bonding ability. Each prospective bidder must have been bondable for 10 consecutive years prior to submission of the experience questionnaire. If a joint venture, all parties must comply.

Subcontractor prequalification specification requirements were also included to provide for prequalification after award of contract and prior to commencement of work on subcontracts of $150,000 or greater.

Contingencies and Exculpatory Language

Recognizing the general usage of exculpatory language employed historically in contractswas of little if any value and could contribute to the development of the adversary relationship, the planning group and specification group diligently endeavored to preclude this type of language from the plans and specifications.

Further, the group recognized there would be certain types of work that would be difficult to define and quantify for bidding purposes, and the decision was made to direct the contractor to conduct this work on a force account basis (Labor, Equipment and Materials).

Items of work directed to be completed on a force account basis were:

	Estimated Cost	Actual Cost
On-the-job Trainee	$16,800.00	$29,246.00
Erosion Control	$100,000.00	$85,436.00
Construction Monitoring	$140,000.00	$152,633.00
Avalanche Control	$50,000.00	$3,265.00
Furnish Employee Shuttle Bus	$25,200.00	-0-
Trial Testing for Rock Reinforcement	$4,200.00	$1,399.00
Miscellaneous Work	$220,000.00	$225,360.00

Payment for Materials on Hand

The need was recognized for a contract provision which would allow payment for permanent materials procured by the contractor. This contract provision specification was included to assist the financing of the project.

Mobilization

A mobilization item (lump sum) and specification were included to assist in financing the project.

The mobilization specification provided for partial monthly payments to the contractor as the work progressed as follows:

-Five percent of the bid price for mobilization will be paid for each one percent of the original contract amount earned until 90% of mobilization is paid.

-The remaining 10% of mobilization will be included in the final payment.

Labor Adjustments

The project planning group recognized the need for inclusion of a labor adjustment provision to provide relief and minimize this risk. It should be pointed out at this time (1973-75), inflation was running rampant and in consideration of the duration of this contract, it was felt a contractor could not reasonably assess this risk. Therefore, a specification provision patterned closely in concept to that utilized by the U.S. Bureau of Reclamation in federal contracts was employed.

A review of the labor adjustment payments made to the contractor reveals the following:

Year	Labor Adjustment Payments
Aug. 1975	0 - not eligible
1976	0 - not eligible
1977	+$314,000.00
1978	+ 991,924.00
1979	+ 363,974.00
Approximate Total	+$1,669,898.00

The total of the labor adjustment payments represents 90% of the actual escalation incurred by the contractor during the allowed escalation period. Adjustments for labor costs were not allowed during the first 545 calendar days of the contract. The total amount of labor adjustment allowed represented 1.62% of the contract amount bid.

Adjustment of Material Costs and Adjustments for Changes in Common Carrier Rates

A provision for adjustment of selected material costs was deemed appropriate for inclusion into the contract based on the inflationary trends (1973-1975), shortages of various steel shapes, and energy dependent products. Generally, AASHTO (American Association of State Highway and Transportation Officials) guidelines were used with some modification. Materials determined to be eligible for cost adjustments were structural steel, reinforcing steel, gasoline, diesel fuel, liquid petroleum gas and electrical power. The bidders were required to use the "Pegged" or Specified Material prices listed in the following tabulation in preparing their bid. The following tabulation reflects the "Pegged" or Specified Price and the material adjustment costs through July, 1979:

Material	"Pegged" or Specified Price*	Material Cost Adjustment
Structural Steel	$0.72/kg-$650/ton	$ +856,434.00
Reinforcing Steel	$0.35/kg-$320/ton	+101,721.00
Gasoline	$0.10/1 -$0.382/gal	+ 26,971.00
Diesel Fuel	$0.09/1 -$0.330/gal	+ 34,540.00
LP Gas	$0.08/1 -$0.300/gal	+ 84,647.00
Electrical Power	Per Rate Schedule (Energy+Demand+Fuel Cost Adjustment)	+228,196.00

*Delivered to Project Site

Total Material Cost Adjustment +$1,332,509.00

This total amount of allowed material cost adjustment represents 1.30% of the contract bid amount.

A specification provision allowing adjustment for changes in the common carrier rates was included as part of the contract. This provision is normally included in all Colorado Highway contracts. This adjustment amounted to $50,054.00 during the life of the contract.

Escrow Documents and Cost Accounting Systems

In consideration of the complexity of this project, the risks involved and the history of the first bore construction, a provision was included in this contract to require the contractor to submit to the owner virtually any and every piece of information that he had used to arrive at his bid. It was required that the unit prices for each bid items be supported and separated into a cost breakdown consisting of labor, equipment, material, on-project fixed costs, and off-project fixed costs. Since mobilization was a separate bid item in this contract, it was supported by the same type of cost breakdown as specified for all other unit price items. The specification provision requiring the bidders submission of the escrow documents states:

Each bidder shall submit with his proposal complete documentation clearly itemizing and separating costs for each Contract Item, except the Contract Item "FIXED FEE," contained in the Proposal. Costs used to determine each unit price shall be separated and identified as costs of: Labor; Equipment; Materials; Fixed Costs - On-Project Site; Fixed Costs - Off-Project Site; any other costs included must be specifically identified.

(a) The documentation shall include copies of all quotes, memoranda, narratives or any other information used to arrive at the bid prices contained in the Bid Schedule and shall be clearly marked with the appropriate Bid Schedule Item Reference Number. For purposes of identification, all such supporting documentation will be known as the ESCROW DOCUMENTS.

(b) The Escrow Documents shall be submitted in a sealed container along with the sealed envelope containing the proposal and will be clearly marked with the bidder's name, date of submittal, project number, and title "Escrow Documents." The Escrow Documents shall be accompanied with an affidavit signed by the bidder, stating that he has personally examined the contents of the Escrow Documents container and has found that the Documents are in the container and are correct and complete. Escrow Documents of the apparent successful bidder shall be examined in his presence for adequacy and accuracy prior to award. After Award of the Contract, the Escrow Documents of all other bidders will be returned unopened.

(c) The Escrow Documents of the successful bidder will be returned at such time that the contract is completed and final settlement has been achieved.

(d) Escrow Documents shall be stored at a location and in a manner agreeable to the Division and the Contractor.

(e) Escrow Documents may be examined any time deemed necessary by the Chief Engineer to determine the Contractor's bid concept. This examination may be required for payment purposes for any and all contract items, subject to the following requirements:

1. Examination of documents shall be made by those specifically delegated by the Chief Engineer and a Contractor representative.

2. These Documents are considered proprietary and confidential in nature and shall be treated as such by those designated to review them. These documents, or any of the contents thereof, shall not be made available to any person or persons not herein designated without the specific consent of the Contractor.

The owner's reasoning for requiring submission of the contractor's bid documents was to establish and insure the basis of bid would be available for review to facilitate determining just and fair compensation in the equitable settlement of major disputes which might arise during the course of construction. Secondly, the Escrow Documents documented the basis of bid and provided a means of evaluating the contractor's bid proposal.

The owner committed to procedures to insure the contractor's bid documents would be maintained confidential, such as storage in bank safe deposit box with access attained only by mutual consent and presence of designated officials for the contractor and the Colorado Division of Highways.

Appropriate sections of the Escrow Documents were reviewed on occasion to facilitate adjustments involving substantial quantity underruns and overruns made in accordance with the specification, "Alteration of Character or Quantities of Work." This usage greatly facilitated this type of adjustment.

It is noteworthy to mention that the contractor, although not obligated to do so, volunteered to make the documents available to members of the Project Review Board in the event of a dispute where resolution of the dispute could be facilitated through use of the documents.

Upon completion of the project and agreement to final payment, the Escrow Documents were jointly removed from the safe deposit box by the owner's representative and the contractor's project manager and returned to the contractor.

A cost accounting system was required by the project specification to be maintained by the contractor. The cost accounting system assimilated incurred costs on a current basis and was structured to identify incurred costs of labor, equipment, materials, fix costs on-project site, fixed costs off-project site and other costs. These cost records were available to the engineer as required for monitoring project costs.

Monitoring of the contractor's cost accounting system was by the owner's auditor. The cost accounting system was utilized by the owner's auditor to audit costs associated with labor and material adjustments, alteration of quantity adjustments, force account work and claims.

One can readily see how the Escrow Documents and the cost accounting system would be jointly utilized to quantify costs and facilitate determining fair and just compensation in the event of a claim adjustment or major dispute during the course of the work.

Dispute Resolution

The need for an outside non-biased authority to facilitate resolution of project disputes was amply demonstrated during construction of the first bore.

The following specification was included in three of the major contracts employed. (Contracts numbered one, two and four listed on page 5).

Claims for adjustments and disputes shall be handled according to the following procedures:

(a) Notification of Dispute

If the Contractor objects to any decision or order of the Engineer, the Contractor shall ask, in writing, for written instructions from the Engineer. While waiting for the written instructions, the Contractor shall proceed without delay to perform the work or to conform to the decision or order. Cost records of the work shall be kept in accordance with subsection 109.04. Within 10 days after receipt of the written instructions, the Contractor shall file a written protest with the Engineer, stating clearly and in detail the basis of the objection.

(b) Determination of Dispute

The Engineer will consider any written protest and make his decision. The decision, in writing, shall be furnished to the Contractor. This decision shall be final and conclusive, subject to written appeal by the Contractor requesting a Review Board. The appeal must be instituted within 30 days of the date of receipt of the Engineer's decision. Pending final decision of a dispute, the Contractor shall diligently proceed with the work as directed.

Should the Contractor appeal the Engineer's decision, the matter will be referred to a Review Board consisting of one member selected by the Division and one by the Contractor, the two to select a third member. The Contractor and the Engineer shall each be afforded an opportunity to be heard by the Review Board and to offer evidence. All matters brought before the Review Board will be reported to the Chief Engineer.

The decision of the Review Board shall govern unless the Chief Engineer shall determine that such decision is not in the best interest of the State; in such instance, he may override the Board's decision. The Division and the Contractor shall each be responsible for one-half of the Review Board's fees and reasonable expenses.

The above provisions were incorporated into the second bore contract to provide for a three-member Review Board to resolve disputes which might arise during construction. The Board consisted of three authorities in the field of construction who were contracted with individually by the owner and contractor jointly to monitor progress of the construction and to hear disputes between the owner and contractor. The Board routinely visited the project at 90-day intervals for joint briefings by the contractor and owner. Approximately 15 meetings were held at the site for routine briefing purposes and resolution of three disputes involving claim amounts of approximately $580,000.00.

The costs of utilizing the project Review Board amount to approximately 0.045% of the contractor's bid price for constructing the project and approximately 8.06% of the amount of claims presented to the Board. The Review Board cost was equally shared by the owner and contractor.

The Review Board concept worked well on this contract and was very effective in settling the three disputes which arose during construction of the project.

It is worthy to mention that it was felt, at least by the owner's construction personnel, that the Review Board's presence most probably precluded the development of other disputes during the construction. In other words, the author feels the Review Boards's presence, in addition to the stature of the individual board members, exerted an unwritten stabilizing influence over both the owner's and contractor's supervisory personnel which precluded the potential for development of the adversary relationship.

This specification was also included in the Tunnel Finish Contract and Electrical-Mechancial Contract.

Detailed Plans

Based on the many lessons learned and observations made during construction of the first bore, the owner concluded the plans for the second bore should be carefully and completely detailed to convey the designer's intent for a workable, buildable design.

Input for the design was provided by construction, safety, contractor personnel and design consultants who were familiar with the construction of the first bore.

The second bore contractor followed the plans and specifications and very few changes were necessary.

Other Specifications

Other equitable specification provisions included in the second bore contract which were considered essential and standard were:

- Cancellation of Contract
- Price and Time Adjustment - Delays
- Alteration of Character or Quantities of Work
- Changed Condition Clause

Construction Management

The owner-construction team, assisted by the design consultants, administered all second bore contracts.

To insure efficient management, the owner assembled a construction team principally from "in house" personnel who were employed during construction of the first bore. This supervisory team was assembled and trained well in advance of the start of construction and additional training was provided during construction and prior to the awarding of successive construction contracts. It is noteworthy to point out the contractor's personnel was invited and attended many of the owner's training sessions involving safety, quality control and plan familiarization. The contractor reciprocated by inviting the owner's staff to attend many of his training sessions and meetings involving safety, scheduling, material procurement, subcontract matters and construction coordination.

Clear lines of authority and communication were established within the owner's construction organization and secondly, with the contractors and outside agencies having jurisdcition. Procedures involving contractor-owner coordination with the "press" were established early in the construction phase.

Weekly meetings were routinely scheduled between the owner's and contractor's staff to discuss progress of the contract work, to plan and coordinate joint work activities and to discuss any current or anticipated problems. The project clearly reflected good communication between the owner and contractor.

One example of the cooperative effort that could be cited was the joint use of rock instrumentation data taken by the owner's construction team which was provided and discussed with the contractor.

The owner's construction monitoring program (Rock Instrumentation) was geared to provide data on rock behavior in conjunction with the contractor's tunnel work. The monitoring program was tailored to provide usable data on rock behavior to the owner and contractor within hours after the instruments were read underground. In several cases, this data alerted and afforded both the contractor and owner the luxury of time to plan and remedy a potential structural support problem.

CONCLUSION

It is concluded the contract and contract provisions for this project were very workable and successful. The tunnel contract came in within budget, slightly under the contract time allowed and three percent under the engineer's estimate. The adversary relationship common to many contracts did not develop.

Substantial credit must be given to the contractor, Peter Kiewit Sons Co.-Brown and Root, Inc. for their outstanding organization and management of the project and to the Department of Highways consultant, Mr. Tom Lang, of the firm Leeds, Hill & Jewett, Inc. for his expertise during design and construction.

The author wishes to personally thank the Federal Highway Administration Division, Region and Headquarters for their participation during the development of the design and specifications and the Division's assistance during construction. Accordingly, it is a pleasure to thank the members of the Tunnel Review Board for their fine assistance and willingness to serve on the board. The Review Board members were Mr. A. A. Mathews, Mr. B. Palmer King, Mr. Nixon F. Crossley and Mr. Charles E. McGraw (deceased).

It is also appropriate to acknowledge the valuable reference the National Academy of Science has provided through the report titled, "Better Contracting for Underground Construction," authored by Subcommittee No. 4 - Contracting Practices, U. S. National Committee on Tunneling Technology.

EXHIBITORS

AEC Inc.
State College, PA

Balco, Inc.
Bridgeville, PA

Bonanza Fans, Inc.
Irvine, CA

Chem Grout
La Grange Park, IL

Commercial Shearing, Inc.
Youngstown, OH

The Dosco Corporation
Pittsburgh, PA

Drilco Industries
Midland, Texas

Du Pont Co.
Wilmington, DE

Elgood-Mayo Corp.
Brooklyn, NY

Englehard Industries Div.
Union, NJ

Ensign Bickford Co.
Simsbury, CT

Fan Line Manufacturing
Los Angeles, CA

Geofreeze
Lorton, VA

Golder Associates
Golden, CO

Hayward-Baker
Odenton, MA

Irad Gage, Inc.
Lebanon, NH

Jarva, Inc.
Solon, OH

Milwaukee Boiler Mfg. Co.
Milwaukee, WI

Northern Systems, Inc.
Cleveland, OH

The Robbins Company
Seattle, WA

Schwing America, Inc.
White Bear, Minn.

Serata Geomechanics
Berkeley, CA

Slope Indicator Co.
Seattle, WA

Sullair Mining Equipment Corp.
Garland, Texas

Terrametrics, Inc.
Golden, CO

The Torrington Co.
Torrington, CT

U.S. Dept. of Transportation
Washington, DC

U.S. Gypsum Co.-Metal Products Div.
Chicago, IL

Verlag Gluckhauf GmbH
Essen, West Germany

Western Contractors Service Corp.
Santa Ana, CA

Zokor Corporation
Aurora, IL

Chapter 101

THE CARDIFF CABLE TUNNEL

By A. C. Lyons
Partner, Sir William Halcrow & Partners
Consulting Engineers, London

ABSTRACT

The presentation describes the history, preliminary report, site investigation, including examination of old records, design of tunnel including choice of levels, alternative linings and working sites, the preliminary contract involving shaft sinking on the site of the Tower Block; design modifications, the main contract, including shaft sinking, ground treatment, compressed air installation, machine tunnelling, tunnelling enlargements for chambers, waterproofing and equipment.

PLANNING

The study group that examined the requirements for external plant for the new Cardiff Telephone Exchange recommended that to cope with the number of cables required and to avoid disruption of existing services and traffic diversions and congestion, a feasibility study should be carried out into the construction of a cable tunnel from Bute Monument to the south-east to the Telephone Exchange and from there north to the Castle area and on to the Law Courts. (See fig.1) Sir William Halcrow and Partners were engaged to carry out this study.

PRELIMINARY REPORT

The Consultants produced a preliminary report based on information that was obtained from the site investigation that had been carried out for the foundations of the high rise building of which the telephone exchange was to form a part and from various other site investigations which had been undertaken near the proposed route of the tunnel, many of which did little more than determine the level of the top of the Keuper Marl Strata. It should be borne in mind that the site investigation for the high rise building had been carried

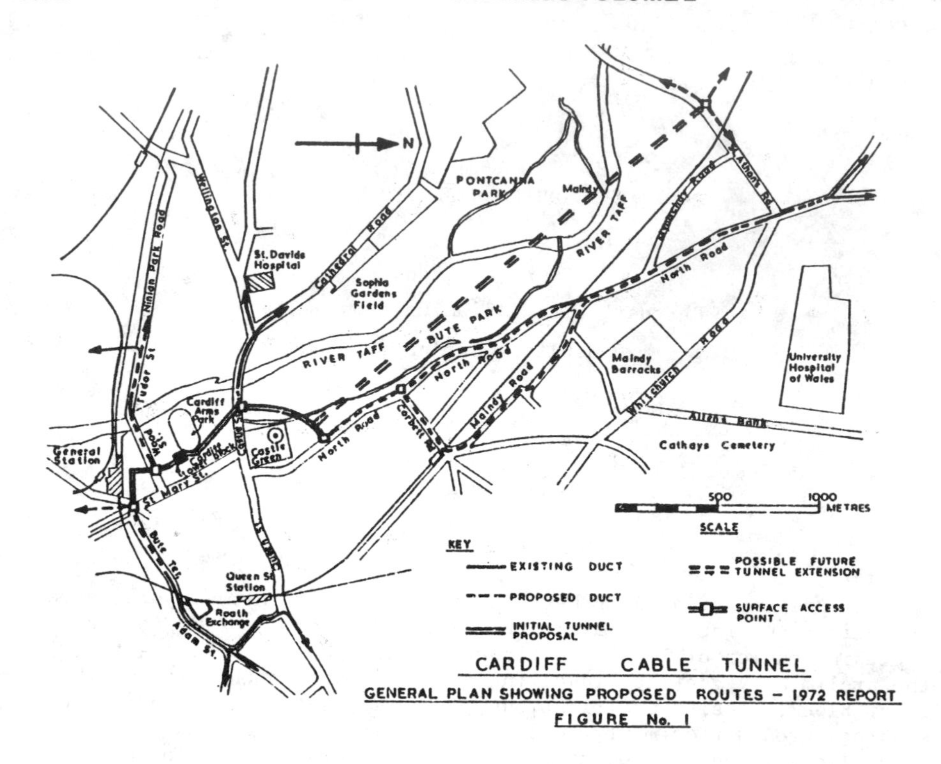

CARDIFF CABLE TUNNEL
GENERAL PLAN SHOWING PROPOSED ROUTES - 1972 REPORT
FIGURE No. 1

out for the purposes of foundation design and not all the information required for full tunnel design had been obtained. That most conspicuously absent was details of the permeability of the ground without which the design of the rings could not be finalised and methods of construction could not be determined to any degree of certainty.

It appeared probable that there were two aquifers. (See fig. 2) Below the surface there was a layer of made ground beneath which was a layer of coarse sandy gravel containing cobbles which was approximately 7 metres thick and lay on top of the Keuper Marl. This was very permeable and had a ground water table equal to approximately river level giving a head of up to 10 metres above the marl. This was very difficult material through which to tunnel and would have required chemical consolidation or freezing throughout the length of the tunnel. The predominance of cobbles would have made slurry shield work, by then current standards, extremely difficult and if compressed air working had been attempted very heavy air losses would have made the work costly, if not unfeasible.

The Keuper Marl provided another aquifer. It was jointed and fissured and water accumulated in the joints and fissures in large quantities, the fissured rock being very permeable. Several

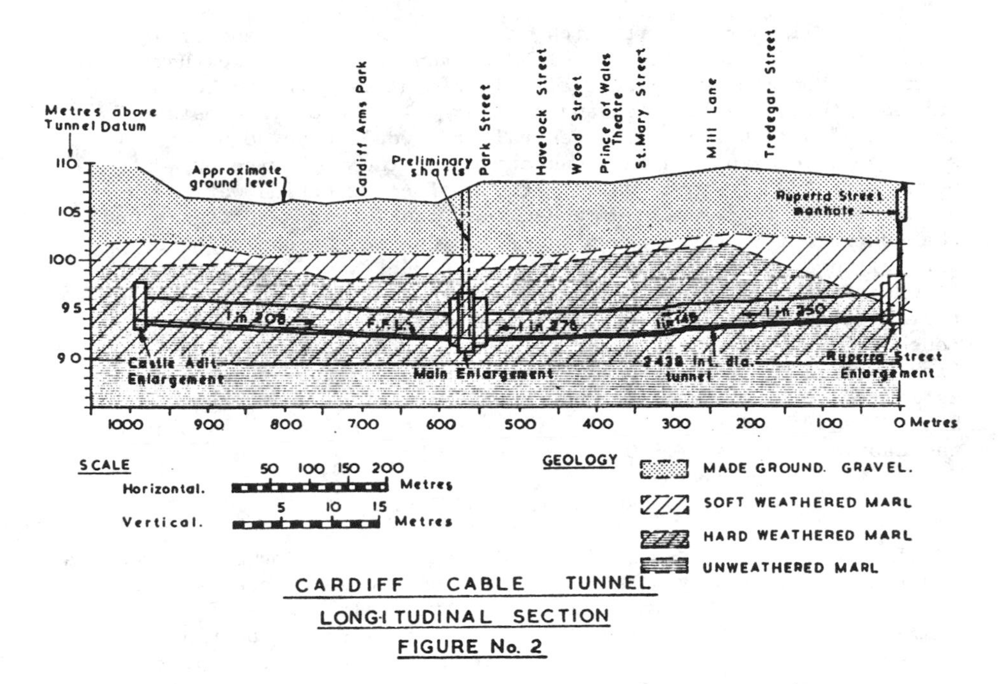

CARDIFF CABLE TUNNEL

LONGITUDINAL SECTION

FIGURE No. 2

industrial concerns, including a brewery, drew their water from wells sunk into this aquifer. It was by no means ideal material for tunnelling for although it was hard, to tunnel through it without compressed air or ground treatment of any form would have led to large quantities of water being pumped and may have had serious effects on others using the aquifer for water supplies. If compressed air had been used, pressures would have been high and air losses would have been considerable. Chemical consolidation would have been feasible but expensive and if considerable disruption was not to be caused to traffic on the surface, the consolidation or ground injection would have had to be carried out from the tunnel face, probably through a bulkhead initially and rate of progress would therefore have been very slow.

Between the two aquifers lay a band of weathered marl which was up to twelve metres thick. The upper horizon was quite permeable and although the rock became more permeable with depth, the upper parts had characteristics of hard fissured clay in which the fissures had closed up or filled. It appeared from what little borehole information was available and from the study of an outcrop that it would be feasible to drive the tunnel through this stratum using a tunnel shield and bolted reinforced concrete rings for the great part without the use of compressed air or any form of ground treatment.

The preliminary report which was published at the end of January 1973 recommended that the tunnel be driven through the weathered marl, from Bute Monument via a central enlargement beneath the Telephone Exchange to the Castle area and gave an estimate of the costs. The three shafts required in the Central Area would have to be constructed before work on the foundations of the high-rise building were commenced if simple cheap methods of construction were to be used. It was therefore recommended that the shafts be designed and the contract let as soon as possible to enable the shafts to be sunk without interference to or from the construction of those foundations. It was also recommended that a soils investigation contract be let so that a detailed soils survey could be carried out along the proposed route to enable a final report to be produced which would cover the final design, methods of construction and estimates of cost. The estimated cost of the shaft contract in the preliminary report was £55,000 and the estimated cost of the tunnel from Bute Monument to the Castle Area was £1,100,000.

PRELIMINARY CONTRACT

The Central Shafts were designed, the Contract Documents produced and tenders invited by 30th April 1973. There were three shafts, one lift shaft of 4572 mm diameter and two cable shafts of 3050 mm diameter. As the Post Office had some surplus cast iron rings from a previous contract it was proposed to use these for the upper lengths of the shafts that passed through the highly permeable sand and gravel and construct the lower sections in the less permeable weathered marl using reinforced concrete bolted segmental rings.

The shaft contract was let on 16th July 1973 and completed on programme on 22nd September 1973 before the work on the main foundations of the high rise building was due to commence.

The shafts were sunk by the underpinning method. An excavation was made deep enough for three rings to be erected in it. The rings were surrounded by a concrete collar and the ground grouted. Excavation was then made for a ring at a time and each successive ring erected and bolted to the one above. The annulus around each ring was grouted with cement ground immediately after erection.

The contract used injections of AM9 to control the water in the very permeable sands and gravels. The top of the weathered marl proved to be impervious as expected but the permeability increased as the shafts were sunk deeper and the concrete plugs in the bases were constructed by allowing the shafts to flood and the hydrostatic pressure to balance before tremying in the shaft plug concrete. The contract price was £48,131.

SITE INVESTIGATION CONTRACT

The soils investigation contract was put out to tender on 28th June 1973 and tenders received 13th July. The starting date was 6th August and although the final report was not received until March 1974 the results were utilised as soon as they became available. Boreholes were sunk at approximately 100 mm centres along the length of the proposed tunnel which now included a spur under the River Taff to the Fitzhammon Embankment. The latter addition was made to avoid disrupting traffic on the main route to the west which ran over Wood Street bridge. (See fig. 3)

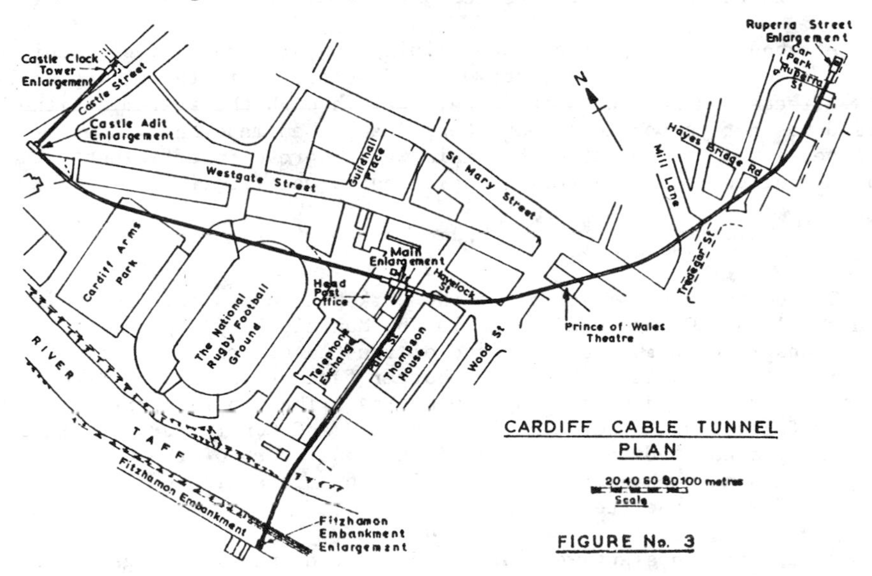

FIGURE No. 3

"Shell and Auger" methods were used to sink the boreholes down to the marl and rotary drilling was carried out through the marl. Undisturbed samples were taken of predominantly cohesive soils using a 4 inch open drive sampler. Large disturbed samples were taken of non-cohesive soils. After rotary drilling commenced a continuous core was obtained. Insitu standard penetration tests were carried out in accordance with BS 1377. The laboratory tests carried out included particle size distribution, water content, index properties, specific gravity, undrained triaxial compression, unconfined compression tests on rock cores and chemical analysis.

In order to estimate the amount of water likely to enter the face at various depths, piesometers were fixed in six of the boreholes in order to ascertain the permeability of the ground. The head of water was recorded and the probable water inflow in to the tunnel working face assessed.

REVISED REPORT

As a result of the site investigation the tunnel level was raised in order to bring as much as possible of it into the relatively impermeable weathered marl, reducing the gradients to 0.5%, the minimum permissible for drainage purposes with a view to decreasing the maximum head of water to 10 metres. A revised report and estimate were sent to the Post Office on 18th July 1974. The new estimate of cost was £1,675,000 and included an allowance of £35,000 for compressed air plant, and an amount of £17,000 for compressed air working under the River Taff and a contingency sum of £100,000 for working in compressed air elsewhere.

At about this time the tunnel mining industry was being unionised and this was beginning to cause a rapid escalation in tunnelling costs. The affects had not yet worked their way through the system and the trend was not yet obvious. The Consultants had made an allowance of 10% per annum for inflation but this was to prove insufficient. Tunnelling costs during the next six months were to rise by 25%.

DESIGN

The design was completed and the work put out to tender in mid-January 1975. Owing to a change in the Municipality's programme for road construction the southern end of the tunnel was moved from Bute Monument to the site of a disused butter factory in Ruperra Street, lengthening the south drive by 150 metres. The upper floors of the butter factory would serve as Consultant's and Contractor's offices and the ground floor proved suitable to house much of the Contractor's electrical and mechanical plant leading to a reduction in the likely level of plant generated noise on site.

Alternative designs were prepared for the tunnel linings. The diameter of the tunnel was determined by the area occupied by the cable brackets and supports and the space needed down the centre of the tunnel as a walkway. A design using standard reinforced concrete segmental rings 2438 mm in diameter and 600 mm wide was produced which gave sufficient space for current and future cable requirements in the section with the highest demand. (See fig. 4) An alternative design was produced in which the cable brackets were inset into the body of the tunnel rings which reduced the diameter to 2187 mm and the length of the rings increased to 1000 mm to reduce the number of bolts and length of caulking required. (See fig. 5) The water pressures anticipated were of the order of one atmosphere and asbestos cement caulking material, which had proved successful on the central shafts, was considered to be capable of making the tunnel sufficiently water-tight and was specified.

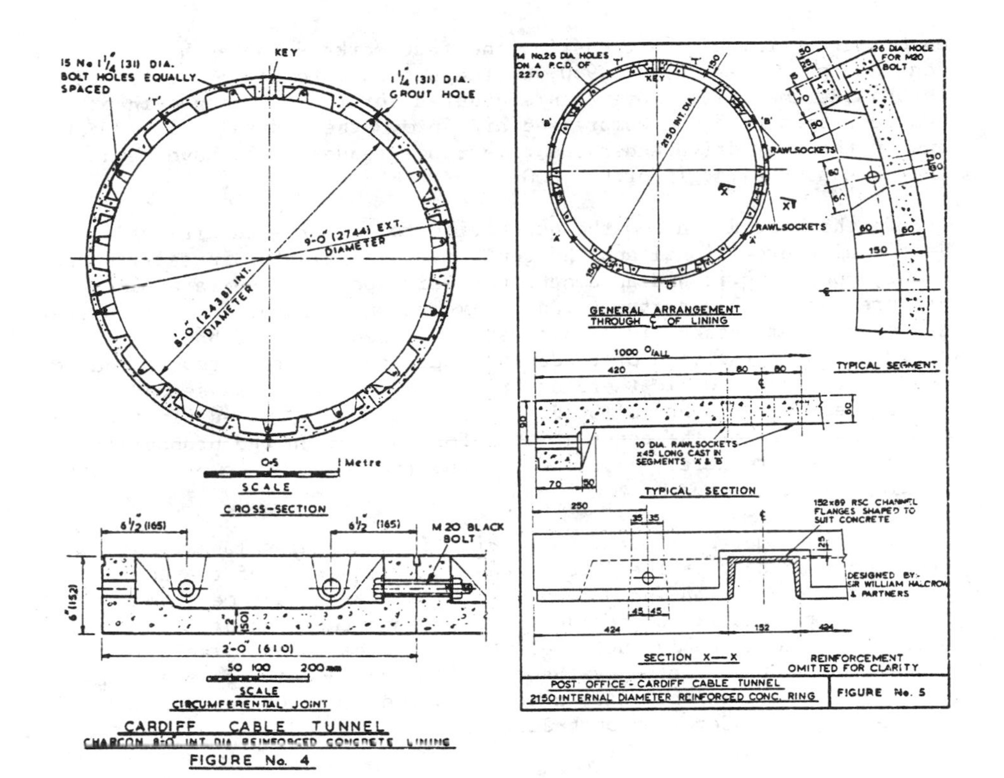

MAIN CONTRACT

Tenders

The tenders were received on 17th March 1975. The lowest tenderer proposed using a full face rotary digging machine which was already in his possession in conjunction with standard 2438 mm dia. rings. He proposed to use the tunnelling machine for the drive from the main working site at Ruperra Street, throughout the central area to the Castle enlargement. The spur to Fitzhammon Embankment was to be driven using a hand shield after the construction of the Central Enlargement. He anticipated using low pressure compressed air for the construction of the enlargement and for the Fitzhammon spur under the River Taff. The shafts were to be sunk with the aid of chemical consolidation. The contract price was £1,900,000.

The second and lowest tenderer proposed to use the alternative design incorporating the specially designed 2148 mm internal diameter reinforced concrete rings. He proposed to use two hand shields and hand operated pneumatic breakers or clay spades. He also proposed to use low pressure compressed air for the whole of the tunnelling to ensure dry working conditions for the face workers and as his contract price was only £1,950,000 the proposal to use compressed air throughout the drives more than accounted for the difference in price. Had he proposed to use compressed air in only the Central Enlargement and in the spur drive under the river, his tender would have been the lowest by a margin of £60,000.

In the United Kingdom the quantities for compressed air are conventionally provisional and the Contractor is paid for installing the plant, operating it and an amount per shift per face operated under air pressure. This contract was no exception. If the lowest tenderer had to use compressed air at places other than those he had anticipated at the time of tender he would be paid for its use and the cost of the works would therefore rise above that of the second lowest tenderer who had allowed for the use of compressed air throughout. The award of the contract therefore hinged on the probability of the lowest tenderer's estimate of requirements for compressed air working being correct.

By this time the affect of unionisation of mining labour had had its effect on costs: the lower tender was in excess of the estimated price by £225,000, an increase of 13%. As there was some slack in the programme the Client decided to look into the feasibility and cost of providing cable ducts below the surface before placing the tunnel contract. Eventually the decision was made to proceed with the tunnel solution and after discussion the contract was awarded to the lowest tenderer on 30th July 1976.

CONSTRUCTION

Shaft Sinking

Work commenced on site in September 1976. The 3658 mm diameter shaft, the Ruperra Street Shaft, was sunk by underpinning. An excavation three rings deep was made and the top three rings set in it in a concrete collar. The work then proceeded by excavating for a ring at a time, constructing the next ring beneath those already built and grouting the annular space behind the cement grout. Before the shaft had reached the designed depth of 20 metres the ground changed to hard marl with wide fissures containing water at about twice the pressure that had been recorded in any of the boreholes. As a result of the late extension of the tunnel the nearest borehole was about 100 metres away but as the borehole spacing was at 100 metre centres the possibility that similar ground existed elsewhere could not be dismissed.

Redesign

The tunnel had been designed to have a continuous fall in gradient from North to South for ease of drainage both during and after construction. As the main working site was at the southern end from which the tunnel would therefore be driven, drainage would have always been away from the working face. This advantage was reconsidered against the disadvantage of probably having to double the air pressure for certain lengths of tunnel drive. It was considered better to redesign the tunnel so that all lengths drained towards the centre enlargement thus keeping the required air pressure to a minimum. The decision was taken in a matter of hours and the shaft plugged at the new reduced depth.

Ground Treatment

Before breaking out of the shaft to construct the tunnel and a short 3048 mm back-shunt, the fissured ground was grouted from the surface using bentonite and cement.

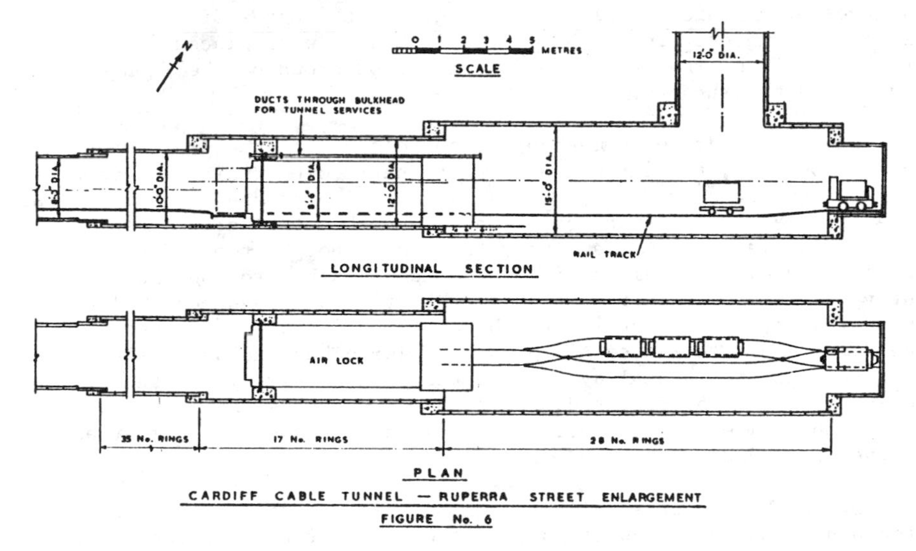

CARDIFF CABLE TUNNEL — RUPERRA STREET ENLARGEMENT

FIGURE No. 6

Ruperra Street Englargement

The Contractor's method of working was to break out of the west side of the shaft and construct by hand mining nine rings of 3048 mm diameter bolted rings, the first six to act as pilot tunnel and the remainder to act as a back-shunt. He then broke out of the East side of the shaft and constructed a further seventeen rings, also to act as a pilot tunnel. The pilot tunnel was then enlarged ring by ring to 4571 mm diameter reinforced concrete bolted rings to act as the permanent enlargement. The floor of the enlargement was then concreted.

Seventeen rings of 3658 mm diameter lining were then erected to act as a shield chamber and to hold the air lock, followed by thirty five rings of 3049 mm dia. concrete rings. During the construction of the latter occasional open fissures were found by probing ahead of the face. These were grouted up using bentonite and cement grout. The face was then boxed up and grouted.

Machine Tunnelling

The tunnelling machine was constructed in the 3658 mm shield chamber and shoved forward into the 3048 mm section where sufficient of the shield train was erected behind it to operate it as a mechanical digger shield. The air lock was then constructed and tested after which the drive for the 2438 mm dia. standard reinforced bolted ringed tunnel commenced. To prevent the runners supporting the sledges of the shield train from damaging the flanges of the reinforced concrete rings, shaped timber blocks were placed in the recesses of the invert segments which stood proud of the flanges and supported the runners.

The tunnel drive commenced in compressed air at a pressure of plus one atmosphere, the intention being to carry out trial compressed air working and then gradually to reduce the air pressure to normal. When the air pressure was reduced it was found that the water in the face caused the marl to form a slurry that could not be removed by the shield conveyor system and it was found necessary to continue the drive in compressed air. Later in the drive although the marl became harder so that rock cutting teeth had to be installed on the cutting head, attempts to reduce air pressure always had the same effect. The moisture in the face always caused the marl to slurry and the air pressure had to be restored. To reduce air losses the joints of the rings above knee-joint level were caulked with asbestos cement as the drive proceeded.

After the digger shield had got over its teething troubles it reached a maximum speed of 15 metres per day of two working shifts and averaged 8 metres per day. The machine drove past the main enlargement and stopped for four weeks when the shield train was clear of the enlargement length. The southern end of the enlargement comprising twentyeight rings of 4572 mm dia. bolted segments was constructed by enlarging the pilot tunnel ring by ring, the timber support frames or horseheads erected at the position of the break-out for the Fitzhammon Drive and the digger shield then driven on to the end of the North Drive, a total length in all of 1.1 kms. Later the Castle Adit Enlargement, which was 3658 mm in diameter, was constructed around the tunnel and digger shield, the shield turned through a right angle and the Castle Adit driven into the Castle Clock Tower Enlargement which had already been constructed. This final drive had a temporary bulk-head erected at the end of it until the air pressure was reduced to normal in the North Drive. (See figs.7 and 8)

Fitzhammon Drive

Concurrently with the driving of the latter half of the North Drive the Fitzhammon Breakout and Shield chamber were constructed, a hand shield erected in the Shield Chamber and the Fitzhammon Drive commenced. The face was excavated by means of pneumatic hand tools and the rate of construction achieved and maintained was 5 metres per day. This 300 metre drive was completed in 15 working weeks.

Main Enlargement

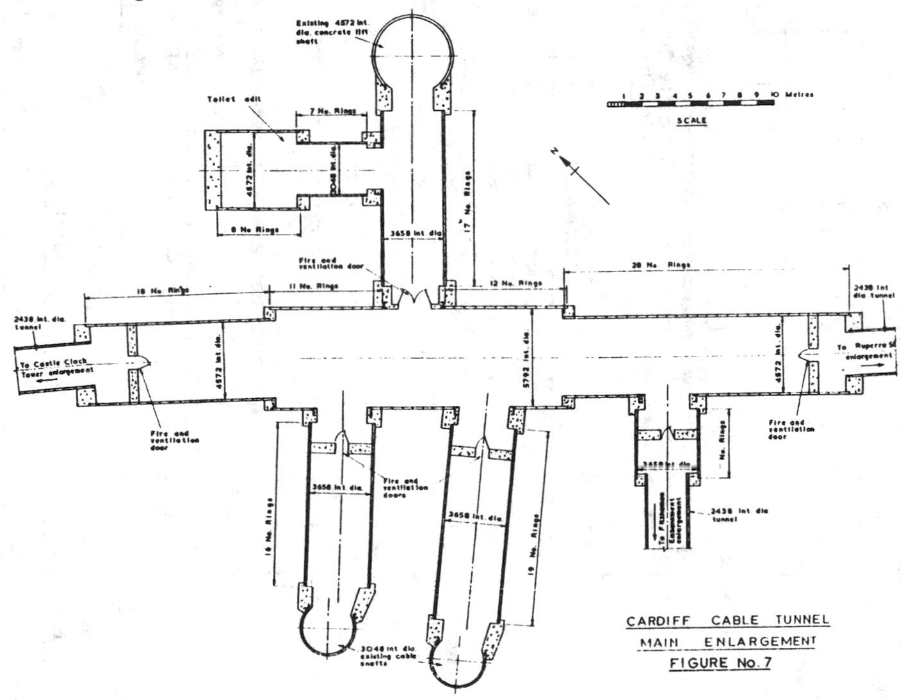

CARDIFF CABLE TUNNEL
MAIN ENLARGEMENT
FIGURE No. 7

The main enlargement was commenced as soon as the Castle Adit Enlargement had been completed. (See fig. 7). Firstly the 2438 mm dia. pilot tunnel was enlarged to 4572 mm dia. working from South to North one ring at a time. The twentynine ring main chamber in the centre was then enlarged to 5792 mm internal diameter. This work was carried out concurrently with the Castle Adit Drive, the spoil from and rings and materials for the latter being carried through the enlargement work. On completion of the 5792 mm section heavy timber frames or "horseheads" were erected to support the rings where the openings for the lift and cable adits were to be constructed.

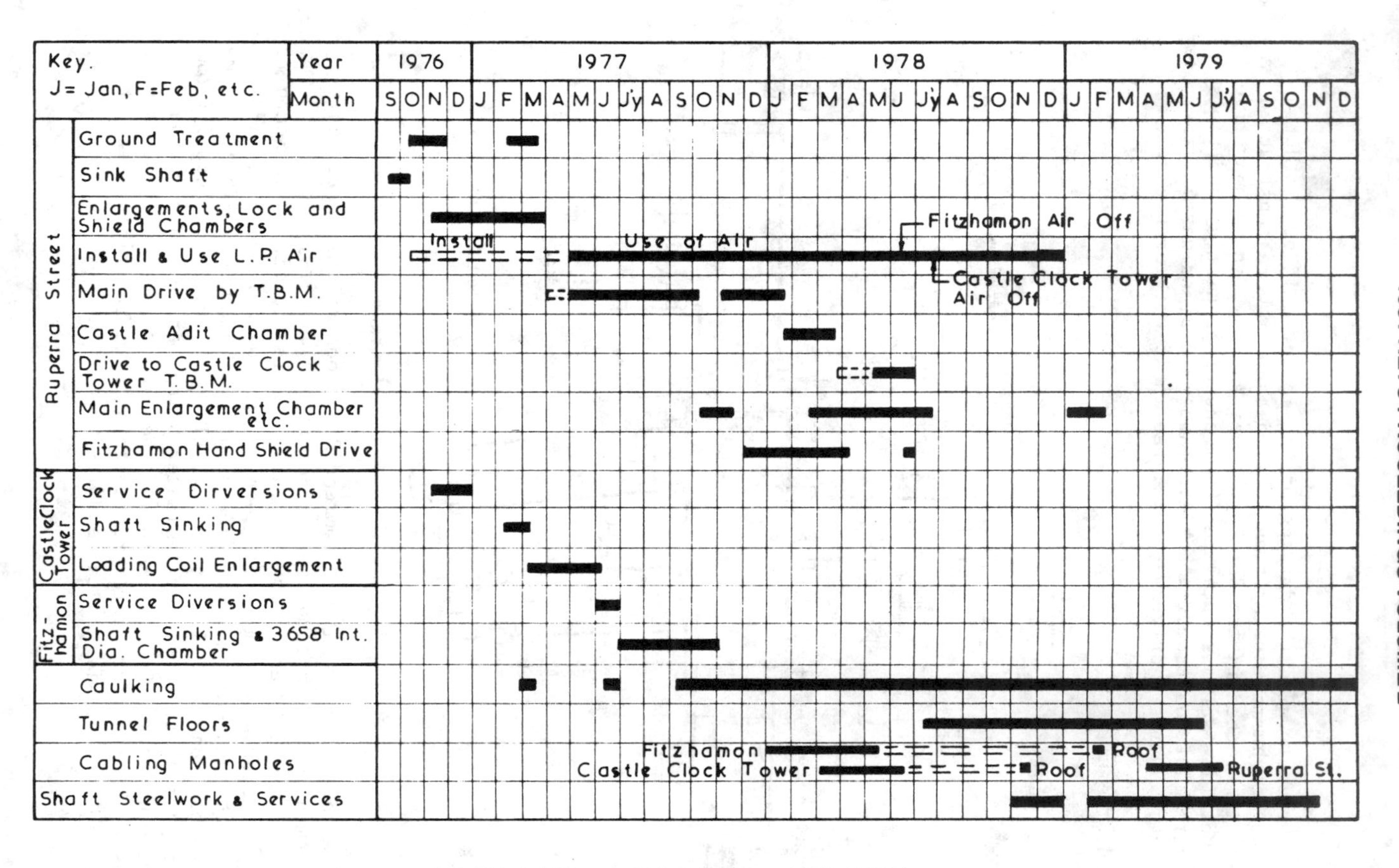

CARDIFF CABLE TUNNEL

PROGRAMME OF TUNNEL WORKS - FIGURE No. 8

Cable and Lift Adits

The cable and lift adits were constructed by removing segments from the 5792 mm rings which had been rolled so that the keys were in the right position for the openings. A length was then excavated and the first three rings constructed. The concrete junction length between the first ring and the side of the main tunnel was then concreted. The adits were then driven to junction with the lift and cable shafts. The toilet adit was then driven in a similar manner. All the enlargement and adit work was carried out by hand using pneumatic spades for excavation and supporting the ground as necessary by timbering. Air winches attached to rings already constructed were used to handle the segments into position.

TYPICAL CABLE TUNNEL

Concrete Invert

Then each drive was completed, the tunnel was cleaned out, any damaged segments were repaired or replaced, and the joints of the invert segments caulked. The compressed air was maintained at a level of plus one atmosphere until all the caulking had been completed. As each caulked length of ten metres was inspected and passed the concrete inverts were poured and drainage channels formed. The granolithic topping 40 mm thick with a non-slip finish was laid in a single pass after the invert concreting was completed.

Waterproofing

The joints were sealed by caulking 25 mm deep grooves between the segments (see fig. 4) with asbestos cement. The bolt holes were made water tight by pairs of hemp grummets impregnated with silica gel. This work was carried out under compressed air, the grooves above knee-joint being caulked as the tunnel was driven and those on the invert after the invert had been cleaned out. When air pressure was reduced to normal the full differential head of water acted on the joints and any bad faults became apparent. Minor faults were not always obvious due to the presence of condensation and it became necessary to use air dehumidifiers to reduce the humidity sufficiently for the condensation to evaporate.

Major faults were grouted and recaulked. Minor faults were re-caulked and where sweating occurred a water proofing compound was applied which penetrated the surface of the caulking material and formed a crystalline seal. The waterproofing was accepted when the total inflow into the whole tunnel complex had been reduced to five litres per minute.

Drainage

The drainage system had to cope with any water which might percolate into the tunnel through the linings plus any wash down water. A sump was constructed in the base of the lift shaft, the lowest point in the system and two pumps were installed capable of raising water to the surface. The capacity of each pump was 273 litres/min at that head. They were controlled by electrodes and should the inflow of water exceed the combined capacity of the pumps an alarm would be given in the control room.

Toilet facilities were provided which were served by a sewage pump.

Ventilation

The ventilation system was designed to provide between three and four air changes per hour. Bulkheads with fireproof doors were provided in the main enlargement at the entrances to all tunnels. (See fig. 7) Fans in ducts in the top of the bulkhead draw air from the lift-shaft via the central enlargement and pass it into the tunnels. Exhaust air passes out through the access shafts and through ventilation ducts in the cabling manholes.

Cabling Manholes

There is a cabling manhole at the top of each of three remote cable shafts. These consist of two part chambers, one of which is immediately over the shaft and the other connected to the surface. They are separated by a watertight bulkhead containing a watertight door.

Shaft Steelwork

In the cable shafts which were 3049 mm dia. were erected a series of platforms at 3000 mm centres which were connected by sloping ladders for man access. Tacking bars, or cable supports, were provided at a maximum of 1500 centres throughout the depth of the shaft. A rectangular steel tower was erected in the lift shaft in which ran the 5t goods lift. The tower was faced with steel mesh as a safety precaution. The shaft also contained a service bay for pumping and water supply mains, electricity supply and ventilation trunking and a ladder bay with platforms at 3000 mm centres for man access.

SUMMARY

The owner is	Wales and the Marshes Telecommunications Board, Cardiff, Wales.
The Engineer is	Sir William Halcrow and Partners, London, England.
The Contractor is	Sir Robert MacAlpine and Sons (South Wales) Ltd., Newport, Monmouthshire.

MAIN CONTRACT

The tender price was £1,900,000

The final price is £2,400,000 approximately

Additional price due to price escalation £800,000 approximately.

Cost of L.P. air £500,000 approximately.

Cost of ground treatment £60,000.

Start date, 2nd September 1976

Substantial completion 16th December 1979

Contract Period 87 weeks

Extension of time recommended 17 weeks

Maintenance period 52 weeks

Contractor for Preliminary Contract	- Thyssen (Great Britian) Ltd. Llanelli, Carmarthen
Contractor for Soils Investigation	- Cementation Ground Engineering Ltd. Hertfordshire.